Insect Hormones

Dedicated to
the centenary of the appearance of the book
*On the Origin of Species by Means of
Natural Selection*
by Charles Darwin
and the 150th anniversary of its author's birth

Insect Hormones

V. J. A. NOVÁK

R.N.Dr., C.Sc.

Head of the Department of Insect Physiology
in the Entomological Institute of the
Czechoslovak Academy of Sciences, Prague

METHUEN & CO LTD

11 NEW FETTER LANE LONDON EC4

First published in Czechoslovakia
in the German language 1959
Second edition 1960
English translation first published 1966
© Vladimir Novák 1966
Printed in Great Britain by
Butler & Tanner Ltd, Frome and London

Preface to the First Edition

Research into insect hormones is a biological discipline which has appeared only during the last twenty years and has only become fully developed since the nineteen-fifties. The number of papers on insect hormones has increased geometrically over the last few years. It is therefore a rather difficult task to present a systematic review of the current state of our knowledge in such a rapidly enlarging subject. New information is accumulating at a surprising rate and new theories appear almost daily. An attempt, however incomplete it may be, to summarize and synthesize the present state of our knowledge has nevertheless a use in encouraging the profitable orientation of future research. In the case of insect hormones such a review may be of additional benefit as the data are important in other biological disciplines, especially in general biology, endocrinology and various branches of entomology including the applied field.

It is clear that, with a literature on insect hormones including more than 1500 papers, it is impossible to attempt even an approximately complete survey of the available references. The author's aim has been rather to summarize as many as possible of the most important papers, to review the overall picture from a single viewpoint, and to list all the available references.

An attempt has been made to deal objectively with all the most important aspects of the subjects discussed, including some conflicting views whether or not the author considers them correct. This does not mean, however, that the author has limited himself merely to reproducing the views of others without reference to his own conclusions, which appear to him to be well founded. Where possible the author has evaluated the available information and has developed further the conclusions quoted from other scientists, particularly from the point of view of the prospects for further research. The author is fully aware that many of his conclusions can only be regarded as provisional working hypotheses with the present limited state of our knowledge. He is, however, convinced that even the contradiction or modification of a wrong hypothesis will do more to further progress in a field such as insect hormones at the present stage of development than a non-critical accumulation of apparently objective facts.

In the field of endocrinology, the facts and conclusions have often been

v

regarded as being inconsistent with the principles of animal evolution. It is, however, the facts about insect hormones which themselves most clearly demonstrate the fallacy of this conclusion. The number of papers dealing with insect hormones from the point of view of phylogeny has increased rapidly, especially in the last few years, and they make an important contribution to a better understanding of animal evolution. One of the chief aims of the present review has been to summarize these papers, enlarging on their approach. This perhaps makes the book at least partly worthy of such an important event in modern biology as the centenary of the first appearance of Charles Darwin's most important work – *On The Origin of Species by Means of Natural Selection* – and the 150th anniversary of his birth.

Last, but not least, the author wishes to express his sincere thanks to all those who took part in making this book possible by their comments, criticism or technical assistance, also to those who made the author's task easier by supplying reprints of their papers. The author is particularly pleased respectfully to acknowledge his debt to his former teacher Dr Karel Wenig, Professor of Animal Physiology at Prague University, for all the care he has taken in his capacity as scientific editor with the compilation and improvement of this book both from the point of view of the subject matter as well as with the style and language.

The opportunity is equally welcome to record gratitude to the most important and distinguished contributor to the field of insect hormones, Professor V. B. Wigglesworth, F.R.S., under whose guidance the author started his study of the subject as a British Council scholar in 1948–49 in the department of zoology at Cambridge University.

The author is similarly grateful to Professor Ivan Málek, Fellow of the Czechoslovak Academy of Sciences and Director of the Biological Institute, and to Professor Otto Jírovec, Fellow of the Czechoslovak Academy of Sciences, for their continued interest in his work and numerous encouraging discussions about this book. Thanks are also due to Dr Vladimír Landa for a careful revision of the typescript as well as for many useful comments, and to Dr Viktor Janda, jr., and Dr Jaroslav Veber for reading the typescript and providing helpful criticism and suggestions. The author is indebted to Mr Kinský and Mrs Kohnová for the careful translation of the manuscript into German and to Professor Fiala for the excellent microphotos. Special thanks are due to my wife for her valuable help with typing the manuscript, for preparing the index and many other time-consuming tasks connected with the preparation of this book.   V. J. A. N.

Prague, 20 March 1958.

Preface to the Second Edition

The fact that the first edition of this book was out of print within a few months of its appearance demonstrates the vivid interest of specialists in the results of research on insect hormones. The number of papers dealing with this subject has increased markedly in the short space of less than two years since the first edition went to press. Many of these papers represent important contributions to our knowledge of insect hormones.

The publishers' aim was to meet the orders of those who missed the first edition as soon as possible. This has made it impossible to incorporate the new information in the original text. The only alternative has been to include all the new data in a special chapter at the end of the book. This will be an advantage to readers of the first edition who will find all the additions in Chapter XI.

The limited time available prevented a more complete survey of the new findings or a balanced assessment of the most important papers. The considerable number of papers, more than 200 in less than two years – including a few earlier references – demonstrates the increasing interest in insect hormones not only of entomologists but also of physiologists and biologists generally.

Thanks are due to the scientific editor, Professor K. Wenig, and the reviser, Dr V. Landa, for many helpful comments; also to Dr G. Petersen (Deutsches Entomolgisches Institut, German Academy of Agricultural Sciences) for his careful corrections of the language.   V. J. A. N.

Prague, 30 January 1960.

Preface to the Third (First English) Edition

The number of papers dealing with insect hormones has increased out of all proportion in the last three years and many important new findings have appeared since the second edition was published. The aim of the author has been to include as many of them as possible into the new edition. However, the more rapidly a branch of science develops the more difficult it becomes to make a complete survey up to a particular date. The material in Chapter XI of the second edition has been incorporated in the appropriate sections of the book. The material in the new edition has been rearranged in several places, particularly in Chapter III. Care has been taken to make a clear distinction between views which are generally accepted and the views and conclusions personal to individual authors, including the author of this book. Thanks are due to all who have helped the author to improve the language and to make this new edition as good and complete as possible.

The preparation of the typescript for print took more time than was originally expected. During this period a large number of new papers on the subject appeared, many of them of primary importance. Since, as in the second edition, even a brief treatment of them could not be incorporated in the text, a new chapter has been added containing the additions for the years 1963 to 1965 referring to the papers available to the author until about 1 June 1965.   V. J. A. N.

Prague, 18 August 1965.

Contents

A*   ix

Contents

xii *Contents*

List of Plates

CHAPTER ONE

Introduction

The first observation of specific 'tissue ferments' circulating in the blood of animals was made as early as the second half of the eighteenth century by de Bordeu (1775). This was followed by Le Gallois in 1801 with a more definite report. The first certain experimental evidence of the existence and the source of such substances carried in the blood was furnished by Berthold (1849), who showed that castration effects in male chickens could be annulled by implanting the testes from other specimens. The term internal secretion in its present sense was first used by Brown-Séquard in 1899. It was not until 1909 that the concept of hormones as 'chemical messengers' from one tissue to another was established by Bayliss and Starling in their classic paper on the control of pancreatic secretion to the intestine.

Since that time the exact definition of the term hormone has changed rather frequently as a result of the increasing number of papers. The narrowest definition is that a hormone is the product, characterized among other things by a high resistance to boiling, of a special incretory gland. The broadest definition includes all physiologically active substances carried in the blood, even inorganic substances such as carbon dioxide.

The following intermediate definition of the term seems the most suitable for use in this book. Hormones are substances which are physiologically active even in minute concentrations, are produced by the organism itself and produce their effects away from their site of origin, being transported by the body fluid.

This definition allows for the character of hormones as a special type of vital function and for our present state of knowledge about their chemical composition, place of origin and mechanism of action. The fact that substances with the defined qualities also agree in other respects, such as the nature of their special effect and their wide non-specificity of action in animals of the same taxonomic phylum or in even wider groupings, together with the resistance to boiling that most of them show, seems to indicate that the definition includes a natural and physiologically uniform group of substances.

At present, even with our very incomplete knowledge, it is apparent that in all the main animal groups the hormones of any individual form a group of substances which are quite indispensable to the organism, having, as a group, a complex relationship with all the important body functions. We may therefore speak of the hormone system of a given individual or species with the same justification as we speak of the nervous system, digestive system, or muscular system etc. This applies to most of the substances which fit the definition given above. There are, of course, substances which fit the definition equally well but which cannot be regarded as part of the hormone system of the body in the same sense. These are various substances which are secreted by tissues having other functions in the body and which are only active away from their site of origin under certain conditions, although their surplus may be discharged into the body fluid. They can most suitably be termed *protohormones* to distinguish them from hormones in the narrow sense. They agree with the hormones, however, in being produced by the organism itself, acting away from their site of origin and being carried in the blood. This suggests, as will be shown later (p. 267), that they correspond to a phylogenetical stage which has been passed in the evolution of each of the true gland hormones. The protohormones include all the gene hormones as defined by Koller (1938) and the neurohumoral factors (cf. p. 209). The term must, however, be distinguished from the term prehormone, or hormone precursor, which refers to a chemical stage from which true hormones are formed in chemical reactions. The term protohormone, on the other hand, in no way refers to the chemical properties of the substance. The same substance may occur in one group of animals as a protohormone, as a neurohormone in another (or as both protohormone and neurohormone together as in insect acetylcholine), or as a neurohormone and a true glandular hormone in a third group (adrenaline in the sympathetic ganglions and in the suprarenal medulla of vertebrates). In most cases the phylogenetic relationships between such conditions are quite apparent. With some substances, of course, the present state of our knowledge makes it impossible to decide whether a given substance which has been demonstrated by its physiological effects is a protohormone or a hormone in the strict sense of the word (e.g. some of the neurohormones discovered by Gersch and his co-workers, cf. p. 242).

The following groups of protohormones can be distinguished: (*a*) The so-called gene hormones which are chemical constituents of tissues and are necessary for the ontogenetic development of particular characters (structures, colours etc.) from the genetic background. Their hormonal character is only apparent under experimental conditions, this property being more or less fortuitous. (*b*) the neurohumoral factors which are substances occurring in minute, microscopically invisible quantities in the synapses and nerve endings – e.g. acetylcholine, adrenaline – where they play a part in the transport of nervous impulses from one neurone to another. In some particular cells of the nervous system (neurosecretory cells) they may be produced in larger quantities and be passed into the blood to affect the activity of various organs, e.g. gut peristalsis and the pulsation of the dorsal vessel. (*c*) The third group includes all other proto-hormones, e.g. the various so-called ommoferments which affect the pig-mentation of the imaginal eyes. These are often produced in superfluous amounts and then diffuse into the surrounding tissues or may pass into the body fluid (blood or haemolymph) and thus affect remote tissues as well. This is perhaps the way the hypothetical gradient-factor developed into the juvenile hormone in the phylogeny of the corpora allata (cf. p. 167).

Some authors also refer to various chemical substances found in proto-zoans as hormones. Some of them may be assumed to be chemically related or even identical to hormones in the metazoa and it may be assumed that at least some of the most important hormones of the higher animals existed when the latter were at the unicellular level in their phylogeny. Even so, by the physiological definition given above, as these substances are both produced and have their activity inside the same cell they no more correspond to the concept of hormones than the organelles of Protozoa correspond to the organs of higher organisms.

According to their place of origin in the body and the way in which they reach the blood, it is possible to distinguish the following types of hormones: tissue hormones, neurohormones and glandular hormones. The *tissue hormones* are produced by various non-glandular tissues in which secretion of the hormone is purely a secondary function. They include, for instance, histamine produced by damaged tissues, secretine produced by the mucous membrane of the duodenum, and choline produced by the mucous membrane of the intestine. The *neurohormones* (cf. pp. 206) originate in special cells of the central nervous system, the neurosecretory cells, and travel via the axons of these cells in the form of neurosecretory granules to special glandular organs (e.g. the corpora cardiaca in insects and the neurohypophysis in vertebrates). In these organs they are stored and subsequently passed into the blood. The *glandular hormones* are phylogenetically the highest type of hormone. They originate in special ductless glands of which hormone secretion is the primary or sole function.

Most, though not all, of the hormones are morphogenetically active. Some authors use this criterion to distinguish two groups of hormones, the morphogenetic and the metabolic hormones. This should not be regarded as implying that morphogenetic hormones do not affect metabolism. Furthermore, not all the morphogenetically active hormones influence morphogenesis directly, but produce their effect through their action on other processes.

Survey of Insect Hormones

The class Insecta is one of the groups of animals which have been most thoroughly studied as regards internal secretions. This does not mean, however, either that our knowledge of insect hormones is complete or that all the types of hormones are necessarily present. For example it appears well established that no hormones associated with the development of the sex glands are present in insects, in contrast to the vertebrates.

The first group of insect hormones to be discovered were those associated with metamorphosis. The earliest of these to be found was the activation hormone produced by the neurosecretory cells of the insect brain (Kopeć, 1917, 1922; Wigglesworth, 1934). Next to be discovered was the juvenile hormone produced by the corpora allata (Wigglesworth, 1935, 1936) and this was followed by the moulting hormone (ecdyson) originating in the prothoracic glands (Fukuda, 1940). This latter was studied thoroughly by Williams (1946-52) and has been isolated as crystals of pure chemical by Butenandt and Karlson (1954). The first attempts to isolate the activation hormone were made by L'Hélias (1956). Her paper, however, lacks both a reliable test for identifying the substance obtained as the activation hormone, and any suggestion as to which of the substances mentioned (by the author) corresponds to this hormone. It is very probable that some of these substances are identical with some of the neurohormones discovered by Gersch (1957) and his co-workers (cf. page 212). Evidence has been brought by Gersch (1952) that one of these neurohormones, neurohormone D_1, is identical with the activation hormone (cf. p. 214). The hormonal character of the ether extract of the male abdomen of *cecropia* described by Williams (1956) and other authors seems to have been reliably disproved (cf. page 119).

Only in the last ten years has there been a marked increase in our knowledge of the neurohormones in insects. Apart from the activation hormone previously mentioned, the first report on neurohormones came from Hanström (1941) who observed effects of extracts of insect brain and corpora cardiaca on the chromatophores of different crustaceans. However, it was Gersch and his collaborators who first demonstrated unambiguously the presence of three independent substances with chromatotropic and myotropic characters, and who succeeded in isolating them by means of paper chromatography and other methods from three different parts of the nervous system of several insect species. One of these substances, which occurs in the ventral ganglionic chain but is absent in the brain and the corpora cardiaca, is stated by Gersch to be identical to acetylcholine in vertebrates. However, this substance is more probably in the nature of a protohormone than a true hormone. The other two

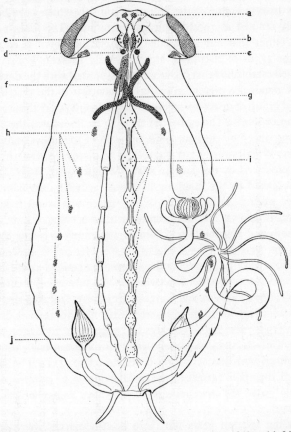

FIG. 1. Diagram of the insect body showing the sources of the chief insect hormones: *a* – neurosecretory brain cells, *b* – corpora cardiaca, *c* – neurosecretory cells of the suboesophageal ganglion, *d* – corpora allata, *e* – ventral glands, *f* – pericardial glands, *g* – prothoracic glands, *h* – oenocytes, *i* – neurosecretory cells of the ventral nerve cord, *j* – corpus luteum.

neurohormones (C and D of Gersch) originate in individual ganglia, including the brain and the corpora cardiaca (p. 211). One can also regard as a typical neurohormone the hormone of the so-called castration cells of the suboesophageal ganglion in *Periplaneta*. The existence of such a hormone has recently been suggested by B. Scharrer (cf. p. 227).

TABLE 1 Survey of the insect hormones known to date:

Type of hormone	Site of origin	Site of action	Effects	Discoverer
Protohormones				
Gene hormones:				
A-substance (= v-s.) antibar-substance	gonads, brain, imaginal discs, haemolymph, etc.	testes, eye-pigments, eye-discs	pigmentation, facets development	Caspari, 1934; Kühn, 1936; Ephrussi etc., 1938
Neurohumoral factors:				
acetylcholine	nerve endings	synapses	stimulus transmission	Gersch, 1956
Desmohormones:				
(?) gradient-factor	imaginal parts	imaginal parts	growth activation	(Novák, 1949)
Hormones s.str.				
Tissue hormones:				
ovary ripening factor	fat body	ovaries	permeability low	Ivanov and Mescherskaya, 1935
ovary inhibiting factor	corpus luteum	ovaries	egg-laying stimulus	(Mokia, 1941)
egg-laying factor	?	female genital tubes	?	(Zavřel, 1935)
(?) oenocytes secretion	oenocytes	epidermis (?)	stimulation of secretion	Beck and Alexander, 1964
proctodone	anterior hindgut	neuroendocrine cells		
heart stimulating factor	pericardial cells	heart	myotropic (acceler.)	Davey, 1961

Neurohormones:	Site of production	Target / organs	Function	References
activation hormone (AH)	neurosecretory cells of pars intercerebralis	prothoracic glands, corpora allata, midgut, ovaries	activation, secretion, water balance	Kopeć, 1917; Wigglesworth, 1934
neurohormone A	corpora cardiaca (?)	various pigment cells	chromatotropic	(Raabe, 1949)
neurohormone C	neurosecretory cells, corpora cardiaca corpora allata	muscles; pigment cells	myotropic, chromatotropic	Giersberg 1932; Janda, 1934; Gersch, Unger, 1956 the same authors
neurohormone D (= AH)	neurosecretory cells, corpora cardiaca	muscles; pigment cells,	myotropic, chromatotropic	Fukuda, 1952; Hasegava,
diapause hormone	suboesophageal ganglion	embryos	inhibition of development	B. Scharrer, 1955
castration hormone	suboesophageal ganglion	?	?	
Glandular hormones:				
moulting hormone (MH)	prothoracic glands, ventral glands, pericardial glands	epidermis, ectoderm	induction of moult	Fukuda, 1940; Butenadt, Karlson, 1954
juvenile hormone (JH)	corpora allata	whole body (larval parts) ovarian follicle cells, ovaries	growth activation	Wigglesworth, 1935
Exohormones				
queen inhibiting substance	mandibular glands	development of workers	inhibition of development	Butler, 1953, 1954
termite inhibiting substance	?	growth and development	inhibition	Light, 1944; Lüscher, 1956
termite stimulating substance	?	growth and development, ovaries	stimulation	

7

The hormone supposedly produced by the fat body of *Periplaneta* and an inhibitory hormone from the corpus luteum of insect ovaries can safely be regarded as tissue hormones. The latter hormone prevents the ripening of eggs in the ovarian follicles as has been demonstrated experimentally by Ivanov and Mescherskaya (1935). However, further experimental evidence is required to clarify their specificity; this also applies to the hormone which, as Mokia (1941) suggested, conditions the rate of oviposition in silkworm females.

Quite certainly, the present state of knowledge does not even approach a complete picture of all the hormonal substances and mechanisms in insects. There are indications of the presence of further hormonal mechanisms: for example, the relation between the stage of maturity of the gonads and the flight instinct in beetles mentioned by Yakhontov. We can be sure that there are other hormones as yet completely unknown.

As regards protohormones in insects, several types of gene-hormones have been described. The term gene-hormone is used to refer to substances which are produced by the tissues and pass into the blood under certain conditions whence they determine various changes in the form and colour of specific organs. For example, the substance affecting eye-pigmentation occurs in the gonads, the brain and other parts of the body. Substances with these characters have been found by Kühn (1927), Caspari (1933), Beadle (1937) and many others in various insect species.

Of the neurohumoral factors which are considered to effect the transmission of the nerve impulse from one neuron to another at the synapses, only acetylcholine has so far been demonstrated. At the same time, acetylcholine appears also to occur as a neurohormone, often in large quantities. For example, in *Periplaneta americana*, fifteen times more acetylcholine has been found than in the central nervous system of mammals. It is not yet clear whether the acetylcholine found in the ventral cord of various insects (cf. p. 210) is a product of special neurosecretory cells or whether it occurs only at synapses; on this would depend whether the acetylcholine should be considered as a humoral factor or a true neurohormone. There is some evidence for supposing the nature of a protohormone also for the hypothetical gradient-factor; this would mean that it occasionally spreads by diffusion and perhaps in some cases also via the haemolymph (e.g. in regeneration) (cf. p. 130).

In a special and broader sense of the word, hormones may include the so-called exohormones (ectohormones, pheromones part. 1), also called social-hormones. These are produced by queens in the social Hymenoptera or by the reproductives (parent pair) in termites, and suppress the development of gonads and other sexual features in most individuals of the colony, turning them into sterile workers. These substances resemble hormones in their main characteristics, i.e. they are active substances produced by a specific region of the body with a site of action different from their site of origin. They differ from hormones in that the site of action of an exohormone is in another organism, outside the body of the individual producing it. This difference assumes a lesser importance, however, if the social colony is regarded as a living individual of a higher order.

The Importance of Hormones in the Organization of Insects and the Applications of Hormonal Research

The present state of our knowledge of the insect hormones, as given in this book, is undoubtedly only a very incomplete picture of the real status and importance of internal secretions in the organization of insects. This is a reflection of the relatively short period of systematic research to which insect hormones have been subject. Nevertheless, even the previous very incomplete survey of these hormones is sufficient to underline their fundamental importance in the life of insects. Among the substances in insects already known to be of hormonal character, we find agencies which interfere with almost all the important functions of the insect body, including growth, morphogenesis, the moulting process, reproduction, heredity, diapause and colour changes as well as digestion, excretion, secretory activity, movement and nervous activity.

The remarkable theoretical importance of insect hormones has resulted in an ever increasing interest in this type of substance. One of the interests of insect hormones to physiologists is that the research worker can interfere with the basic nature of the chief functions of the insect organism in a truly physiological manner, i.e. without disturbing any of the important life processes, and can thus understand the nature of the functions more profoundly. This is also the basis of the great relevance of insect hormone research to general biology.

Research with an insect hormone may be divided into the following stages: the first stage consists of locating the source of the hormone, of ascertaining its effects on various body functions and organs and of elucidating its mode of action. The second stage involves chemical isolation of the hormone, and the determination of its various physical and chemical properties as well as its chemical composition. The third and last stage of hormonal research, as yet scarcely begun, is to use the isolated substance, now perfectly defined, to analyse all the body functions on which it acts, and thus to investigate its biochemical principle in a similar way as the chemist investigates the chemical composition of an unknown substance by subjecting it to the action of standard reagents.

Not only the theoretical importance of insect hormone research, but also its practical implications, have become increasingly obvious in recent years. Thus hormone research affects both the theory and future practice of insect pest control, as well as the rearing of useful insects and the improvement of appropriate techniques.

Besides appearing likely to influence diapause, hormonal research has opened up a field for using the increasing knowledge about endocrine secretions of insects (primarily the hormones associated with metamorphosis and their critical periods) to understand more fully the bionomics of harmful insects. This could lead to discovering the most suitable times and methods for applying insecticides and other control measures.

CHAPTER TWO

Methods and Techniques in Insect Hormone Research

The first demonstrations of insect hormones were obtained by the artificial removal and subsequent replacement, i.e. extirpation and reimplantation, of the supposed source of the hormone. This is similar to the first studies on vertebrate hormones, the classical Brown-Séquard castration experiments with chickens. Although the results of castration and gonad implantation experiments with insects were always negative (cf. p. 235), spectacular effects resulted from the first experiments involving the removal of the suspected endocrine centres in the head. These results, due primarily to the pioneer work of Kopeć (1917, 1922) and Wigglesworth (1934, 1935, 1936), led on to the evolution of further, often very ingenious techniques. The exclusively biological, surgical methods involving histological examination, which were the first stage of insect hormone research, were soon followed successively by chemical treatments based on extraction, isolation and injection. A short survey of these various experimental approaches may be useful, not only for readers who intend to commence their own research in this field, but also for all who seek to obtain a clearer insight into endocrine problems in insects.

Preparation of the Experimental Insect Material

Selection of suitable specimens. The first requirement for a successful experiment on endocrine activity is to use animals at a suitable stage of their ontogeny; i.e. in a period when the respective hormone is being secreted (in experiments with the removal of the source of the hormone) or in a period of its absence (in experiments involving the artificial introduction of the hormone or its source). Secondly, it is important to use perfectly healthy specimens, as diseased or underfed animals as well as those reared in abnormal environmental conditions may show quite abnormal or even suppressed endocrine activity.

Narcosis. In most insect hormone experiments, some form of narcosis will prove necessary to enable surgical treatment to be performed successfully. Not only will the insect be immobilized, but also bleeding, which is often the cause of the failure of experiments, will be prevented.

The organic anaesthetics used for vertebrates are not very suitable for insects. For example the maximum dose, without undesirable side-effects, of the normally used ethyl-ether does not maintain immobilization for a sufficient length of time. Using higher doses in such cases, even of the specially pure medical chemicals classed as 'pro narcosi', results in a slowing down and disturbance of development and may even reduce the percentage of surviving individuals. Results using other common organic narcotics are even less satisfactory. However, CO_2 narcosis is very effective with insects, and a recovery of 100 per cent is usually obtainable. Even so, anaesthesis and immobilization using CO_2 are again of too short a duration, and recovery is almost as rapid as the onset of narcosis. According to Williams (1946), recovery of the insect during the work may be prevented by using a *Buchner* funnel, into which a steady flow of gas is carried in a pipe from a CO_2 cylinder. The narcotized specimen is fixed at the bottom of the funnel, and all operations take place in a continuous stream of CO_2. The required time under narcosis (up to 15 min.) in no way influences either the development of the insects or the percentage surviving. To get a sufficiently deep narcosis of diapausing pupae, Williams (1957) suggests that the animals should be introduced into the CO_2 atmosphere for about 20 mins. before beginning the operation. After a window has been cut in the cuticle of the pupa, the pressure of the haemolymph can largely be controlled by compressing the abdomen of the pupa with a piece of plasticine so that the excised area is filled with haemolymph but does not overflow.

A very simple and successful method is water narcosis, which gives quite long immobilization periods (15–20 mins.) coupled with a 100 per cent recovery. The treatment simply consists in submerging the insect in water for 20 to 60 minutes before operating. The time required depends on the species of insect, its rate of metabolism and the required duration of immobilization. With some insects, however, only much longer periods are effective, e.g. 6 hours with diapausing pupae and as much as 12 hours with maggots and sawfly pre-pupae. In many cases, the process is markedly speeded up by a short pre-submergence in soda (CO_2) water. This soda water pre-treatment (soda water diluted 1 : 1 with tap water) provides a very good narcosis for aquatic insects. Without doubt, the principle of water narcosis rests on the effect of expired CO_2, the action of which is prolonged by the entry of water into the tracheae. This prevents gaseous exchange until the water evaporates.

Fixing the insect prior to an operation. In most cases it is advisable to fix the narcotized animal on to some support (microscope slide) in a suitable position, so that both hands can be kept free for operating. For this purpose ordinary plasticine or the type of plastic rubber used by artists in charcoal painting is satisfactory. It is sometimes preferable to fix the animal, with paper strips and entomological pins, to the bottom of a petri-dish covered with paraffin wax. The problem of fixing the soft and flexible bodies of maggots and other larvae can be overcome by fastening the larva with several rubber threads or strips of scotch tape across the body. In this case bleeding can be controlled by forcing the blood, by repeated pressure of a cover slip, away from the part of the body to be operated on, while the constriction by the rubber or scotch tape prevents the blood from flowing back again (Possompés, 1953).

Highnam (1958a, b) operated on animals (lepidopterous pupae narcotized with ethyl ether) fixed on a paraffin block in depressions corresponding to the shape and size of the body of the individual insects. Thus the part of the body to be operated on (in this case the thoracic tergites) protruded from the block.

After-treatment of the wounds. In many insects, including cockroaches and bugs where there is little danger of infection of the haemolymph which readily coagulates and does not blacken in air, no treatment of wounds is required after implantation or other less extensive operations. All the instruments used should be thoroughly clean, but not necessarily sterilized. More extensive and deep wounds may be covered with melted paraffin (using a cautery needle) or with a thick collodium solution. Some insect groups, e.g. caterpillars and beetle larvae, are more vulnerable to bacterial or virus infections and have haemolymph which blackens on exposure to air due to the formation of poisonous quinones through the activity of tyrosinase. With these, a higher mortality rate may be avoided by applying a few micro-crystals of an antibiotic (in most cases a mixture of penicillin and streptomycin is satisfactory) and of phenylthiourea to the wound. With these insects, it is also advisable to pre-sterilize the area to be operated on with alcohol-ether, sublimate or some other antiseptic, to use sterilized instruments and to cover the wound in the manner mentioned above. Highnam (1958a, b) kept the excised part of the epidermis with its cuticle in insect-Ringer while the operation was performed, and then replaced it. Antibiotics should also be added to this Ringer solution (for concentrations, see p. 27).

The Operating Instruments
Even for very complicated operations on insects simple home-made instruments are completely satisfactory. The most serviceable *preparation needles*

are entomological pins of various sizes down to minutia, melted into glass rods or fixed with sealing wax into glass tubes as handles (cf. fig. 2), their points bent to a suitable shape. Excellent *scalpels* may be made from small triangular pieces of razor blades which have been broken off between two slides. The best of these are selected under a microscope and are

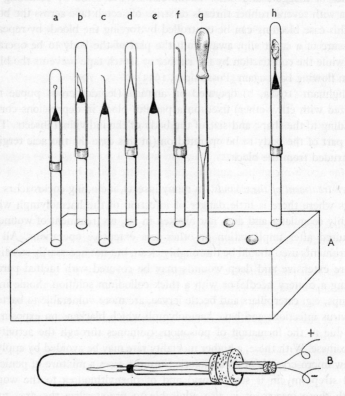

FIG. 2. A. Devices for transplantation experiments: *a* – platinum loop, *b* – razor blade scalpel, *c, e* – mounted needles, *d, f* – glass-rods, *g* – pipette with rubber teat, *h* – needle with cotton wool (for sterilization). B. Electric microcautery with the platinum loop in a protective tube.

similarly sealed into glass handles. For cutting, fine *scissors*, eye-scissors, iridectomy-scissors and so-called Wecker-forceps, are used.

To transport extirpated organs or tissues, a very fine *platinum loop* in a glass handle is used. The loop is sterilized in a gas-flame prior to each use, and when not in use it is protected by a glass cover made from a slightly broader tube (see fig. 2a).

To insert the implants into the incision made in the cuticle, glass-rods of various sizes are used, somewhat smaller in diameter than the organ to be implanted. Otherwise simple bent preparation needles may be used. To implant very small pieces of tissue, e.g. the corpora allata or imaginal discs of young larvae, a specially adapted *micropipette* as described by Beadle and Ephrussi (1937) is employed. Such a micropipette may be prepared from thin-walled glass tubing 1–1·5 cm. in diameter drawn out to a thin capillary in a gas flame to a diameter of 0·5–1 mm. and 2·5–3 cm. in length. By careful heating in a horizontal micro-flame or on a red-hot platinum wire, a constriction is formed in the upper third to prevent the object manipulated being sucked into the broader part of the tube. The micropipette is then connected to a small (tuberculin) syringe by a thin rubber tube. To allow one-handed operation, the pipette may be fixed in a 'Perspex' stand provided with a supporting surface for the hand operating the syringe piston. The stand holds the entire apparatus in the required position, but is unnecessary when an assistant co-operates, as suggested by the above-mentioned authors. Both pipette and syringe are filled with the fluid (insect-Ringer) containing the object to be implanted.

Electric cautery is used both for melting the paraffin wax used for covering the wounds, and for eliminating a source of hormone by burning it out (in cases where it is visible through a transparent cuticle; Burtt, 1938). A very thin platinum wire forms the glowing part of the cautery. It may be heated either by a current of 4 or 6 V from an accumulator, or, more conveniently, from a transformer as used for microscope lamps. The current passes to the platinum loop via a rheostat so that the temperature of the loop can be regulated as required. To cover the wound, a piece of paraffin wax the size of a pin's head is placed on the loop and heated to slightly above the melting point. It is applied by letting the lower edge of the hanging drop touch the wound. To eliminate a gland or other structure an appropriately higher temperature is used, but not red-heat.

Micro-forceps. To remove the neurosecretory cells or other small glands, microforceps of various kinds are used. For allatectomy in *Bombyx*, Bounhiol (1938) used very thin watchmaker's forceps which may be sharpened as described by Avel (1929). True microforceps were made by Sláma (1962[1]) by fixing specially sharpened entomological micro-pins to both tips of a small pair of hard surgical forceps with 'Perspex' solution.

[1] K. Sláma, 'Effects of Allatectomy and Cardiacectomy in *Pyrrhocoris.*, *J. Ins. Physiol.*, 1964.

B

Removal of the Source of a Hormone

The simplest way of demonstrating the endocrine activity of a gland or group of cells is to show that their removal causes a change in the activity of the organism which can be reversed by re-implanting the corresponding tissues from another active animal. The chief condition for success in such treatment is that the tissues should be removed prior to the time at which the secretion of hormones into the blood normally starts. The concentration of the hormone as well as its effects can be assessed from the resultant morphological and physiological changes appearing in its absence; sometimes also by changes in the behaviour of the treated animal. Unequivocal evidence of endocrine activity lies in the disappearance of such effects after re-implantation of a source of the hormone.

Ligaturing. The simplest way of eliminating the source of a hormone is to ligature off the part of the body containing it. With insects, this usually

FIG. 3. Ligating experiments with *Musca domestica*. Immediately after the operation (*left*), ligated before the end of the critical period (*middle*), ligated after the critical period (*right*).

involves ligaturing off the head, as it is this which contains the neuro-secretory and the retrocerebral systems of the body. With some insect larvae, e.g. caterpillars and maggots, the thorax is ligatured off with the head, so that the prothoracic glands also are included. The ligature is made with a fairly thin thread of wool or cotton, but sufficiently thick not to cut the integument and sufficiently thin to prevent damage to adjacent parts of the body.

In ligaturing, a plain loop is used. This is tightened gently and slowly, usually without narcosis. In most cases the loop will be tightened up fully, so as to be equivalent to the removal of the relevant part of the body, e.g. decapitation, without any bleeding. However, it is sometimes an advantage to tighten the loop only sufficiently to prevent free movement of blood between the isolated part and the remainder of the body but leaving the nervous connections unbroken. The loop may thus later be loosened to allow haemolymph to pass into the previously isolated part and to allow the passage of a hormone into the body. The most suitable moment for ligaturing the body occurs with caterpillars at the beginning of cocoon spinning. At this time feeding has finished and the gut has been voided, so that no important physiological functions will be disturbed. Production of the brain hormone (AH), however, starts only just before moulting in many species, so that its passage into the body can still be prevented by ligaturing at this time (cf. p. 56). The actual ecdysis including withdrawal of the insect from the exuvia may often be somewhat hindered by the presence of the ligature. In such cases, the newly moulted specimen must then be freed from the exuvia at a suitable moment, with the aid of dissecting tools under a dissecting microscope. Where the cuticle is very fragile, as with larvae of *Tenebrio molitor*, it may easily be broken by the ligature. Stellwaage-Kittler (1954) used steel springs fixed to a wooden block by one end, and found the technique very successful. The free ends of the springs held suitable parts of the larva's body against the block.

Decapitation. In most cases the head, with its important neurosecretory endocrine centres, is best removed after ligaturing. In this way bleeding of the insect is prevented. In some instances, for example with some beetles, this is impracticable. Decapitation must then be carried out with the insect under deep narcosis, and the wound must be immediately covered with melted paraffin ͵or with collodion.
‸wax.

Cauterization of the endocrine centre. The hormone source may be removed by using a cautery to burn through the cuticle. This technique will be successful where the integument (e.g. the cervical membrane) is sufficiently transparent to render the relevant gland visible as, for example, in some dipterous larvae (cf. p. 219, and Burtt, 1938; Day, 1943a, b). Where the body would have to be first opened up, either surgery or electrocoagulation may be used.

Electrocoagulation. This is the most suitable technique for destroying very small organs, such as the neurosecretory cells of the brain, without affecting the neighbouring tissues. For this a source of high frequency current (1000 Kc, 200 V, 6–8 mA) is required. One of the electrodes is made from very fine platinum wire (0·05 mm.), with one end cut obliquely under a dissecting microscope to produce as fine a tip as possible. This electrode may, if necessary, be fixed in a handle of a micromanipulator. The narcotized insect is placed on a piece of gauze saturated with KCl solution. This is connected to the second electrode. Alternatively the narcotized insect may be in a dish and half submerged in insect-Ringer solution into which the second electrode has been introduced. Kloot and Williams (1954) obtained good results with insects treated by electrocoagulation by keeping them at a constant temperature of 5°C for three days after treatment before returning them to room temperature.

Extirpation. The surgical removal of the actual gland producing the hormone, when this can be done without affecting other organs and tissues, is the most satisfactory technique of eliminating the hormone source. Because of this, special techniques have been developed for different insect species. However, it is extremely difficult to remove completely a loose ramified structure interwoven with other organs, as exemplified by the prothoracic glands of caterpillars. Operation details are very different according to the gland or tissue to be removed. The first step in extirpation is normally to cut a triangular or rectangular window in the overlying cuticle, and the gland is then removed through this opening with the aid of microforceps. Before inserting any tools, a little powdered antibiotic (penicillin and streptomycin) should be introduced into the wound. If necessary, a few microcrystals of phenylthiourea to prevent tyrosinase activity should be introduced with the antibiotic. At the end of the operation the cuticle is replaced and the wound covered with melted paraffin. A piece of coverslip or 'Perspex' may be used instead of the excised piece of cuticle; the process of wound healing may then be observed. Williams (1946, 1947, 1952, etc.) used a small piece of 'Perspex' with a central hole through which evaporated body fluid could later be replaced several times by insect-Ringer.

Allatectomy. A reliable technique for removing the corpora allata of *Leptinotarsa decemlineata* was described by De Wilde and Stegwee (1958) and De Wilde and De Boer (1961). This technique is as follows:— The head of the narcotized specimen is gripped in special forceps with the tips fixed by a screw, and is held at right angles to the body axis. The cervical membrane is thus stretched and must then be split in the median line, the cervical muscles parted and the fragments of fat body removed.

Sufficient illumination will reveal the shining white corpora cardiaca with which the corpora allata are connected. These are removed with fine forceps, either separately or together with the corpora cardiaca. A similar technique was successfully used by Staal (1961) with second instar nymphs of *Locusta*, and by Sláma (see above) in *Pyrrhocoris*.

Introduction of Hormones into the Organism

Transfusion of haemolymph. The first attempts to introduce a hormone from one insect individual into another were made with a blood transfusion technique. Buddenbrock (1930b, 1931; cf. Koller, 1938) effected a partial exchange of haemolymph between two groups of sphingid caterpillars, those just prior to a moult and those after moulting. He cut the end of the terminal horn of the caterpillar, and from the cut horn sucked haemolymph into a syringe. The haemolymph was then injected through the cut horn into another specimen. In his earlier experiments Tauber (1925) used a narrow surgical cannula to transfuse haemolymph from sphingid cater-pillars just prior to a moult into younger specimens. The first requirement for success with transfusion experiments is to use specimens with the maximum amount of hormone in the haemolymph as donors and speci-mens with no hormone in the haemolymph as recipients. The disadvantage of transfusion experiments is that only the quantity of hormone already contained in the donor's blood at the moment of transfusion can be used and of that only the proportion contained in the volume of blood trans-fused. Further reduction of concentration must occur as only part of the recipient's blood can be replaced. An additional decrease in concentration of the hormone in the recipient's blood is rapidly brought about by the excretory activity of the Malpighian tubules. For these reasons only qualitative effects of transfusing haemolymph have so far been observed.

Parabiosis or grafting consists of joining two or more individuals in such a way that their blood systems are connected. In insects this is usually achieved by cutting off the tip of the head of one animal and inserting the rest of the head into an incision in the cuticle of the other specimen. The two animals are then sealed together with paraffin wax. Sometimes a connecting glass tube filled with insect-Ringer or haemolymph is used (cf. fig. 4). The place where the tube enters each animal is then thickly covered with paraffin wax. This technique has frequently been referred to as blood transfusion (cf. Wigglesworth, 1936, 1940a). However, parabiosis has the great advantage over transfusion in its strict sense that the source of the hormone remains present within the joined specimen. Again, it has the advantage over implantation of a gland that the hormone level in the recipient specimen is increased instantaneously. With implantation it usually takes 2 or 3 days before the transplanted gland attains its maximum secretory activity and the normal level of the hormone in the haemolymph

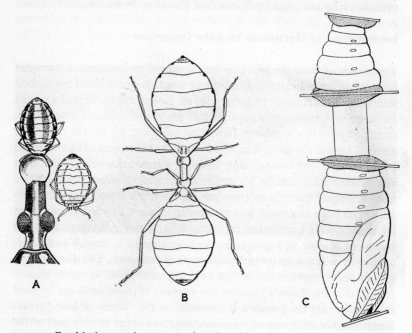

A   B   C

FIG. 4. Parabiosis experiments. A – decapitated 1st instar nymph of *Rhodnius prolixus* after joining to a 5th instar nymph (cf. control on the right); B – two decapitated nymphs joined with a glass tube; C – a pupa joined with a pupal abdomen by means of a glass tube through openings in the glass covers. (A, B after Wigglesworth, 1940a; C after Williams, 1947, modified.)

is reached. For parabiosis, of course, only those stages or individuals are suitable which do not take any food (e.g. pupae), or those which take food only once between moulting, e.g. blood-sucking insects. It is also rather important that the insects should have a hard cuticle.

Implantation. The most reliable evidence of the secretory activity of a given organ or tissue is obtained by transplanting it into a specimen at a stage when the relevant hormone is absent. The gland to be transplanted is best excised in an embryo dish filled with insect-Ringer solution (NaCl – 0·65 g., KCl – 0·25 g., CaCl$_2$ – 0·03 g., made up to 100 ml. with distilled water. After sterilization by boiling add 0·025 g. NaHCO$_3$). With small and fragile organs such as the corpora allata of some species (e.g. *Periplaneta*) and the prothoracic glands of most insects it is first necessary to cut individually all the nerves and tracheae entering the organ, using a bent preparation needle. Only then can the isolated organ be lifted out with a needle or platinum loop and placed into a second dish of fresh Ringer. A little anti-biotic may be added to this dish when insects rather liable to infections are involved. The cuticle of the narcotized specimen which is to receive

FIG. 5. Copulating male and female of silkworm (*Bombyx mori*), each having been in parabiosis with another specimen since the beginning of its pupal instar, showing that the vitality of the parabiotic specimens is not the least reduced.

the gland is then cut with a razor-blade scalpel. The length of the cut should not exceed the diameter of the organ to be implanted by more than one-third. After this cut has been made, the gland is carried in a drop of insect-Ringer on a platinum loop to the incision and carefully slipped under the epidermis with a glass rod (cf. fig. 2d). When implanting very small organs, such as the ring gland of *Drosophila* larvae, it is advisable to inject the gland in insect-Ringer by means of a micropipette. Where necessary (e.g. with most larvae of Lepidoptera and Coleoptera) a few small crystals of phenylthiourea and a little antibiotic (penicillin and streptomycin) should be inserted into the insect before implantation. With other insects (e.g. bugs) both are quite unnecessary. In some species, the haemolymph coagulates so rapidly that no covering of minor wounds is necessary; in others wounds should be covered with paraffin wax or collodion.

The location and eventual removal of an implanted gland was achieved by Johansson (1958) working with the corpus allatum in *Oncopeltus fasciatus*. The gland was implanted using a loop of fine hair tied round the end of the dorsal vessel left attached to the organ. The free end of the hair then protruded from the wound.

Epidermal vesicles. A novel method of studying insect hormone effects is
that used for the first time by Piepho and his colleagues (1936, 1938, 1951
etc.). Instead of transplanting the hormone source, a small piece of excised
cuticle is inserted into an epidermal incision on the specimen whose
hormone system is to be studied. The epidermis of the implanted integument grows rapidly along its cut edges until the growing edges meet to

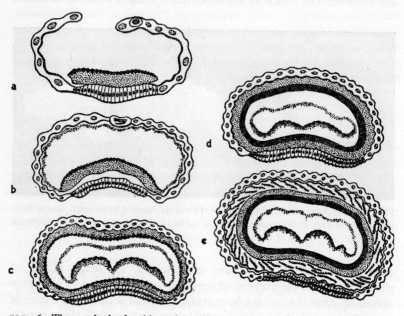

FIG. 6. The method of epidermal vesicle according to Piepho. *a* – before the
closing of the vesicle, *b* – before the first moulting inside the host specimen,
c – after a larval moult, *d* – after a subsequent pupal moult, *e* – after a subsequent
imaginal moult. (After Piepho, 1951.)

form a bladder enclosing the cuticle. This epidermis bladder then carries
out all the moults of its host simultaneously, growing all the time and
enclosing successive exuvia one within the other. The result is a lamellated
structure including all the exuvia from the time of implantation onwards.
The bladder may later be removed and re-implanted into a new host.
The type of cuticle of each exuvium usually corresponds closely to that of
the host; thus a larval cuticle will form in the presence of the juvenile
hormone, and pupal or imaginal cuticles in its absence (cf. p. 90). The
structure of the successive cuticles can be studied in detail by cutting
histological sections through the bladder (cf. fig. 6).

Evaluating the Secretory Activity of an Endocrine Gland

In hormone research it is often important to know whether a given gland is active and to what extent. The degree of activity can be judged histologically by the volume of the gland, or by transplanting it into specimens with their corresponding glands either inactive or extirpated. Each of these three methods has advantages and disadvantages.

The histological evaluation of the activity of a gland depends on determining the quantity of nuclear material, viz. the nuclear/cytoplasmic ratio (the relative quantity of nuclear material per unit volume of tissue, the size of the nuclei, the form and staining properties of the cytoplasm etc.).

For determining the absolute number of nuclei, Engelmann (1937) has, for the corpus allatum, suggested the following equation:—

$$N = \frac{N' \cdot V}{A \cdot (T + 2r)}$$

where N is the total number of nuclei in the gland, N' the number of nuclei counted in the area of a selected section, V the volume of the gland, A the area of the section, T the thickness of the section, and $2r$ the average diameter of the nuclei. An inactive gland is characterized by reduced cytoplasm, a low ratio of cytoplasm to nuclei, less basophilic cytoplasm with indistinct cell boundaries, a lower volume of nuclei etc. Pycnotic nuclei are often observed in inactive glands following a period of activity (B. Scharrer, Harnack, 1958). During secretory activity the amount of cytoplasm increases both absolutely (volume of the gland) and relatively (in comparison with nuclei), the cells become swollen, and the cytoplasm is more basophilic. The histological evaluation of gland activity is very reliable, and its disadvantages lie in the rather long time required to make the preparation.

Much discussion has centred on whether it is possible to judge the degree of activity of a gland (corpus allatum) from changes in its volume (cf. Pflugfelder, 1948, 1952; Kaiser, 1949; Novák, 1951b; Legay, 1950, 1959; Lüscher and Engelmann, 1960; B. Scharrer and Harnack, 1958; see also the panel discussion in the symposium on Insect Ontogeny in Prague).[1] It may be concluded even if there were many cases where the volume of the gland increases without corresponding changes in secretory activity, that the volume of the gland can be regarded as directly proportional to the amount of secretion produced in a unit of time. This is assuming that normal development has occurred under optimal conditions and that the experiments concern the same stage of development

---

[1] See *Acta Symp. Evol. Ins.*, Prague (1961), pp. 213–19.

with all internal and external conditions identical. So far the activity of the corpus allatum has mainly been studied from this aspect.

Several methods have been developed for determining the volume of the corpora allata. To make relative estimates of changes in the volume of the gland, the average diameter of the gland (Legay, 1950), the square root of the product of two linear dimensions (Novák, 1954), and even the cube root of three dimensions of the elliptical gland have been used. In other cases, models have been prepared from the drawing of a complete series of histological sections; the volume of the models was then measured by immersing them in water (Pflugfelder, 1948). Elsewhere, planimeter measurements of camera lucida drawings of representative sections have been made, and the volume of the gland calculated from these (B. Scharrer and Harnack, 1960). For estimates on the corpora allata another approach has been the use of the 'activity volume', this being the difference between the volume of the gland and the minimum volume of a gland with an equal number of nuclei (Lüscher and Engelmann, 1960).

In transplantation experiments, the time must be taken into account which elapses between an operation and the moment when it becomes possible to judge the effect of the gland's secretion. Secretion, after transplantation, may start earlier or later, dependent on the hormonal environment of the host and regeneration (cf. p. 108). Even a completely inactive corpus allatum from a freshly moulted adult may prevent metamorphosis when it is implanted into a very young last instar larva (cf. Novák, Červenková, 1959/1961). Therefore the morphogenetic effects of a transplanted gland would appear to be not very suitable for an evaluation of its activity. On the other hand, the effect of the gland on oxygen consumption or on other metabolic features might be very instructive.

Isolation of a Hormone

The ultimate stage in research on a given hormone is reached with its isolation and the determination of its chemical properties. With insects this stage has as yet only been reached with ecdyson. The main chemical procedures used by Butenandt and Karlson (1958) to isolate the pure moulting hormone they called ecdyson are outlined on page 77.

The results of Williams (1956 etc.), Schneiderman (1958 etc.) and other authors are questionable so far as they concern the identity of the substance showing a juvenile-hormone-like activity (cf. p. 119) obtained from extracts of male *cecropia* adults. We must await further confirmation concerning the other alleged brain-extracts from *Bombyx mori* obtained by Kobayashi and Kirimura (1958) (cf. p. 55).

Gersch and Unger (1957) obtained promising results with paper chromatography of the neurohormones of *Carausius morosus* as did L'Hélias (1957) with the same insect using Tisselius and Macheboeuf's micro-electrophoresis technique (cf. p. 213).

Testing a hormone preparation. The first requirement for the chemical isolation of a hormone is a simple and reliable technique for testing the concentration of the given hormone. After each chemical as well as physical process, such as extraction, washing, filtration, division, etc., each fraction obtained must be tested for its hormone content, in order that it may be decided which fraction is to be used in further work.

For test material, a developmental stage or species can be considered suitable, if it does not contain any effective quantity of the given hormone but nevertheless is still capable of producing a recognizable reaction to the presence of the hormone. Such material can be obtained most reliably by removing the source of the hormone artificially. To prevent wastage of material, the smallest possible test subjects should be used.

Butenandt and Karlson (1954) in their experiments with ecdyson success-fully used the so-called *Calliphora* test which had been developed by Becker and Plagge (1939) fifteen years earlier. Mature maggots of the blow fly, just prior to puparium formation, were used as the test material. They were ligatured, without narcosis, in the first third of their body and all specimens in which the frontal part of the body pupated within 24 hours were used in tests. Immediately before use, the front pupated part was cut off and exactly 0·01 ml. of the solution to be tested was injected via the ligature. After 24 hours the number of hind parts which pupated were recorded. The hormone quantity which induces pupation of 50–70% of the injected individuals within 24 hours is designated as a *Calliphora*-unit.

The last instar caterpillar of the moth *Cerura vinula* may be mentioned as a very sensitive test insect. It reacts even to very low hormone concentra-tions with a very pronounced colour change preceding pupation. This colour change is caused by pigments of the ommochrome group (cf. Bück-mann, 1953; Karlson, 1956b). The effect of the hormone is probably just to condition that stage of morphogenesis at which the brown xanthom-matin is chemically reduced to red xanthommatin.

The myotropic effects of the neurohormones on the heart of *Periplaneta americana* were tested by Ralph (1962). In these experiments, the mem-branes between the thoracic and abdominal terga and sterna were cut and the dorsum, with the heart attached, dissected free. The isolated heart was perfused at regular intervals before and between tests by dropping Pringle's solution on to its ventral surface. A drop of a hormone extract in the same solution was placed on the heart and the beats in the following minute were counted and compared with those after the application of the saline alone.

To test the effect of hormones on the colour change of *Carausius morosus* in vitro, Gersch and Mothes (1956) and Mothes (1960) used strips of larval cuticle of approximately equal size in Ringer solution. For testing neurohormones in *Corethra* larvae, Gersch (1956b) used the filtrates of ganglia finely triturated in insect-Ringer and finally boiled. Ivanov and Mescherskaya (1935) used extirpated ovaries in Ringer as test material.

The necessity for testing the various lipid extracts for their juvenile hormone activity has led to the development of new, very sensitive tests. Wigglesworth (1958) applied substances with a supposed juvenile hormone activity to the surface of the body. He allowed the substance to penetrate the epicuticle (the cement layer) by abrading the surface of the body. A standard level of abrasions can be achieved by applying a suspension in distilled water of a variety of microcrystalline substances with sharp edges, e.g. barium sulphate, crystalline aluminium-hydroxide, carborundum 500, activated charcoal. The abrasives are then washed off with a stream of water, after which the degree of abrasion of the epicuticle can be ascertained by immersing the specimen in ammoniacal silver hydroxide for a short time. The substance to be tested is applied either concentrated or diluted with olive oil in various concentrations. The results obtained in this way have been found to be more reproducible than those with a casein emulsion injection technique.

Gilbert and Schneiderman (1957) have elaborated the so-called wax test for juvenile hormone activity. This involves applying the extract under investigation to a normal pupa immediately after pupation. Applied at this time, the active substance affects the newly grown regenerating cells which are the most sensitive. The disadvantage of this method is that the development of the cuticle of the regenerating epidermis is not quite normal, even in the control specimens to which only olive oil or paraffin wax has been applied, and it is often very difficult to decide to what degree the effect obtained is due to the activity of the relevant hormone.

De Wilde (1959) used homogenates from diapausing adults of *Leptinotarsa decemlineata* to test for a juvenilizing effect (cf. p. 119) of extracts from abdomina of *H. cecropia* adult males. The homogenates were prepared from beetles, after removal of their elytra, by one minute of homogenization at a low temperature in a glass homogenizer. The medium used was cooled M/30 phosphate buffer of pH = 6·8 to which sodium succinate had been added in a concentration of 0·075 M. The oxygen consumption of the homogenate was measured in a Warburg respirometer before and after the addition of corpora allata – 2 to 4 pieces per beetle.

Tissue Culture

The culture of insect tissues in vitro is a technique which could make possible very important advances in our understanding of the mechanisms and modes of action of the various insect hormones. However, results with this technique have not yet been entirely satisfactory, and only the latest findings have indicated that there are no fundamental obstacles to obtaining continuous cultures in the same way as is normal for vertebrate work. It may be assumed that an important condition is that metamorphosis hormones, which are indispensable for growth inside the body, must be added. This condition can partly be fulfilled by adding insect haemolymph provided, however, that this has been obtained at a suitable time in the intermoult period when all the necessary factors are present in an effective concentration. Among the earlier papers those by Bělař (1929), Trager (1937) and Fischer (1942), also Wyatt (1956) and Demal (1956) more recently, all mention partial success. Demal achieved differentiation of the imaginal discs of *Drosophila melanogaster* and *Calliphora erythrocephala* in hanging-drop cultures using a medium made up of 5 parts insect-Ringer, 1·5 parts chicken embryo extract, and 0·5 part pupal extract. A little penicillin and streptomycin were added. The cultured discs were washed and subcultured daily. Under these conditions they survived for 3 to 4 days and partial differentiation (without growth) occurred. According to Demal, the presence of the chicken embryo extract is a prerequisite for survival, while the pupal extract is a prerequisite for differentiation. Similar results have been obtained by Gouldon and Karlson (1951) using histoblasts of the grasshopper *Chortophaga viridifasciata*. Wyatt (1956) reports an important improvement in her roller tube culture technique with ovarial tissues of *Bombyx mori*. She uses a physiological solution augmented with cations and amino-acids, with 10% haemolymph from which coagulating proteins have been removed by heating at 60°C for 5 min. and with a small amount of embryonic extract obtained by crushing centrifuged silkworm eggs five days after they were laid. Under these conditions, mitoses have still been found in the tissues two weeks after excision.

Martignoni, Zitger and Wagner (1958) developed a technique for preparing tissue suspensions of thoracic segments of *Peridroma margaritosa* (Haworth) caterpillars. They used the following modification of a physiological solution by Dulbecco and Vogt (1954): (I) NaCl – 8·0 g., KCl – 0·2 g., NaHPO$_4$ – 1·15 g., KH$_2$PO$_4$ – 0·2 g., phenylthiourea (twice recrystallized from hot alcohol) – 0·5 g., distilled water – 800 ml; (II) CaCl$_2$ – 0·2 g., MgCl$_2$.6H$_2$O – 0·1 g., phenylthiourea – 0·52 g., water – 200 ml. Both solutions were sterilized separately in an autoclave and were mixed together only after cooling. Before use, 200 units of penicillin and 100 units of streptomycin per ml. were added. The thoracic segments of the larvae were surface sterilized by successive rinses in 50% ethyl alcohol with 4% formaldehyde and two rinses in 70% ethyl alcohol. Disintegration of the cells was effected in an extract of the hepatopancreas and crop of the snail *Helix aspersa*. This homogenate was centrifuged and the supernatant liquor sterilized by filtration through a Milleposche filter. Disintegration occurred

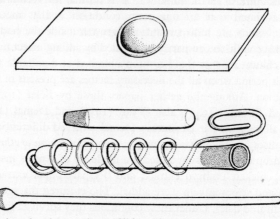

FIG. 7. Devices for tissue culture. Slide with a depression and furrow; micro-container with a fitted stopper, inside a wire spiral for holding it in an ice-container; homogenizing rod.

at room temperature with continuous stirring in an Erlenmeyer flask for 5 to 7 min.

After centrifuging, several washings in physiological solution and de-canting, the cells were suspended in the culture medium. The thoracic segments from one larva yielded about 160,000 cells. They were round in form and clear with a distinct nucleus. They thrived in the culture, remaining healthy for 4–5 days.

In recent years Trager (1959) reported good results with tissues of the tse-tse fly (*Glossina palpalis*). He used a culture medium of the following composition (solutions A_1–A_3 in mg. per 100 ml. water):

Solution A_1: NaCl – 90, KCl – 300, $NaH_2PO_4.H_2O$ – 110, $MgSO_4.7H_2O$ – 310, $CaCl_2$ – 80, glucose – 150, lactalbumin hydrolysate – 1,000.

Solution A_2: As for A_1, with yeast extract (Difco) – 200.

Solution A_3: As for A_1, with trehalose – 50, L-malic acid – 50, a ketoglucosic acid – 25, succinic acid – 5, yeast extract – 200

In all solutions the pH was adjusted to 6·8–6·9 with 1·0% NaOH. Solutions were sterilized through Selas 03 porcelain filters.

Solution B: Reduced glutathione – 200 mg, ascorbic acid – 2 mg, in 10 ml. double distilled water. The solution was sterilized through an ultra-fine glass filter.

Solution $C_{1,2,3}$: 8 ml. of solution A_1, A_2, A_3 respectively with 2 ml. sheep serum.

Solution C_4: the same as C_3 with 0·5 ml. B.

Solution D: 1,2,3,4, in 1 ml. $C_{1,2,3,4}$, respectively with two sterilized 12 days old pupae of *Glossina palpalis* crushed gently and centrifuged for 15 mins. at 2000 revolutions per min. The supernatant liquor together with the resuspended fatty layer at the surface constitutes the culture medium (pH 6·7–6·9).

Trager's solution with 10% silkworm serum (centrifuged at 2,000 r.p.m. for 10 min. to remove the blood cells) was used for incubation of ovarian and testicular cells by Gaw, Liu and Zia (1959) who claim to have succeeded in obtaining permanent silkworm tissue cultures. After 2 or 3 days of culture the cells formed a continuous layer and were at a stage suitable for subculturing. To separate the cells from the cover slip, 0·25% trypsin in Trager's solution was added. The cultures were heated in a water bath at 26°C for 15 min. until the cells separated from the glass surface. 22 successive subcultures were made, and the cells were still alive when the paper was written.

Another at least partly successful experiment was that by Jones and Cunningham (1960) with cultures from *Philosamia adversa*. The medium was changed every fifth day. The cultures remained healthy for up to four weeks, the cells resembling chick fibroblasts. In cultures 5 to 6 days old the mean mitotic index was 1·0. It later decreased similarly to the primary cultures of mammalian tissues (cf. p. 281).

Tissue Culture in Vivo

An interesting technique of insect tissue culture was developed by Lüscher (1948) in Prof. Wigglesworth's laboratory. He replaced a cut leg of the bug *Rhodnius prolixus* by a glass capillary containing insect-Ringer and closed at the end with paraffin wax. In a few days a proliferation of epidermal cells and other types of tissue was observed. With this technique, the cells inside the capillary tube could be freely observed, even under a high-power microscrope, by fixing the bug on a slide and including it under a coverslip together with a fluid with a high refractive index, e.g. a medium containing cedar wood oil. Besides producing suitable test objects for studying the effects of different chemicals on insect tissues as Lüscher suggested, the method is undoubtedly also very suitable for observing cytological effects of various insect hormones in vivo.

The Histology of Endocrine Glands

Most of the usual histological fixatives are suitable for fixing endocrine glands dissected from insects, and much will depend on the subsequent staining method. For whole insects Carnoy's fluid (2–10 min.) or Dubosq-Brazil are the most suitable. It is advisable to narcotize the specimens in ether before fixation in order to prevent damage to internal tissues caused by nervous shock before death. The hard chitinous cuticle is a serious obstacle to sectioning with a microtome. Apart from the normal softening agents, such as diaphanol, dehydration through a sequence of butyl alcohol-70% ethyl alcohol mixtures followed by several changes of pure butyl alcohol has given good results. Each bath lasts about 12 hours. From pure butyl alcohol, the specimen passes through a mixture of butyl alcohol and paraffin wax (1 : 1) at 45°C to three changes of melted paraffin wax with a high melting point (65°C) but with the addition of 5 to 10% beeswax. However, where possible, the embedding of dissected organs is preferable.

For staining, most of the standard methods are suitable, e.g. haematoxylin (Ehrlich's or Delafield's), eosin, Mallory's and Prenant and Gabe's trichrome (cf. Gabe, 1953a, b). In this connection, the papers of B. Scharrer (1952), Arvy and Gabe (1952), de Lerma (1956) and Herlant-Meewis (1950a, b) may be recommended.

Special stains have been developed for staining neurosecretory granules, such as Gomori's haematoxylin phloxin and various formulations of paraldehyde-fuchsin (cf. Gabe, 1953b). De Lerma (1956) stained chromophilic substances in neurones which had been fixed in a mixture of sublimate and picric acid, using Giemsa or toluidine blue at a very low concentration (1 : 10,000 at pH = 6). Highly selective methods are alcian blue-performic acid (Sloper, 1957) and astral blue (Müller, 1957) (cf. p. 229).

Staining in vivo. Some endocrine glands in most insect species are almost transparent, both in situ in the dissected body and in physiological solutions, and may therefore be practically invisible. Perhaps this is the reason, as B. Scharrer (1948) has suggested for e.g. the prothoracic glands of cockroaches, why many glands escaped the attention of research workers for so long. But even well-known and clearly visible organs may have to be stained to show up various anatomical details. The most commonly used stains for this purpose are methylene blue and neutral red. Their advantage is that different structures can be intensified by varying the concentration and staining time. Thus, for example, in her study of the prothoracic glands in *Leucophaea maderae*, B. Scharrer (1948) injected methylene blue and neutral red in a concentration of 1 : 10,000 into the animals at a set interval before dissection. Pflugfelder (1937a, b) stained nerve fibres in the corpora allata and corpora cardiaca with methylene blue diluted 1 : 400 in 0·5% NaCl. Pflugfelder also states that the osmiophilic cells in the corpora cardiaca stain bright red with neutral red while the contents of vacuoles remain yellow. The author (Novák, 1951b) has used methylene blue in insect-Ringer (1 : 10,000, with 3 hours of staining and 10 min. washing) to stain corpora allata (strongly) and corpora cardiaca (lightly) in the bug *Oncopeltus fasciatus*.

Observations in vivo. E. and M. Thomsen (1954) described a method for studying neurosecretory material in living cells from the brain of *Calliphora erythrocephala* using dark-ground illumination. Carlisle (1953, cf. Carlisle and Knowles, 1959) showed the importance of phase-contrast microscopy in the study of crustacean endocrine organs, and doubtless it would be equally promising for similar studies with insects. Little is yet known about the possibilities of using the fluorescence microscope in insect hormone research. However, it has been shown that several insect neurohormones and the corresponding neurosecretory cells show a primary blue fluorescence in u.v. light, connected with the presence of pterines in solution. This fluorescence shows up in a lightly acid medium (cf. p. 280).

Research with the electron microscope. Meyer and Pflugfelder (1958) studied the structure of the corpora cardiaca in *Carausius morosus* by means of the electron microscope. The glands were fixed in situ through a dorsal incision of the integument with a mixture of phosphate buffer (Sörensen) pH = 7·2, 5% formaldehyde and 0·85% NaCl at low temperature (+2°C) for 3 hours and after preparation they were placed in fresh fixative for a further hour. The preparation was then washed and the glands were fixed again for an hour in a 1% solution of OsO_4 (after Palade). With this technique the very delicate cytoplasm remained especially well preserved.

Mercer and Brunet (1959) fixed the collaterial glands in *Periplaneta americana* in a 1% solution of OsO_4 in veronal-buffer with pH = 7·4 (cf. Palade, 1952) for 2 hours at 0 to 5°C. The fixed organs were washed in running water for 10 min. and then dehydrated, passed through absolute alcohol, xylol and a xylol-araldite mixture (1 : 1) to araldite (1 hour at 60°C) and finally embedded in fresh araldite in a gelatine capsule. Methacrylates have been found unsuitable for embedding gland cells as the cells become damaged during polymerization (cf. Glauert and Glauert, 1958). Schultz (1960) used the electron microscope to study the corpora allata and associated nerves in the sphingid *Celerio lineata*.

Physiological Methods in Insect Hormone Research

Parallel with the extremely intensive research on the morphogenetic effects of insect hormones, there has been a steady increase in the number of papers dealing with the effect of hormones on the physiological and biochemical functions of the insect body, from both qualitative and quantitative aspects.

Almost all the methods used in physiological research could be cited in this context.

Just to mention the most important methods which have actually been used in specific branches of insect hormone research would involve going far beyond the scope of this book. Nevertheless, it may perhaps be useful to mention at least the most important papers where such methods have been specially adapted for the study of insect hormones.

Williams and his colleagues (1950, 1954, 1956 etc.), and Shappirio and Williams (1952, 1953 etc.) studied insect respiration under normal and experimental conditions as well as the action of various respiratory enzymes, describing many improvements of procedure and technique. E. Thomsen (1949, 1952 etc.) used various delicate techniques in her research on the physiological effects of the corpora allata and neurosecretory brain cells. Janda, jr., and his colleagues (1952, 1959, 1960 etc.) studied metabolism during development in various insect species. Sláma (1960, 1961 etc.) studied the effects of the metamorphosis hormones on metabolism and enzyme activity and described a special volumetric micro-respirometer which had a sensitivity about 100 times greater than a Warburg apparatus. Especially useful methods have been described by De Wilde (1958, 1959, 1960 etc.) from research on the metabolism of the Colorado beetle during imaginal diapause and its endocrine nature. Punt (1950, 1956a, b etc.) described the use of a diapherometer for the continuous determination of oxygen consumption and carbon dioxide output in insects.

CHAPTER THREE

The Metamorphosis Hormones

The longest and best known of the insect hormones are those which influence postembryonic development. At present, three of these metamorphosis hormones are recognized: (A) the activation hormone produced by neurosecretory cells in the insect brain, which conditions the reactivation of the body after each moult and the production of the other two metamorphosis hormones; (B) the moulting hormone produced by the prothoracic glands or corresponding tissues, which conditions the moulting process and thus, indirectly, growth and morphogenesis; (C) the juvenile hormone produced by the corpora allata, which conditions the growth of the larval parts in all metabolous insects (Pterygota), the function of the ovarial follicles of adult females in most insects, and several other structures and functions of the insect body which are unable to develop in its absence. All three hormones are essential for the normal course of postembryonic development. The activation hormone is a typical neurohormone, the other two are true glandular hormones, highly species unspecific or even class unspecific. They are closely mutually interdependent, both in their production and function.

Terminology

Although the problem of insect hormones and metamorphosis has been intensively studied in recent years, or perhaps for this reason, no generally accepted terminology has been developed. It might, therefore, be as well to start with a closer definition of the terminology used in the present work.

Metamorphosis. By metamorphosis is understood that part alone of the postembryonic development which takes place in the absence of a morphogenetically active concentration of juvenile hormone, i.e. the last larval instar of Hemimetabola and both the last larval and the pupal instars of Holometabola. This is in agreement with most other physiological works. Although it must not be denied that a part of the adult differentiation is realized at the beginning of each larval instar, there is no more reason to call this metamorphosis than there is in the case of the similar successive postembryonic differentiation in ametabolous insects (Ametabola).

Postembryonic development of insects is thus divided into two parts or stages:
the larval stage (or larval development) beginning with the hatching of the
larva and ending with the penultimate larval instar (the ecdysis from the
penultimate to the last larval instar); and the subsequent metamorphosis
stage (or metamorphosis) ending with the emergence of the adult insect.

Instar: Both the larval and the metamorphosis stages are subdivided into
instars. An instar is that part of the postembryonic development which
takes place between two successive ecdyses. In contrast to many other
authors, the term is used in both the morphogenetical and the chronological
sense of the word. A new definition was suggested by Hinton (1958),
according to which, the instar begins at the moment of deposition of the
new cuticle and ends with the moult, which is the next separation of the
cuticle from the epidermis. From the point of view of morphological
description this has the advantage that the term 'instar' refers to one and
the same cuticle whereas in the definition used here each instar starts inside
the old cuticle which is replaced by a new one during the instar. It has also
the merit of drawing the attention of morphologists to those stages in the
moulting process which take place beneath the opaque cuticle. Irrespective
of the fact that postembryonic development is subdivided into a succession
of overlapping cyclic processes, so that the determination of the limits of
individual instars is to some extent arbitrary, the first mentioned definition
of the instar seems more suitable for the purposes of this book for the
following reasons:

1. Ecdysis is connected with a series of other processes, such as the
resorption of the moulting fluid, the occupation of the new shape of the
body by distension of the newly formed cuticle (even though this was laid
down some time previously), the deposition of the wax and cement layers
of the epicuticle, the tanning and hardening of the new cuticle, etc. It is
therefore the most important and most conspicuous section of each moulting cycle.

2. Even if successive moults are connected with an uninterrupted succession of various physiological processes, most of these are, nevertheless,
clearly arranged in cycles within each interecdysis, but not intermoult,
period. Feeding and its associated increase in weight, respiration and
hormone production, for example, are interrupted during ecdyses but not
during moults. By selecting the detachment of the cuticle as the start of
an instar, all of these evidently individual processes are divided between
two different instars.

3. The size and shape of the body, even though determined by the newly
deposited cuticle, particularly that of heavily sclerotized parts such as the
head capsule, is also changed at each ecdysis but not at the moults.

4. The detachment of the cuticle can only be observed in histological sections (rather difficult to make because of the hard sclerotized cuticle). The moment of ecdysis is therefore also preferable as the dividing point from a practical point of view.

Most of these reasons remain valid even in such cases as the last larval instar of higher Diptera. There, although the chief characteristic of ecdysis, the shedding of the exuvium, is obviated, as is the tanning of the newly formed pupal cuticle, other characteristics, such as, for example, the removal of the moulting fluid and the formation of the epicuticular layers, remain; and these are sufficient to enable the instars to be distinguished.

Stage of development. The stage of development is a general term for a section of ontogenetical development characterized by significant biochemical or morphological processes or by both, such as the protopode, polypode, oligopode, and postoligopode stages in embryogenesis, the larval stage (comprising the first to penultimate larval instar), the metamorphosis stage (comprising the last larval and the pupal instars), the maturation stage, the stage of sexual maturity, etc.

Moulting process. The succession of biochemical, physiological and morphological changes preceding each ecdysis constitutes the moulting process or *moulting*. This commences with the swelling of the epidermis followed by detachment of the old cuticle, usually referred to as the *moult*. Then the moulting fluid is produced, in which the inner layers of the cuticle are gradually digested, and a new cuticle is laid down by the epidermis cells. The process culminates in *ecdysis* which is preceded by the resorption of the moulting fluid and followed by the tanning and hardening of the exocuticle and the secretion of the wax and cement layers of the epicuticle. The laying down of the inner layers of the endocuticle by the epidermis cells continues after the ecdysis and usually does not stop until immediately before the start of the next moulting process. This is the end of the moulting process which has just occurred (cf. fig. 38).

Growth. By growth is understood, generally speaking, the increase in the amount of living matter of the body (organized protein molecules). The following special types of the growth may be distinguished in insects:

Isometric growth (harmonic or proportionate growth). The type of growth where there is an equal rate of increase in all parts of the body, i.e. there are no morphological changes. The shape of the body at the end of an isometric period is a homothetic figure of that at the beginning.

Anisometric growth (disharmonic or disproportionate growth). The type of growth where there is a different rate of increase in different parts of the body, with a resulting change of shape. Two kinds of anisometric growth are distinguished in this book (cf. Novák, 1960, 1962). These are:

(*i*) *Allometric growth* (or anisometric growth in the strict sense). Here all parts of the body grow although at different rates, as for instance in the post-embryonic development of mammals.

(*ii*) *Gradient growth*. In this type of growth, only certain parts of the body, the gradients, grow. Growth of the remaining parts is stopped and eventually they are wholly or partly removed by histolysis. This occurs for example in the embryogenesis of most animals and in the metamorphosis of insects. Gradient growth is the chief factor in morphogenesis.

Differentiation. The chief feature of development, the sequence of changes which occurs in the body in a given period of ontogenesis, irrespective of growth. The three following types are distinguished: (1) *chemical* (biochemical) differentiation, the sequence of changes in the chemical composition of the body irrespective of changes in weight, shape, function, etc., (2) *morphological* differentiation or morphogenesis, the sequence of changes in the shape of the body, (3) *functional* differentiation, the sequence of development of the various functions of the body. These three types of differentiation are all closely interrelated in normal development. In ontogenesis, chemical differentiation usually precedes morphological differentiation, which in turn precedes functional differentiation. In phylogenesis, functional differentiation usually precedes chemical and morphological differentiation of the corresponding part of the body. (This must follow from the action of natural selection and its role in evolution: it means that structures of the body can be favoured by selection and thus developed and specialized for a given function only where this function already exists to some extent.)

Larval structures. The parts of the body which can grow only in the larval stage (see above), i.e. in the presence of a certain minimum concentration of the juvenile hormone (cf. p. 164). They lose the ability for further growth during the metamorphosis and usually undergo partial or complete histolysis at that time (cf. Novák, 1951b, 1956).

Imaginal structures. Those parts of the body the growth of which is independent of the presence of juvenile hormone. Their development is accelerated during the metamorphosis when the growth of the larval structures ceases. They constitute the greater part of the imaginal body.

Larva. The term is used here in its broadest sense, as in Wigglesworth (1939 etc.) and Hinton (1958, etc.), but not Yeshikov (1941) and Snodgrass (1954), to include the entire postembryonic stage of development which precedes the metamorphosis in all insects. The term 'nymph' as a special type of larva is retained for the larval stage of *Hemimetabola* and 'larvula' is kept for the first larval instars of *Odonata* etc. 'Eonymph', 'mesonymph' and 'pronymph' in the sense of Berlese (1913) and Sláma (1960 etc.) refer to the prepupal stages of sawflies. Prepupa is the term for the latter portion of the last larval instar of *Holometabola*, which is characterized by the advanced pupal moulting process with an abundance of moulting fluid and retraction of the body.

Pupa. This term is used for the last postembryonic instar (second metamorposis instar) in Holometabola, which is the period between the pupal and imaginal ecdyses. Internal morphological changes, which vary considerably in extent according to the insect, occur during this instar, whilst most of the external changes are realized in the first metamorphosis instar (last larval instar).

Hemimetabola and Holometabola. These terms are used in the taxonomic sense as in Imms (1946) and Obenberger (1952) but unlike Weber (1954), Snodgrass etc. *Hemimetabola* (= *Heterometabola*, = *Exopterygota*) have only one metamorphosis instar, *Holometabola* (= *Endopterygota*) have two. The prefix 'hemi-' does not refer to the amount of morphogenesis which, on the average, is not very different in the two subclasses, but to the number of metamorphosis instars.

A. THE ACTIVATION HORMONE, AH

(= 'moulting hormone', part. Wigglesworth, 1934; = 'Larvenhäutungshormon' = 'Verpuppungshormon' = 'Imaginalhäutungeshormon', part. Piepho, 1938; = 'Growth and differentiation hormone', part. B. Scharrer, 1948; = thoracotropin, B. Scharrer, 1952; = 'adenotropes Gehirnhormon', Weber, 1954; = 'Aktivationsfaktor', Wigglesworth, 1952.)

The first suggestion regarding a hormonal function of the insect brain was made by Kopeć (1917, 1922) whose experiments with *Lymantria dispar* caterpillars proved conclusively that the brain is necessary for pupation. This was the first evidence for an internal secretion of any kind in insects. Tauber (= Taabor, 1925), working independently, concluded, from several years' work on blood transfusion and ligaturing using *Deilephila euphorbiae* caterpillars, that insect metamorphosis is controlled by endocrines. Further evidence for the existence of a humoral control of moulting in other species of Lepidoptera is contained in the papers by Koller (1929, cf. 1938) and Buddenbrock (1930a, b, 1931, cf. 1950).

The first evidence, however, for the existence of a special hormone, produced by the brain and controlling moulting, was obtained by Wigglesworth (1934, 1935, 1936) from his classic experiments with decapitation, parabiosis and transplantation in the blood-sucking bug, *Rhodnius prolixus*. This was the true beginning of insect endocrinology which has now developed into a special, very intensively studied, biological discipline. It was the same author who, in collaboration with Hanström (1938, 1940, 1943), first discovered the source of the activation hormone in the neurosecretory cells of the brain (Wigglesworth, 1939b, 1940).

At about the same time, Fraenkel (1934, 1935) showed a similar hormonal control of pupation in *Calliphora* larva by his well known ligaturing experiments. Similar conclusions were reached by Bounhiol (1936, 1938) from his experiments with *Bombyx mori*; by Bodenstein (1937, 1938a, b, c) on the basis of several years' experimental work on the transplantation of appendages from young to fully grown caterpillars; by Kühn and Piepho (1936, 1938, 1940) for *Galleria mellonella* and by Hadorn (1937a, b, 1938, 1939), Hadorn and Neel (1938a, b) and Hadorn and B. Scharrer (1938) for *Drosophila*. Since then, the number of papers on endocrine control of moulting has increased very rapidly.

Fukuda (1940a, b, 1941a, b, 1944) was the first to show that the AH does not affect the moulting process directly but by controlling the secretion of the prothoracic glands. These findings were confirmed and closely examined by Williams (1946, 1947a, b, c, d, 1948, 1952 etc.) and his colleagues (Schneiderman, 1953b, 1954a, b etc., Susman, 1952, and others).

The first suggestion regarding the possible function of the corpora cardiaca in neurosecretion was made by De Lerma (1933, 1934) and its connection with the neurosecretory cells of the brain was elucidated by Hanstrom (1936, 1939, 1942 etc.), by Pflugfelder (1937, 1938c, d) and particularly, by B. Scharrer (1937, 1941) and B. and E. Scharrer (1937, 1944 etc.) who showed by a detailed histological and experimental study that the neurosecretory cells of the brain with their axons, together with the corpora cardiaca, form a single neurosecretory system corresponding to that of the neurosecretory cells of the hypothalamus with their axons and the neurohypophysis in vertebrates. Since that time the neurosecretory function of the insect brain and corpora cardiaca, and its connection with moulting and metamorphosis, has been found whenever it has been seriously looked for, that is, in practically all the chief orders of metabolous

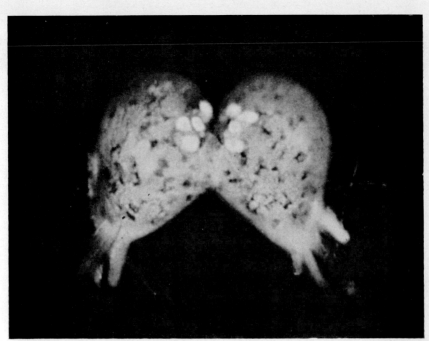

PLATE I. *Above:* Brain of the silkworm (*Bombyx mori*) caterpillar with two median groups each of four neurosecretory cells, conspicuous by their bluish-white coloration. Reflected light.

Below: Transverse section of the pars intercerebralis of protocerebrum, with two groups of neurosecretory cells of the pars intercerebralis, in *Pyrrhocoris apterus*. Stained with Gomori, chromhaematoxylin-phloxin.

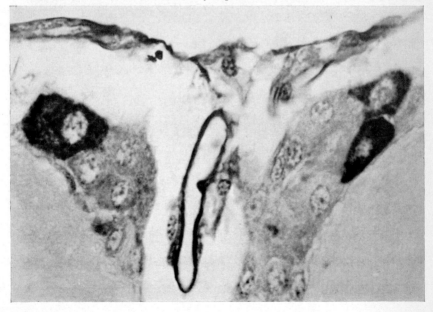

insects (Pterygota). There is also histological evidence for its existence in Apterygota (Cazal, 1948, Paclt, 1956 etc.).

A series of papers by Gersch and his school (cf. p. 211) on the chromato-phorotropic and myotropic activity of insect brain extracts has raised the question as to whether some of the newly discovered factors (e.g. neuro-hormone C and neurohormone D of Gersch and Unger, 1957a, cf. 1960) could be identical with AH. This problem has been discussed in detail by Raabe (1959) and a recent paper by Gersch (1962) brings experimental evidence in favour of the identity of the AH and the neurohormone D_1. Nevertheless, further experimental evidence is needed regarding the relationship between AH and the humoral factor of the insect brain which affects water balance, however tempting it might appear (cf. p. 214) to consider them identical. On the other hand, there is no doubt regarding the relationship between, on the one side, the nervous stimulus induced by changes in photoperiodism and the role of the AH with a temporary break in its production and, on the other, the larval and pupal diapause which is caused by an insufficiency of MH and ovarial diapause in adults caused by lack of JH. The mechanism of action of AH on the prothoracic glands and corpora allata is, however, not yet clear. The possibility that AH has a general effect on most of the body functions, such as metabolism, secretory activity, water balance etc., by influencing the cell membranes, would appear to offer a very promising field for future research.

The conclusions of B. and E. Scharrer (1944) that a close analogy exists between the neurosecretory system of three large groups of animals, Crustacea, Insects and Vertebrates (cf. p. 273), are in full agreement with such a possibility. They confirm the earlier views of these authors (1944 etc.), Hanström (1939 etc.) and others. The relationship between AH production and the secretory activity of the corpora allata, which regulates the activity of the ovarial follicle cells (studied in detail by Johansson, 1958), is in agreement both with the general nature of the AH effects and with the features of the neurosecretory system common to the three groups of animals mentioned.

The Neurosecretory Cells of the Brain

Morphology. The neurosecretory cells of the brain, the source of the AH, are usually arranged in two groups, placed symmetrically on the upper surface of each hemisphere near the median furrow in the pars inter-cerebralis protocerebri. There are 4 to 15 or more neurosecretory cells in each group (4 in *Bombyx mori*, 6 in *Calliphora* larvae, 7 in *Pyrrhocoris apterus*, 7–8 in various Hymenoptera, 15 in cockroaches). They are often very conspicuous in a living brain dissected in Ringer because of their milk-white or slightly bluish colour. The transparent nucleus shows as a dark spot in the middle of each cell. The cells are still more conspicuous when examined under dark-ground illumination, appearing shining white against the dark background (cf. Thomsen and Thomsen, 1954). The axons of these two groups of cells form a pair of nerves – the nervi corporum cardiacarum interni. These two nerves cross inside the brain in the mid-line and each enters the corpus cardiacum on the opposite side of the body (cf. fig. 9). External to each of the two above-mentioned groups of neurosecretory cells is, in most insects, a smaller group, usually of 2–4 cells, the axons of which form the nervi corporum cardiacarum externi, either of them entering the corpus cardiacum on the same side of the body.

Several authors have described the transportation of the material originating in the neurosecretory cells of the brain into the corpora cardiaca via the nervi corporum cardiacarum. The neurosecretory material has been observed in histological preparations (M. Thomsen 1951) and under dark ground illumination (E. Thomsen, M. Thomsen, 1953). Severing of the nervi corporum cardiacarum led to an accumulation of neurosecretory material in the distal end of the portion connected to the brain and the disappearance of the granules in the end on the other side of the cut (B. Scharrer, 1952, cf. fig. 9). A similar observation was made by E. Thomsen (1954), using dark-ground illumination, when the cardiac-recurrent nerve[1] of adult *Calliphora* females was ligatured with a silk thread. The passing of part of the neurosecretory material from the corpus cardiacum via the nervus allatus into the corpus allatum, where it is said to stimulate the gland and increase its size, has recently been studied by Nayar (1958). The same author also observed that the neurosecretory granules pass via the nervus recurrens into the walls of the dorsal aorta, which is innervated by this nerve. From here they appear to pass directly into the blood stream.

Histology. The use of special staining techniques, such as Gomori (chrome-haematoxylin-phloxin; cf. p. 30) and paraldehyde fuchsin (cf. p. 30), renders the neurosecretory cells very conspicuous in histological preparations and the neurosecretory material may easily be followed along their axons (cf. fig. 8 and p. 208).

Using histochemical methods, a considerable amount of acid phosphatase was found in the cytoplasm of most of the neurosecretory cells in the bug *Iphita limbata*, whilst it was absent in the cytoplasm of the other nerve

[1] In *Calliphora* the nervi corporum cardiacarum I and II fuse with the nervus recurrens before entering the corpora cardiaca.

cells. On the other hand, the phosphatase content of the nuclei of the above-mentioned cells was lower than that in the neighbouring nerve cells. On the basis of his detailed histological studies on the brain of the lygaeid bug *Oncopeltus fasciatus* Dallas, Johansson (1958a, b) distinguished four different types of cells the staining characteristics of which suggested a neurosecretory function. *A-cells*, the most conspicuous of all, stain dark

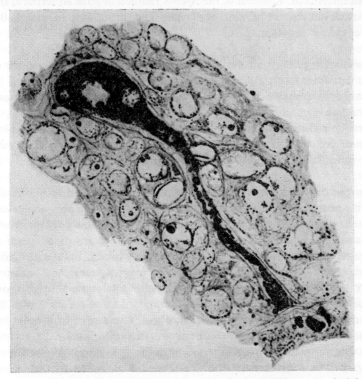

FIG. 8. A neurosecretory cell of the brain in a larva of *Tabanus* sp. Staining: Flemming-Heidenhain. (× 1200) after M. Thomsen, 1951.

purple-red with paraldehyde fuchsin and blue-black with Gomori chromehaematoxylin. They contain a large number of granules which fill most of the perikaryon. The cells are pear-like or sometimes irregular in shape, and occur immediately beneath the neurilemma. When examined alive, under dark-ground illumination, they are conspicuous by their shining bluish-white colour. Their axons form the nervi corporum cardiacarum I. *B-cells* stain green or blue-green with paraldehyde fuchsin and red with Gomori. They are somewhat smaller than the A-cells and more irregular in shape.

They contain no granules and occur deeper in the mass of ganglion cells. *C-cells* stain purple-red with paraldehyde fuchsin and reddish with chrome haematoxylin-phloxin. They occur in the same layer as the B-cells, are irregular in shape and contain a flaky cytoplasm. *D-cells* have a fine granular cytoplasm which stains pale purple-red with paraldehyde fuchsin and pale blue-black with chrome haematoxylin-phloxin. They are somewhat larger than the A-cells. Removal of the A-cells resulted in reduced fertility, and delayed, but did not prevent, egg laying. The corpus allatum was smaller after their extirpation.

Embryogenesis. The only available data on the origin and development of the neurosecretory cells during embryogenesis are given in the papers by Jones (1953, 1956a, b). This author found, in embryos of *Locustana pardalina* when mitotic activity had re-appeared after the diapause, several particularly large cells in those places in the brain where, later, the typical neurosecretory cells occur. These cells have a particular connection with the function of the ventral glands of the head and with moulting.

Phylogenesis. There is an abundant literature on the origin and evolution of the neurosecretory cells in phylogenesis. It has been reliably established that neurosecretory cells occur not only in all insects including Apterygota (Hanström, 1937; Marcus, 1951) but also in other arthropods such as Crustacea (Hanström, 1937), Xiphosura (B. Scharrer, 1941) and Chilopoda (Gabe, 1953b), in Annelida (Sactor, 1951; Scharrer and Scharrer, 1937) and, phylogenetically lowest, in Turbellaria Polyclada (Turner, 1949; Clark, 1956). Hanström (1940, 1953) assumed them to originate with the so-called lateral frontal organs in the lower Crustacea which lie in the epidermis quite separate from the brain. In the higher Crustacea they become very close to the brain and form the well-known pair of frontal organs. The neurosecretory cells of these are connected by their axons to the corresponding sinus gland at the side of the brain, where the secreted material is stored. In the Apterygota, they form two groups of cells on the surface of the protocerebrum which are enclosed by a connective tissue membrane. From each of these groups a nerve arises which passes through the brain in a typical chiasma and reaches the corpus cardiacum of the opposite side. These neurosecretory cells and the granules in their axons give the same Gomori positive reaction as the neurosecretory cells of Pterygota. The typical neurosecretory cells of Pterygota develop from these two groups by a process of inclusion into the brain mass during which the connective tissue membrane disappears.

From what has been said it is evident that the activation hormone is phylogenetically the oldest of the three metamorphosis hormones. As regards the origin of the neurosecretory cells of the pars intercerebralis, Clark (1955) derives their function from the original epidermis cells from which they have developed as nervous tissues and assumes their secretory function to be primary and their nervous function secondary. He points out that they are the most primitive and phylogenetically oldest parts of the brain (cf. p. 229).

Corpora cardiaca[1]

Morphology. The first mention of the corpora cardiaca in the literature is without doubt that by Lyonet (1762) in his work on the anatomy of *Cossus cossus*. They consist of a pair of bodies situated immediately behind the brain, between the anterior end of the dorsal vein and the oesophagus, in front of the corpora allata with which they are connected by the nervi allati. They are usually fused medially and in some cases they are also fused with the corpora allata (cf. p. 81). In the ring gland of Diptera Cyclorrhapha, they form the lower median part of the ring, which is characterized by the small size of the cells, and fuse in the middle with the hypocerebral ganglion and at the sides with the R-cells (cf. p. 67). They are innervated by two pairs of nerves from the brain, the nervi corporum cardiacarum interni and externi which are composed respectively of the axons of the median and lateral groups of neurosecretory cells of the pars intercerebralis protocerebri, as previously mentioned. The corpus cardiacum is composed of two parts, a nervous part (originally, the corpora cardiaca were supposed to be normal ganglia, the 'pharyngeal ganglia'), and a glandular part. They differ, at first glance, from the corpora allata and from all nervous ganglia by their bright, milky-white coloration.

Histology. In addition to the neurons, the following two types of cells can be distinguished: (1) The chromophobic cells whose cytoplasm is not stained by the usual staining methods. They form the main connective tissue in the corpus cardiacum in which there are, usually, scattered cells of the other type. (2) The chromophilic cells which are deeply stained by various stains and furnished with characteristic pseupodia-like processes. Cazal (1948) assumed them to be modified neurons which had lost their nervous function and intensified their secretory function. Arvy and Gabe (1954) found small granules in the cytoplasm of the corpora cardiaca cells

---

[1] For similar reasons to M. Thomsen (1951), the author prefers the original and more generally used term corpora cardiaca to Cazal's (1948) 'corpora paracardiaca'.

in Plecoptera, which stained deeply with phloxin. Numerous fibres of the nervi corporum cardiacarum are present in the corpora cardiaca in addition to the above-mentioned cells, these ramify and most of the branches reach the surface. Some of the granules produced by the neurosecretory cells of the brain are stored here, but the remainder reach the surface where they are washed off by the haemolymph. A small amount of the neurosecretory

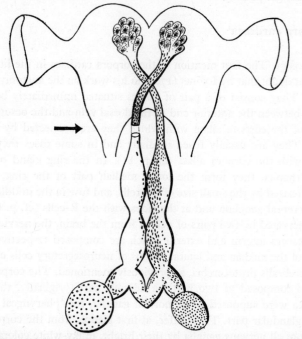

FIG. 9. The effect of breaking one of the two nervi corporum cardiacarum. Note the accumulation of neurosecretory granules in the proximal nerve stump, its disappearence from the corpus cardiacum and the swelling of the corresponding corpus allatum. (After B. Scharrer, 1952.)

material has been shown to pass through the corpora cardiaca into the corpora allata via the nervi allati (M. Thomsen, 1954b, etc.) in several species without producing any evident effect.

In addition to the neurosecretory granules, Nayar (1957b, 1956) found a secretion, which he does not think to be of neurosecretory origin, in the chromophilic cells of *Iphita limbata*. De Lerma (1956) also suggests the existence of a special secretion of the corpus cardiacum in *Hydrous piceus*. It occurs in the form of homogeneous acidophilic inclusions which are more or less abundant in the chromophilic cells of the corpus cardiacum.

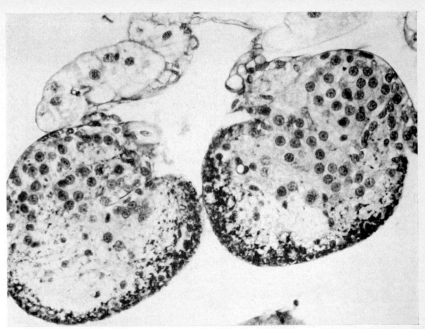

PLATE II. *Above:* Transverse section through either corpus cardiacum in *Periplaneta americana* showing both the glandular (chromaffine) and the neural (chromophobe) part with abundant neurosecretory granules in the peripheral layer. Stained with Gomori, chromhaematoxylin-phloxin.

Below: Longitudinal section of a corpus allatum and the adjacent part of the nervus allatus in *P. americana*, stained as above.

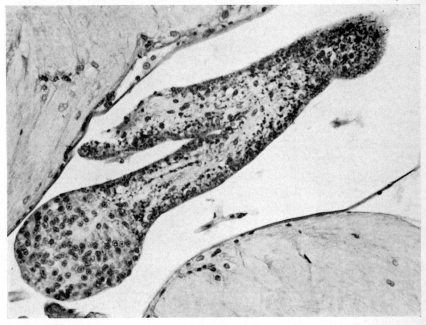

No intracellular Gomori-positive granules were found inside the corpora cardiaca cells.

Arvy and Gabe (1953a, b, 1954) also emphasize the occurrence of a true intracellular neurosecretion in the corpora cardiaca on the basis of their great knowledge of many groups of insects. The same conclusion was reached by Hanström (1953) for Apterygota.

Johansson (1958) was able to distinguish three different types of cell in the corpora cardiaca of *Oncopeltus fasciatus*. Two of these are large chromophilic cells which occur in different parts of the corpus cardiacum and differ in their staining characteristics with paraldehyde fuchsin. Those of the frontal and lateral portions of the gland stain green whereas those of the hind and median portions take on a pale red colour. The third type are interstitial chromophobic cells. These are dispersed throughout the corpus cardiacum but are most abundant medially. It is interesting to note that Johansson did not observe any accumulation of neurosecretory material in the corpora cardiaca of *Oncopeltus*; here the granules are stored exclusively in the walls of the aorta dorsalis as in *Iphita limbata* (Nayar, 1953, 1956) but distinct from *Rhodnius prolixus* (Wigglesworth, 1956) where they are stored in the corpora cardiaca. A similar condition was found in *Hydrocyrius columbiae* by Junqua (1956). It appears to be, phylogenetically, a secondary utilization of the tissue which makes possible a quicker passing of the neurosecretory material into the haemolymph.

Mayer and Pflugfelder (1958) found only two kinds of cells in the corpora cardiaca of *Carausius morosus* (cf. p. 31): the osmiophilic cells containing granules of neurosecretory material and generally forming well delimited groups in the corresponding part of the gland; and the osmiophobic cells containing a system of vacuoles, special lamellated granules and peculiar oblong mitochondria. In the nerve endings inside the gland, granules 500 to 2,000 Å in size were found, which correspond to those known from the neurohypophysis of vertebrates and are without doubt of neurosecretory origin (cf. p. 273).

Function. Johansson (1958) assumed the corpora cardiaca to have two functions: the storage and mixing of the products of different groups and types of neurosecretory cells and, in addition, the production of a separate hormone of their own. A similar suggestion was made by Cameron (1953). He showed that the corpora cardiaca produce a special active substance (?orthodiphenol) which is quite different from the neurosecretion and affects the heart-beat and peristaltic movements. A similar conclusion was reached by Altmann (1956) who studied the myotropic effects of corpora cardiaca extracts of the bug *Iphita limbata* on the gut peristalsis of another bug *Aspongopus janus* (Fabr.) and their chromatophorotropic effects on the red pigment cells of the decapod *Coridina laevis* (Heller). The neurosecretory cells of the brain of the same species had no similar effects. Johansson's (1958) experiments on the influence of the corpora cardiaca on reproduction produced negative results.

Embryogenesis. The development of the corpora cardiaca during the embryonic period was studied by Wiesmann (1926) and Pflugfelder (1937) in *Carausius morosus*; by Mellanby (1936) in *Rhodnius prolixus*; by Roonwal (1937) in *Locustana pardalina*; by Poulson (1937) in *Drosophila*, and by several other authors. According to their findings, the corpora cardiaca, together with the hypocerebral ganglion, originate as an unpaired dorsal evagination of the oesophagus. Not until later are they separated and their cells differentiated into nervous and secretory ones. They are assumed to have originally been normal visceral ganglia which secondarily attained a neurosecretory function and became innervated by the nervi corporum cardiacarum.

Phylogenesis. The corpora cardiaca are well developed in the Apterygota with the probable exception of *Collembola* (cf. Cazal, 1948). They are much more developed here than the corpora allata (cf. p. 87) and have been described in Japygidae and Lepismatidae. They are rather reduced in Campodeidae and occur in other Diplura and in Thysanura (cf. Cazal, 1948; Paclt, 1956 etc.). It may be concluded that the corpora cardiaca have developed during the phylogenesis of Apterygota, but earlier than the corpora allata. If Cazal's (1948) observation that they are absent in Collembola is confirmed, this will agree with the conclusion of B. Scharrer (1952) who stated, from experimental evidence, that the corpora cardiaca merely store temporarily the secretion from the neurosecretory cells of the brain and are not essential for the action of the activation hormone. Thus, for example, transplantation of a brain with active neurosecretory cells may break the diapause in *cecropia* pupae without the simultaneous transplantation of the corpora cardiaca (cf. Williams, 1952 etc.). There is as yet no definite evidence for the existence of a special corporum cardiacarum hormone as was supposed by L'Hélias (1956b) (cf. p. 99).

The Effects of the Activation Hormone

(1) *The activation of the prothoracic glands.* The first papers by Kopeć (1917) and Wigglesworth (1934, 1940) pointed out the necessity of the brain for moulting, pupation and metamorphosis. The discovery by

Fukuda (1940 etc.) of the function of the prothoracic glands in *Bombyx mori* showed, however, that the effect on moulting is an indirect one which depends on the activation of these glands. This was proved conclusively by Williams (1952) who found that active prothoracic glands alone are able to induce moulting in isolated pupal abdomens of *cecropia* whereas an active brain can only produce the same effect in the presence of (inactive) prothoracic glands. Similar results were obtained by Wigglesworth (1952b) with *Rhodnius prolixus* and by several other authors with various insects.

At first glance, some of the recent findings appear to contradict this. Johansson (1958), for instance, found that complete extirpation of all ten of the type A neurosecretory cells of the pars intercerebralis of *Oncopeltus fasciatus* carried out not more than four hours after the last larval moult did not affect imaginal moulting although this started two to three days later than in the controls. Without doubt, this is due to the A-cells secretion stored in the form of granules in the walls of the aorta, as mentioned above. According to Raabe (1959b), the way in which the prothoracic glands are stimulated by the AH has not yet been explained. A possible explanation was suggested by Church (1955) who considers it might be directly concerned in the synthesis of ecdyson. The findings of E. Thomsen and I. Moller on the influence of AH on intestinal activity in *Calliphora erythrocephala*, as well as other effects mentioned, would however suggest an action of a much more general nature, as would also its relationship to the adiuretin of the vertebrate hypothalamus.

(2) *The activation of the corpora allata.* The effect of AH on the function of the corpora allata appears now to have been adequately demonstrated. AH is necessary for the re-activation of the corpora allata in the same way as it is in the case of the prothoracic glands. This was suggested in some of the earlier accounts (cf. Thomsen, 1952), and is quite evident from the recent work of Johansson (1958a, b), de Wilde (1958a, b, c) and his collaborators, Nayar (1957) etc. Johansson (1958a) observed the effect of the extirpation of the A-cells of the brain on the volume of the corpus allatum and found that complete extirpation of these cells results in abnormally reduced corpora allata. A similar effect was observed by E. Thomsen (1952) in *Calliphora*. If, however, only a few A-cells are left, the volume of the corpora allata remains normal. The proper understanding of how the corpus allatum is activated by AH has proved difficult for two reasons: (1) The action of the corpus allatum seems to depend on nervous stimuli; (2) the activation hormone does not reach the corpus allatum only through the haemolymph but also directly from the brain, in the form of granules,

c

via the nervi corporum cardiacarum, corpora cardiaca and nervi allati. Neither of these factors appears to play a primary role in the regulation of corpus allatum activity, except in the case of diapause (see below), but such has been attributed to both by different authors (e.g. Engelman, 1957 etc.; Nayar, 1958 etc.). It is through the activation of the corpus allatum that the chief effect of the activation hormone on the ovaries is produced.

(3) *The control of diapause.* As suggested by E. Scharrer (1952), the author of the conception of neurosecretion, the specific role of neurohormones in the animal body depends on a long-term co-ordination between the nervous system and internal secretion. A classic example of this interdependence is the direct influence of the AH on both larval (pupal) and imaginal diapause. In each case, it is a nervous stimulus induced by external conditions which leads to a temporary interruption of the AH production which in turn results in the inhibition of the functions concerned (cf. p. 193).

As shown by Williams (1946, 1947, 1948) and several other authors, a stage corresponding to the natural diapause can be induced by the removal of the brain, the source of the AH. Similarly, a natural diapause can be broken at any time by implanting an active brain or other source of AH (corpora cardiaca, corpora allata; see below). It seems that this dependence is the result of a phylogenetic utilization and improvement by diapausing insects of a tendency present in all insects. This tendency is the control of the AH production in response to a variety of unfavourable environmental conditions and it is highly adaptable.

Thus the diapause generally occurs in the winter period in temperate regions, whereas it is usual in the hot dry season in the tropics and sub-tropics. The same is true of the dependence of AH production on the nervous impulse produced by the distension of the abdomen in blood-sucking insects as described by Wigglesworth (1936, 1948, etc.) and by Detinova (1954, etc.). The condition in blowfly larvae first observed by Cousin (1933) may be taken as an intermediate stage in the development of diapause (cf. p. 187).

(4) *The effect on ovarian development.* In addition to its indirect effect on ovarian development through the activation of the corpora allata, the existence of a direct effect of the AH on the development of eggs has been suggested. A careful analysis of the endocrine mechanisms controlling ovarian development in adult *Calliphora erythrocephala* showed that the removal of the neurosecretory cells of the brain can be completely compensated by the implantation of active neurosecretory cells from another specimen but not by the active corpora allata. The effects of the AH

deficiency are different from those of allatectomy. Implantation of corpora cardiaca from an active specimen has a similar, though lesser, effect to the reimplantation of neurosecretory cells. The corpora cardiaca alone are not able to induce maturation of the ovaries in this species. Thomsen concludes that the function of the AH in the insect organism is rather complicated and that the neurosecretory cells of the brain form an 'all-over controlling centre of the endocrine system' (cf. p. 272).

(5) *The effect on the accessory glands.* The effect on the male accessory glands, first observed by Wigglesworth (1936) and since confirmed by many workers using various other insects, is, as in the case of the ovaries, primarily an indirect one through activation of the corpora allata. No direct effects have hitherto been observed though they may be assumed.

(6) *The effect on morphogenesis.* In his experiments with the cricket *Pteronemobius haideni,* Sellier (1956) observed that the implantation of an active brain into the larvae (8th instar) at the start of the diapause resulted not only in a suppression of the diapause but also in a lengthening of the wings in the resulting adults. No such effect was noted where the implantation was effected at a more advanced stage in diapause. The implantation of brains from other species of the genus *Gryllus* gave similar results. This, however, appears to be much more an indirect effect depending on the time of activation of the corpus allatum.

(7) *The effect on the fat body.* E. Thomsen (1952) observed that the fat bodies of *Calliphora* females, whose AH source had been removed, had a higher glycogen content though the quantity of fat was reduced. The glycogen content corresponded with that following allatectomy but the reduction in the quantity of fat was greater.

(8) *The effect on intestinal proteinase activity.* E. Thomsen and Möller (1959a, b) studied the effect of extirpation of the neurosecretory cells of the pars intercerebralis on intestinal proteinase activity in *Calliphora* females. The colorimetric method of Day and Powning was used to determine this activity in gut homogenates. The proteinase activity in the treated specimens was 5 to 8 times lower than in the control. The effect of the removal of AH was identical with that caused by lack of proteins in the food. As proteinases are themselves proteins so that their production may be considered as a protein synthesis in the gut epithelium cells the authors conclude that the AH affects proteosynthesis. This, however, is not the only possible explanation – a more general activation effect corresponding to

that observed in other tissues, such as, for example, some kind of membrane activation, would be at least equally satisfactory. Corresponding results were reached independently by Strangways-Dixon (1959, 1961) using the same species. He showed by selective feeding on sugar and protein diets that flies deprived of their neurosecretory brain cells digested no proteins even when forcibly fed on them for six days and neither their corpora allata nor their eggs showed any increase in size.

(9) *The effect on water balance.* A series of papers is concerned with the effect of AH on water balance. Altmann (1956a, b) for example studied the effect of extracts from different endocrine glands on the intake, retention, and excretion of water by the honey-bee. Injections of corpora allata extracts increased water consumption and decreased the viscosity of the haemolymph; corpora cardiaca extracts increased the viscosity and decreased the water consumption. Excretion was increased by the corpora allata extract and decreased by that of the corpora cardiaca. Injections of adrenalin produced similar effects to corpora cardiaca extracts. In the case of the corpus allatum extracts the problem remains as to whether the effects observed are due to juvenile hormone or to neurosecretory material reaching the gland via the nervus allatus, the second possibility being much more probable.

Nayar (1957) studied the relationship between water content and the release of neurosecretory granules in *Iphita limbata* and obtained the following results: When distilled water was provided for drinking for a few weeks, bugs were obtained with an increased amount of neurosecretory material in the walls of the aorta, and the neurosecretory cells were practically free of granules. On the other hand, when the insects were forcibly fed on salt water for the same length of time, the release of neurosecretory material through the walls of the aorta almost ceased and the neurosecretory cells were filled with granules. Similar results were obtained with specimens where the wax layer of the epicuticle was removed by washing with benzene or chloroform. In those kept in an atmosphere dried with calcium chloride, neurosecretory material accumulated in the neurosecretory cells; in those kept in a more humid atmosphere, the material was released and an increased quantity of granules was found in the walls of the aorta. Similar observations were made by Gutmann and Novák[1] using *Pyrrhocoris apterus*. It may be concluded that the neurosecretory cells enable the animal to maintain the water balance within certain limits. The analogy with the adiuretin of the vertebrate hypothalamus is striking (cf. p. 265).

[1] Unpublished observations.

Raabe (1959a) obtained similar results with *Carausius morosus* where the corpora cardiaca had the same effect as the neurosecretory cells of the brain. This agrees with the findings of Stutinski (1952a, b). He injected rats with extracts of the pars intercerebralis protocerebri and the corpora cardiaca of the cockroach *Blabera fusca* and found that the urine was reduced in quantity in the same way as after the administration of pitressin. The opposite result was obtained by Nuñez (1956) using the beetle *Anisotarsus cupripennis*. There, the extracts of brain neurosecretory cells and corpora cardiaca appeared to produce diuretic effects. These experiments, however, need to be repeated under comparable conditions.

(10) *Other effects.* The various known effects of AH, as well as the possibility that they may be due to a common and very general action, leaves no doubt that further research will reveal a number of further effects. It also remains to be determined whether some of the observed effects of brain and corpora cardiaca extracts, such as the various chromatophorotropic and myotropic actions, are due to AH or to other neurosecretory products. The experimental evidence available at present provides little support for any conclusion in this connection (cf. p. 212).

The Indirect Effects of the AH

The control of the moulting process must be interpreted as an indirect effect of the activation hormone. Moulting is inhibited by removal of the AH source and re-evoked by its reimplantation. For this reason, the brain hormone was originally described as the moulting hormone by Wigglesworth (1934). It was called a 'growth and differentiation hormone' (*partim*) by B. Scharrer (1948) and Williams (1947, 1952a). The corpus allatum hormone was also originally interpreted by several authors (Pflugfelder, 1937, Bodenstein, 1943 etc.) as a moulting hormone. Conclusive proof of an indirect as opposed to a direct effect is provided by the fact that the effect can be produced by another hormone but not by the given hormone alone (see above and Williams, 1952b). On the other hand, the mere finding that removing another organ inhibits the effect is in no way proof of an indirect effect. In such a case there is always the possibility that the effect of the hormone was prevented by breaking another link in the chain between the hormone and the part of the body responding. With the metamorphosis hormones it is particularly important to differentiate the direct and indirect action for a given hormone. The interaction of their effects is very complicated, as in metamorphosis and moulting. From this point of view a revision of many of the present opinions on the metamorphosis hormones and their mode of action is desirable.

The Control of AH Production

The functional cycles of the neurosecretory cells. The existence of specific,
so-called 'critical' periods in each instar as far as the hormonal activity is
concerned was shown experimentally shortly after the discovery of the
first metamorphosis hormone (cf. Wigglesworth, 1934, 1936 etc.). During
these periods, the presence of the source of the given hormone is essential
for normal development whereas afterwards it is no longer necessary. This
shows that there is a certain cyclicity in the function of the AH, which
has been confirmed by subsequent histological research on the neurosecretory system. The course of neurosecretion and the function of the
corpora cardiaca during postembryonic development has recently been
studied in detail by Herlant-Meewis and Paquet (1956). They found a
decrease in the amount of neurosecretory granules in the pars intercerebralis and corpora cardiaca at the time of each moult. Neurosecretory
activity reached its maximum after about one-third of the next intermoult
period had elapsed. At this time also the largest amount of neurosecretory
material was seen to pass into the corpora cardiaca. This time of maximum
secretory activity agrees well with what has been observed regarding the
critical period for AH in other species. The quantity of neurosecretion in
the corpora cardiaca decreases markedly about half way through the intermoult period, i.e. when the critical period for the juvenile hormone has
been reached. Another increase in the neurosecretory material was
observed in the last quarter of the intermoult period. Cyclical changes in
the amount and character of the neurosecretory material were observed in
Phasmids and other insects by a number of other authors (De Lerma, 1954,
1956, in *Hydrous piceus*; L'Hélias, 1956a, b, in *Carausius morosus*; Formigoni, 1956, in *Apis mellifica*; Dupont-Raabe, 1954, in Phasmidae, etc.).
On the other hand, Füller (1959) described frequent cyclical changes in
the amount of secretion in the individual neurosecretory cells of the pars
intercerebralis of *Periplaneta americana* without any noticeable cyclicity
in the neurosecretory system as a whole.

The question arises as to what factors govern the changes observed in
neurosecretory activity. One of the first answers to this was provided by
Wigglesworth (1936a, 1940a) in his classic experiments with the blood-
sucking bug *Rhodnius prolixus*. He showed that production of the brain
hormone and thus also the start of the moulting process, as well as all the
interrelated developmental processes, is induced by a nervous stimulus
produced by a certain distension of the abdomen due to ingested blood.
This stimulus depends on the quantity, not the quality, of the fluid intake.
so that the same effect is caused by a corresponding volume of pure water.

Several small blood meals do not, however, produce any effect, even though their sum exceeds the necessary minimum quantity. Severing of the ventral nerve cord anywhere between the brain and the abdomen prevents this stimulus. It may therefore be viewed as a typical case of the transformation of a nervous stimulus into an endocrine impulse effected by the neurosecretory cells of the pars intercerebralis protocerebri, as claimed by E. Scharrer (1952, see above). A very similar neurosecretory effect was found by Detinova (1954) in *Anopheles*. On the other hand, no such connection was found by Novák (1951b) in the plant-feeding bug *Oncopeltus fasciatus* and many other insects where poorly fed specimens can undergo a normal moulting process. It is also well known that meal-worms undergo several extra moults when left without food, and starving clothes-moth larvae can moult as many as 40 times. The above-mentioned dependence of AH production on a nervous stimulus from the distended abdomen seems therefore to be a secondary phylogenetic adaptation in blood-sucking insects. It enables them to survive for long periods in the absence of a suitable host in a state of reduced metabolism corresponding to that of a true diapause (cf. p. 192). In most other insects, AH production is automatically renewed at the beginning of each instar with the passing of the first digested food into the haemolymph. The phylogenetic character of this dependence on the stimulus from the abdomen was shown by Larsen and Bodenstein (1959) in the mosquitoes *Culex pipiens* and *Aedes aegypti*. Whereas *A. aegypti* and normal *C. pipiens* show the normal dependence of AH production (and through this the juvenile hormone production which regulates egg development and oviposition) on the distension of the abdomen by blood, AH production by the autogenic form, *Culex molestus*, is independent of this stimulus.

A detailed analysis of the function of the neurosecretory cells in insects which feed continuously throughout their growth has recently been made by Clarke and Longley (1962) using *Locusta migratoria* L. No changes were found in the amount of neurosecretory material in the median neuro-secretory cells or in their axons (nervi corporum cardiacum I) or in the corpora cardiaca during the postembryonic development or at different times during the intermoult period. The neurosecretory material appears to be produced continuously throughout growth in this species. As the AH is supposedly not used during the ecdyses, the authors assume it to accumulate in the haemolymph at these times. The increased concentration of the hormone in the haemolymph at these periods would then reactivate the prothoracic glands (cf. p. 75).

A very interesting connection between the frontal ganglion and the production of neurosecretion was also found. Its extirpation resulted in the complete inhibition of further growth and moulting. The same effect was obtained by cutting the frontal connectives whereas cutting the recurrent nerve or the ventral nerve cord in front of the first abdominal ganglion had no effect. Histological examination of the neuroendocrine system five days after the operation revealed a marked accumulation of neurosecretory granules in the corpora cardiaca, the nervi corporium cardiacarum I but scarcely any in the neurosecretory cells. No neurosecretory cells were found in the frontal ganglion. The authors suppose that the frontal ganglion plays a part in transmitting the nervous impulses from stretch receptors in the oesophagus to the neurosecretory cells of the pars intercerebralis which would thus correlate the release of the hormone with the intake of food.

A temporary inhibition of AH production caused by various external impulses, the mechanisms of action of which are not yet fully understood, is the direct internal cause of all types of insect diapause except the early embryonic one (cf. p. 199). In addition to photoperiodism, temperature and the above-mentioned distension of the abdomen in blood-sucking insects, several other factors controlling AH production have recently been described. Thus, for example, the interrelationship between juvenile hormone production and the carrying of oothecae by female cockroaches, incorrectly interpreted as a direct effect on the corpus allatum secretion, is without doubt governed by neurosecretion (B. Scharrer, 1958). Similarly, neurosecretion, or AH production, appears to be the chief mechanism influenced by the quality of the food as shown by E. Thomsen (1952, 1959) and Strangways-Dixon (1959) (cf. p. 49); and the effect of feeding on proteosynthesis is also governed in this way (cf. E. Thomsen and I. Möller, 1959, Strangways-Dixon, 1961 etc.).

Chemical Features of the AH

Very little information is available at present regarding the chemical nature of the AH. As far as the neurosecretory granules originating in the pars intercerebralis protocerebri are concerned, it may be assumed on the basis of an analogy with the neurosecretory materials in vertebrates that, in addition to the active substance, i.e. the AH, which is polypeptide in character in vertebrates, they also contain a carrier substance, soluble in organic solvents, that is responsible for their staining properties (cf. p. 207).

There is as yet no explanation for the processes involved in the storage of these materials. L'Hélias suggested that the product of the brain cells might be simply one component of the active substance which she called the brain-prehormone which does not become the active hormone, i.e. the AH, until after reaching the corpus cardiacum where it is affected by the secretion of this gland. The prehormone which reaches the corpus allatum is changed into juvenile hormone (JH). According to the interpretation of L'Hélias (l.c.), both AH and JH are protein in character and contain a pterine group in the molecule. All would be identical with folic acid or one of its equivalents whilst JH is assumed to be a folic acid derivative with antifolic effects. This hypothesis is based on the author's findings, using *Carausius morosus*, regarding the effects of both hormones on the fluorescent properties of substances isolated by electrophoresis from homogenates of the organs concerned, as well as the fact that these hormones have a positive effect on cultures of bacteria requiring folic acid for their growth. It does not, however, agree very well with data on this subject accumulated by other authors and even if pterine derivates are present it has been shown recently by Gersch and Unger (1962) (cf. p. 207) that they have nothing in common with either of the hormones.

The following discoveries by B. Scharrer (1952) and others appear to speak conclusively against the hypothesis of L'Helias (1956) on the inter-action of the brain secretion with those of the corpora cardiaca or allata: (1) extirpation of the corpora cardiaca has no qualitative effect either on moulting or metamorphosis; (2) the effects of brain extirpation may be at least partly compensated by the implantation of active corpora cardiaca (B. Scharrer, 1956, E. Thomsen, 1952); (3) the careful histological studies on the neurosecretory activity of the brain and corpora cardiaca in some Hymenoptera and Diptera carried out by M. Thomsen (1951, 1954a, b) give full support to the conclusion that the neurosecretory material passes through the corpora cardiaca directly into the haemolymph.

Isolation of the active ingredient of the AH has been reported by Kobayashi and Kirimura (1958). They used 8,500 silkworm (*Bombyx mori*) pupae preserved in methanol 24 hours after pupation and centrifuged three times after homogenization. 200 ml. of the methanol solution obtained were concentrated to 30 ml. and extracted with 145 ml. ethyl ether. On evaporation, the ether solution yielded about 2 mg. of an oily yellowish brown material; the evaporation temperature did not exceed 38 °C. An injection of this substance into decerebrated permanent pupae, in which no ecdyson had previously been found, caused these to moult to adults 16–20 days later. It has recently been claimed by Kirimura *et al.* (1962) that the active principle of these extracts is cholesterol and its identity with the AH was postulated. This view has, however, little if any support from other facts known regarding the AH. It is nevertheless very interesting in connection with the recent finding of Karlson and Hoff-meister (1963) that cholesterol is the precursor of ecdyson (cf. p. 78).

The Mode of Action of AH

The movement of the neurosecretory granules through the axons of the nervi corporum cardiacarum from the neurosecretory cells of the pars intercerebralis protocerebri into the corpora cardiaca is well known, but their fate in the corpora cardiaca and their passage from here into the haemolymph is less clear.

Interesting experimental evidence for the transporting of the AH from the corpora cardiaca to the prothoracic glands in *Rhodnius* by the haemocytes was produced by Wigglesworth (1956b). He showed that blocking of the haemocytes by injecting chinese ink, trypan blue or iron saccharate, the particles of which are phagocytosed, results in a significant delay of the next moult if the injection is carried out before the end of a specific critical period which corresponds approximately to that of AH. When, however, he at the same time implanted active prothoracic glands or injected a sufficient amount of a solution of crystalline ecdyson, no such delay occurred. Wigglesworth concluded that under normal conditions the haemocytes transport the AH from the corpora cardiaca to the prothoracic glands or, perhaps more likely, that they secrete a further substance necessary for the activation of the prothoracic glands under the influence of the AH. As suggested by Wigglesworth, other explanations are also possible such as, for example, that the AH is absorbed on the injected material and removed with that from the haemolymph by phagocytosis; or the haemocytes, damaged by phagocytosis, discharge some AH inactivating substance into the haemolymph. An alternative explanation could be that, in normal insects, the role of haemocytes is to phagocytose the neurosecretory granules, thus freeing the AH whilst digesting the carrier substance. This would be in agreement with the observed occurrence of neurosecretory granules in the aorta dorsalis of various insects (cf. Nayar, 1951 etc.) and with the observation of Hodgson and Geldioy (1959) who found that the hyperactivity in Blaberus craniifer and, to a lesser extent, electrical shock treatments, resulted in an invasion of all parts of the brain by blood cells.

Scarcely any data are available regarding the mechanism of activation of the prothoracic glands and other organs influenced by the AH. It has, however, been found by Williams (1952) that the same activating effect may be obtained by implanting another, active prothoracic gland. This is to be interpreted, together with Wigglesworth's (1957) conclusions, as meaning that continuous action by the AH is necessary for the prothoracic gland to provide an effective amount of moulting hormone. This is based on the discovery that the first change in the epidermis definitely attributable to the prothoracic gland hormone commences about two days before the end of the critical period for AH, during which time the removal of the AH-source (by decapitation) prevents the continuation of the moulting process.

B. THE MOULTING HORMONE (ECDYSON), MH

(Growth and differentiation hormone, Scharrer, 1948; Williams, 1952; = Larvenhäutungshormon = Verpuppungshormon = Imaginalhäutungshormon, Piepho, 1938; = Metamorphosehormon, Weber, 1954)

The first evidence for the existence of a humoral factor controlling moulting can be seen in the experiments of Kopeć (1922) and Wigglesworth (1934 etc.). At about the same time as Wigglesworth, Fraenkel (1934, 1935) showed that a similar hormonal factor, necessary for puparium formation, was present in the brain region of *Calliphora erythrocephala* larvae. Prior to this, however, Hachlow (1931), on the basis of his experiments with butterfly pupae (*Vanessa io, Aporia crataegi*), suggested the existence of a 'thoracic centre' which was necessary for development. A similar conclusion was reached by Bodenstein (1933a, b, 1934) in his transplantation experiments with the legs of caterpillars.

The credit for the first clear distinction between the hormone of the brain cells and that of the prothoracic glands belongs to Fukuda (1940a, b, 1941a, b, 1944) who showed the importance of the prothoracic glands for moulting by transplantation experiments in silkworms. After this the papers on the moulting hormone started to appear at an increasing rate. The role of the prothoracic glands, or the analogous peritracheal glands in lower Diptera Cyclorrapha and the pericardial gland and ventral head glands in Hemimetabola, in the moulting processes has been demonstrated in all the chief groups of insects (cf. e.g. Pflugfelder, 1947, in Phasmidae; B. Scharrer, 1948, and Bodenstein, 1933a, d, in cockroaches; Possompès, 1946, 1949, 1953 etc., in both lower and higher Diptera; Ochsé, 1944, and Rahms, 1952, in Megaloptera; Wigglesworth, 1952, in Hemiptera; Arvy and Gabe, 1952, and Schaller, 1960, in Odonata; Formigoni, 1956, in Hymenoptera; Sellier, 1951, and Strich-Halbwachs, 1953, in Orthoptera; Stellwaag-Kittler, 1954, and Srivastava, 1959, 1960, in beetles, etc.).

Whilst the earlier authors recognized and were mainly concerned with the importance of the MH for inducing the moulting process, many of the later investigators emphasized its indispensability for growth and morphogenesis and used for it the less suitable terms 'growth and differentiation hormone' or 'metamorphosis hormone' (see above and p. 71). A certain amount of confusion appears to have been caused by the discovery of the effects of the ring gland in flies, which is a composite structure that contains the sources of all three metamorphosis hormones (cf. p. 67); also, the role of the MH in diapause and imaginal differentiation in *cecropia* pupae as resolved by Williams (1946, 1947, 1948, 1952 etc.) seemed at first to favour the growth and differentiation concept (cf. p. 193).

The most important stage in the MH investigation, after its separation from the AH by Fukuda, was its isolation in crystalline form by Butenandt and Karlson (1954) from a silkworm pupae extract. An important pre-requisite for this was the discovery by Becker and Plagge (1939) of a suitable test organism and a quantitative measure for judging concentration, the so-called *Calliphora*-unit. Their technique was improved by Butenandt and Karlson and used in their isolation experiments. On the other hand, the specificity claimed by Williams (1951a, b) for the so-called spermato-cyte-test appears to be questionable in the light of the recent findings of Laufer (1960). Becker and Plagge (1939) were also the first to show the broad inter-Order unspecificity of MH, which was confirmed by Wiggles-worth for such widely separated orders as Hemiptera and Diptera. Another important step was the successful extirpation of the ventral glands in migratory locusts by P. Joly, L. Joly and Halbwachs (1956).

The concept of the prothoracic gland hormone as a moulting hormone, which agrees with the original findings of Kopeć and Wigglesworth (1934) as well as with the gradient-factor theory of the present author, has been confirmed in recent years by two independent pieces of work: Halbwachs and Joly (1957) showed, using *Locusta migratoria*, that transplantation of the prothoracic glands accelerates the moulting process without exerting any positive effect on growth and differentiation; Lüscher and Karlson (1958) observed moulting but no growth or imaginal differentiation follow-ing the injection of a large quantity of ecdyson into the nymph of *Kalotermes flavicollis*. The results of Bückmann on the effect of ecdyson on colour change in *Cerura vinula* caterpillars also agree with this concept. These show that the higher the dose of hormone injected the quicker moulting takes place, whilst the effect on the colour change decreases with an increase in the hormone amount. For example, the original green epidermis changed to red following the injection of 66 *Calliphora* units, the epidermis remained green with the fat body and gut contents slightly reddish after 330 *C*.u., whilst after 3,300–6,600 *C*.u., moulting to the pupa took place without any change in colour.

The Prothoracic Glands

Morphology. The prothoracic glands of the *Cossus cossus* caterpillar were fairly accurately described by Lyonett as early as 1762. A more complete description together with data on embryonic development is given by Toyama (1902) who called them 'hypostigmatic glands'. Ke (1930) used the term prothoracic glands for the first time.[1] Since then, because of the

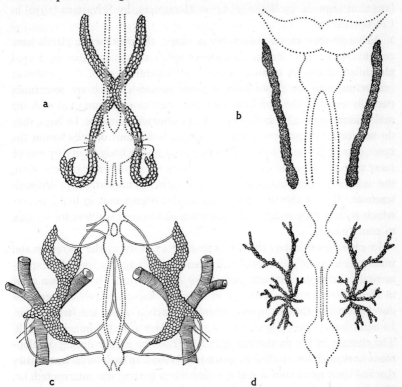

FIG. 10. Prothoracic glands in four different insect orders: *a* – Blattoptera, *b* – Hemiptera, *c* – Lepidoptera, *d* – Hymenoptera, diagrammatic, after various authors, modified.

interest aroused by the discovery of their function, they have been described in detail for practically all the chief groups of insects (cf. fig. 10 and p. 60).

Several comparative morphological studies of the prothoracic glands

[1] Some authors, e.g. Fukuda (1940 etc.), Wigglesworth (1952 etc.), normally use the term in the singular because the glands, although distinctly paired in origin in most insects, coalesce medially. They are exceptional in Gryllidae where they are completely fused to form one organ, as described by Sellier (1951). Wigglesworth (1952) used the broader term 'thoracic' glands because of their position in *Rhodnius*. From general and phylogenetical considerations, however, the earlier term 'prothoracic glands' appears to be preferable.

and analogous organs in various groups of insects have also appeared. For example, they were described by Lee (1948) in many lepidopterous larvae, by Pflugfelder (1947d) in various orders of Hemimetabola, by M. Thomsen (1951) in Diptera, by Wells (1954) in Hemiptera, by Srivastava (1959) in Coleoptera, etc.

Although they vary considerably in shape, the prothoracic glands have certain features in common in all groups where they occur: they are paired glandular structures located in the ventrolateral areas of the prothorax (extending into the mesothorax in some species), which are sometimes partially fused in the mid-line. They are often closely connected with the main lateral tracheal branches near the prothoracic spiracles. In bugs, they do not form independent compact organs, but chains of cells within the inner pair of fat-body lobes. They are fixed in the body cavity by one or more muscle fibres and by a nerve ring from the prothoracic or, less often, the suboesophageal ganglion. They are rather abundantly supplied with tracheae. The prothoracic glands are almost transparent in living insects which is why they escaped the attention of research workers for so long in many groups.

In each larval instar, there is a distinct cyclicity in the secretory and mitotic activity of the prothoracic glands which agrees with the experimentally determined critical periods for MH activity. The secretion cycle in *Pieris brassicae* was described in detail by Kaiser (1949). The greatest development of the prothoracic glands is reached in the last larval instar. In adult insects they degenerate two to ten days after the imaginal moult. The changes in the prothoracic glands of *Tenebrio molitor* during development were critically studied by Srivastava (1960). In each larval instar, they reached their maximum size at the time when feeding was interrupted, i.e. about two days before ecdysis (cf. critical period for MH); they produced most of their secretion at this time and afterwards became reduced. A new cycle starts with the feeding of the next instar. The critical period occurs less than 24 hours after the interruption of feeding in the last larval instar. The glands are completely reduced at the commencement of eye pigmentation.

Histology. The prothoracic glands are generally composed of two strips of glandular tissue. The basic components of these are glandular cells very similar to those of the corpora allata. Their cytoplasm is basophilic and stains deeply with methylene blue, neutral red and other stains. Numerous deeply stained granules are found in the cytoplasm with the use of either of the stains mentioned. Abundant black granules, probably lipoid in character, are found after fixation with osmium tetroxide. The glandular cells are joined by intercellular bridges which stain blue with azan and are connected by their anastomoses with the membrane enveloping the axial muscle fibres. A rich supply of thin tracheae was observed by Wigglesworth (1952a) in *Rhodnius prolixus* in contrast to the feeble tracheation of the surrounding fat body. As opposed to the prothoracic glands in cockroaches and butterflies, no nerve fibres were observed here either in dissected glands or by histological investigation.

Embryogenesis. It has already been shown by Toyama (1902) that prothoracic glands appear at a very early stage in embryonic development as an epidermal invagination of the lateral portion of the maxillary segment and from here later extend into the prothorax and, where this is reduced, even into the mesothorax (cf. Pflugfelder, 1958). A similar conclusion was reached by Wells (1954) for the bug *Dysdercus cingulatus*. Here, two pairs of invaginations arise in the second maxillary segment; the anterior, larger, pair develops into labial glands whilst the posterior pair gives rise to the prothoracic glands (fig. 16). If, however, their supposed origin from the nephridian tubules and their innervation, in most insects by nerves from the prothoracic ganglion, is taken into account, it appears more probable that the invagination mentioned does not start in the second maxillary segment but in the most anterior portion of the prothoracic segment. The figure given by Wells (p. 236, fig. 4, cf. fig. 16 of the present work) does not exclude this explanation which is consistent with what was meant by B. Scharrer (1948) who stated: 'it is quite possible that in certain insects the prothoracic glands may be shown to be the derivatives of nephridia of the first thoracic segment . . .'

Phylogenesis. The prothoracic glands or their equivalents are today known in practically all groups of metabolous insects (Pterygota). The conclusion, however, that their occurrence is not restricted to the Pterygota is well founded. Pflugfelder (1958) suggested the possibility of a homology between the ventral glands of Hemimetabola and the so-called head nephridia of Apterygota which are also developed from the second maxillary segment. The papers by Gabe (1953b, 1956) and Echalier (1955, 1956) suggest the possibility of a homology between the prothoracic glands and the so-called moulting gland ('la glande de mue') or organ Y in Crustacea Malacostraca. This view appears to be strengthened by the recent findings of Karlson (1957), who was able to induce pupation in ligated *Calliphora* larvae with a concentrated extract obtained from *Crangon vulgaris* (cf. p. 261). The earlier conclusions of Pflugfelder (1947, 1952) and B. Scharrer (1948) that both the prothoracic and ventral glands, as well as

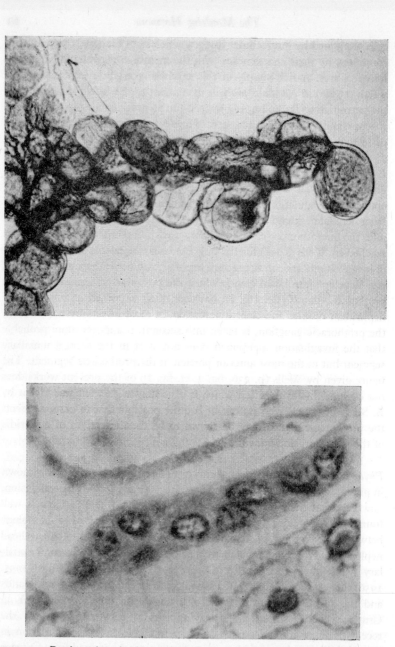

FIG. 11. Prothoracic glands. *Above – Galleria mellonella*, in insect-Ringer,
×400; *below – Pyrrhocoris apterus*, sagittal section, Ehrlich-eosin, ×400 (above the
gland a tracheal wall, below on the right two fat-body cells).

the corpora allata, originated from the nephridia of the ancestral Annelids during the evolution of the Class Insecta are also in agreement with this. It may be concluded that, if suitable techniques are used, the equivalent of the prothoracic glands will be found in all groups of arthropods such as Crustacea, Arachnida, Myriapoda, etc. If this is true, the production of the moulting hormone may be looked upon as a phylogenetical adaptation which has developed in close relationship with the chitinous cuticle as a mechanism to ensure the simultaneous moulting of the whole body surface. This is necessary to allow the organism to escape from the inextensible chitinous covering.

The Ventral Glands

Morphology. Ventral glands, often called ventral head glands or tentorial glands, were first found by Pflugfelder (1947a), in the hind ventral region of the head in Phasmidae. Boisson (1947) described corresponding structures in *Bacillus rossii* as corpora incerta and discovered a cyclicity in their secretory activity which was connected with moulting. Pflugfelder (1947d) assumed that they were absent in Hemiptera and in all Holometabola.

An important feature of the ventral glands is that they degenerate at the end of the metamorphosis or in the first few days after the imaginal moult in the same way as the prothoracic glands. Exceptions in this respect are the ventral glands (= tentorial glands) of the worker and soldier castes of termites, which are less developed than in the sexuales but are active during the whole life period (Springhetti and Bernardini, 1955; Kaiser, 1956). This appears to be connected with the neotenic character of these castes in some lower termite groups, evidenced by the underdeveloped state of their ovaries, in which they are maintained by inhibitory substances (cf. p. 245) produced by the reproductives (cf. Pflugfelder, 1958).

The influence of the ventral glands on the moulting process was shown by Strich-Halbwachs (1954, 1958) and by Halbwachs, Joly and Joly (1957) in migratory locusts. The implantation of an active gland at the beginning of the 4th or 5th instar causes an acceleration of the moulting process with a feeble prothetelic effect (cf. p. 132). The so-called corpora adnexa in *Dinjapyx marcusi* which are epithelial in structure and situated caudally to the suboesophageal ganglion are viewed by Marcus (1951) as a homologue of the ventral glands in Apterygota. Some authors have expressed the view that the ventral glands can be looked upon as homologous with the prothoracic glands of Holometabola. It seems, however, more probable that they are serial homologues of prothoracic glands (see further below).

A regular cyclical secretory activity of the ventral glands in *Carausius* was described by Pflugfelder (1947, cf. 1958). The drops of secretion appear, closely connected with the nuclei, during and for a few days after the ecdysis. This period of abundant secretion is followed by a phase of exhaustion. Between the 3rd and 7th day of the intermoult period both the nuclei and cytoplasm grow intensively. On the 8th to 9th day there is great mitotic activity resulting in abundant cell aggregates between the 10th and 11th days. Ecdysis takes place on the 12th day associated with the strong

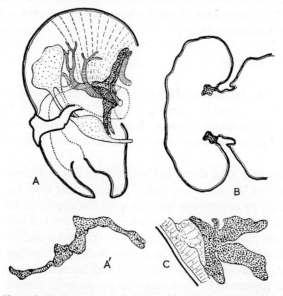

FIG. 12. Ventral glands. A – *Locusta migratoria*, position in head, A′ – the same, separately (after Strich-Halbwachs, 1959, modified); B – *Grylloblatta campodeiformis*, position in head (after Rae and O'Farrell, 1959); C – *Aeschna cyanea*, with a piece of cuticle and an epithelial cushion (after Plugfelder, 1947, modified).

secretory activity. Similar observations have been made in Odonata, termites and other Hemimetabola.

Histology and embryology. The histological structure of the ventral glands is very similar to that of the prothoracic glands. Their embryogenesis was studied by Pflugfelder (1947, cf. 1938 and 1958) in *Carausius morosus*. They develop from epidermal proliferations in the ventrocaudal part of the head, but are soon separated from the epidermis and become bladder-like. Jones (1953, 1956) found ventral glands in *Locustana pardalina* and *Locusta migratoria* as invaginations in the head region of embryos at the end of the katatrepsis stage. He assumed them to be homologous with the prothoracic glands of other insects. He studied their function in regard to the start of secretory activity of the neurosecretory brain cells and the first embryonic moulting process.

Phylogenesis. Rae and O'Farrell (1959) studied the formation of the ventral glands and the retrocerebral complex in *Grylloblatta campodeiformis*, a representative of the primitive Orthopteroid Order Notoptera (= Grylloblattidae). They described structures evidently endocrine in function in the ventrocaudal region of the head and in the cervical area which resembled very closely the so-called 'head lobes' of *Blatella germanica* and the 'cervical glands' of *Periplaneta americana*. These authors assume that the coxal muscles they describe in *Grylloblatta* are the remnants of the degenerated prothoracic glands of cockroaches and homologous with the axial muscle cord in Blattidae described as Scharrer's organ by Chadwick (1955).

The existence of both prothoracic glands and a homologue of the ventral glands in the above-mentioned cervical structures of cockroaches seems to

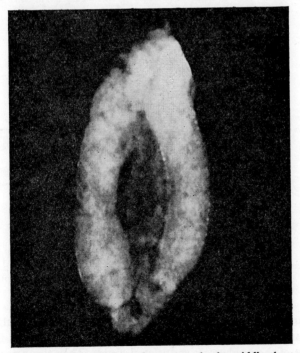

FIG. 13. Pericardial glands of *Carausius morosus*, in the middle the transparent dorsal vessel.

be well substantiated by the morphological and experimental evidence of
Rae (1955) and Chadwick (1955, 1956). Thus a complete extirpation of the
prothoracic glands of *Periplaneta americana* does not prevent moulting.
Cyclical changes in the volume of the above-mentioned 'ventral lobes' in
Blatella associated with the moulting process and regeneration were
observed by O'Farrell *et al.* (1958, 1959).

The Pericardial and Peritracheal Glands

The first suggestion regarding the existence of ductless glands of the dorsal
vessel was made by Verson (1911a, b). They were fully described by
Pflugfelder (1938a–d, 1949b) for various species of Phasmidae (*Phyllium,*

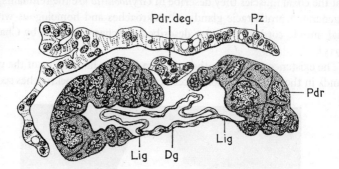

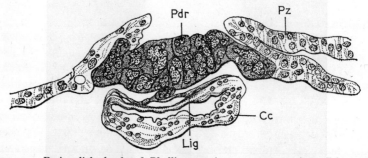

FIG. 14. Pericardial glands of *Phyllium* sp. in transverse sections. Pdr – pericardial glands; Pdr. deg – degenerated part of a pericardial gland; Pz – pericardial
cells; Dg – dorsal vessel; Cc – corpora cardiaca; Lig – ligaments (after Plugfelder,
1938).

Carausius etc.). Here they occur in the form of a paired gland, the histological structure and function of which, unlike their origin, is identical
with that of the prothoracic and ventral glands. They also agree in that
they degenerate in the adults. Corresponding structures were described by

Possompès (1949a–c, 1953a, b) and by other authors (M. Thomsen, 1951 etc.) in lower Diptera (Chironomidae, Simuliidae, Tabanidae) under the name of peritracheal glands. They have not been found in Tipulidae. M. Thomsen (1951) observed them in various other groups of Diptera. Both authors agree regarding their homology with the pericardial glands of Phasmidae. The relation of these to the moulting process was shown experimentally by Pflugfelder (1949b). No moulting was observed in specimens in which the pericardial glands were extirpated.

Histology, embryology and phylogenesis. In their histological structure the pericardial glands of Phasmidae and the peritracheal glands of Diptera correspond closely to the prothoracic and ventral glands of other groups of insects. As regards their embryogenesis, the pericardial glands were originally assumed to be of mesodermal origin by Pflugfelder (1938). In his latest work dealing with this subject, however, the same author (1958) mentions their ectodermal-like structure and emphasizes the difficulty in distinguishing between the mesenchymal and ectodermal cells in the early embryonic period of the insects mentioned. This would remove the only possible objection to their identification with the peritracheal cells which are of ectodermal origin according to Possompès. The problem of their homology has, however, been rather complicated by their confusion with pericardial cells of obvious mesodermal origin which have nothing in common with the pericardial glands (cf. Thomsen, 1951, Steinberg, 1959).

The Ring Gland

A special endocrine organ which combines the source of all three metamorphosis hormones has been developed in higher Diptera and the first signs of this can be seen in Tipulidae. It was first described by Weismann (1864) in *Calliphora vomitoria* and is therefore referred to by some authors as 'Weismann's ring'. Since its discovery, its structure and function have been studied by many authors. The first worker to suggest its endocrine character was Hadorn (1937a–c) although the experiments of Fraenkel (1934, 1935), as mentioned above, showed its function. In these papers the ring gland was assumed to exert a positive influence on metamorphosis. The opposite point of view was, however, taken by Burtt (1937, 1938) according to whom the prothoracic gland produced the opposite, i.e. inhibitory, effect on metamorphosis, so that he identified it with the corpus allatum. Hanström, on the other hand, attempted to identify the ring gland with the corpora cardiaca on the basis of his having found nerve cells, which do not occur in other endocrine glands.

The first suggestion as to the composite character of the ring gland was perhaps that by B. Scharrer and Hadorn (1938) who claimed to have found both the corpora allata and the corpora cardiaca therein. The structure of the ring gland during metamorphosis and the development of the adult corpora cardiaca and corpora allata in *Calliphora* were thoroughly studied by E. Thomsen (1941, 1947). She identified the lateral portions of the structure, which are formed of large glandular cells, with the pericardial glands of Phasmidae by showing that they disintegrate during metamorphosis. She also discovered that the hypocerebral ganglion is associated

FIG. 15. The brain and ring gland (*above*) of *Musca domestica*, with suboesophageal ganglion and a pair of imaginal discs (*below*).

with this composite structure. Her findings were corroborated and elaborated by Vogt (1941c, d etc.) for *Drosophila*, M. Thomsen (1951) for several species of Diptera, and by Possompès (1953) in a monograph chiefly concerned with the structure and function of the ring gland in *Calliphora erythrocephala* on the basis of individual implantations of parts of the ring.

On the basis of our present state of knowledge the following four main components of the ring gland may be distinguished: (1) corpus allatum of the small cell type (cf. p. 82) situated in the dorsomedian part of the ring, often covered by large cells of the lateral portions; (2) pericardial (peritracheal) glands formed by the large glandular cells of the lateral portion of the ring; (3) corpus cardiacum in the ventromedian part of the ring, with only one pair of nervi corporum cardiacarum formed by the coalescence of the nervi corporum cardiacarum interni and externi before they enter the ring gland (cf. Hanström, 1942, Fraser, 1955); (4) hypocerebral ganglion composed of transparent ganglionic cells and closely connected with the corpus cardiacum.

Embryogenesis and phylogenesis. The origin of the ring gland in embryonic development was studied in detail by Poulson (1945a). Amongst other things, the ectodermal character of the lateral large gland cells, which correspond to the peritracheal glands of Possompès, was shown. Very little is known as yet regarding the phylogenesis of the ring gland. Possompès distinguishes four different types of development: (1) *Tipula* type; 2 corpora allata, 2 corpora cardiaca (no equivalent of the prothoracic glands has so far been found here). (2) *Chironomus* type; 2 corpora allata, 2 corpora cardiaca, 2 peritracheal glands, each of them being connected with the corpus cardiacum and the corpus allatum. (3) *Tabanus* type; 1 corpus allatum, originating by fusion of the two glands, 2 corpora cardiaca and 1 peritracheal gland (formed by fusion of two original ones). (4) The true ring gland of *Calliphora* with 1 corpus allatum (fusion of two), 1 corpus cardiacum (fusion of two), a peritracheal gland (fusion of two). This is in full agreement with the earlier findings of M. Thomsen (1951).

The Effects of the Moulting Hormone

(1) *The initiation of the moulting process.* The implantation of active prothoracic glands or their equivalent can induce moulting not only where secretory activity is naturally suppressed, as in the case of diapause (cf. p. 191), or where the gland has been experimentally removed (cf. Deroux-Stralla, 1948a, Pflugfelder, 1952, Joly-Halbwachs, 1956), but also in cases where neither the prothoracic gland nor the moulting process normally occurs, as in adult insects (cf. Wigglesworth, 1940a, 1952, and Rae, 1955). The moulting process and associated growth can be induced by the active prothoracic gland alone, without a simultaneous implantation of the source of the AH (cf. Williams, 1952). On the other hand, the implantation of an active brain or corpora cardiaca alone is not able to induce moulting in the absence of an effective concentration of the MH. This conclusion was fully confirmed by experiments with isolated MH prepared in crystal form by Butenandt and Karlson (1954) (cf. Karlson, 1957, Williams, 1954, Wigglesworth, 1955a).

(2) *The regulation of growth.* One of the basic conditions of growth in insects, as in any other arthropod, is the loosening and subsequent freeing of the body from the inexpansible cuticle. As the MH is indispensable for the moulting process it is therefore no less indispensable, though indirectly so, for growth. It is not yet certain whether there is also a direct effect on growth. There are some suggestions in favour of such a conclusion as, for instance, the influence of the MH on the mitotic activity which precedes the detachment of the old cuticle. On the other hand, there is an increasing amount of evidence to the contrary: (1) Growth is possible without any moulting process and thus without the MH (e.g. the growth of ovaries and other internal organs as well as of regenerating tissues). (2) The implantation of ventral glands as well as the injection of ecdyson induces moulting, often without any effect on growth or even with a negative one (cf. p. 79). (3) As distinct from the juvenile hormone the MH itself is not able to induce mitotic activity in larval parts of the body (cf. Wigglesworth, 1940a). In the absence of further evidence the presence of the MH is thus to be viewed as one of the conditions of growth but there is no justification for accepting it as a true growth hormone of the JH type.

(3) *The influence on larval and pupal diapause.* On the other hand there is no doubt regarding the direct character of the effect of the MH in breaking both the types of diapause mentioned. This is clear from the fact that the presence of the MH alone is able to break this kind of inhibition at any time during its occurrence, as seen from the experiments of Williams (1952b) and many others. Here, however, it must be remembered that it is the absence of this factor (as a consequence of the absence of the AH) which is the immediate internal cause of diapause.

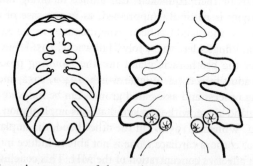

FIG. 16. Embryonic precursors of the prothoracic glands in the bug, *Dysdercus* sp. The external pair of invaginations between the third and fourth (prothoracic) segment – the labial glands, the internal pair – prothoracic glands (after Wells, 1954).

(4) *The influence on enzyme activity.* Views have been expressed that the MH interferes with the reaction chain of some of the principal enzymes of the insect organism that regulate normal metabolism and growth, as for example the cytochromoxydase system (Williams, 1949, 1954; Shappirio and Williams, 1952, 1953). However interesting and important these findings may be in the study of the corresponding enzyme activity – showing amongst other things the functional importance of insect hormones in research on any question of insect physiology and physiology in general – they do not bring any unambiguous evidence in favour of the assumption of a direct participation of the MH in the corresponding reactions.

(5) A series of papers has dealt with *the influence* of the internal medium *on the puffing patterns* of giant chromosomes in the salivary gland cells in *Drosophila* and *Chironomus* (Beermann, 1959, Kroeger, 1960, Clever and Karlson, 1960, Clever, 1961). Distinct changes in the pattern were observed following the injection of ecdyson. It is, however, difficult to interpret them otherwise than as a part of the regular sequence of changes in the secretory cycle of the glands characteristic of a given stage of the moulting process which has been induced by the MH. They are therefore only indirectly dependent on the presence of the hormone (cf. p. 286).

Indirect Effects of the MH

(1) *The effect on differentiation.* In addition to the effects of MH on growth, many authors also speak of its effects on differentiation. While, however, the question of the direct nature of the effect on growth may still be viewed as a matter for discussion, there is no more justification for assuming any direct influence of the MH on differentiation. The dependence of any surface morphological change on the moulting process is, however, unquestionable. Even the slightest morphological changes on the surface of the body can only be realized during the relatively short interval between the detachment of the old cuticle and the deposition of the new.

Any inhibition of the moulting therefore necessarily means the inhibition of growth and differentiation. But the initiation of the moulting process does not in any way mean a simultaneous initiation of differentiation. On the contrary, a premature introduction of the MH, as in the ecdyson experiments, results not in more differentiation but in less. This was shown in Fukuda's (1944) experiments with prothoracic gland implantation, and in the experiments of Wigglesworth (1940a, b, 1948) with the parabiosis of moulting specimens of *Rhodnius* joined to those which had passed the critical period for the moulting hormone.

The same conclusion necessarily results from the findings regarding the effects of the juvenile hormone on growth and differentiation. By implanting active corpora allata the gradient growth, resulting in differentiation, may be changed into an isometric one without change in form. Such an inhibition of differentiation does not only mean any inhibition of the moulting process but it is, in fact, distinctly accelerated. There is no basis for assuming any antagonism between the MH and the JH. Differentiation can be completely separated from both moulting and growth and there is no connection between the effect of the MH on one or the other. The indisputable influence of the MH on the differentiation is therefore purely indirect.

Joly (1958) when analysing the ventral gland hormone effects on the mitotic activity of the epidermis cells and on the allometric growth during the metamorphosis reached the conclusion that the MH only affects the moulting process.

(2) *The influence on the ovarian development.* The indirect character of the morphogenetical effects of the MH is most evident from its effect on the development of the ovaries. It was shown by Strich-Halbwachs that the removal of the ventral glands at the start of the last larval instar in *Locusta migratoria*, which prevents moulting, also suppresses the development of ovaries but only to a certain extent. The oocytes, which averaged 0·70 mm. in length at the time of the operation, reached 1·80 mm. within one month in the permanent larvae thus obtained, whereas they reached 7·20 mm. in the metamorphosed controls at the moment of egg-laying. Some of the oocytes were abnormal or even degenerated in the experimental series. It is clear that, here, the same factor operates, i.e. the inhibitory influence of the inexpansible cuticle, the only difference being that its effect on the internal organs is less direct than on the epidermis. The relationship between the moulting process and the development of the ovaries also permits a rational explanation of the findings of Bodenstein (1953a–d) and Wigglesworth (1940b, 1954, 1957 etc.) (cf. p. 118). From these the induced character of this type of MH effect is also evident.

It may be added that the independence of the development of the ovaries from the moulting process and the MH is quite evident from the fact that it normally takes place in adults where no prothoracic glands are present and no moulting occurs.

(3) *The influence on the corpora allata and reproduction.* Engelmann (1959) studied the effect of the implantation of active larval prothoracic glands into adult females of the cockroach *Leucophaea maderae* on the function of the corpora allata and the development of ovaries. He obtained moult-

ing of the adult in some cases and nearly always a partial inhibition of the corpora allata secretion. He explained this as a direct effect on the corpora allata and an indirect one on the neurosecretory brain cells. Both these inhibitory effects were prevented by the simultaneous implantation of a brain and suboesophageal ganglion. An injection of ecdyson had an effect similar to that of the implanted prothoracic glands. In both cases cell division was observed in the corpora allata with a subsequent increase in the number of their cells. As Engelmann himself suggested his results to some extent contradict those obtained by Bodenstein (1953a, e) for a related species, *Periplaneta americana* (cf. p. 118). There is also a marked inconsistency in the conclusions of both the authors mentioned, as in the fact that the prothoracic gland secretion is produced during larval instars almost simultaneously with that of the corpora allata without producing the slightest inhibitory effect. Some results in recent years have even shown that corpora allata may produce a direct positive effect on the inducing of moulting which has, however, no connection with the JH (cf. Ichikawa a. Nishiitsutsuji-Uwo, 1959, Gilbert a. Schneiderman, 1959). There is, nevertheless, a possibility of a simple single explanation of all these facts in what has been called the *law of correlation in consumption* by the different tissues inside the body (Novák, 1956 etc., cf. p. 116). When comparing the above-mentioned findings of Engelmann with those of Bodenstein we see in the first case that the moulting process, even when not accomplished, necessarily consumes part of the available reserves of the body. Their deficiency then becomes evident in the reduced corpora allata activity and in the restricted growth of the ovaries. In the second case, on the other hand, such a serious interference with the physiological processes of the body as that of allatectomy and the resulting regeneration processes may in itself produce an impulse strong enough to prolong the activity of the prothoracic glands.

It was shown by Joly (1958) for *Locusta migratoria* that the cutting of the nervi corporum cardiacarum and the resulting increase in the volume of the gland has no inhibitory effect on the moulting process. Interesting in this connection is the paper by L'Hélias (1959a) on the effect of folic acid on diapausing pupae of *Pieris brassicae* which increases the ribonucleic and desoxyribonucleic acid amount and causes tumour growth in the absence of the MH. The author attempts to explain these findings as agreeing with the hypothesis of the artificial induction of endogen viruses.

(4) *The influence on regeneration.* What has been said regarding differentiation is also true for regeneration which is also independent of moulting though there is an indirect interdependence, at least as far as more extensive

regeneration is concerned. It can either be accelerated by the action of the MH, or suppressed or greatly delayed by the removal of the MH (extirpation of the prothoracic glands; cf. O'Farrell, Stock, Morgan, 1953, 1954, 1956 etc.). Less extensive regeneration, however, including mitotic activity etc. may occur independently of MH (cf. Wigglesworth, 1937 etc.).

(5) *The influence on the morphogenetical colour change*. Conspicuous morphological colour changes occur in various insect species during metamorphosis. Some of them persist into the adult stage, but the majority of the others are of a transient character (cf. p. 219). These changes may be considerably influenced by the suppression or premature introduction of the MH and can be either suppressed or prematurely induced. Because of this, many authors have assumed that there is a direct effect by the moulting hormone on the chemical synthesis of the corresponding pigments. Bückmann (1956–9), for example, in his very thorough studies of morphological colour changes in *Cerura vinula* larvae during metamorphosis reached the conclusion that these changes are caused by low concentrations of the MH, whilst large doses of the same hormone induce pupation. Normally the green caterpillars turn dark at the time the cocoon is made due to the production of a red ommochrome, first in the epidermis and one day later in the fat body. The morphological processes of the pupal moulting do not start until five days later. The colour changes are completely inhibited by ligaturing the part of the body lacking the MH. When 66 *Calliphora*-units were injected into such a permanently green abdomen, they caused reddening of the epidermis. 330 *C*.u. caused reddening of the fat body only, whilst very large doses of 330–6600 units caused pupal moulting without any colour change. Bückmann (1947a) concluded that here the effect of ecdyson could be due to a simple reduction of the ommochrome pigment and he suggested that 'das wäre ein idealer Modelfall einer chemisch einfach definierten Hormonwirkung'.

Even though a secondary direct dependence of a pigment reaction on the hormone cannot be excluded on the basis of phylogenetic considerations (the morphological colour change mentioned is phylogenetically much later than the occurrence of MH in crustaceans, so that the ommochrome system has developed in the presence of MH and could be thus dependent upon its presence), the following explanation seems much more probable: the effect of the MH depends, as in the case of other metamorphosis changes, on the conditioning of both chemical and morphological changes, specific to the given species, in the normal course of development. The discovery by Bückmann (1959) that removal of the corpora allata (by decapitation) in the earlier larval instars results in similar changes in the larval period is in full agreement with this as are also the recent findings of the same author (Bückmann, 1961, 1962).

A similar dependence would doubtless be found in all other cases of morphological colour change described for various other insect species, using a similar experimental approach to that used by Bückmann with *Cerura* (cf. p. 219). It is evident from the experiments of Wigglesworth (1940) with *Rhodnius* that there is no direct influence of the MH on pigment formation: in the imaginal moulting of this species black pigment disappears in some places where it existed previously.

The Control of the MH Production

The secretion of the MH by the prothoracic glands and their equivalents is dependent on the presence of a certain effective concentration of the AH in the haemolymph. It is therefore the control-system of the AH (cf. p. 53) which initially also controls the production of the MH. It was shown by the experiments of Williams (1952 etc.) that the prothoracic glands may be activated to produce the MH even in the absence of the AH by the introduction of the MH. Thus, diapause in *cecropia* pupae may be broken by the implantation of active prothoracic glands or by the injection of ecdyson into pupae with inactive prothoracic glands, even in an amount which itself would not be sufficient to initiate the moulting process (in specimens with their prothoracic glands removed). On the basis of these experiments Williams suggests that a co-ordination is ensured in this way in the secretory activity between the left and right prothoracic gland. Furthermore, an effect was observed (cf. O'Farrell, Stock, Morgan 1953, 1954, 1956 etc.), of extensive or repeated injuries, or of the regeneration process caused by them. They may even in some cases cause supernumerary moulting in adult insects (Bodenstein, 1953a–d). This effect, however, seems to be restricted to the phylogenetically lowest groups of Hemimetabola such as cockroaches, not yet very far removed from the Apterygota where moulting continues in adult insects.

Chemical Features of the MH

Isolation of the MH. The prothoracic gland hormone was the first of the insect metamorphosis hormones to be prepared in crystalline form. Butenandt and Karlson (1954) used 500 kg. of silkworm pupae to prepare an extract using the following technique:

The pupae preserved in methanol were subjected to a pressure of 50 atm. and the resulting extract reduced by evaporation in vacuo. The 30 litres remaining from about 650 litres of the original extract were shaken several times with butanol. The separated butanol extract was then washed successively with 1% H_2SO_4, 10% Na_2CO_3 and 5% acetic acid. It was evaporated and the remaining red-brown oily substance (79 g.) was redissolved in butanol and after filtration through about 800 g. aluminium oxide, following Brockmann (activity v), re-evaporated and dried in vacuo. It was then dissolved in water, shaken successively with ether and ethyl acetate and the water phase again evaporated. The remaining 1·15 g. of red-brown oil showed an activity of 1 *Calliphora*-unit (cf. p. 25) in 0·5γ. It was then purified by chromatography in aluminium oxide (activity IV) and, using ethyl acetate-buthanol (3 : 1) and ethyl acetate-methanol (3 : 1), 167 mg. of a highly active fraction (1 *Calliphora*-unit in 0·1γ) was obtained. After recrystallizing from ethyl acetate and methanol 25 mg. of a crystalline substance was obtained which showed an activity of 1 *C.u.* in 0·0075γ (cf. p. 284).

Chemical characteristics. The above-mentioned crystalline preparation formed silky fibrous needles. These change their appearance at 161–162°C due perhaps to loss of water of crystallization, and melt at 235–237°C. Within these limits the substance is heat stable; it is soluble in water and very soluble in methyl alcohol; it shows distinct absorption bands in the ultraviolet and infrared parts of the spectrum. The ultraviolet spectrum reaches its maximum at 244 mμ (in ethyl alcohol) and at 249 mμ (in water); and the infrared at 6,120 mμ. It is optically active:

$$(d)\frac{20^\circ}{D} = +58\cdot5^\circ \pm 2^\circ \qquad (d)\frac{21}{546} = 82\cdot3^\circ \pm 2^\circ$$

(at a concentration of 7·00 mg. in 2 ml. ethyl alcohol).

On the basis of these findings the presence in the molecule of α and β unsaturated keto groups was assumed. The infrared part of the spectrum also suggests the presence of at least two hydroxyl groups. It was further inferred that a C_2H_5 group and perhaps also a CH_3 group are present. Both acids and bases easily inactivate the MH. There is another band in the spectrum at 265 mμ which may be assumed to have originated by the splitting off of water which led to the formation of the double unsaturated system (cf. p. 285).

The hormone decomposes quickly in alkaline solutions, the decomposition being accompanied by a successive change of spectrum. The first analysis of the dried substance showed elements in the following ratio: $C_{4,4}H_{7\cdot3}O_1$. The molecular weight was originally shown to be about 300; the empirical formula was $C_{18}H_{31}O_4$ (Karlson, 1959 – see further, p. 285). The formula suggested a bicyclic system. Concentrates from *Crangon vulgaris* which have been found to be more active in crustaceans than in insects point to the existence of several different chemical and physical characteristics (e.g. increased polarity etc.) in the crustacean hormone. Further research has shown that at least two different substances are present with identical physiological activity, which are separable into α-ecdyson and β-ecdyson by extracting with a cyclohexane-butanol-water mixture. The two substances may be separated by their melting points and solubilities though their spectra are very similar. Their relationship is assumed to be similar to that of oestradiol and oestriol in the vertebrate hormones. α-ecdyson is about twice as active as β-ecdyson. (1 *Calliphora*-unit corresponds to 0·0075 of α-ecdyson and to 0·015 of β-ecdyson.)

Karlson and Hoffmeister (1963a) have recently continued the work on the chemical properties of ecdyson. 1,000 kg. of dried pupae of *Bombyx mori* removed from cocoons obtained from the silk factory were used. From these 250 mg. of crystalline ecdyson with a specific activity of 100,000 *Calliphora* units per mg. was obtained by the following improved method of preparation:

1,000 kg. dried silkworm pupae extracted with 3,000 litres methanol

↓

methanol extract reduced to 600 litres

↓ diluted with water, 4, 5 litres oil removed

methanol-water solution

↓ extracted 4 times with 60 litres butanol

butanol extract (240 litres)

| washed successively with 60 litres iced water, 60 litres 1% H_2SO_4, 60 litres 10% Na_2CO_3, 60 litres 5% CH_3COOH, 60 litres iced water

↓

butanol concentrate reduced to 4·1 kg.

| diluted in 30 litres water, extracted 3 times with 6 litres petroleum ether, 3·85 litres petroleum ether fraction

↓ removed

232 g. water concentrate (50 *C*.u. per mg.)

↓ Al_2O_3 chromatography

36 g. of active fraction with 500 *C*.u. per mg.

↓ 'counter current' chromatographic extraction (Craig)

14·6 g. of active fraction (2,500 *C*.u. per mg.)

↓ Al_2O_3 chromatography

2·90 g. of active fraction

↓ 'counter current' chromatographic extraction (Craig)

250 mg. crystalline ecdyson

By means of X-ray analysis and mass-spectroscopy a molecular weight of 464 was ascertained. This corresponds to the empirical formula $C_{27}H_{44}O_6$. Evidence was obtained of the steroid nature of ecdyson, one oxy-group and five hydroxyl-groups were found. On the basis of the empirical formula a relationship with cholesterol was suspected. Injection of tritium-labelled cholesterol into *Calliphora*-larvae (Karlson and Hoffmeister, 1963b) yielded positive results. Crude radioactive ecdyson was obtained by extraction and purification from the injected larvae. It was concluded that cholesterol is a precursor of ecdyson. The activation of the prothoracic glands in decerebrated *Bombyx* by ether extracts of brains and by cholersterol, found by the Japanese authors (cf. p. 55), could probably be explained by this. It in no way contradicts the fact that cholesterol is inactive in diapausing sawfly larvae (Sláma, 1963, unpublished observation) (cf. p. 226).

The substance was shown to be active not only in various Lepidoptera but also in Hymenoptera (Williams, 1954, in *Cimbex americana*) and Hemiptera (Wigglesworth, 1955, in *Rhodnius prolixus*). Karlson (1957) later succeeded in isolating a similar substance from the shrimp *Crangon vulgaris*, using the same method. The *Calliphora*-test shows a distinct, but much lower activity in this substance (1 *C*.u. = 50 mg. of the dried oil; cf. p. 76). Similar preparations have been obtained from *Carcinus moenas* and *Portunus holsatus*.

A similar but more active MH preparation has recently been obtained by Stamm (1958) from the grasshopper *Dociostaurus maroccanus*. The author used 10 kg. of adult specimens which yielded 11 mg. α-ecdyson and 12 mg. β-ecdyson in crystalline form. The substances were shown to be chemically identical with the silkworm α- and β-ecdyson and were found to be more active in *Calliphora*-tests. The reduced activity of the silkworm preparations is assumed to be due to the presence of kynurenin and another substance harmful to *Calliphora*.

The Mode of Action of the MH

Even though the moulting hormone is at present the best known of the insect hormones and the only one the chemical composition of which is at least partly known, its mode of action is not yet properly understood. The way it affects the cytochrome oxidase system has already been mentioned as has its action on the ommochrome changes. Its effect on development of the epidermal glands in *Ephestia kuehniella* has recently been analysed experimentally by Hanser (1957), using the ecdyson preparation of Karlson and Butenandt. His paper allows the following important conclusions:

(1) The injection of the MH at any time during the intermoult period induces the moulting process. This commences with the loosening of the old cuticle and the secretion of the moulting fluid and continues with the formation of a new cuticle (pupal cuticle).

(2) A single dose, even if rather strong (40 *C*.u. or more), is not sufficient to complete the moulting process. If no further dose is supplied the moulting process stops in one of its later stages and can only continue when further ecdyson is injected. The presence of the MH is therefore necessary during the whole of the moulting process.

It may be concluded from the findings of Hanser (1957) and the results of earlier experiments with parabioses and prothoracic gland transplantations that the influence of the MH on the moulting process depends on the activation of all the enzyme systems of the epidermal cells. The first phase of this activation consists of the swelling of the cells, which may or may not result in mitotic activity. It is followed by the second phase – secretory activity of the cells, resulting in the production of moulting fluid, the first effect of which is the loosening of the old cuticle by chitinase which subsequently dissolves the inside layers of the cuticle. In the third phase the new cuticle is deposited and the secretory activity of the cells continues with the production of inner layers of the new cuticle, most probably under the action of the same enzyme (chitinase). The phases naturally overlap one another. It seems that the presence of the MH is necessary at least to initiate all these phases.

C. THE JUVENILE HORMONE (NEOTENIN), JH

(= inhibitory hormone, Wigglesworth, 1935; = status quo hormone, Williams, 1952; = das Larvalhormon, Weber, 1954)

The metamorphosis-preventing secretory activity of the retrocerebral gland, the corpus allatum, which is paired in most insects, was first shown by Wigglesworth in his classic parabiosis experiments with the blood-sucking bug *Rhodnius prolixus* in 1935. Wigglesworth demonstrated conclusively that the joining of a nymph in the penultimate or a younger instar to a nymph in the start of the last larval instar results in the delaying or total suppression of the metamorphosis without preventing an increase in size. In this way sixth instar giant nymphs originate which may eventually change after the next moult into giant imagines. When, on the other hand, the corpus allatum of the younger nymph is removed by decapitation, without preventing the moulting process, a miniature precocious imago results.

D

Wigglesworth not only showed the source of this inhibitory effect but was also the first to provide definite evidence of its hormonal character by showing that the same happens with two specimens connected by a glass tube so that only the haemolymph communicates. The original term 'inhibitory hormone' was soon altered to 'juvenile hormone' after its active role in producing larval characters in adults was recognized (Wigglesworth, 1940). This discovery was confirmed by a number of other authors for various insect species, Bounhiol (1936, 1938a) for *Bombyx mori*; Pflugfelder (1937a, b) for *Carausius morosus*; Piepho (1938b, c, d) for *Galleria mellonella*; Bodenstein (1938b) and Weed-Pfeiffer (1938) for *Melanoplus differentialis*.

At the same time as he found its effect on metamorphosis, Wigglesworth (1935, 1936) also discovered the effect of the corpus allatum hormone on the ovarian development. This was later confirmed for a number of other species whilst in others, such as *Bombyx mori*, no interference by a corresponding humoral factor was observed. The other JH effects were ascertained subsequently. An apparent contradiction appeared between the inhibitory, metamorphosis-suppressing effect of the corpora allata hormone and its total-metabolism-increasing influence and the hypothesis of two or more corpora allata hormones with different effects was accepted by a number of authors. This had, however, little if any support from experimental evidence and the possibility of explaining all the available data on the basis of only one substance, the JH, with the character of a growth hormone, was soon recognized (Novák, 1951a, b, 1956 etc.). Experimental and observational evidence was accumulated in favour of this explanation. The existence of an interordinal unspecificity of the JH was shown by the transplantation of corpora allata between Blattoptera and Hemiptera (Novák, 1949,[1] 1951a, b) and Phasmida and Lepidoptera (Piepho, 1950). The first attempts at elucidating the chemical nature of the JH were made by Williams (1956 etc.), Schneiderman and Gilbert (1958) etc. (cf. Schneiderman (1960) etc.), using ether extracts of male abdomens of the Saturniid *P. cecropia*. Recent findings on the so-called pseudo juvenilizing effects (Sláma, 1961), however, appear to suggest that this substance has little in common, either in chemical structure or effects, with the corpus allatum hormone (cf. p. 119).

The Corpora Allata

The first suggestion regarding the possible endocrine activity of the insect corpora allata is perhaps that by Müller (1828), using *Blatta orientalis*; he,

---

[1] Verbally communicated by Prof. V. B. Wigglesworth, F.R.S., at a departmental afternoon tea, March 1949.

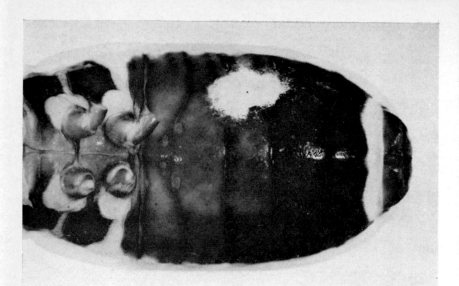

PLATE III. Localized effect of an implanted corpus allatum from *Periplaneta americana* on the epidermis of the ventral abdominal surface of *Pyrrhocoris apterus*. *Above:* External appearance. A limited area of red matt larval cuticle, which is clearly distinguishable from the black shiny adult cuticle, forms above the implanted gland. *Below:* A section through the implanted corpus allatum. At the top right of the picture is the normal thin and black adult cuticle; above the corpus allatum is the thickened larval cuticle with a rough outer surface.

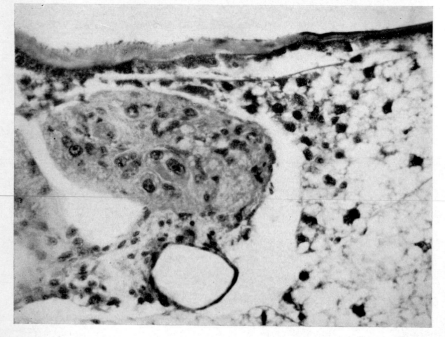

however, assumed these glands to be nervous in character, taking them for visceral ganglia supplying the dorsal aorta and the anterior portion of the gut. This view was accepted by a number of later authors. The first doubts regarding the nervous character were expressed in 1899 by Janet, to whom we owe the term corpora allata, in his detailed anatomical study of the female of the ant *Lasius niger*. In the same year, Heymons (1899) reached a similar conclusion for *Carausius morosus*. The first systematic, comparative morphological study of the insect corpora allata was carried out by Nabert (1913) who clearly expressed the opinion that they were endocrine in function. Since their effects were recognized the number of papers dealing with their structure and function has increased rapidly.

Morphology. The corpora allata are now known in all the chief groups of pterygote insects. Several different types of corpora allata may be distinguished on the basis of their relationship to each other and to the corpora cardiaca and pericardial glands (cf. fig. 17). The simplest and most primitive type known is perhaps the paired lateral corpora allata with paired corpora cardiaca as in Ephemeroptera, Lepidoptera, etc. (fig. 17a, f). One evolutionary trend from this stage developed through the approximation and later fusing of the corpora cardiaca, as in Blattoptera, Orthoptera, Mecoptera and some of the Diptera (e.g. Culicidae). The other tendency was to the fusing of the corpora allata which can take place either below the dorsal aorta as in Hemiptera (d) or above it as in Tabanidae. A special type with both corpora cardiaca and corpora allata fused and connected by the fused prothoracic glands to form a single structure, is represented by the ring gland of Diptera Cyclorrapha (cf. p. 67).

Cyclical changes in one direction occur in the corpora allata in each larval instar as well as in the adult. The corpora allata in the plant-feeding bug *Oncopeltus fasciatus* have the smallest volume at the beginning of each larval instar and increase gradually in size to reach a maximum at about the middle of the intermoult period. They then decrease in size with the decrease in the secretory activity of the gland before the next moult, the minimum size at the beginning of each instar being distinctly smaller than the maximum in the preceding one. In the last larval instar a distinct increase in the volume of the gland also occurs; it is, however, relatively less than in the earlier instars. In the adult stage a distinct increase in the size of the gland commences 3 or 4 days after the imaginal moulting and continues for the whole period of the egg laying (from the 8th and 30th day) when the volume of the corpora allata increases by about 30 times compared with that immediately after the moulting. Legay (1950) found a distinct increase in the volume of the gland in *Bombyx* at the time of each larval ecdysis and a very small increase during the intermoult periods. This type of growth is probably connected with the displacement of the critical period for the AH and thus, necessarily, also of that for the JH towards the end of the intermoult period. It appears, however, to be more a secondary

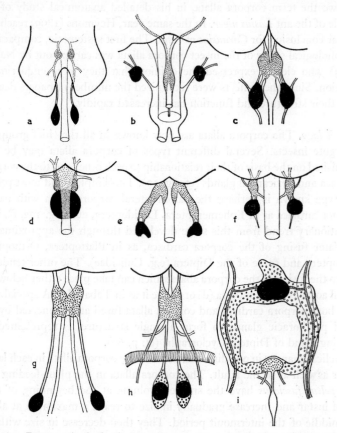

FIG. 17. Retrocerebral glands in various groups of insects. *a – Japyx* sp.; *b – Ephemera vulgata*; *c – Blatta orientalis*; *d – Pyrrhocoris apterus*; *e – Hydrous piceus*; *f – Sphinx ligustri*; *g – Sialis lutaria*; *h – Culex* sp.; *i – Calliphora erythrocephala*. Black – corpora allata, dotted – corpora cardiaca, with circles – peritracheal (pericardial) glands, white – brain, suboesophageal ganglion, hypocerebral ganglion (after Cazal, 1948, and other authors, modified).

adaptation in the phylogenetically highest insect orders, connected with the shortening of the moulting process. The growth of the corpora allata in *Carausius morosus* and in both larvae and adults of the honey bee (*Apis mellifica*) was systematically studied by Pflugfelder (1937a, 1948, cf. 1958).

He found a marked increase in the volume of the corpora allata of worker bees in the first two days of imaginal life, at the height of activity of the pharyngeal glands (between 6th and 12th day), in connection with the first orientation flight (9th and 10th day) and at the time of maximum secretion of the wax glands (14th and 15th day), and a slow decrease afterwards. The corpora allata of the queen larvae are larger than those of worker larvae during the whole of their development but especially during the pupal instar, perhaps connected with the development of the ovaries, as confirmed by Lukoschus (1955). In the adult queen their volume remains practically constant, distinctly below the maximum in the workers. The increase in the volume of the corpora allata between the first and last larval instar in 18 different species of both Heterometabola and Holometabola was studied by Novák (1954). It is much slower than the increase in the volume of the body, but somewhat faster than that of the volume of the brain and the nervous ganglia (cf. p. 112).

Kaiser (1949) studied the relationship between the growth of the corpora allata and the thoracic glands during larval development in Lepidoptera (*Pieris*). Whilst the ratio was 1 : 2 in favour of the prothoracic glands at the moment of hatching, it increased to 1 : 29 at the time of cocoon spinning. During the last larval instar the volume of the corpora allata increased very little whilst that of the prothoracic glands was doubled. The conclusions made by the author from these observations and based on the hypothesis of antagonism between the MH and JH does not seem, however, to find any support in the experimental evidence. Amongst other things it must be kept in mind that even if the volume of the prothoracic glands does increase as compared with that of the corpora allata, it definitely decreases as compared with the body as a total. The fact that the moulting process is distinctly accelerated in the presence of the active corpora allata certainly speaks against any antagonism between the two hormones.

In *Platysamia cecropia* adults a noteworthy sexual dimorphism in the size of the corpora allata was found by Schneiderman and Gilbert (1959) in contrast to that in bugs and most other insects. Whereas the pupal corpora allata show the same weight of about 30 γ in each sex, those of adult males reach about 400 γ whereas those of the female adults stop at about 65 γ. This is in agreement with the activity of ether extracts of male and female abdomens, that of the female being only about 1/40th as active as that of the male (cf. p. 119). The authors suggest a connection with the analogous difference between the lipids extracted with ether (0·201 g. in male and 0·045 g. in female) on the one hand and the much higher flight activity in the male on the other hand. Similarly Rehm (1951) found a 20-fold increase in the adult male corpora allata of *Galleria mellonella*, whilst that in the female was only three-fold. The number of cells per corpus allatum is, however, approximately the same in each sex.

Histology. The corpora allata are spherical, ovoid or pad shaped bodies in most insects, connected with the corpora cardiaca by a nerve (nervus

FIG. 18. Corpora cardiaca and corpora allata of *Acheta domestica*. Nervi allati ending in spindleshaped clubs. Below: a pair of nervi recurrentes with a part of dorsal vessel.

allatus) which may become reduced so that the two bodies are closely approximated or, in some cases, partially fused (cf. fig. 17). They are enclosed in a mesenchymatous connective tissue membrane formed by plate-like cells with an oblong nucleus and homogeneous surface layer (Cazal, 1948). Mendes (1948) found the following three types of glandular cells in the corpora allata of *Melanoplus*: undifferentiated cells, normal secretory cells and polyploid giant cells. A noticeable feature of the glandular cells of the corpora allata is that they increase considerably during the period of their secretory activity and shrink during the inactive period (cf. Pflugfelder, 1948). The period with histological signs of secretory activity agrees with the period of their hormonal activity as shown by parabiosis and transplantation experiments (cf. Wigglesworth, 1936a, Pflugfelder, 1952, Novák, 1951 etc.). There is no histological evidence in favour of the concept of more than one corpus allatum hormone in any of the species studied in this respect (cf. Mendes, 1948, Pflugfelder, 1952).

On the basis of their histological structure the following four types of corpora allata may be distinguished:

(*i*) *The epithelial vesicular type*, containing, in their central cavity, secretion (in *Aeschna*), connective tissue (in *Japyx*) or a system of concentric lamellae (in Phasmidae). This is the original, phylogenetically lowest type (even though secondarily simplified in some cases), which shows the ectodermal origin of the gland.

(*ii*) *The pseudolymphoid type*, formed by small cells with reduced deeply staining cytoplasm resembling that of the lymphoid tissue in vertebrates. Corpora allata of this type have been found in Ephemerida and Odonata.

(*iii*) *The small cell type*, which is the most common found for example in Blattoptera, Orthoptera, Hemiptera, Coleoptera etc. It is formed by numerous small irregularly shaped cells in the intercellular lacunae of which the secretion accumulates during the periods of activity. The nuclei are eggshaped to oblong, their cytoplasm being relatively clear.

(*iv*) *The large cell type*, phylogenetically the highest occurring in Panorpata, Hymenoptera, Trichoptera, Lepidoptera and many Diptera. The gland consists of few large cells with large, often lobular nuclei and numerous uniformly distributed chromatin granules (cf. Cazal, 1948).

The histophysiological changes in the corpora allata in adult *Leucophaea maderae* were studied in detail by B. Scharrer and Harnack (1958) and Harnack (1958a, b). No great changes in the low secretory activity of the male corpora allata were observed during the whole adult life except for a short 'activation period' shortly after the imaginal moulting. In females, on the other hand, important changes occur in connection with the ovarian cycles. A conspicuous increase in the amount of cytoplasm, both absolute and relative (in relation to the size and number of nuclei), occurs during the activation period. The authors describe the changes minutely. Harnack (l.c.) also observed the effect of starvation on the imaginal moulting. The corpus allatum volume decreased markedly shortly after a limited increase at the beginning of the instar. Feeding following a long period of starvation results in a marked increase in the volume of the gland which greatly

exceeds that in normally fed specimens not only in the first ovarian cycle
but also in the later ones where it increases. The author suggests an analogy
with the adenohypophysis in vertebrates.

B. Scharrer (1956, 1958) studied the effect of ovariectomy on the corpus
allatum in the same species and observed an increase in volume of the
gland, the number of nuclei, and an increased amount of cytoplasm in

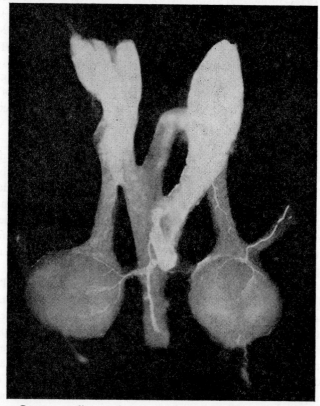

FIG. 19. Corpora cardiaca and corpora allata of *Periplaneta americana*. In the
middle the hypocerebral ganglion.

relation to nuclei following the operation (cf. p. 109). Similar changes
appear following denervation of the corpus allatum (interruption of the
nervi corporum cardiacarum). The author calls attention to the analogy
with the neuroendocrine cycle in vertebrates. The succession of developmental changes in the corpora allata in the adult bug *Oncopeltus fasciatus*
was studied by Johansson (1958a) and that in the pupae of *Mimas tilae*
(Lepidoptera) by Highnam (1958b).

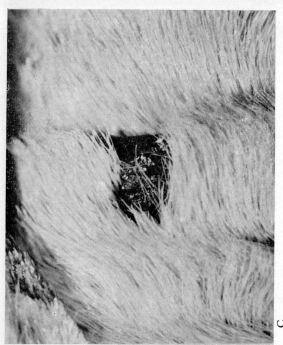

A

B

C

PLATE IV. Localized effect of an implanted corpus allatum from *Periplaneta americana* on the epidermis of the abdominal tergites of *Bombyx mori*. A – Pupa with a very small area of larval cuticle above the implanted corpus allatum. B – The same more strongly magnified. C – The same individual after the moult to adult. The small area above the implanted gland remains bare of scales and has a surface which is similar to a pupa yet wrinkled.

The ultrastructure of the corpora allata and its functional changes were studied by B. Scharrer (1961, 1962) in adult females of *Leucophaea maderae*. The secretory cells interlock by means of long cytoplasmic processes. Their cell membranes are folded in a characteristic way in inactive glands. In active glands the cytoplasm of the cells becomes more abundant, the quantity of mitochondria and ribosomes increases, an endoplasmic reticulum and very numerous granular inclusions appear. The gland is ensheathed by a thick membrane from which processes of varying thickness branch off and penetrate the spaces between the secretory cells. These processes form a 'stroma', containing denser bodies, through which the neurosecretory axons of the nervus allatus penetrate the corpus allatum. The 'stroma' seems to be continuous with the adjacent corpus cardiacum. The author suggests that the processes serve as a pathway through which food and other chemical exchanges between the gland and the haemolymph including diffusion of the hormone take place.

Embryogenesis. Contrary to earlier views that the corpora allata were of mesodermal (cf. Wheeler, 1893), or even of entodermal, origin (cf. Nussbaum, 1889), their ectodermal origin now seems to be sufficiently proved. Mellanby (1936) showed that they originate as ectodermal invaginations in the area between the mandibular and maxillary pleurites in *Rhodnius prolixus*. The original paired rudiments fuse into a single median body in Hemiptera towards the end of the embryonic period. Abnormalities due to incomplete fusion of the two embryonic invaginations, sometimes even showing two separate bodies, were often found by the author in the plant-feeding lygaeid bug *Oncopeltus fasciatus* (Novák, 1951b). An increased number of such aberrations, amounting to 20%, was observed in animals kept at higher temperatures. An explanation has been suggested that they are the result of a selective influence on the process of fusion exerted by the increase in temperature. Similar changes have been observed in *Pyrrhocoris apterus*.[1] The same origin was found by Pflugfelder (1937a) in *Carausius morosus* where the glands retain their original vesicular shape both in nymphs and adults. The embryogenesis of the corpora allata as a part of the ring gland was clarified by Poulson (1945a, b) for *Drosophila*. Their origin from ectodermal invaginations in bugs is also mentioned by Wells (1954).

Phylogenesis. Corpora allata have been found in all groups of metabolous insects (Pterygota) where they have so far been looked for. As regards Apterygota, they are fairly well developed in Japygidae (Cazal, 1948), and

[1] Novák, 1956, unpublished observations.

in a more primitive stage of development, in a lateral position closely connected with the mandibulo-maxillar area of their origin, in *Ctenolepisma* (Yashika, 1960a, b). A distinct juvenilizing effect of the glands of *Cteno-lepisma* implanted into *cecropia* pupae has been described. From this point of view the earlier suggestions as to the possible homology of the corpora allata with the so-called corps jugales in Thysanura must be considered (Chaudonneret, 1946, 1949; cf. Paclt, 1956). It seems probable that the original function of the corpora allata was the activation of the ovarian follicles and that only subsequently did they gain the function in larval

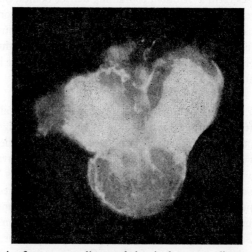

FIG. 20. A pair of corpora cardiaca and the single corpus allatum of *Pyrrhocoris apterus*.

development which led to the origin of Pterygote insects (cf. p. 167). The structure and development of the corpora allata in the larvae of higher Diptera is most complicated. Here they form a part of the ring gland (cf. p. 67). The following phylogenetic stages may be distinguished in the development of the ring gland: (1) the dorsal fusing of the originally paired corpora allata; (2) the fusing of their nervi allati with the neighbouring pericardial glands; (3) the strengthening of the lateral arms and the dorsal part of the gland with tracheal trunks; (4) the bending of the ring with its upper part forward by a backwards shift of the brain. As emphasized by Cazal (1948) the formation of the retrocerebral endocrine system corresponds in a surprising way to the modern views on the phylogeny of metabolic insects based on the system of Martynov (1937) and Jeannel (1949).

The Effects of the JH

(*a*) MORPHOGENETIC EFFECTS

(1) *The inhibition of metamorphosis.* As mentioned above, implantation of the active corpora allata at the beginning of the last larval instar partially or completely prevents metamorphosis and results in adultoid forms or supernumerary larval instars. These extra instars (giant larvae) may actually change into giant adults at the next moult. The removal of the corpora allata by decapitation or extirpation in earlier larval instars is followed by a precocious metamorphosis resulting in miniature adults, preceded (in Holometabola) by miniature pupae. In Hemimetabola only one instar occurs in most cases following allatectomy (e.g. Hemiptera), whilst in a number of the phylogenetically oldest groups, such as Blattoptera and Phasmidae, two more moults appear following the operation, a special 'praeadultoid' instar preceding miniature adults (cf. p. 162).

The suppression of metamorphosis connected with the positive effect on larval (isometric) growth is the most conspicuous and important effect of the juvenile hormone but is not the only one. Implantation of the corpora allata markedly accelerates the moulting process. For example, the inter-moult period of the last larval instar in *Rhodnius* takes 24 days, whilst following the implantation of active corpora allata at the beginning of the instar, the animal moults in 17 days. On this Wigglesworth (1936) based his original concept of the juvenile hormone effect, applying Goldschmidt's theory of differential velocities (1923). He concluded that morphogenesis could not be completed because of the acceleration of the moulting process. Such an effect really appears to exist but only to a limited extent in the case of the so-called progressive prothetely (cf. p. 133).

Under certain conditions the JH appears also to be capable of accelerating the metamorphosis. At least this would be the most probable explanation of some of the observations of Wigglesworth (1948a) according to which the removal of the corpora allata at the start of the last larval instar results in somewhat nymphoid adults. From this it would follow that the presence of the JH in a concentration below the morphogenetical threshold is necessary for complete imaginal differentiation. On the other hand the positive effect of the implantation of last instar corpus allatum on imaginal differentiation in earlier nymphs appears to have a quite different cause (cf. p. 160).

The introduction of an active corpus allatum into an adult by implantation or parabiosis can produce a partial suppression of the imaginal characters when an artificial imaginal moulting is induced simultaneously, either by parabiosis with the nymphs (cf. p. 160), or by implantation of the active prothoracic glands, or by injection of the ecdyson (cf. Wigglesworth 1940a; Bodenstein, 1953a–c etc.), or by exposing a part of the imaginal epidermis

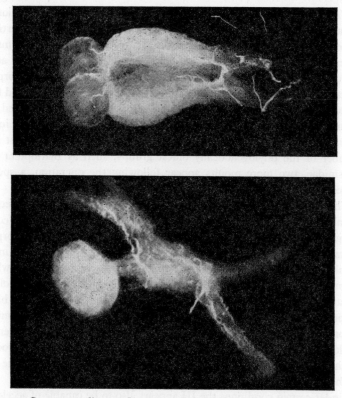

FIG. 21. Corpora cardiaca and corpora allata of *Carausius morosus* (above) and a corpus cardiacum and corpus allatum of *Bombyx mori*.

to the action of the larval hormone as in the epidermis bladder method (Piepho, 1951 etc.; cf. p. 22). All the JH hormone effects mentioned under this heading can be produced to exactly the same extent with both the larval and adult corpus allatum (Slámia and Hrubešová, 1963).

(2) *The influence on the ovarian follicular cells.* The influence of the corpus allatum hormone on the development of eggs in the ovaries was shown in the first of Wigglesworth's papers on the juvenile hormone. Wigglesworth (1935, 1936) showed that the presence of an active corpus allatum is absolutely indispensable in *Rhodnius* for the ripening of eggs in the ovaries

beyond a certain developmental stage at which the ovarian follicle cells become active. Following allatectomy the growth of the eggs stops at a certain stage due to the degeneration of the follicle cells. This effect may be prevented by the simultaneous implantation of an active corpus allatum from another specimen. The larval and imaginal corpora allata show the same activity in this respect. Results similar to those with *Rhodnius* were obtained by Joly (1945a, b) with the beetle *Dytiscus*, by Weed-Pfeiffer (1945) with the grasshopper *Melanoplus differentialis*, by B. Scharrer (1946) with the cockroach *Leucophaea maderae*, by E. Thomsen (1952) with the blow-fly *Calliphora erythrocephala* and by other authors with other groups of insects. The research on *Calliphora* was further developed by Possompès (1955), according to whom the extirpation of the corpora allata suppresses the ripening of the eggs only when it is done in the adult; the removal of the corresponding part of the ring gland has no similar effect. L'Hélias (1956a) suggests that this might be due to the ability of the corpus cardiacum extract to replace that of the corpus allatum which she assumed to be related chemically and to have similar effects. The question remains whether there is not here at least a partial regeneration of the corpora allata. In the higher Diptera, the adult corpora allata are quite different from those of the larvae (the dorsal part of the ring gland) so that their development may not be prevented even by the complete removal of the larval structures. The necessity of JH for ovarian development has been found in most of the species examined in this respect. There are, however, species where no such connection exists, such as *Carausius morosus* (Pflugfelder, 1937a), *Bombyx mori* (Bounhiol, 1938b) etc. This independence of the development of the eggs seems to be a phylogenetically secondary adaptation connected with a particular type of egg laying: for example, in *Bombyx* all the eggs are deposited in a short time, not long after the imaginal moulting. In *Carausius* on the other hand, they are laid singly after long intervals.

The existence of a special gonadotropic corpus allatum hormone has been suggested by various authors, some years ago (e.g. Vogt, 1943a, d; P. Joly, 1945a etc.) and recently (e.g. Engelmann, 1957; Engelmann and Luscher, 1958; Sagesser etc.). As emphasized by Pflugfelder (1952, 1958), there is no definite evidence in favour of this conclusion. There are, on the other hand, important arguments in support of the one hormone theory (Novák, 1951b, Novák and Sláma, 1962, etc.). One of the most important of these is the fact, already mentioned, that the effects of the imaginal glands can be reproduced by the glands of any larval instar not only of the same species but also of any other insect Order. Also, conversely, the imaginal corpus allatum of any insect species can replace the larval corpus

allatum in any insect (Pterygote) species. For example, the corpus allatum
of adult female of *P. americana* in the process of ootheca formation can
prevent imaginal differentiation in the last larval instar of *Oncopeltus
fasciatus* (Novák, 1951a, b). The histological evidence also lends no support
to the theory of two or more hormones (Mendes 1948 etc.; cf. p. 85). The
male gonads are in all cases independent of the presence of the JH.

FIG. 22. Result of allatectomy (at the beginning of 4th larval instar) in *Bombyx
mori* – a miniature pupa prematurely formed (regressive prothetely).

(3) *The influence on the sexual accessory glands.* The necessity of the JH for
the functioning of the accessory glands in the male *Rhodnius prolixus* was
shown by Wigglesworth (1936a) in his first paper on the corpus allatum
hormone. Since that time a similar dependence on the JH has been shown
in many other insect species, not only in males but, in some cases, also in
females. For example, the female accessory glands in *Calliphora erythrocephala* reach an average length of 2·58 mm, but in allatectomized females
they do not surpass 1·7 mm. The effect of allatectomy in males is less
conspicuous. Here the normal length is 1·18 mm, but they reach only
0·91 mm following allatectomy. Their secretory activity is not completely
suppressed by allatectomy (E. Thomsen, 1942). B. Scharrer (1946c) found

an effect of the corpora allata on the functioning of the accessory glands in males but not in females. On the other hand, no such action of the JH has been found on the accessory glands of *Lucilia* and *Sarcophaga*.

(4) *The influence on polymorphism.* Of the various types of polymorphism in insects (cf. p. 246) the following have been found to be closely connected with the JH:

(*a*) The mechanism of *caste polymorphism in social insects*, wherever studied from this point of view, has so far been found to bear some relationship to the JH activity, as for example in ants (Brian, 1959 etc.) and in termites (Lüscher, 1961, Kaiser, 1955). As, however, various exo-hormones play the principal role here, it seems preferable to discuss them later in the chapter devoted to this subject (p. 243).

(*b*) *Phase polymorphism in locusts.* The influence of the JH on the development of locusts, *Locusta* and *Schistocerca*, has been studied by Staal (1959, 1961 etc.), L. Joly (1960 etc.), Kennedy (1956, 1961), Loher (1960), and others. Their findings point to a complicated dependence on JH activity. As shown by Staal, implantation of active corpora allata into young larval instars induces the green coloration typical of the solitary phase even in environmental conditions which would otherwise produce the gregarious phase. The adaptive value of either phase in environment which induces the particular type of development has been emphasized by Kennedy (l.c.). The existence of a volatile factor acting through antennal chemoreceptors seems possible, on the basis of the results of Loher (1960) who discovered a substance accelerating sexual maturation in adult male locusts.

(*c*) *Seasonal polymorphism in aphids.* A very complicated type of poly-morphism is encountered in aphids. There is a strict seasonal alternation of forms with a preponderance of parthenogenetic generations. The poly-morphic forms differ as regards the occurrence of wings, the presence or absence of vivipary and in a number of other, less marked, characters, both morphological and physiological. Even though little is known regarding the various mechanisms involved in its determination, there are definite suggestions that the metamorphosis hormones and perhaps other chemical factors play a part in the determination of the characters of the various forms. The apterous virginoparae of *Megoura*, for example, appear to be produced by the neotenic effect of increased JH activity. This activity, however, seems to take place during the embryonic period through the action of the maternal endocrine system on the corpus allatum of the older embryo. The still earlier activation of the embryonic corpus allatum by the maternal body appears to be the cause of differentiation of the oviparae. Similar conclusions were reached by Johnson and Birks (1960) with an

Australian aphid species (*Aphis craccivora* Koch.). They assume that all
aphids start their development as presumptive winged forms and that they
may be diverted away from this direction of development by various
stimuli in the determination period between the late embryonic stage and
the second larval instar. These authors attempted to apply their conclusions to other types of insect polymorphism.

(*d*) *Alary polymorphism in bugs.* Alary polymorphism or the occurrence
of varying degrees of wing development in one and the same species is a
wide-spread phenomenon in Heteroptera. A theory has been elaborated by
Southwood (1961) based on Wigglesworth's findings (1954, 1960) on the
hormonal control of this type of polymorphism. Brachyptery is assumed to
originate on the principle of metathety in some species, particularly in
colder, mountain conditions. It may be classed as a juvenile character
in adults following the normal number of instars (five in Heteroptera).
In these insects (such as *Gerris*, *Nabis*, *Bryocoris*, various *Tingidae* etc.)
macropterous forms are found mostly in warm localities. On the other
hand, brachyptery is assumed to originate in other species on the principle
of prothety (paedogenesis). In species such as *Dolichonabis limbatus* and
Microvelia, long-winged specimens appear in cold, mountain conditions
whilst in the normal warm environment only brachypterous forms occur.
This theory awaits[1] further experimental evidence, as suggested by its
author.

(*5*) *The influence on tumour growth and other alterations in histogenesis.* In
addition to the morphological effects mentioned the JH has a profound
influence on histogenesis which becomes evident with its removal. The first
detailed analysis of the histological effects of corpora allata extirpation was
carried out by Pflugfelder (1937a, 1938a–d, 1952) with *Carausius morosus*.
He found numerous changes of a pathological character following allatectomy carried out in earlier instars. He distinguished tissue degenerations
and tissue proliferations both of which often occurred in one and the same
tissue. The following may be mentioned as the most frequent of these
pathological changes: (*a*) Degeneration sometimes connected with a partial
histolysis of fully developed tissue and often connected with a subsequent
partial or complete phagocytosis. At the same time, proliferations usually
appear as knotty structures scattered throughout the tissue, which sometimes contain single differentiated cells in the form of giant muscle cells (cf.
fig. 23). (*b*) Degeneration of the nervous system and the adjacent mesoderm
and glial cells in which the formation of large irregular cysts often occurs.

[1] The number of instars can scarcely be taken as a definite criterion of practical
value for distinguishing between metathety and prothety; cf. p. 132.

castrated females (E. Thomsen, Hamburger, 1955) apparently suggest that this may be a direct, and not an indirect effect on the metabolism and not, as earlier supposed by Pflugfelder (1952), caused by oxygen consumption of the developing ovaries. Pflugfelder himself (1952) observed an increase in oxygen consumption in *Carausius morosus* following the implantation of corpora allata and a decrease following their extirpation. Both effects were, however, rather weak and only temporary. L'Hélias (1956a) found a decrease in oxygen consumption in the same species following allatectomy. An even greater decrease was observed when the corpora cardiaca were removed at the same time. L'Hélias tried to explain this as being connected with the accumulation of glycids and mineral phosphorus in the tissues and with the loss of energy caused by the breaking down of esters due to the increase in alkaline phosphatases.

On the other hand, a series of experiments on the oxygen consumption of normal and castrated adult females of *Pyrrhocoris apterus*, implanted with corpora allata (Novák, Sláma, Wenig, 1959, 1961), appears to point towards an indirect action of these glands on metabolism. It was found that castrated females do not show any increase in oxygen consumption compared with normal controls following corpora allata implantation, very probably because of the increased share in the total metabolism of the ripening ovarian follicle cells which do not grow in the absence of the corpora allata. Examination of the effect of corpora allata implantation into the last larval instar of the same species (Novák, Sláma, 1962) gave corresponding results. A direct connection was found between the extent of the induced morphological changes and the rate of oxygen consumption. It was concluded from both series of experiments that the JH-effect on the oxygen consumption is an indirect one depending on the increase in the amount of metabolically active tissue. The direct effect of the JH seems more likely to be concerned with proteosynthesis.

On the other hand, Sägesser (1960) claims to have found an increase in the oxygen consumption after corpora allata implantation in the cockroach *Leucophaea maderae* even in castrated females and concludes, in agreement with E. Thomsen, that JH affects metabolism directly. His point of view based on the theory of two corpus allatum hormones does not, however, appear to be without its faults, as shown by Novák and Sláma (l.c.).

Results which seem to contradict the above to some extent are reported by Samuels (1956). He found a significant increase in the oxygen consumption of the isolated thoracic musculature of *Periplaneta americana* adults of both sexes 2-3 months after allatectomy. Samuels attempted to explain the differences observed in the oxygen consumption in the whole

4th instar moult occurs at the same time as that of the controls. This can also be accepted as a consequence of the positive effect of regeneration on the functioning of the glands concerned.

The question of the effect of the metamorphosis hormones on the regeneration process in insects was thoroughly discussed by Bodenstein (1955, 1959) on the basis of his numerous experiments. He emphasized the necessity of the MH for regeneration. It is only the degeneration of the prothoracic glands connected with the metamorphosis which makes the adult metabolous insects unable to moult. All the tissues of the imago retain their full ability for regeneration and this occurs in the extra imaginal moulting process brought about by the implantation of an active prothoracic gland or by parabiosis of the adult with a nymph. It is not made clear to what extent the observed effect of MH on regeneration is a direct one or, perhaps more probably, whether it is only indirectly brought about by the inducing of the moulting process. Bodenstein discusses his results as contradicting those of Pflugfelder with *Carausius morosus* (see above) and attempts to find a common explanation.

(b) THE PHYSIOLOGICAL EFFECTS OF THE JH

It is often difficult to distinguish between the morphogenetical and the physiological effects of a hormone as well as between the direct and the indirect effects. All morphogenetical effects are necessarily based on physiological (biochemical) ones and, on the other hand, most of the physiological effects can, but may not, cause morphogenetical changes. It may, therefore, be useful to make the following distinctions:

(7) *The effect on proteosynthesis and on the total metabolism (oxygen consumption).* It was suggested by Pflugfelder as early as 1941 on the basis of his work with corpora allata implantations and extirpations in *Carausius morosus* that the JH is a factor which generally favours metabolism. This conclusion was upheld by the later experiments of Pfeiffer-Weed (1945a). She concluded from her experiments on the effects of allatectomy in adult *Melanoplus differentialis* females that the corpora allata exert a positive effect on the basal metabolism. She observed a connection between the presence of the corpora allata and the consumption of the food reserves in the fat body as well as an effect of the JH on the increase in weight of the fat-free dry-matter and water. Further results supporting this conclusion were obtained by E. Thomsen (1949) who found that allatectomized female adults of *Calliphora erythrocephala* show a 19% decrease in oxygen consumption. A similar dependence on the presence of the JH was found in the males. Experiments carried out under the same conditions using

whilst there is this disturbance in the hormonal balance, as shown by Pflugfelder (1948). He attempted to explain this by the known fact that young cells are more easily affected by external stimuli than older ones. Tumorous growth of a malignant character has often been observed following the cutting of various nerves, such as the nervi corporum cardiacarum (B. Scharrer, 1952).

(6) *The effect on regeneration.* A marked decrease in regeneration ability was observed by Pflugfelder (1939d) in *Carausius morosus* following extirpation of the corpora allata. In some cases, particularly when an amputation was effected after the allatectomy, there was a complete loss of regeneration ability. In many cases the degeneration of whole groups of cells was observed in the regenerating epidermis whilst knotty proliferations appeared in other parts of it. On the other hand, no difference was observed in *Blattella germanica*, either in the extent of regeneration or in its effect on the duration of the instar concerned, irrespective of whether the extirpation was carried out during the period of active JH concentration (1st to 5th instar) or in its absence during the metamorphosis (6th instar) (cf. O'Farrell *et al.* 1956, 1959 etc.).

The connection between regeneration and the changes in volume of the corpora allata were studied in detail by O'Farrell *et al.* (1958, 1959, 1961 etc.) in *Blattella germanica*. The duration of the moulting process was only affected when muscle tissue was involved and the greater the amount of tissue affected, the longer the intermoult period. When, however, the regeneration was restricted to the epidermal structures no changes were observed in the moulting cycle. No evidence is available of any nervous influence on the regulation of the moulting process and all the effects observed appear to be the results of self-regulatory processes. A histological study of the volume of the corpora allata and of that of the so-called headlobes (cf. p. 65) carried out at twelve-hourly intervals showed a close connection between the volume changes of the two glands. Regeneration has a positive effect on the functioning of both pairs, which is particularly interesting from the point of view of the experiments of Bodenstein (1953) and Engelmann (1959) on the reciprocal effects of the corpora allata and the prothoracic glands and their effect on the moulting process (cf. p. 73). Immediately after the moult following treatment which causes the regeneration, a hypertrophy of the ventral lobes and corpora allata occurred. This hypertrophy and the subsequent extensive regeneration seems to result in extra moults in the adult stage. The delay caused by regeneration observed in the moulting process in the first larval instar of *Blattella germanica* is followed by a shortening of the following instars so that the (*c*) Degeneration of the fat body during which vacuoles appear in the fat cells, which resemble fat droplets but do not stain with osmium tetroxide and therefore probably do not contain either fat or any lipoid substance. It would be interesting to determine to what extent these JH deficiency syndromes agree with the further mentioned (p. 100) alterations in the fat body of adults of other species, which are not connected with pathological changes in other tissues. The long-term effect of allatectomy is encapsulation of the pathologically changed cells by lymphocytes which often leads

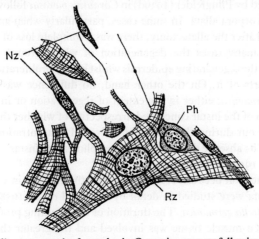

FIG. 23. Malignant growth of muscles in *Carausius morosus* following allatectomy. Rz – giant muscle cell; Nz – normal muscle cell; Ph – phagocyte (haemocyte) (after Pflugfelder, 1938).

to the development of large cysts. Inside these cysts large concretions often appear which show concentrical layers in sections. (*d*) Degeneration features are also often observed in the Malpighian tubules in which cysts and concretions appear similar to those in the fat body. (*e*) Accumulations and proliferation of haemocytes (lymphocytes) often also occur, from which extensive knots of undifferentiated cells sometimes arise resembling those of spindle cell sarcoma in Man. (*f*) Proliferations of a carcinomatous character are observed in the epidermis, gut, and oviducts.

Various disturbances also appear following the implantation of extra corpora allata (from adults into larvae), in, for example, the ovarioles, oviducts and other organs and tissues. They are, however, obviously different from the changes produced by allatectomy (Pflugfelder, l.c.).

Various disturbances in tissue differentiation frequently occur during regeneration particularly when a piece of embryonic tissue is implanted

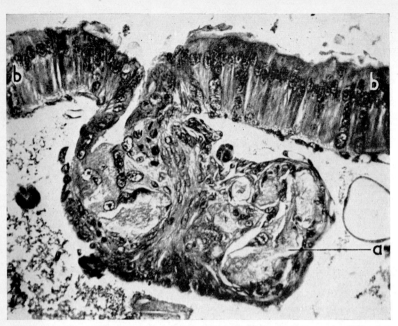

PLATE V. *Above:* Hypertrophy of the gut wall of *Carausius morosus* following allatectomy in an early larval instar. *a* – cancer-like growth of the gut wall; *b* – gut epithelium. From Pflugfelder, 1938. *Below:* Hypertrophy of lymphocytes following allatectomy in *Carausius morosus.* From Pflugfelder, 1938.

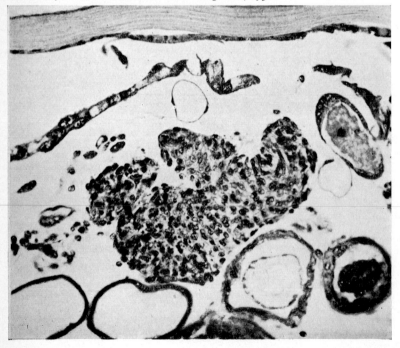

interference with JH production. Some of these are obviously of morphogenetical origin, such as the green coloration in the solitary phase of the
migratory locust. Others are, no doubt, due to the brain neurohormone.
There are, however, other changes which can be assumed to be due to the
JH. Here must be mentioned those causing the coloration of allatectomized
stick insects (Carausius morosus), as observed by L'Hélias (1956 and
etc.). They are supposed to be due to an accumulation of the uric acid in
the tissue together with a decrease in the purine, pterine and melanin
contents. Changes in coloration were also observed in the same species
following implantation of active corpora allata (Pflugfelder, 1938c, d etc.).
A marked morphogenetical effect of the corpora allatum hormone on the
black pattern in the lygaeid bug *Oncopeltus fasciatus* has been described
(Novák, 1951).

(14) *The effect on the mitochondria.* An increase in the oxygen consumption
is reported by Clarke and Baldwin (1960) in mitochondria preparations
from *Locusta migratoria L.* on a sodium succinate substrate, after the
addition of the corpora allata. The increase was however only observed in
mitochondria prepared from *Locusta migratoria* adults, those from 5th
instar nymphs of *Schistocerca gregaria* showing a decrease in oxygen consumption. The addition of 2 : 4 dinitrophenol in physiological amounts, on
the other hand, resulted in an opposite effect: it decreased the oxygen
consumption of mitochondria of adult *Locusta* and increased that of
mitochondria of 5th instar *Schistocerca*. The addition of both dinitrophenol
and corpora allata at the same time increased the oxygen consumption of
the preparations from both species. The authors discuss the possibility of
the corpora allata controlling metabolism by their action on the mitochondria and the possible relationship between the effect of JH and those
of the dinitrophenol. Many questions, however, remain to be answered in
this connection even if the changes observed should be confirmed for other
species.

(15) *The effect on pheromone production.* It has recently been shown by
Loher (1961, 1962) that the JH controls the sexual maturation and the
corresponding changes in the coloration and the mating behaviour in the
locust *Schistocerca gregaria* males in a very interesting way. The maturation of the adult males of the gregarious phase in this species has the following three aspects: the colour change from the light-brownish grey and
white of the freshly moulted adult to the yellow of the mature specimen;
the specific sexual behaviour pattern; and the production by the epidermis
cells of a pheromone which accelerates the maturation process in young

possibility that the effect observed may be merely the result of the inhibition of the moulting process must also be taken into account.

(11) *The effect on the water balance.* In addition to the neurosecretory cells of the pars intercerebralis and the corpora cardiaca, the corpora allata are also said to produce an effect on the water balance (cf. Altmann, 1956, Raabe, 1959). Allatectomy results in a reduction of the water content of the body, including that of the haemolymph. The effect of the JH is particularly evident in castrated females where retention of the corpora allata results in a considerable increase in the quantity of haemolymph with an associated conspicuous distension of the abdomen. In such individuals, however, the amount of dry matter also increases. However, there remains to be distinguished what is due to JH itself and what is the effect of the neurosecretion stored in the corpora allata (cf. p. 73).

(12) *The control of the imaginal diapause.* The relationship of the corpora allata to the imaginal diapause is evident from the necessity, first shown by Wigglesworth (1935, 1936), of the JH for the ovarian follicle cells. Experimental evidence of the dependence of the imaginal diapause on a temporary break in corpus allatum activity as suggested by Detinova (1945) for *Anopheles maculipennis*, was provided by Joly (1945) in his detailed study of *Dytiscus marginalis* and has since been confirmed by a number of other authors in various groups of insects with imaginal diapause, e.g. by de Wilde et al. (1954–61) in a series of papers on *Leptinotarsa decemlineata*; Hodek and Novák (1961),[1] in Eurygaster; Larsen and Bodenstein (1959) in *Aedes aegypti* and other mosquito species, etc. These findings will be dealt with in greater detail in the next chapter (p. 185). Here it only needs to be mentioned that the primary internal cause of the imaginal diapause lies in the neurosecretory system of the pars intercerebralis which appears to be the mechanism of action of external stimuli. The absence of the AH produces, of course, a series of further effects in the body in addition to the inhibition of the corpora allata, as shown by the papers of E. Thomsen and Möller (1959), Strangways-Dixon (1960) and others. This is why the state after allatectomy is not identical with the natural imaginal diapause and why diapause also occurs in the males, the gonads of which are not dependent on the presence of JH. This has recently been clearly shown by Sláma (1963) in his experiments on the effects of allatectomy, cardiacectomy and of the natural diapause on oxygen consumption in *Pyrrhocoris apterus*.

(13) *The effect on colour change.* Conspicuous changes have been observed in the coloration of both larval and adult insects following experimental

---

[1] Unpublished observations.

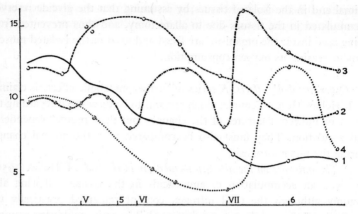

FIG. 24. Blood sugar concentration in normal and allatectomized nymphs of *Carausius morosus*. 1, 2 – concentration of sugar in the blood; 3, 4 – concentration in the tissue; 1 – controls; 2 – allatectomized; 3 – controls; 4 – allatectomized. Abscissa – time (the Roman figures – number of instar of the controls, Arabic figures – number of instar of the allatectomized specimens). Ordinate – concentration % of sugar (after L'Hélias, 1956).

(9) *The influence on the fat body.* It has been shown by Weed-Pfeiffer (1945a) that allatectomy causes an increase in the fat content of the fat body which is only slightly affected by castration. Similar results were obtained by E. Thomsen (1942) with *Calliphora erythrocephala* and by Vogt with *Drosophila*. The last-mentioned author also observed reduction in the size of the nuclei and nucleoli of the fat body cells which she explained as being due to the cytoplasm of these cells becoming filled with fat droplets. Day (1943a) also mentioned conspicuous histological changes in the fat body following extirpation of the ring gland in flies of the genera *Lucilia* and *Sarcophaga*. It is not, however, very clear from his experiments to what extent these changes were due to other components of the ring gland. An increase in the fat content of the fat body following allatectomy was also observed by L'Hélias (1956) in *Carausius morosus*. She assumed it to be due to a blocking of the phosphorylase activity.

(10) *The influence on the oenocytes.* Similar decreases in the volume of the cells and in the size of the nuclei with associated pycnosis were observed by Day (1943a) in the above-mentioned flies and by Vogt (1947) in *Drosophila* following ring gland extirpation. It is also difficult to decide here to what extent the observed changes are the result of JH-deficiency and to what extent they are due to the absence of the other two metamorphosis hormones (AH and MH) which also originate in the ring gland. The

animal and in the isolated tissues by assuming that the glycide reserves, accumulated in the tissues due to allatectomy, and thus prevented from being used inside the organism, are freed and used in the isolated muscle, thus increasing its oxygen consumption.

(8) *Other metabolic effects.* A series of further metabolic effects is claimed by L'Hélias. Here, of course, much remains to be discovered regarding the direct or indirect character of the changes and their mutual dependence and regulation. They must also be compared with the normal changes during the metamorphosis.

(*i*) *The influence on the nitrogen metabolism in the body.* L'Hélias (1956a) observed an accumulation of aminoacids in the tissues following alla-tectomy although the total nitrogen content remained practically un-changed and the protein amount decreased. The aminoacids were assumed to be partially converted into glycogen and the suggestion was put forward that the JH favours the formation of polypeptide chains. The effect of the JH on growth would therefore depend on this.

(*ii*) *The effect on the purine metabolism.* This depends, according to L'Hélias (1956a), on the fact that the JH reduces uric acid production and promotes ribonucleic acid formation. Its effect on the colour change is connected with this (see below). In allatectomized specimens the uric acid content of the tissues increases and the RNA content decreases.

(*iii*) *The effect on the mineral phosphorus content.* After allatectomy the amount of mineral phosphorus in the tissues shows a marked increase. It may also be observed in histological preparations as an accumulation of phosphatases in the tissues and the Malpighian tubules which are filled to bursting point with these (L'Hélias, 1956a). It is assumed that the absence of the JH (in larval tissues) prevents the normal glycide metabolism and thus also the production of the energy necessary for the synthesis of proteins.

(*iv*) *The influence on alkaline phosphatase.* The removal of the JH source results in a considerable increase in the alkaline phosphatases. From this it is concluded that the hormone reduces the activity of these enzymes or perhaps inhibits their synthesis (L'Hélias, 1954, 1956a). The removal of the corpora cardiaca is said to have an opposite effect. No effect on the acid phosphatases has been observed.

(*v*) *The effect on the glycides.* A considerable increase in glycides was observed in the tissues after allatectomy. At the same time the blood sugar content in the haemolymph decreased in comparison with untreated controls. From this it was concluded that the organism is not able to utilize them in absence of the JH (L'Hélias, 1953b).

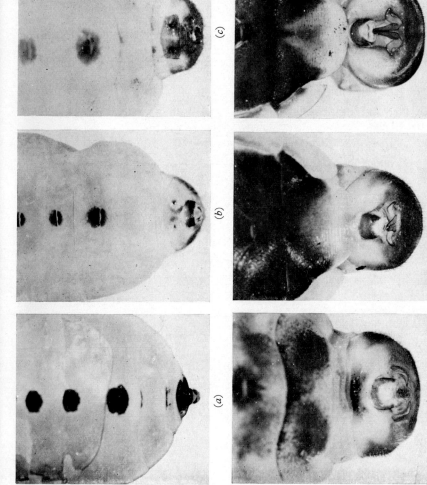

PLATE VI. Abdomina of intermediate forms (b–e) between last instar larva (a) and adult (f) of *Pyrrhocoris apterus* (males) following the implantation of a corpus allatum at different stages in the course of the last larval instar.

things, from the fact that neither the normal nor the experimentally induced
action of the corpora allata in adults causes any sign of moulting whilst this
may easily be induced, in the adult, by the implantation of an active
prothoracic gland.

(2) *The effect on the silk glands of caterpillars.* It is well known that in many
Lepidopterous larvae the labial glands are almost inactive during the first
to penultimate larval instar whereas they produce a large quantity of a silky
material for cocoon spinning in the last larval instar. The exact opposite is
the case in some sawflies such as *Cephaleia* (fam. Pamphilidae) where the
silk glands are active throughout the larval instars producing the so-called
excrement webs in which the larvae live gregariously, and pupation takes
place in cells in the soil without a cocoon. In each case the action of the
glands is connected with the presence of the JH. The hormone, however,
does not affect the silk glands directly but by affecting their morphogenesis in a very general way. Whether its presence affects the function of the
glands positively or negatively depends on genetic, species-specific factors.

(3) *The effect on instincts.* The action of JH on cocoon spinning in *Galleria
mellonella* has been described as a special case of effect on instinct. The
larva of this species spins a cocoon before each moult. This cocoon is, however, different before the larval moults from what it is before the pupal. The
larval cocoon is in the form of a tube open at each end whilst the pupal one
is spindle-shaped and completely closed. It was shown by Piepho (1950b)
that the implantation of corpora allata at certain times before moulting
caused the larva to produce cocoons intermediate between the larval and
the pupal types, depending on the time of implantation. This effect also
cannot be explained as a direct one on the instinct of cocoon spinning but,
undoubtedly, as an indirect one through the morphogenesis of the brain.
By inhibiting the morphogenesis of the imaginal brain at the required time
the JH determines whether and to what extent the material basis for a given
instinct is developed, i.e. the corresponding nervous (cerebral ganglion)
structure. A detailed analysis of this and similar effects will no doubt make
possible an exact localization of various imaginal instincts in insects,
especially when these differ from those in the larvae, as for instance in the
case of insects with aquatic larvae, very distinctly (cf. 287).

Is there more than one Corpus Allatum Hormone?
The seemingly contradictory effects of the JH, such as the negative effect
on the metamorphosis and the positive effect on growth, the activation of
larval tissues and, on the other hand, its necessity for the development of

adult males in the immediate vicinity of the mature specimen by an olfactory effect on their chemoreceptors. None of these indications is shown by allatectomized males. They are however induced by implantation of the active corpora allata from a mature specimen.

A similar type of pheromone was described by Barth (1962) in the cockroach *Byrsotria fumigata*. The virgin female of this species produces a volatile sex attractant which stimulates the courtship behaviour of the male. The production of this pheromone is also controlled by the JH. It does not occur in allatectomized specimens, but its production can be induced by the implantation of active corpora allata from another specimen. In this species no other role of the JH in the reproductive behaviour of either female or male was found.

The Indirect Effects of the JH

In many of the JH effects mentioned above it is difficult to decide whether the observed action is caused by this hormone (or its absence) directly or whether it is merely the consequence of an effect caused by the hormone in another part of the body. There are, however, several cases where the indirect nature of the JH effect is unquestionable.

(1) *The effect on moulting.* Several of the earlier authors who dealt with the corpus allatum hormone assumed it to be a moulting hormone (Pflugfelder, 1937a; Bodenstein, 1943a). This was based on the fact that, after the implantation of active corpora allata into a last instar larva, one or several extra moults and supernumerary larval instars occurred. Further investigations have, however, shown without doubt that the moulting process is directly influenced by the prothoracic gland hormone (MH) and that the observed, very marked, effect of the JH is simply the indirect effect of prolonging the action of the prothoracic glands which are normally histolysed during or immediately after the metamorphosis. The seemingly contradictory observation of Bodenstein (1953a–e) that allatectomy towards the end of the last larval instar in the cockroach *Periplaneta americana* may result in preservation of the prothoracic glands and thus in supernumerary moults can also be explained in this connection (cf. p. 118). As shown by O'Farrell *et al.* (1953, 1956), the amputation of legs or a more extensive injury to another part of the body may have the same effect as corpora allata extirpation. This, as noted above (cf. p. 73), is an effect of the regeneration process, perhaps improved by selection into a self-regulatory mechanism, in the case of insects with a well-developed autotomy, and has nothing to do with the action or absence of the corpora allata. The indirect character of the effect of JH on moulting is quite obvious, amongst other

such typically imaginal structures as the ovarian follicle cells, led to the hypothesis of two or more corpus allatum hormones. A number of indications have recently been collected in favour of this theory. It was argued by Lüscher and Springhetti (1960) that the corpora allata in *Kalotermes flavicollis* F. produce two different hormones which have different effects in caste differentiation, a 'juvenile hormone' and a 'gonadotropic hormone'. The first of these is supposed to increase the ability for supplementary reproductive differentiation and the other to initiate the pre-soldier differentiation. There is, however, no evidence in other insects for the absence of one of the two effects in a gland in which both would be present. The application of this theory therefore results in various contradictions.

Sägesser sees another reason in favour of two corpus allatum hormones in his finding that there is no qualitative difference in the oxygen consumption curve between the penultimate and the last larval instar in the cockroach *Leucophaea maderae*. Actually, however, there is no more than a quantitative difference in the supposed production of the juvenile hormone, and the qualitative changes in its effects on morphogenesis can be completely explained on the basis of this (cf. Novák, 1951b, 1956 etc. and p. 290). Moreover, there are many other processes acting during each instar, e.g. all those connected with moulting which are practically identical in both the penultimate and the last larval instar and which more or less mask the changes due to the differences in endocrine balance. All other experimental findings may therefore be as well if not better understood by the assumption that there is only one corpus allatum hormone (cf. Novák and Sláma, 1962).

Schneiderman uses the fact that the extract of the *cecropia* male abdomens (cf. p. 119) does not induce the development of ovaries as another argument in favour of two corpus allatum hormones.[1] This, however, is much more another argument against the identification of the extract mentioned with the corpus allatum hormone. On the other hand Wigglesworth (1961) found a positive effect of another morphogenetically active lipoid substance, farnesol, both in preventing metamorphosis and activating ovarian development. Wigglesworth interprets his results as a 'support for the belief that the yolk formation hormone and the juvenile hormone are likely to prove identical'.

There are a number of other important arguments in favour of this identity: (1) As shown by the histological investigation of the corpora allata during the secretory cycle, there is no evidence for more than one type of secretion. There is only one type of secretory cell in the corpus allatum (cf. Mendes, 1948; Highnam 1958a; B. Scharrer and Harnack, 1960; B.

[1] Personal communication to the author.

Scharrer 1961). (2) There is no difference in the endocrine activity of the corpora allata in either direction during the whole life cycle: the corpora allata of larvae from the first to the penultimate instar effect both morphogenesis and ovarian development in the same way as those of the adults, whereas those of the last larval instar and the pupal instar have a reduced activity on both processes. (3) As shown elsewhere, there is no major difference in the effect on the growth and function of the larval parts of the body and that on the ovarian follicle cells and both of these effects necessarily result in an increase in oxygen consumption. Even if none of these arguments can be taken as definite evidence of the existence of only one corpus allatum hormone, they are, nevertheless, much more relevant than the argument in the opposite direction. There is therefore at present no real justification for the hypothesis of two corpus allatum hormones (cf. p. 290).

The Control of JH Production

Criteria of corpora allata activity. The activity of the corpora allata may be estimated either indirectly, by the size and the histological appearance of the gland, or directly, by its effects on the recipient after transplantation. Each of these methods has its advantages and disadvantages. There has been a great deal of discussion regarding the reliability of estimating the function of the corpora allata by the increase in the volume of the gland.[1] It must be taken into account, that there are various cases of increase in volume, both normal and pathological, which are not connected with a corresponding increase in hormone production. For example, the gland increases in size from one instar to the next and this increase is not connected with an increase in activity per volume unit. It may be estimated by comparing the size of the gland at two consecutive moultings. Similarly, the increase in volume observed following castration in adult females is probably due not to an increase in the secretory activity of the gland but to a restriction in the removal of the secretion by the haemolymph.

It may well be supposed, however, that under normal conditions in comparable developmental periods or during short periods an increase in volume is a reliable sign of an increase in the secretory activity of the gland. Histologically, the active stage is characterized by the swollen cytoplasm which stains more deeply with acidophilous (nuclear) stains. The amount of cytoplasm increases in relation to that of the nucleus even if the nuclei also become swollen. The local or general inhibitory effect on metamorphosis following the implantation of a corpus allatum into the last

---

[1] See the Panel discussion in the *Symposium on Insect Ontogeny*, Prague, 1959, published 1961.

larval instar is usually taken as experimental evidence of JH production. The drawback to this method lies in the fact that the effect cannot be estimated until after the next ecdysis. During this time the activity of the implanted gland may change markedly (cf. p. 109).

The possibility of a quantitative test for corpus allatum activity based on its metabolic effects has recently been suggested by Sláma (1963). The implantation of an active gland into an allatectomized adult female of *Pyrrhocoris apterus* causes a specific increase in the oxygen consumption of the recipient. This increase appears to be directly proportional to the activity of the gland.

The changes in corpora allata activity during the instar. Practically all the experimental (Wigglesworth, 1936, 1940a etc.), histological (Mendes, 1948), and morphological (Novák, 1951b) data agree that the corpora allata are inactive at the beginning of each instar and that the haemolymph does not contain an effective quantity of JH at that time (cf. p. 84). The amount of hormone gradually increases afterwards and the maximum volume of the corpus allatum is usually observed in the second half of the intermoult period. The production of the hormone ceases as the moulting process progresses and, as a result, its concentration in the haemolymph decreases. The main reason for this decrease is, without doubt, the excretion of the JH by the Malpighian tubules, as shown by the experiments of Bounhiol (1953). He found that ligaturing the Malpighian tubules of the silkworm at the beginning of the last larval instar has a similar effect to corpus allatum implantation, i.e. it suppresses metamorphosis to a greater or lesser extent. The operation is effective during a period which corresponds to that for an effective corpus allatum implantation. It is longer than the critical periods for AH and MH. The length of this period may, however, vary considerably in different species. In Lepidoptera, for example, the critical periods for all these hormones seem to be greatly prolonged as a result of the long feeding period and short moulting process (cf. p. 81). This may explain the discovery by Legay (1948) that the corpora allata of silkworm larvae reach their maximum volume at about the time of each ecdysis.

The corpora allata activity during postembryonic development. The production of the JH starts in the final period of embryogenesis after the corpora allata have been formed (cf. p. 87). The secretory activity of the gland continues during larval development with a temporary interruption at the time of each ecdysis, as mentioned above. A certain time is therefore necessary at the beginning of each instar before the active concentration of the hormone is again reached. It is not reached at all in the last larval

instar in Hemimetabola. The production of the hormone continues in adult
insects. It is distinctly cyclical in the females of those species which lay eggs
in several separate batches, such as cockroaches and many beetles and

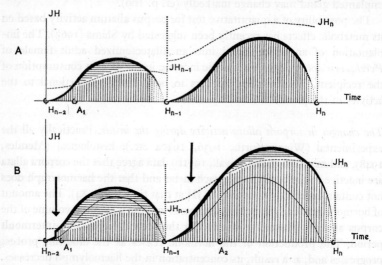

FIG. 25. Diagram of the dependence of the type of the growth on the JH-
concentration during the penultimate and last larval instar. A – controls; B – after
the implantation of corpora allata (the arrows indicate the moment of implantation).
Area with horizontal lines – proportionate growth, vertical lines – disproportionate
(gradient or allometric) growth, H_{n-2} – penultimate larval instar, broad line – the
actual concentration of the JH, ecdysis; H_{n-1} – last larval ecdysis; H_n – imaginal
ecdysis; dotted line – minimum effective concentration of the JH; A_1, A_2 =
moment of the reaching the effective concentration of the JH. Abscissa – time,
ordinate – JH – concentration.

bugs. No such cycles are observed in males and in females which lay only
one batch of eggs (e.g. *Bombyx mori*) or which lay single eggs at long
intervals (e.g. *Carausius morosus*) (cf. fig. 25).

The secretory activity of the corpora allata in the last larval instar. Wigglesworth (1940, 1948) originally supposed that the JH production ceases
completely in the last larval instar or even that the corpus allatum actively
eliminates the JH from the haemolymph during this period. Piepho (1951),
on the other hand, put forward the hypothesis that the presence of some
JH in the last larval instar of Holometabola (*Galleria*) is a necessary condition for the development of the pupa: in the complete absence of JH,
adult differentiation should occur. This hypothesis was later accepted by
Wigglesworth (1954 etc.), Karlson (1956 etc.), Schneiderman (1960 etc.)

and a number of other workers. That the corpora allata continue to produce the JH in the last larval instar was shown by Novák and Červenková (1959). They implanted corpora allata from the last instar nymphs of *Pyrrhocoris apterus* into other last instar nymphs immediately after moulting and at different times during the intermoult period and in most cases they obtained juvenilizing effects of varying extent. This does not prove, however, that the corpora allata were producing a morphogenetically active concentration of the JH as assumed by the above-mentioned hypothesis. There is definite evidence against that supposition: when the corpora allata are removed from the last larval instar nymph immediately after moulting (Wigglesworth, 1936; Bounhiol, 1938; Williams, 1947 etc.) no morphological change is observed. On the other hand, the implantation of another last instar larva corpora allatum which itself is inactive in the donor, is able to produce a juvenilizing effect. This may, however, be completely explained by the theory of surface and volume dependence of the JH activity mentioned below (cf. p. 112).

Hypertrophy of the corpora allata. Castration of *Calliphora erythrocephala* females shortly after the imaginal moult results in hypertrophy of their corpora allata, as shown by E. Thomsen (1946). The most probable explanation for this phenomenon is that in the absence of the ovaries the JH is not removed from the haemolymph. When the concentration of the hormone here exceeds that inside the gland cells, further diffusion of the hormone into the haemolymph is inhibited. It therefore accumulates in the gland causing its hypertrophy and a subsequent decrease in secretory activity. This appears to be at least a more probable explanation than the hypothesis suggested by E. Thomsen (1946, 1947) of a specific hormonal influence of the ovaries which suppresses the activity of the corpora allata. The hypertrophy of the corpora allata observed in functional termite females (cf. Pflugfelder, 1938b) appears, however, to be of quite a different type, being connected with the hyperfunction of the glands (cf. p. 86).

Effect of an implanted corpus allatum on that of the recipient. It was shown for the first time by Pflugfelder (1939a) that the implantation of an active corpus allatum causes a more or less complete degeneration of the recipient's gland. A detailed biometrical analysis of this relationship was carried out by Novák and Rohdendorf (1961) using adult females of *Pyrrhocoris apterus*. They implanted active corpora allata into freshly moulted adults and measured the volume of the recipient's glands on the 3rd, 6th and 9th days after implantation and compared this with that of the controls implanted with a piece of muscle of similar size. The corpora allata of the recipients were distinctly smaller than those of the controls. No such effect on the recipient's gland was observed if the implantation was made later in the instar (6th day after moulting), when the recipient's gland had reached its full activity. The following explanation of the effect of the implanted gland was suggested:

The discharge of the hormone from the gland into the haemolymph can take place only by diffusion through the surface of the gland as there is no special mechanism (e.g. muscular) for this. Diffusion is, however, only possible when the concentration of the hormone inside the gland is higher than that in the haemolymph. This condition is not maintained when an active gland is implanted before the recipient's gland has reached its full activity. In this case the concentration of the hormone in the haemolymph, produced by the implanted gland, exceeds that inside the recipient's gland and so diffusion and thus also the secretion of the hormone is prevented. Of course, if the implantation is effected later in the instar, when the corpus allatum of the recipient has reached its full activity, there is already a high concentration of hormone in the haemolymph. This exceeds the concentration in the implanted gland so that the position is now reversed and the secretion of the implanted gland is inhibited.

External factors controlling the activity of the corpora allata. Little is known as yet regarding the direct influence of various factors on the JH production. The only paper analysing the effects of external factors on development is that by Wigglesworth (1952a) on *Rhodnius prolixus*. He found that subjecting ıvth instar nymphs to a high temperature approaching the living maximum (ca. 35°C in *Rhodnius*) causes an extension of the inter-moult period and the development of somewhat adultoid 5th instars (regressive prothetely). A low temperature approaching the developmental minimum (below 20°C in *Rhodnius*) prolongs the intermoult period more than the high temperature, but the resulting 5th instar nymphs are some-what juvenile (progressive metathetely). The results may of course also be explained as an effect on the action of the hormone in the tissue or as an unequal effect on the growth of larval and imaginal tissues. A reduced oxygen concentration (below 5°C) has a similar effect to the high temperature.

A detailed morphological investigation of the shape and size of the corpora allata in the bug *Eurygaster integriceps* during postembryonic development and in adults in the different seasons of the year was made by Teplakova (1947). She observed an increase in the size of the gland in adult females in the spring connected with the development of the ovaries. The corpora allata of bugs parasitized by larvae of flies of the family Tachinidae were very small. In the Summer period of increased activity, the corpora allata of some of the females with functional ovaries were extraordinarily large, whereas in most others they were of medium size. Differences in the size of the gland were also found among females from different heights above sea-level.

Internal factors controlling the activity of the corpora allata. Several different explanations have been attempted for what has been called by Wigglesworth (1948) the 'counting of instars'. Wigglesworth concluded on the basis of his experiments with *Rhodnius prolixus* first that the decrease in the JH activity in the last larval instar is not connected with the age of the gland. This is clear from the fact that the corpus allatum of the 4th (penultimate) larval instar when implanted into the 5th (last) instar is able to induce juvenilizing effects, i.e. it retains its activity even when its age is equivalent to that of the last larval instar when it would normally cease functioning. From this Wigglesworth concluded that 'it is not the corpus allatum itself which counts the instars' and he suggested the possibility of a nervous stimulus being the cause of this decline in corpus allatum activity in the last larval instar. The strong innervation of the gland by the nervus allatus appears to point towards a nervous control of the corpora allata.

The hypothesis of a nervous control was supported by Engelmann and Lüscher (1956, 1957) on the basis of their experiments with adult females of *Leucophaea maderae*. They investigated the stimulating effect of an interruption of the nervi corporum cardiacarum on the swelling of the corpus allatum previously observed by B. Scharrer (1952). They found that a similar result could be obtained by destroying specific parts of the protocerebrum. On the other hand, no effects were observed after the electrocoagulation or surgical removal of the neurosecretory cells of the pars intercerebralis. The treatment induced egg formation in adult females and several extra larval instars in last instar nymphs. The authors consider their results as evidence for the nervous control of the corpora allata. They assume, that the absence of JH both in females carrying oothecae and in last instar larvae is caused by nervous inhibition. This, however, is not the only possible explanation of the observed facts. It seems more likely, and in agreement with the other known facts, that the observed swelling and activation of the corpus allatum is due to a stimulation by the nervous irritation and regeneration process induced by the operation. The fact that no effect was observed after the removal of the neurosecretory cells may be due to neurosecretory material accumulated in the corpora cardiaca, as the corpora allata are incapable of either secretory activity or growth in the absence of AH (cf. p. 47). A nervous stimulus inhibiting AH production

E

and in this way, undoubtedly, the JH production might, however, be the mediator of the negative effect of the oothecae on the activity of the corpora allata, in the same way as the distension of the abdomen has a positive effect on the AH production in *Rhodnius* (cf. p. 250).

A nervous control of the corpus allatum was also assumed by Johansson (1958) in his work with adult *Oncopeltus fasciatus*. He found that interruption of the corpus allatum innervation in a starving female can induce egg-laying in the same way as the implantation of an active corpus allatum. This treatment was however not effective when the brain with unbroken nervi corporum cardiacarum was implanted at the same time as the corpus allatum. Further evidence in favour of a nervous control of corpora allata activity was provided in the papers by Joly (1945a, b) on *Dytiscus marginalis*, by Detinova (1954) on *Anopheles messeae*, by de Wilde (1958 etc.) on *Leptinotarsa decemlineata*, etc.

The following conclusion from the available experimental evidence seems to be the most probable. The brain controls the activity of the corpora allata both by neurosecretion (AH) and by nervous activity. The latter may produce either a positive (distension of the abdomen in blood-sucking insects) or a negative effect (carrying of oothecae) according to the biology of the species concerned. Neither of these factors, however, seems to be responsible for the decrease in activity of the JH in the last larval instar which is the immediate cause of the metamorphosis. The nervous system here is simply a mediator of the external stimuli which on the average remain unchanged in each instar.

The dependence of the JH production on gland volume. A different approach to the question of the control of metamorphosis was made by Kaiser (1949) who emphasized the increasing disproportion between the size of the corpora allata and the prothoracic glands and concluded that the amount of JH produced quickly decreases compared with that of the MH, and the surplus of MH causes the metamorphosis. This idea was further developed by L'Hélias (1956). It is based, however, on two suppositions which have been disproved: that of a direct positive effect of the MH on the metamorphosis; and that of an antagonism between the MH and JH (cf. p. 83). In addition, the actual amount of MH as estimated by the volume of the prothoracic glands in relation to the volume of the body, and thus also the concentration of the MH in the haemolymph, does not increase.

A similar explanation, which considers the surface area and volume of the gland in relation to the volume of the body as responsible for the time of reaching the active concentration of the hormone, was used by the author (Novák, 1949, 1951, 1954; cf. 1956). The concentration of the hormone in the haemolymph depends on the following factors: (1) the quantity of hormone produced in a unit of time; (2) the volume of the haemolymph and, in direct proportion to this, the volume of the body; (3) the quantity of hormone consumed in the body; (4) the quantity of hormone removed from the haemolymph by the Malpighian tubules (and perhaps other organs) in the unit of time.

Let us now consider what happens to these values during larval development.

Little is known regarding the actual productivity of the corpora allata, but the following can be assumed: The circulatory system of insects is open so that no blood capillaries enter the gland. Histological evidence shows that there is no muscle or other special mechanism to discharge the hormone so that its passage into the haemolymph takes place only by diffusion through the surface of the gland. It may therefore be supposed that the surface area of the corpus allatum is one of the limiting factors which determines the quantity of hormone reaching the haemolymph in a unit of time. Another factor is necessarily the size (volume) of the gland. As nothing is known regarding the effect of the other factors during development we cannot take them into account. The interdependence of the known factors may thus be expressed by the following equation, where P represents the concentration of the hormone produced in the haemolymph (the quantity in a given volume of haemolymph), S_g is the surface area of the gland, V_g is the volume of the gland, V_b is the volume of the body, and c is a constant:

$$P = c\,\frac{S_g V_g}{V_b}$$

This means that, all other conditions remaining constant, the concentration of the hormone is directly proportional to the surface area and to the volume of the gland and indirectly proportional to the volume of the body. As the surface area increases with the square of the linear dimension whereas the volume increases with its cube, it is evident that the productivity of the gland increases much more slowly than the volume of the haemolymph and than the quantity of the hormone which is necessary to maintain the same concentration as the body increases in size.

As shown above, the amount of JH in the haemolymph falls below the active concentration before each ecdysis, towards the end of each intermoult period. A certain time is therefore necessary in each instar before the minimum effective concentration is again reached. Because of the above-mentioned interdependence between the productivity of the corpora allata during growth and the concentration of the JH, the effective concentration is reached later and later in each subsequent instar. The length of the intermoult period, however, remains practically unchanged during the whole larval development, with the exception of the last larval instar. This is no doubt caused by the fact that the above-mentioned dependence on the surface area of the gland does not apply to the same extent for the activation hormone with its special way of reaching the haemolymph (cf. p. 40); the production of MH is also probably less dependent on the surface area of the prothoracic glands as this is very large. An instar thus necessarily comes earlier or later in each species, in which the effective concentration of the JH is not reached before the advanced moulting process inhibits further growth and differentiation. This is the last larval instar, the instar of metamorphosis.

The relationship between the surface area and volume of the corpora allata and that of the body, during development. To test this theory, measurements were

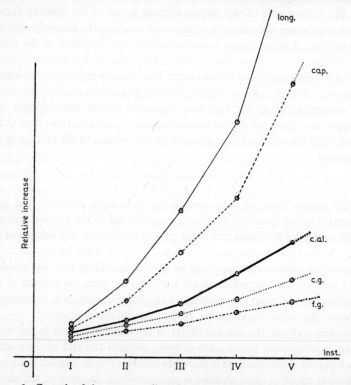

FIG. 26. Growth of the corpora allata (c. al.) compared with other parts of the body during the five larval instars of *Bombyx mori*. Abscissa – larval instars, ordinate – relative increase; f.g. – frontal ganglion; c.g. – cerebral ganglion; cap. – breadth of the head; long. – length of the body (from Novák, 1954).

made of the surface area and volume of the corpora allata and the volume of the body in freshly hatched larvae (the beginning of the first larval instar) and freshly moulted larvae in the last instar (Novák, 1954). The results obtained in 18 different species of both Hemimetabola and Holometabola show that there is a marked decrease in the volume of the corpora allata compared with that of the body, in addition to a very great decrease in the surface area of the corpora allata compared with the volume of the body. This relative decrease in the volume of the corpora allata is due to the very slow growth of this gland which, during the whole larval period, is only a little quicker than that of various parts of the nervous system and much slower than the growth of most other parts of the body, such as the breadth of the head, breadth of the pronotum, length of the tibia etc. (cf. fig. 26). It is concluded that the relative decrease in the surface area and volume of the corpora allata in all the species studied is too great not to manifest itself in the production of the JH and is large enough to explain the lack of its effective concentration in the last larval instar and thus the onset of the metamorphosis.

The disproportionate growth of the imaginal parts of the body. The above-mentioned theory not only explains the 'principle of counting instars' but also permits the understanding of the slight increase of the imaginal parts of the body (imaginal discs in Holometabola) compared with the larval parts which occur in the earlier larval instars. The growth in each larval instar may be interpreted as consisting of two parts: the isometric growth of the whole body (both larval and imaginal) and the disproportionate increase of the imaginal parts by allometric growth. As shown above, isometric growth only takes place in the presence of an effective concentration of JH. From this it may be concluded that the period of isometric growth is preceded, in each instar, by an allometric growth period before the minimum effective concentration has been reached. This conclusion agrees with both experimental results and histological observations. As shown by Wigglesworth (1952b) the implantation of an active corpora allata at the beginning of the IVth (penultimate) larval instar in *Rhodnius* produces a juvenile last instar nymph, that is, a nymph with the imaginal parts (wing pads) less developed than in normal last instar nymphs. In the most successful case, a nymph may be obtained which shows no allometric growth at all and is simply an enlarged version of the penultimate instar. The disproportionate growth may therefore be prevented by prematurely raising the JH concentration. Still more convincing is the finding that mitoses occur only in the imaginal parts of the epidermis before the critical period for the JH, whereas they occur equally over the entire surface of the body after this period. From this it is clear that the critical period for the JH, and thus the allometric growth period in each larval instar, corresponds to that part of the intermoult period before the minimum effective concentration is reached.

The allometric growth period therefore increases in duration at the expense of the isometric growth period with each subsequent instar. The last larval instar of Hemimetabola may therefore be interpreted as the larval instar the isometric growth period of which has been reduced to zero so that allometric growth occupies the whole of it. In this respect, the metamorphosis corresponds to the allometric growth period, that is to the first part of each of the preceding intermoult periods. This is equally true for the metamorphosis of Holometabola, where this period is divided by the pupal instar. The postembryonic growth of the imaginal part of the adult body (to say nothing of the surviving larval parts) is thus formed by the following components: The total allometric growth from the 1st to the penultimate larval instar; the total isometric growth from the first to the penultimate larval instar; the allometric growth of the last larval and pupal instar.

The Law of Correlation in Consumption

Another dependence of the allometric growth of the imaginal parts of the body during the metamorphosis may be derived from the theory discussed above, cf. Novák, 1956, 1959. The following argument enables us to understand the increased rate of growth of the imaginal parts of the body during this period. The amount of food at the disposal of a given part of the body R_x is dependent on the amount available for the organism as a whole (R_o) and on the amount consumed by the remaining parts of the body $(R_o - R_x)$. If this is true, the interdependence can be expressed by the following equation[1]:

$$R_x = c \, \frac{R_o}{(R_o - R_x + 1)} \qquad (1)$$

This means that all other conditions being constant, (c) the amount of food available for a given part of the body is directly proportional to the amount available for the body as a whole and indirectly proportional to the amount of food consumed by the rest of the organism. For this theoretically derived relationship the term 'law of correlation in consumption' has been suggested.

Assuming that the average consumption of both parts of the body

[1] The addition of 1 in the denominator, not used in the original paper (Novák, 1956), ensures that the value of the fraction cannot rise over the value of the numerator, when the value of $R_o - R_x$ falls below 1.

(R_x and $R_o - R_x$) is equal, the amount of food consumed by a given part of the body will be directly proportional to its mass (the amount of its living tissue). This condition is more or less completely preserved during the postembryonic development of insects. Here both the imaginal and the larval structures represent large parts of the body and both are formed by various types of tissue with no specific differences (except the ability of the imaginal parts to grow in the absence of JH). In this case the above equation (1) assumes the following form:

$$R_i = c \frac{M_o}{(M_o - M_i) + 1} = c \frac{M_o}{M_l + 1} \qquad (2)$$

This shows that the amount of food available for the imaginal parts of the body is directly proportional to the mass of the whole body (M_o) and indirectly proportional to the mass of the remaining part of the body ($M_o - M_i$), i.e. to the mass of the larval parts of the body (M_l). This approximation holds so long as the share of the larvo-imaginal parts is negligible. In the last larval instar the larval parts lose the ability for further growth in the absence of an effective quantity of JH. Their share of the food thus falls to zero before they become histolysed (partly in Hemimetabola, completely in Holometabola) ($M_l \to 0$). When this happens the total supply of food is at the disposal of the imaginal parts, and is further increased by the mass of the histolysed larval structures. This may be expressed in terms of the above equations as follows:

$$R_i = \frac{R_o}{O + 1} + M_l = R_o + M_l \qquad (1 + 2)$$

The Mode of Action of the Juvenile Hormone

Various theories have been expressed regarding the mode of action of the JH, some of them obviously contradictory. According to Wigglesworth's original idea (1936) the JH affects the morphogenesis on the principle of Goldschmidt's hypothesis of different reaction velocities. He supposed that the degree of differentiation reached by a given specimen after corpus allatum implantation is the product of competition between two simultaneous processes: the differentiation of the imaginal structures, and the moulting. Differentiation is only possible in the period between the moment of detachment of the old cuticle and that of the deposition of the new one. The effect of the JH was assumed to depend on accelerating the moulting process so that the prematurely deposited new cuticle would inhibit further differentiation before it could be completed. On this basis, Wigglesworth originally used the term 'inhibitory hormone' for the secretion of the corpora allata. Wigglesworth (1940) himself replaced this theory by the hypothesis of two alternative enzyme systems inside each epidermis cell, the larval and the imaginal one, where the larval system was supposed to be dependent on the presence of the JH and the imaginal one to work in the absence of the JH. The term 'inhibitory hormone' was therefore later changed to neotenin (1954). The hypothesis of polymorphism discussed elsewhere (p. 149) was based on this concept.

Pflugfelder (1939, 1941) and Weed-Pfeiffer (1945a, b), on the other hand, emphasized the positive effect of JH on the total metabolism as shown by their experiments. This line was later pursued by E. Thomsen (1949, 1955 etc.), Engelmann (1957 etc.) and by Sägesser (1961), who claim to have shown experimentally a direct effect of the JH on metabolism. To prevent the evident contradictions, the hypothesis of two different corpus allatum hormones was created; one of them being identified with the JH of Wigglesworth and supposed to affect the larval development only. The other, a 'gonadotropic' hormone, was assumed to activate the ovarian follicles and the metabolism. No definite evidence against the original Wigglesworth concept of only one corpus allatum hormone was however produced (cf. p. 290).

A specific theory was put forward by Bodenstein (1953a–d etc.) to explain his very interesting findings on the negative effect of the implanted corpus allatum on the survival of the prothoracic glands in *Periplaneta americana*. He assumed the need for a very complicated balance between the three metamorphosis hormones, as well as a specific corpora cardiaca activity. There is, however, a possible alternative explanation which does not contradict the bulk of the knowledge of the JH and the other two metamorphosis hormones (cf. p. 103).

Another complicated hypothesis was formulated by L'Hélias (1956) which unfortunately does not take into account most of the known facts. The author supposes a specific prehormone produced by the neurosecretory brain cells, from which originates the AH in the corpora cardiaca and the JH in the corpora allata. She supposes pterin bases to be common to both principles and identifies the AH with folic acid or some of its derivates whereas the JH is thought to possess antifolic activity so that it would partly inhibit the AH. By an interaction of both factors, which changes in favour of the AH towards the end of the larval development, metamorphosis would be induced with the co-operation of the prothoracic glands. As shown recently by Gersch *et al.* (1962) even if the pterin compounds are closely connected with the AH and other neurohormones in the neurosecretory granules and are difficult to separate, they are not identical with either of the hormones (cf. p. 213).

On the basis of the gradient-factor as a factor conditioning the JH-independent growth of the imaginal parts of the body, a theory which is discussed later, a hypothesis on the mode of action of the JH has been suggested by the author (Novák, 1951a, b, 1956; cf. p. 156). This seems to explain the above-mentioned contradictions in the experimental results and to be of the nature of a synthesis of the earlier views. According to this theory the JH produces its effect by taking the place of the GF in those parts of the body which lost it in the course of development. Such parts are the larval parts of the body during larval development, the ovarian follicles in the adult females, and a number of other tissues at particular times during development (cf. p. 164). As suggested in the papers by Novák, Sláma, Wenig (1961), Novák, Sláma (1962) and Sláma (1963), the effect of the JH seems to depend on the conditioning of proteosynthesis as well as other functions in the larval parts of the body. Its effect on oxygen consumption is therefore merely an indirect one arising from an increase in the amount of the metabolizing tissue (larval structures, ovarian follicles). The negative result on oxygen consumption of the implantation of the corpus allatum into castrated females seems to show that the JH has no direct effect on the imaginal parts of the body. This question, however, needs further experimental evidence. All the other described effects of the JH would therefore be due to the altered biochemical balance in the body connected with the experimentally added share of larval tissues in the metabolism or to the abnormal absence of their share after extirpation of the corpora allata.

The Juvenile Hormone-like Effects

Much attention has been paid to the discovery by Williams (1956a) of the morphogenetical activity of the lipoid extracted from the adult *cecropia* silkworms (*Platysamia cecropia*, fam. Saturniidae). It was shown that the abdomens of male *cecropia* moths yielded a relatively large quantity of an oily substance with a strong morphogenetical effect on *cecropia* pupae similar to that of the implanted corpus allatum. When injected into pupae at the commencement of adult differentiation it inhibits further differentiation without suppressing moulting, so that either second pupae or various transitional forms between larva and pupa result. It is effective not only in *cecropia* pupae but also in *Pieris brassicae*, *Tenebrio molitor*, *Rhodnius prolixus*, *Periplaneta americana* (cf. Wigglesworth, 1958 etc.), *Leptinotarsa decemlineata* (de Wilde, 1959 etc.) and other groups of insects.

Special testing methods have been worked out to determine the activity of the extractions. The simplest of these is merely the injection of the extract into the body cavity of the experimental animal, either alone, or, as was found to be more effective, diluted with olive oil (Williams, 1956). Another method is a surface application on the cuticle, the surface layer of which was abraded by treatment with aluminium oxide or by some other means (Wigglesworth, 1958). Sláma (1961) applied the substances to be tested to the very thin cuticle beneath the wings in *Pyrrhocoris apterus*. As the most sensitive test (but not necessarily the most reliable) of morphogenetical activity Gilbert and Schneiderman (1960) used the following procedure, which they called the wax test. The extract was dissolved in a mixture of paraffin wax and peanut oil to form a greasy wax and applied in the molten state to cover a small incision in the epidermis.

The extraction was carried out using various organic solvents such as ethyl ether, petroleum ether, methanol, ethanol etc. The most effective appeared to be ethyl ether. The evaporated extract yielded a non-poisonous golden-yellow oily substance with a low viscosity. On the average, 0·2 ml. of the active oil was obtained. From the abdomen of one male 0·025 ml. was active when injected into a pupa of *Telea polyphemus*. It is a substance insoluble in water which cannot be extracted by chloroform, benzole or carbon tetrachloride. It can be dissolved in acetone only after the addition of diethyl ether. The substance is resistant to high temperatures as well as to aqueous alkali solutions up to a concentration of 5N, acids up to a concentration of 2N and is not affected by jonex filtration.

The substance is present in large quantities in various tissues in the abdomens of male adults; only traces are found, however, in the head and thorax of the same specimens. The activity of extracts prepared from various developmental stages of *Platysamia cecropia* was tested in *Antherea polyphemus* pupae by Gilbert and Schneiderman (1957, 1960; cf. Schneiderman 1961). The results are tabulated below.

TABLE I. Juvenile hormone content of *cecropia* during its development
(After Schneiderman, 1961, combined)

Stage of development	Hormone content per gram fresh wt. compared with adult male (%)
Unfertilized eggs	4·3
7-day-old embryos with yolk	3·7
1st instar larvae (freshly hatched)	6·4
5th instar larvae (mixed ages)	0·50
Freshly moulted pupae	0·75
Diapausing pupae (1 month old)	0·55
Chilled pupae (6 months old)	0·0
Pupae 2 days of adult development	0·0
„ 11 days of adult development	0·0
„ 17 days of adult development	0·0
„ 20 days of adult development	0·50
„ 22 days of adult development (males)	50·0
♂Adult (2 days)	100·0
♀Adults (2 days)	3·2

According to these data the content of the active component is rather high in unfertilized embryos and freshly hatched larvae but decreases during the postembryonic development, being lowest in the last instar larva and in diapausing pupa. It practically disappears when development starts again after the diapause. It reappears before the end of adult development and increases slowly in the female but very quickly in the male.

Although the effect of this morphogenetically active substance appears to be quite general amongst insects (see above), its occurrence is rather specific, even if very widespread. Very little if any active extract was obtained in closely related species such as *Antherea polyphemus*, according to Schneiderman (1961), whilst in extracts of many other insects of various groups a greater or lesser activity was observed. Remarkably enough, however, further investigation has revealed various amounts of the active principle in the most varied groups of animals (cf. Schneiderman, Gilbert and Weinstein, 1960) including various tissues of vertebrates. A rather high activity is reported to have been found in beef adrenal extracts, in extracts of calf thymus and several other tissues (Williams, Moorhead, and Pulis, 1959). Moreover, it has also been reported from various micro-organisms (though it appears to be absent in many others) and even from several, both lower and higher, plants, e.g. in the extract from soya bean meal.

The similarity in the effect of the substance and that of corpus allatum hormone led to the hypothesis that the two factors are identical. As a matter of fact the authors of the papers mentioned generally refer to the active principle of these extracts as the juvenile hormone. There is a good argument, in addition to the similar effects, in favour of this supposition: males allatectomized at the beginning of the pupal period completely lack the active principle. Similarly, the unfertilized eggs of allatectomized females also lack it completely whilst extracts of those laid by normal females are rather effective (cf. table).

Nevertheless, further research has shown the need for a different approach to this problem. In a paper dealing with the morphogenetical effects of a number of natural and synthetic organic substances, such as fatty acids, colchicine and others, absolute unspecificity of the testing methods used was shown by Sláma (1961) who suggested the term pseudo-juvenilizing for these effects. Oleic acid, linoleic acid and other higher fatty acids, particularly unsaturated ones, were found to be rather active in locally inducing larval characters.[1] The effects of colchicine are similar, if

[1] The work was performed at the beginning of 1960; the results were mentioned in the communication by V. J. A. Novák at the XIth International Congress of Entomology in Vienna, 1960 (cf. Novák, 1961c).

not identical. It was further shown by Schmialek (1961) that an open-chain terpene alcohol, farnesol, isolated from the excrements of the meal-worm (*Tenebrio molitor*), is particularly active in the tests mentioned. In a subsequent paper Wigglesworth (1961) reports that farnesol reproduces all the effects of the juvenile hormone when applied to the surface of the cuticle in *Rhodnius*. It causes not only retention of larval characters when applied to the last instar larva but, as emphasized by Wigglesworth, in contrast to the *cecropia* extract it also induces ripening of the ovarian follicles in females deprived of their corpora allata (by decapitation). In this respect it appears to be closer to the true corpus allatum hormone than the *cecropia* male extracts.

The effects of farnesol, its isomers and related substances have been further studied recently by Yamamoto and Jacobson (1962) and again by Wigglesworth (1963). Of a series of farnesol derivatives (farnesanic acid, farnesyl pyrophosphate, farnesyl diethylamine, furan of farnesol (= den-drolasin), squalene), farnesyl methyl ether was found to be the most effective in preventing metamorphosis and in inducing yolk formation in *Rhodnius*. The question of its relationship with the corpus allatum hormone remains open but a close similarity was found between the effects and the mode of action of farnesol and its derivatives on the one hand and the *cecropia* extracts on the other.

A distinct juvenilizing effect is produced by dendrolasin which is the product of the mandibular glands of the ant *Lasius* (*Dendrolasius*) *fuli-ginosus*. Chemically it is the furan of farnesol. Another related substance of pheromone character, geraniol, the active substance of the secretion of the Nassonoff glands in the honey bee, is also a chemical closely related to farnesol. In this way, the above-mentioned effect of the JH on phero-mone production (cf. p. 249) could perhaps be understood, as well as its positive effect on the development of the juvenilizing activity of the *cecropia* male extract (cf. p. 123). The synthesis of the lipoid substances with juvenilizing activity appears in some way to be dependent on the JH.

The minimum effective doses of farnesyl methyl ether, 24 μg. per gram of body weight of *Rhodnius* larva to obtain morphological effects and 8 μg./g. to influence the epidermal cells were compared with those of ecdyson where 10 μg./g. are able to induce moulting in *Rhodnius* larva, and with the vertebrate hormones thyroxine (5 μg./g.), somatotropine (1·4 μg./g.) and testosterone propionate (35 μg./g.). It is interesting to note that 1 μg. represents about 9 times the volume of the corpus allatum in *Rhodnius*. About twenty times more of the active substance is necessary for the development of a complete batch of eggs in *Rhodnius* female

(Wigglesworth, 1963). This might be the reason why, according to the author, the *cecropia* male extract is ineffective in inducing yolk formation.

Nevertheless there is another great difference between the effect of these different substances and the true corpus allatum hormone. As shown by Sláma (1961) the effect of these substances depends on the suppressing of imaginal differentiation, i.e. it has the character of a regressive metathetely, whilst the effect of the JH is that of a progressive metathetely, i.e. the lack of adult differentiation is caused indirectly by the promotion of growth of the larval parts of the body (Novák, 1951b, 1956). Even if the results might be practically identical in many cases, in that metamorphosis is inhibited, it is mainly caused by opposite effects: the regressive metathetely is caused by the suppressing of the growth (of the imaginal parts), without affecting other processes of the body, such as the moulting; the progressive metathetely depends on the promotion of growth in the other direction (i.e. that of the larval parts of the body) which indirectly limits the growth of the imaginal parts and thus the morphogenesis. That is why these effects have been called 'pseudo-juvenilizing' (cf. Sláma, 1961).

The effect of the *cecropia* male extract is somewhat stronger than that of the fatty acids mentioned and perhaps not exactly the same. As recently shown by Wojczak,[1] however, the extract of the *cecropia* male abdomens contains no less than 95% of unsaturated fatty acids. This being so, even if the *cecropia* extract produced some positive effect of the JH type on growth, it could hardly be distinguished, in the experiments described, from the necessarily strong pseudo-juvenilizing effects of the greater part of the extract and, in fact, nobody has yet attempted to do this. It must therefore be concluded that there is no definite reason for identifying the *cecropia* extract with the JH. It is quite probable that the JH is quite different chemically. The close analogy between it and the somatotropine of the vertebrate adenohypophysis (cf. p. 275) rather suggests the possibility of its being protein or polypeptide in character.

This conclusion in no way contradicts the fact that the pseudo-juvenilizing activity of the extract is prevented by allatectomy in an earlier stage. It has been shown by several authors (cf. p. 100) that the JH greatly affects the fat metabolism, directly or indirectly, by regulating the consumption of food reserves. It can therefore be seen that the composition of the fats in the body may change considerably in the absence of the JH and that the active component may disappear from the extract.

What has been said does not necessarily mean that none of this type of material could produce a positive effect on growth. In fact, in addition to the true JH effect which seems not to be possible here, there are three

[1] Personal communication to the author.

other possibilities for a positive influence on growth: (1) The substances of this type may improve the nutrition of the tissues and thus their growth, either locally or generally in the body via the haemolymph. (2) They may kill or partly damage the tissues with which they come into contact and thus induce their regeneration. It has been shown in many cases, that an extensive regeneration process stimulates the secretory activity and growth of the neighbouring tissues. (3) It may unspecifically stimulate the growth of the affected tissues. A detailed histological analysis would be necessary to decide which of the possibilities mentioned should be taken into consideration in a given case.

Full confirmation of the finding that the active substance of the insect extracts mentioned is not identical with the JH but produces just the opposite effect will in no way decrease interest in the morphogenetical activity of this type of chemical, but rather increase it. As suggested by Novák (1962), the extreme case of an effect of this type is the inhibition of growth without a simultaneous inhibition of moulting and other physiological processes produced by the so-called queen inhibitory substance in the honey bee and termites, or, that of its components which suppress the growth of the ovaries in the worker caste (cf. p. 247). This seems to be a special case of biological exploitation – as a result of natural selection – of this type of morphogenetically active substance in the phylogeny of social insects.

D. THE QUESTION OF THE GRADIENT-FACTOR, GF

As mentioned above all three metamorphosis hormones play an important part in morphogenesis, either by indirectly promoting it or by suppressing it. None of these, however, can be regarded as a true morphogenesis hormone. The fact that the greater part of the morphogenesis takes place during the embryonic period when no hormones are operating shows that it has no primary dependence on any hormone. On the other hand, data have been obtained which suggest the existence of a tissue-bound factor that determines the morphogenesis by the way it is distributed within the body.

The conclusions regarding the existence of such a morphogenetical factor are based on the author's experiments with juvenile hormone effects in the lygaeid bug *Oncopeltus fasciatus* Dall. (Novák, 1951a, b). This species has proved very suitable for the study of morphogenesis because of its prominent black pattern, which is very different in the last stage nymph from the adult. In this insect, a cuticular pigment of the melanin type occurs exclusively in the imaginal parts of the surface of the body in larvae. This tracing of the imaginal parts of the larval body is so perfect that the melanin pigmentation can be viewed as a kind of indicator of the imaginal parts of the body. It therefore permits a detailed analysis of what happens to both the larval and imaginal structures during the metamorphosis period of morphogenesis. *Oncopeltus* is even more suitable because

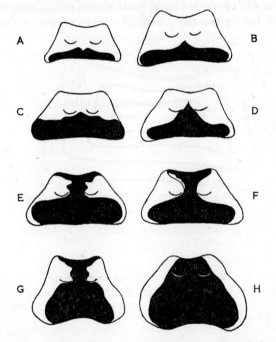

FIG. 27. The development of the shape of pronotum and its black pattern in the lygaeid bug *Oncopeltus fasciatus*. A – a normal 5th (last) instar nymph; B – a supernumerary, giant, 6th instar nymph (result of corpus allatum implantation before the onset of adult differentiation); c–g – transitory forms between nymph and adult (result of implantation of the corpus allatum during adult differentiation), H – normal adult (from Novák, 1951).

the metamorphosis in Hemiptera is, in many respects, of a type transitional between the incomplete metamorphosis of Exopterygota and the complete metamorphosis of Endopterygota, the difference between the two types being in the main one of degree and not of quality, at least from the physiological point of view as suggested by Wigglesworth (1939). The results obtained with this species therefore help the generalization of all the experimental data obtained in insects with both incomplete and complete metamorphosis. The results of the analysis of a continuous series of transitional forms between last instar nymph and the adult in *Oncopeltus* allow the following conclusions:

The growth of the body during the larval period is an isometric one (irrespective of the increase of the imaginal parts of the body) when all parts of the body grow at practically the same rate. It changes later into an anisometric (gradient) growth the result of which is the metamorphosis from larva to adult in the last larval instar. In this period, only the imaginal parts of the body grow, the growth of the larval parts having stopped.

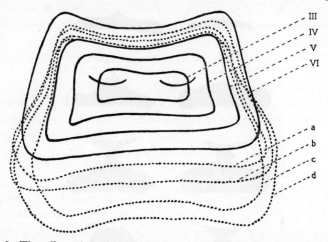

FIG. 28. The effect of the juvenile hormone on the shape of the pronotum in *Oncopeltus fasciatus*. 3rd–6th – pronotum in 3rd to 6th (supernumerary) instar nymphs (in presence of the active JH–concentration since the beginning of the corresponding instar); *a–c* – adultoid nymphs and nymphoid adults; *d* – normal adult (in absence of the effective JH-concentration) (from Novák, 1951).

The examination of the outlines of the pronotum in a series of transitory forms produced by the corpora allata implantations at different periods in the last larval instar shows:

(1) The larval parts[1] of the body grow only in the presence of the JH (following the implantation of active corpora allata). (2) The increase in the larval parts is the greater, the longer the period of JH activity (the earlier the implantation of the corpora allata). It is greatest in nymphs in the extra, sixth, instar and lowest, i.e. absent, in normal adults. (3) The increase in the imaginal parts of the body (in this case, the posterior margin of pronotum) is inversely proportional to that of the larval parts (anterior margin of pronotum). That is, the more the larval parts grow, the less the imaginal parts grow, and vice versa (fig. 28).

[1] Cf. the definition on page 36.

The same relationship as in the pronotum was found in all other parts of the body, the proportion of larval to imaginal parts being approximately the same in different parts of the body of one and the same individual. Similar relationships occur in all other species of both Hemimetabola and Holometabola which have been so far studied from this point of view. On the basis of this, the following three laws of morphogenesis during the insect metamorphosis may be derived:

(*i*) The JH affects morphogenesis by stimulating the growth of the larval parts of the body, which are unable to grow in its absence.

(*ii*) The increase in the imaginal parts of the body is inversely proportional to that of the larval structures.

(*iii*) The growth of imaginal structures is not suppressed in the presence of JH; it is only reduced to the rate of growth of the larval parts.

Experiments on the removal of the source of the JH in the earlier larval instars through decapitation (Wigglesworth, 1936) or allatectomy (Bounhiol, 1937, 1938b) show that a more or less complete metamorphosis can occur in the earliest larval instars in the absence of the JH. From this it necessarily follows that the larval structures are unable to grow in the absence of a specific minimum effective concentration of the JH. It is therefore this lack of ability of the larval parts of the body to grow in the absence of JH which is the immediate internal cause of the continuation of gradient growth at the end of larval period, known as the metamorphosis. The question arises as to what is the cause of this inability to grow on the part of the larval structures.

The Hypothesis of the Gradient-Factor

No definite experimental data are so far available to answer this question. Two facts, however, must be taken into account. First, the larval parts of the body do not lack ability to grow in the absence of the JH from the beginning. They were necessarily able to grow during their differentiation in the embryonic period, otherwise they would not have arisen, and no JH is acting at that time. Secondly, the fact that their ability for growth can be completely restored by the effect of just one physiologically, and no doubt also chemically, individual substance, the JH, permits the conclusion that the loss of this ability was caused by the loss of a similar single chemical substance physiologically equivalent to the JH.

On this basis the hypothesis of a factor conditioning the growth of the imaginal parts of the body has been raised. This assumes that the loss of the ability of the larval parts of the body to grow in the absence of the JH is caused by the inactivation in them of a specific factor indispensable for growth. This factor continues to be active in the imaginal parts of the body, controlling their gradient growth in the absence of the JH during the metamorphosis. This is what has been called the gradient-factor (GF – Novák, 1951a, b). According to this hypothesis the only general difference between the larval and the imaginal parts of the body depends on the absence of one substance, the active GF, in the former.

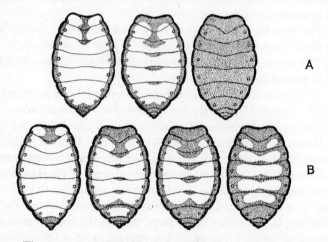

FIG. 29. The occurrence of mitoses in the epidermis of the dorsal surface of the abdomen in *Rhodnius prolixus* in various periods of the penultimate (A) and last (B) larval instar. Dotted – area with mitoses; white – no mitoses (after Wigglesworth 1940a, modified).

The inactivation of the GF. As mentioned above it may be assumed that the GF is just as active in the larval parts of the body as in the imaginal ones up to a certain time. Its inactivation can be completely compensated by the effect of the JH and therefore becomes apparent only in the absence of the JH. The pattern of its inactivation in space and time is genetically fixed in a given species, controlling its morphological characters. Experiments with X-rays and u.v. irradiation of embryos of *Drosophila* show that this pattern was determined in the early embryonic period long before the actual differentiation (Geigy, 1931). The supposed inactivation of the GF is, however, completely reversible by means of the JH until a certain length of time without JH. After a certain time, the JH is no longer able to prevent the degeneration of the larval parts of the body. More time is necessary before the first visible histological signs of degeneration appear. A two-stage degeneration such as observed in the prothoracic glands of *Rhodnius prolixus* by Wigglesworth (1952) appears to be quite general in insects.

The course of the GF inactivation. When the behaviour of individual parts of the insect body is examined in the absence of the JH it soon becomes obvious that the mere separation into larval and imaginal tissues is unsatisfactory. Even the intermediate category of larvo-adult structures, suggested by Geigy (1941), is not sufficient to cover all the types encountered up to the present. It may be concluded that the GF is not inactivated in all larval structures at the same time, but that this occurs gradually in individual parts of the body according to a regular pattern. The eight types of structure which may be distinguished on the basis of the assumed time of their GF inactivation and the time of their disintegration in ontogenesis are listed on page 164 below.

The site of action of the GF. The GF is concerned in some very fundamental growth processes. This follows necessarily from its conception as a factor indispensable for growth (cf. definition above). Its relationship with the JH and the fact that it can be completely replaced by this hormone together with recent findings on the probable role of JH in proteosynthesis make it very probable that the GF is one link in the chain of substances indispensable for proteosynthesis. As such it is of necessity an intracellular factor (which, however, does not exclude the possibility of its occasionally spreading outside the cell limits). This, however, does not mean that it is necessarily only active at the cell level. A large amount of data are available which appear to suggest that the action of GF takes place on a molecular

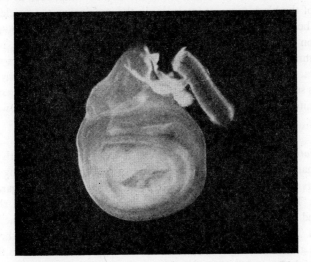

FIG. 30. Imaginal disc of leg in *Musca domestica*. Vital, in insect-Ringer, × 200.

level. This may be concluded first of all from the morphological differentiation of one and the same cell as seen in the epidermis cells (cf. p. 158). In this way, of course, it may affect not only cells but also whole organs and tissues, as observed in metamorphosis.

The supposed features of the GF. The possibility of a complete replacing of the GF by JH permits the supposition of a physiological specificity of this factor corresponding to that of the JH. This does not mean, however, that the GF is necessarily an individual chemical principle. As a secondary hypothesis, it has been stated that it might be of a desmo-hormone nature, i.e. a tissue-bound active agent from which a true lyo-hormone, spread by the haemolymph, is produced in the corpora allata (cf. p. 169). Even though this hypothesis is rather tempting from the phylogenetical point of view, a different concept seems to be more likely from recent conclusions on the general importance of the GF (cf. p. 180). According to these the effect of the GF is in fact due to the action of a group of closely related chemicals which have a common configuration of atoms, i.e. chemicals such as the nucleic acids, which are of general occurrence in animals and other organisms. In any case it is very probable that the GF is a substance, or group of substances, which has been known for a long time for some other of its features.

From what has been said above regarding the GF, the question arises as to whether it is the same in the different parts of the body and at different periods of ontogenesis. There are reasons for assuming, such as the ocurrence of the black pigment (melanin) in the imaginal parts (cuticle) of the whole body surface in *Oncopeltus* (cf. p. 124), its general distribution and common character. Another possibility, perhaps the most likely, is that it is a common feature, or features, of a group of related substances such as, perhaps, the nucleic acids, depending on their ability to be inactivated by various substances originating in the course of ontogenetical differentiation. A definite answer to this can be obtained only by experimental work (cf. p. 181).

The relationship of the GF to the metamorphosis hormones. Irrespective of the true character of the GF, the possibility of its being replaced by the JH suggests a close relationship between both factors, at least as regards their effects. The only actual difference between them depends on the pronounced lyo-hormone character of the JH, i.e. its transport by the haemolymph. The possibility remains, however, that the ability of the JH to restore growth activity to the larval tissues is due to its effect on the GF. This might be explained as due either to the release by the JH of the atom

group the blocking of which was the cause of the GF inactivation or to the replacing of a loss by the JH-molecule. In any case there is no reason for supposing any antagonism between these two factors. The parts containing the GF grow in the presence of the JH as well as in its absence (cf. p. 127).

In spite of the views expressed by various authors, there is no experimental evidence for any kind of selective effect of either AH or MH on the growth gradients. There is also no theoretical reason in favour of such a mode of action. As mentioned above there is no definite evidence for assuming any direct effect of the MH either on growth or on differentiation, which cannot be explained by its inducing of the moulting process. The influence on the breaking of diapause in spermatocytes in vitro as observed by Williams (1952a, b) must not be generalized; in other insects the same effect has been observed after addition of a physiological solution (insect-Ringer) alone (cf. e.g. Bělař, 1929). Unlike JH and GF, AH and MH have no direct effect on the principle of morphogenesis and, therefore, none on the GF.

The aims of the hypothesis of the GF. The supposed existence of the GF is therefore, up to now, only a more or less probable working hypothesis, the definite proof of which will not be easy to obtain for several reasons. It seems, however, to be justified by the fact that it permits a simple and uniform explanation of various, not yet fully understood, phenomena and apparent contradictions, and has made possible the formulation of a general theory of metamorphosis, the gradient-factor theory (p. 156). This also clarifies the evolution of metamorphosis and the mode of action of the metamorphosis hormones (p. 158) as well as some general questions of morphogenesis. In the opinion of the author, many of these conclusions and generalizations will retain their validity irrespective of the confirmation of the gradient-factor hypothesis.

A number of new findings have been obtained since the formulation of the GF theory, all of which appear to speak unambiguously in favour of this concept (cf. p. 160 and p. 162). On the other hand, no indisputable facts are available which contradict it. The assumption of the GF as a special tissue-bound growth-factor regulating the growth of the imaginal parts of the body in the absence of the JH simply remains to be proved experimentally. This, however, would appear to be rather difficult because of its specific character and possible identity with some very common and perhaps well known growth-factor. The GF-theory has been discussed and appreciated by many authors (cf. e.g. Wigglesworth, 1951b, 1954; Pflugfelder, 1958; O'Farrell, 1954 etc.); on the other hand it does not appear to have been completely understood by several others (Hinton,

1954, Steinberg, 1960 etc.). It might therefore be useful to show the relationships and complicated connection between the GF with the various metamorphosis hormones and the internal and external conditions by the diagrams in figs. 38–44.

Ontogenetical Abnormalities of the Metamorphosis

Heterochrony may be defined as a disturbance of the normal ratio between the extent of development in larval and imaginal parts of the body. Within the ontogenetical heterchronies, prothetely, metathetely, and hysterotely are usually distinguished. Prothetely may now be defined, as a developmental disorder in which the development of the imaginal parts precedes in time that in normal specimens; metathetely is a disorder in which the development of imaginal structures is delayed. Local disorders or hysterothetelies in which only specific organs or limited areas of the body are either accelerated or delayed in their development must be distinguished. From the different types of prothetely and metathetely on the basis of the above-mentioned criterion it is also necessary to distinguish further between the progressive and regressive changes in each of the types of heterochrony mentioned. The following six types of heterochrony may be distinguished in this way (cf. Novák, 1951b):

Progressive prothetely. Here, the imaginal structures are more developed than in normal specimens without any decrease in the development of the larval structures. Into this category, for example, come the adultoid 5th instar nymphs of *Rhodnius prolixus* with imaginal structures more differentiated, obtained by Wigglesworth (1948, 1952b) by the implantation of 5th instar corpora allata into 4th instar nymphs or by raising the temperature. In its broadest sense, this type would also include the adultoid silkworm caterpillars (transitions between larva and pupa) obtained by Fukuda (1944) as the result of implantation of active prothoracic glands into freshly moulted specimens of last instar larvae. These are, however, not produced by the abnormal growth of the imaginal parts but by an acceleration of the moulting process which breaks the morphogenetical process prematurely at a stage when the imaginal structures are not yet fully developed and the larval parts still not completely histolysed. The acceleration of the moulting process denotes the prothetelic character of the process.

Regressive prothetely. Here the growth and differentiation of the imaginal parts of the body are accelerated by the inhibition of the growth of the larval parts so that the total growth of the body is decreased. A typical

case of regressive prothetely results from the removal of the corpora allata (by decapitation or allatectomy) in the earlier larval instars. This causes a precocious metamorphosis resulting in miniature adults, as first shown by Wigglesworth (1935, 1936) and Bounhiol (1936, 1938).

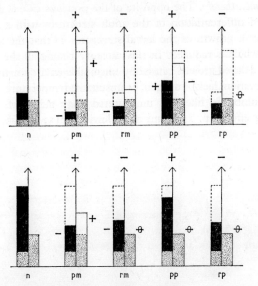

FIG. 31. The four chief types of heterochrony in the postembryonic development of insects (diagram), in the penultimate (*above*) and last (*below*) larval instars. *n* – normal specimen; *pm* – progressive metathetely; *rm* – regressive metathetely; *pp* – progressive prothetely; *rp* – regressive prothetely; the area on the left side of each arrow – the relative growth of imaginal parts of the body; on the right side – the relative growth of the larval parts; dotted area – state before the affected instar; black – growth of the imaginal parts; white area – growth of the larval parts; the sign + above the arrow – the growth is accelerated (intermoult period shorter); the sign − above the arrow – the growth is retarded (intermoult period longer); the sign + laterally – increase of the corresponding parts of the body; the sign − laterally – decrease compared with the normal growth; o – no growth. (From Novák, 1956.)

Progressive metathetely. Stimulation of the growth of larval structures in the last larval instar reduces the growth of the imaginal parts at this time. Here the total amount of growth is increased, but the increase in the imaginal structures is delayed as compared with normal specimens. This is a typical result of the implantation of an active corpora allata into the last larval instar, which manifests itself, according to the degree and time of action of the JH, in extra instar larvae, adultoid larvae and larvoid adults. The same effect is obtained by subjection to low temperatures during the earlier larval instars or by the influence of some parasites, as in the larvae of black-flies (Simuliidae) infected by Microsporidia or Mermithidae.

Regressive metathetely. The opposite of the previous case is an incomplete and delayed differentiation of the adult structures with a simultaneous suppression of growth of the larval structures so that the growth of the body as a whole is reduced. In this category belong all the cases of suppressed or delayed growth caused by unsuitable environmental conditions such as starvation, lack of oxygen, or unsuitable temperature, or by various chemical inhibitors like the unsaturated fatty acids (cf. the pseudo-juvenilizing effects, p. 119; and also Dewitz, 1913; Novák, 1951b etc.).

FIG. 32. Developmental anomalies of a hysterothetelic nature. The remains of larval pseudopodia in *Hyphantria cunea* pupae.

Progressive hysterotely. Here the growth or differentiation of one organ or paired structure precedes the development of the others, as for instance in caterpillars with pupal antennae or external wing rudiments, without corresponding changes in other imaginal organs.

Regressive hysterotely. The growth and differentiation of one organ or paired structure is delayed compared with the others, as for example in pupae with larval abdominal pseudopodia (cf. fig. 32). Here the cause of the disorder is not due to the action of hormones but perhaps to variation in the GF pattern, i.e. in the course of its inactivation.

The disturbances mentioned above, the principle of which is illustrated by the diagram in fig. 31, do not, however, cover all the possible cases of developmental malformations which may originate due to the influence of various environmental factors. An exact classification of the observed disorders is of prior importance for the discovery of their cause and mechanism (cf. Sláma, 1961).

Phylogenetical Abnormalities of the Metamorphosis

Accelerations and retardations. Most of the abnormalities mentioned which represent heterochrony of the ontogenetical development may appear as genetically fixed species specific features of individual species in phylogeny also. Two main categories of these abnormalities may be distinguished (cf. Severcov, 1931): the accelerations, among which are the changes due either to a speeding up of the maturation of the body in general or of the differentiation of a particular organ; and the retardations which are the opposite cases. The most frequent type of acceleration and heterochrony in insects is perhaps neoteny.

Neoteny may be defined as a case of acceleration where the organism attains sexual maturity before morphogenesis is complete and further development is suspended. Neoteny of variable extent is a very common feature in the development of insects. It is on the basis of this that the worker caste of termites and social Hymenoptera is developed. Neoteny is also the mechanism of origin of wingless, larva-like females in various insect groups such as Lepidoptera (Psychidae, Geometridae etc.), Coleoptera, (Lampyridae), and Strepsiptera. It appears to be one of the commonest and simplest mechanisms of origin of new species in insects. It may be explained as a small genetically fixed deviation in the quantity of the JH as the result of which different further phylogenetical changes have arisen secondarily. More or less extensive neoteny is also the basis, in most other cases, of polymorphism, as in aphids, locusts, bugs, cicadas, psocids etc. Most of these morphological deviations are connected with the deviations in the normal course of metamorphosis such as the regressive metamorphosis. In other cases, irrespective of the deviations in the course of metamorphosis, normal adults result as in the case of hypermetamorphosis.

Regressive metamorphosis is a term for a type of postembryonic development during which some of the imaginal parts of the body which developed during the larval period, such as the imaginal discs of wings, lose their ability for growth and are partly or completely histolysed during the metamorphosis. In most cases, it occurs only in wingless females, whilst the winged males have a normal metamorphosis.

Two different types of regressive metamorphosis may be distinguished (cf. Fedotov, 1955a, b): the first is where the imaginal discs grow until the pupal period and almost reach the size of the normal pupal wing before losing the ability for further growth and becoming histolysed. This is the type of metamorphosis in wingless females of Geometridae. In the other type, which occurs in Psychidae, the reduction of wings starts in the first instar larva and no doubt continues during the short periods of gradient growth at the beginning of each larval instar. It seems probable that the first type is phylogenetically younger. It would be interesting to study the secondarily wingless insect orders such as Anoplura and Aphaniptera, to see whether some trace of the ancestral wings would occur, after the JH application. In this connection the finding of Sharif (1935) that some species of fleas have pupal wing rudiments on the mesothorax is of interest.

Even though no experiments with corpora allata have been carried out so far, it seems probable that the JH is also in some way involved in these changes. The chief factor here, however, is the time of inactivation of the GF.

Hypermetamorphosis. A rather frequent abnormality in the course of metamorphosis is where there is more than one anisometric growth period during the postembryonic development, these periods being separated by several instars with isometric larval growth. Hypermetamorphosis occurs in the parasitic groups of the three largest orders of holometabolic insects, Coleoptera, Hymenoptera and Diptera, and in several other insects. Even though here again no experimental evidence is yet available, it seems very probable that the primary influence was the acceleration of the hatching time (desembryonization) relative to the morphogenesis. Hatching therefore takes place at a primitive oligopodous stage as in the campodeiforme larvae of the hypermetamorphic Coleoptera: Meloidae and Diptera

(Bombylidae), or even at a protopodous stage as in parasitic Hymenoptera, instead of the specialized oligopodous stage common to most other insects of these orders. In this way the larvae appear to hatch before the JH starts to act, so that the embryonic gradient growth continues after the hatching. Two or more moults may therefore occur in the different morphogenetical stages before the JH starts to act and the normal larval period of isometric growth begins. The very primitive type of metamorphosis in Ephemeroptera with the so-called larvula may also be understood (cf. p. 168) on this basis.

E. THE PRINCIPLE AND ORIGIN OF INSECT METAMORPHOSIS

Various Concepts of Metamorphosis

The Berlese-Jeschikov theory. Insect metamorphosis with its touch of mystery has attracted the attention of scientists since the early beginnings of Natural History. Until the appearance of the first paper on metamorphosis hormones, however, all the attempts to explain its principles were based exclusively on morphological and histological data. One of the first systematic papers dealing with this question on the basis of the state of knowledge of the time was that by Berlese (1913). His conception is based on the earlier views of William Harvey (1651), Rahmdors (1811) and Lubbock (1883) which emphasize the resemblance between the larva and embryo of insects on the one hand, and that between the pupa of Holometabola and the nymph of Hemimetabola on the other. His theory may briefly be defined as stating that metamorphosis arose by a shifting of the hatching of the larva to an earlier stage of embryonic development so that the completion of the morphogenesis of the imaginal structures must necessarily take place during postembryonic development. This is why the theory has been called the desembryonization theory (Steinberg, 1956). According to it the hemimetabolous insects (Exopterygota) hatch at a later stage of morphogenesis, the oligopod stage, with only thoracic appendages (legs), whilst the holometabolous insects (Endopterygota) hatch in the earlier, so-called polypod, stage which is characterized by the presence of embryonic appendages on the abdominal segments. Some of the parasitic Hymenoptera hatch even earlier, at the protopod stage, with embryonic appendages on the first three segments of the embryonic body only. This conception of Berlese was further developed and later elaborated by Jeschikov[1] (1929, 1936, 1940, 1941), so that it is now generally known

[1] (German translit.), read Yezhikov.

as the Berlese-Jeschikov theory. The contribution of Jeschikov consists mainly in his pointing out the connection between the stage of morphogenesis at which the insects hatch and the quantity of yolk: the less yolk the egg of a given group contains on the average, the earlier in its morphogenesis the larva hatches. Whilst the Hemimetabola which hatch in a late oligopod stage, called postoligopod (Jeschikov), generally speaking possess large eggs with a relatively large yolk content, the much smaller eggs of Holometabola, which hatch in an earlier stage of their morphogenesis, contain on the average much less yolk, the poorest of all being those of the parasitic Hymenoptera.

The Berlese-Jeschikov theory has recently been the subject of numerous objections by many prominent morphologists and physiologists; Hinton (1948, 1955) for example has reached the conclusion, on the basis of his very detailed morphological study of the larval prolegs of the Superorder Panorpoidea (Diptera, Lepidoptera, Trichoptera, Mecoptera and Siphonaptera), that the prolegs have developed independently in all these groups so that they have nothing in common and cannot be homologous either one with the others or with the embryonic appendages of the polypode stage as has been assumed up to now by the Berlese-Jeschikov theory. Hinton assumes that the fact that most of the groups in which larvae with well formed pseudopods occur have developed from groups without larval pseudopods, shows that no such homology occurs, as this would be in contradiction to Dollo's law of the irreversibility of evolution. However persuasive and important the morphological facts shown by Hinton may be, his conclusions cannot be accepted. The fact that 'prolegs have been independently evolved at least twenty-seven times within the Order Diptera' appears to show in itself that a connection of some kind must exist among all of them. The more so as the abdominal appendages are developed in the embryos of all insects irrespective of whether they occur afterwards in the larvae or whether they are obliterated during the following period of phylogenesis. Their stated disappearance in the ancestors of the larvae possessing prolegs does not, therefore, mean that they would have really disappeared in these groups in the sense of Dollo's law. They are thus no true exceptions to this law. The general occurrence in insects of 'exceptions' of this type to Dollo's law may be clearly shown, amongst other things, by the presence of completely developed imaginal thoracic appendages in all of those insects, in the larvae of which they have disappeared morphologically (cf. the apodous larvae of higher Diptera and of Aculeate Hymenoptera). There are no doubts regarding the homology between the embryonic appendages which disappear in the larval stage and the thoracic legs of adults. The disappearance of a structure from the

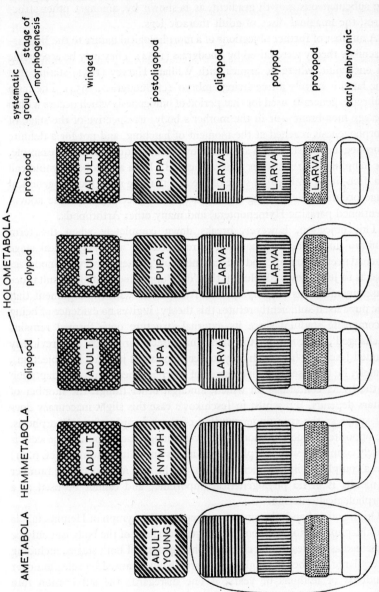

FIG. 33. Diagram of the interrelationships of the morphogenetical stages in the ontogenesis of insects as assumed by the Berlese-Jeschikov theory.

external morphology in no way means a disappearance of the corresponding subcutaneous growth gradient, as is shown by, amongst other structures, the imaginal discs of adult thoracic legs.

A number of further objections of a morphological nature to the Berlese-Jeschikov theory were raised by Snodgrass (1954). They may be acceptable on one point, where he argues with William Harvey (1651) stating that 'the larva is merely a free-living embryo' (cf Snodgrass, 1954). The term embryo is generally used for that period of ontogenesis which occurs within the egg membranes (or in the mother's body) irrespective of the stage of morphogenesis reached at the moment of hatching, and not for a definite morphogenetical stage as is suggested by the above quotation. For example, the nauplius of Crustacea is generally called a larva and nobody would call it a 'free-living embryo' in spite of the fact that the same morphogenetical stage occurs inside the egg membranes in all insects (except the above-mentioned parasitic Hymenoptera) and many other Arthropods.

This objection, however, breaks down completely when the term 'embryo' in the above quotation is replaced by 'morphogenetical stage reached in embryonic period in Hemimetabola'. When, however, Snodgrass objects to Jeschikov's conclusion that 'die Puppe erscheint als Resultat des Zusammenfliessens aller nymphalen Alterstufen' with the argument that 'the pupa itself sufficiently refutes this theory; it gives no evidence of being a composite stadium since its external structure once formed remains unchanged', he commits the same inaccuracy for which he previously blamed Jeschikov (or which only to a certain extent justified his objection), namely, he confused the given stage of morphogenesis with its adaptation to the living conditions on which, amongst other things, the number of instars depends. But whilst in Jeschikov's case this slight inaccuracy does not suppress the true understanding of the principle of metamorphosis, the opposite is true for Snodgrass. Even though each moulting process is closely connected with morphogenesis and is one of its conditions (cf. p. 71) it is a completely independent process. In the case mentioned the number of moults is of no phylogenetical importance and cannot be used as a morphological criterion.

On the other hand, the agreement between the nymph of Hemimetabola and the pupa of Holometabola in the general shape of the body can only be explained as the result of a common phylogenesis of both stages, including a very large number of single hereditary changes caused by selection over hundreds of millions of years, if one disregards the subdivision into different stages with special ecological functions and adaptation. There is in fact scarcely any major difference in the general course of morphogenesis between Hemimetabola and Holometabola (cf. fig. 34). When

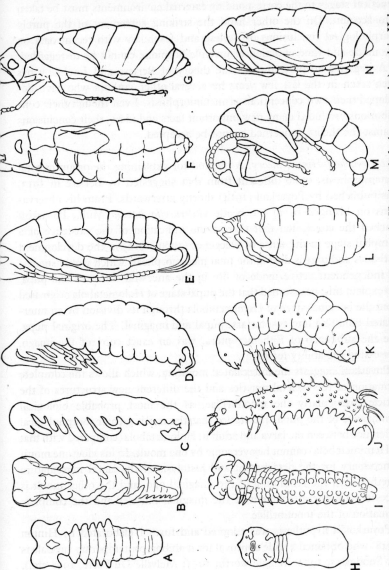

FIG. 34. Comparison of the corresponding morphogenetical stages in Hemimetabola (upper series) and in Holometabola (lower series). A,H – protopod stage; B,C; J – polypod stage; D,K – oligopod stage; E,F,G; L,M,N – postoligopod stage; A,B – *Xiphidium* sp., embryos; C,D – *Blattella germanica*, embryos; E – *Periplaneta americana*, embryo before hatching; F – *Oncopeltus fasciatus*, penultimate instar nymph; G – *Aprophora salicis*, last instar nymph; H – *Platygaster herrickii* Packard, first instar larva; I – *Bombyx mori*, embryo; J – *Panorpa klugi*, larva, 1st instar; K – *Mylabris variabilis*, 2nd instar larva; L – *Musca* sp., prepupa; M – *Sialis* sp., pupa; N – *Calliphora* sp., pupa, (From Novák, 1956.)

evaluating the theory, differences among the species and higher taxonomic groups, specific variations, and the necessity of adaptation of the morphogenetical stages to the corresponding external environments must be taken into account. On the other hand the striking agreement of the purely morphological conclusions of Berlese and Jeschikov with recent data on the mode and time of action of juvenile hormone cannot be disregarded.

A negative attitude towards the theory of Berlese and Jeschikov has been taken in the last few years by several other authors who have developed their own conceptions of metamorphosis. Even though their contributions produced many new important facts and ideas, their conclusions against the theory concerned cannot be accepted.

The Poyarkoff-Hinton theory. A method for explaining the origin of total metamorphosis, quite different from that suggested by Berlese in 1913, was published by Poyarkoff (1914) shortly afterwards. From his observations on histogenesis in the beetle *Galerucella luteola* Müll., Poyarkoff reached the conclusion that there is no indication of the existence of a nymphal stage in the sense of Deegener (1909, 1911) in the development of tissues and organs during the total metamorphosis which would suggest an independent active mode of life in the ancestral forms of the pupa. To explain this, he assumed that the pupal stage of Holometabola originated from the imaginal stage of Hemimetabola through its division by an intercalated moulting into two instars: pupal and imaginal. The original pupa, like the subimago of Ephemeroptera, was an exact copy of the imago, possessing the ability for flight.

Poyarkoff suggests the intercalated moulting, which allows the complete formation of the skeletal muscles and the different new structures of the cuticle, particularly the tonofibrillae, as the most probable biological significance of the pupa. He argues that the much greater morphological difference between the larva and adult in Holometabola (compared with that in Hemimetabola) cannot be overcome by one moult. In his view one moult is necessary for the detachment and histolysis of the larval musculature together with the rebuilding of the imaginal one, and the other moult is necessary for the attachment of the imaginal muscles and the complete formation of the tonofibrillae.

Poyarkoff's hypothesis was adopted and further elaborated by Hinton (1948) who obtained a wide approval for it among contemporary specialists (cf. Snodgrass, 1954; Wigglesworth, 1954; Melville Du Porte, 1958 etc.). Hinton, on the basis of his very detailed study of the morphology of the three main types of pupae in Endopterygota (pupa dectica, pupa obtecta and pupa exarata) and of the histogenesis of the simuliid pupa (1958), together with an intimate knowledge of larval morphology, discusses the theory in detail and compares it with other conceptions of the metamorphosis. He also suggests, from the occurrence of a corresponding instar (subimago) in the may-flies and in the males of some Homoptera, that the pupal stage arose before the larval wings had begun developing internally and that these two structures developed independently of each other. On the other hand he expresses doubts on the necessity of the pupal moult for the evagination of the internal wing buds.

The following objections have been raised, amongst others, to this theory: the original conception of Poyarkoff is of a teleological character wherever the author speaks of the necessity for the pupal moult etc. and Hinton did not remove this error (cf. Melville Du Porte, 1958). This is, however, a mistake which depends more or less on formulation and, as shown by the author mentioned, the result may be fully explained in terms of natural selection.

There is also no doubt that the two instars, instead of one in the absence of the juvenile hormone, allow a more complete formation of the different imaginal characters, including the skeletal muscles. The difference is, however, in quantity and not in quality. As a matter of fact, a very complete imaginal musculature may develop in a hemimetabolous way as in cicadas and various other Exopterygota. As to the attachment of muscles by tonofibrillae, the special relationships emphasized by Hinton (1949) do not appear to be decisive if the distension of the body following each ecdysis and the fact that the insertion of the muscles develops after the start of their histogenesis are taken into account. Regarding the tonofibrillae, their development is not restricted to a special period of the moulting process, but of necessity continues even after the ecdysis throughout the time the new cuticle (endocuticle) is secreted. On the other hand, as will be further argued (cf. p. 175), the intercalated moulting in the middle of the metamorphosis period is quite indispensable for the evagination of the internal wing buds and the complete formation of the wings.[1]

Koshanchikov criticized the Berlese-Jeschikov theory from what may be called a physiological point of view. He emphasized the histological specificity of the pupa and its physiological peculiarities, the supposed differences in total metabolism (the U-shaped curve of oxygen consumption)

[1] The arguments in favour of and against both theories were discussed in detail with Dr. H. E. Hinton, F.R.S., during his stay in Czechoslovakia in September 1961 and as neither he nor the author feels inclined to accept the other's point of view, the only reasonable procedure appears to be to deal with the arguments in favour of both theories together and leave a final judgement to the consideration of the reader and until our knowledge on the subject is further advanced.

and the differences in hormonal environment – the absence of juvenile hormone in pupa, whilst it is present in the nymphal instars (except the last one) – and various other peculiarities. From this he concluded that the pupa is an independent stage of ontogenetical development in the phylogenesis of Holometabola, without any homologous stage in the ontogeny of Hemimetabola. Although the factual basis of Koshanchikov's views is irreproachable, his phylogenetic conclusions cannot be accepted. The experimental findings on the mode of action of the metamorphosis hormones show that a small variation in their action, even purely quantitative in character, may result in far-reaching morphological and metabolic changes. These variations of a hereditary nature can only be explained as single quantitative genetic changes of the mutation type. No greater phylogenetical significance may therefore be ascribed to such changes. The same is true of the other physiological features mentioned above (cf. Koshanchikov, 1946c).

As shown by Sláma (1959, 1960) in a recent paper on the oxygen consumption in sawflies the typical U-shaped curve of the O_2-consumption of the pupal stage of most Holometabola may in some cases be sub-divided into two instars (the pronymph and the pupa as in sawflies, cf. p. 196). It is, no doubt, the result of a small variation in the production or function of the moulting hormone. The occurrence of this type of respiratory curve in Tenthredinoidea, and its absence in other Hymenoptera, shows that the moulting process (from larva, i.e. pronymph, to pupa) has little effect on the total metabolism and, again, that the number of moults is of little, if any, phylogenetical importance. The same conclusion necessarily follows from experiments with the isolated moulting hormone, ecdyson (cf. Karlson 1957).

The embryonization theory of Zakhvatkin. Further objections to the Berlese-Jeschikov theory were raised by Zakhvatkin (1953a, b). His point of view may be summarized as follows: The individual larval characteristics in Holometabola, such as the homonomous type of metamery, the primitive form of the mouth parts, the simple stemmata instead of complicated eyes etc., resemble larvae more than embryos of Hemimetabola (Polyneoptera) and exhibit no specific embryonic characters. Zakhvatkin concludes from these and other facts that an opposite process took place in the phylogenesis of metabolic insects, i.e. instead of the desembryonization of the larvae in Holometabola, as postulated by Berlese and Jeschikov, there was an embryonization of the larvae in Hemimetabola which therefore hatch on the average at a later stage of morphogenesis. Zakhvatkin, however, also admits desembryonization to a limited extent, as for example in the so-called

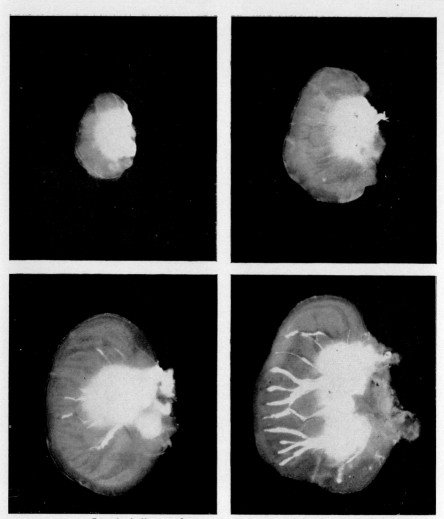

PLATE VII. Imaginal discs at four successive stages of development of the last larval instar of *Galleria mellonella*.

protopod larvae of some parasitic Hymenoptera. He sees, erroneously, the ancestors of the contemporary Holometabola in the insects, with assumed aquatic larvae, allied to the paleozoic Paleodictioptera, in agreement with Handlirsch (1927) and Martynov (1938); on the basis of this assumption he compares the larva of Holometabola with a freshly hatched nymph of the present Ephemeroptera, the so-called larvula. His mistake was unambiguously shown by Šulc (1927), Ghilyarov (1949) and Sharov (1953). The larvula seems more likely to be the product of an independent, even though phylogenetically earlier, case of desembryonization, most probably connected with the secondary transition of the group to development in a fresh-water medium.

Regarding the more embryonic character of the holometabolous larvae Zakhvatkin is right in stating that many of their features are completely larval. Here, however, as in the objections by Snodgrass, two different things must be distinguished: the stage of morphogenesis at a given period of ontogenesis and its adaptation to environmental conditions, which is completely different inside the egg membranes from a free living state. Both the shape of the embryo and of the larva are, of course, the results of evolution under the influence of natural selection. But whilst the first is of a palingenetic character in the sense of Haeckel (1906), the other is of a coenogenetic nature. If, however, the various coenogenetic features of the holometabolous larvae cannot be taken as evidence in favour of an embryonic character, as supposed by Jeschikov, they can no more testify against it. The chief palingenetic characters of the given stages, such as the number of segments and their appendages, definitely point in favour of the Berlese-Jeschikov conclusions.

The ecological theory of Ghilyarov. The ecological factors controlling the evolution of the insect metamorphosis were evaluated by Ghilyarov (1947, 1957, 1959) in his well-founded theory. Unlike Handlirsch, Martynov and Zakhvatkin and in agreement with Berlese-Jeschikov he emphasizes the origin of the class Insecta from dry-land ancestors, myriapod-like animals (Protomyriapoda), supposed to be the direct descendants of Annelida. The first insects (Protohexapoda) were tiny wormlike animals living in moist soil which only subsequently adapted themselves to life on its surface. Their further development was dependent on the strengthening of the cuticle as well as oligomerization and the development of special movement (springing) apparatus as in present day Collembola, Machilidae etc.

Springing was, no doubt, the prerequisite for the development of wings from the paranotal outgrowths of the meso- and metathorax, the original function of which was protection against dessication. The evolution of two different types of ontogenesis started from the first Pterygota: the Hemimetabola, in which the larva and adults are more similar morphologically and inhabit, with some exceptions, the same biotope; and the Holometabola, which have the advantage of making use of two different biotopes. As the original larval type the author accepts the campodeiform (thysanuroid) type and he also accepts, following Zakhvatkin, the principle of embryonization for Hemimetabola and, following Berlese-Jeschikov, that of desembryonization for Holometabola. The further evolution continued in the direction of adaptation to diurnal activity, and by increasing the metabolic energy and independence from heredity. In some groups a secondary adaptation to fresh-water life developed. He agrees with the morphological relationship between the pupa of Holometabola and the nymph of Heterometabola and attempts to find the common thread between the views of Berlese-Jeschikov and Koshanchikov. As an ecological counterpart of the Berlese-Jeshikov theory, the Ghilyarov theory is a very important component of our present understanding of the problem of the phylogenesis of metamorphosis.

The repetition theory of Henson. Henson's conclusions are based on a very thorough study of the embryonic development of the mid-gut in *Calliphora* and its comparison with the internal metamorphosis in Diptera Cyclorrhapha and other insects, and on experimental results on juvenile hormone, particularly those obtained by Wigglesworth. He assumes that insect ontogenesis consists of a series of repeated developmental cycles all similar in principle to embryogenesis. In the larval development each of these cycles, which correspond to the individual instars, is controlled by juvenile hormone. In the nymphs of Hemimetabola the embryonic cycle is modified to a slight degree in each succession, being less and less subject to modification by the JH so that the various instars make a gradual progress towards the adult form. At the last ecdysis its influence entirely ceases – the result is metamorphosis. In holometabolous larvae the suppression due to the JH is greater than in the case of the nymph so that the larva changes very little in form until the metamorphosis starts (cf. Henson, 1946).

Henson attempts to explain the larval forms in various insects, and he suggests the following sequence of the larval forms according to the degree of reduction in the level of their organization: (1) the nymph, (2) the campodeid form, (3) the modified oligopod larva, such as in primitive Trichoptera, (4) the reduced oligopod larva, such as *Tenebrio*, (5) the caterpillar, (6) the grub-like larva, e.g. *Apis*, (7) the maggot. He assumes the existence of intermediate forms between all of them except perhaps between the nymph and campodeiform larva. Outside this series are placed the protopod and polypod stages of parasitic Hymenoptera, which he takes for precociously hatched embryos and not definite larval forms like the rest.

Henson's conception of the metamorphosis is very valuable in that it takes, in contrast to the others, full account of the metamorphosis of internal organs and of the experimental results. As to its conclusions, the following comments must be made: (1) Even if the morphogenesis within the individual moulting processes has something in common with embryogenesis and metamorphosis as a whole, it can in no way be taken as equivalent to either embryogenesis or metamorphosis. First, because all of them are simply parts of one and the same process, the morphogenesis, which commences with the segmentation of the egg and ends with the formation of wings and the development of the gonads, and which is qualitatively different in its various parts. Secondly, because all the larval instars together form one morphogenetical stage – the larval stage, subdivided by a series of moulting processes, which, as such, corresponds to only one of a sequence of morphogenetical processes of the embryonic period. Thirdly, the repeated epithelial renovation of the mid-gut during the moulting process, wherever it occurs, is in no way phylogenetically primary, being a secondary adaptation, most probably connected with the nature of the food; it cannot therefore serve as a reliable criterion on which to judge the character of the metamorphosis, more so as it is only one of many processes which is repeated here. As will be shown later, the metamorphosis is in fact not a repetition but a continuation of the embryonic morphogenesis. Further, the juvenile hormone is not a suppressing factor but a growth factor the extreme effect of which suspends further differentiation. It can therefore only fix a given stage of morphogenesis but cannot cause reduction of structures once developed. It is thus necessary to distinguish between the primary organization level in each larval form, the temporary perservation of which may be due to the JH influence, and its secondary reduction, as in maggots, which is due to other phylogenetically secondary morphological factors. In Henson's series of larval forms (cf. p. 146) there are clearly evident the four morphological stages of Berlese-Yeshikov (No. 1 = postoligopod, 2–4 oligopod; 5 to 7 polypod, the larvae of parasitic Hymenoptera not classified by Henson being protopod). Any doubts on the polypodous character of lepidopterous larvae are untenable if the structure of the abdominal appendages of the first instar larva in the phylogenetically lowest Lepidoptera of the genus Micropteryx is taken into account. The reduced polypod stage of the apodous grubs of many of the Hymenoptera is clearly evident from their tenthredinoid ancestors, and the finally reduced polypod stage of larvae lacking the head and legs as in Diptera Cyclorrhapha seems to be very probable, judging from the structure of their Mecopteroid ancestors. In any case the positive contribution of the repetition theory is to emphasize the significance of the JH in insect metamorphosis.

The question of the midgut renovation in *Galleria mellonella* has recently been thoroughly studied by Piepho and Holz (1959). It was shown that the whole midgut is destroyed during each moulting process and is formed again from the so-called basal cells. The process in the larval moult is different from the pupal and the imaginal moult. The new epithelium is always formed before the old one disintegrates. The same happens with a midgut transplanted into earlier larval instars. In such cases the implanted epithelium regenerates in the form of that of the host, i.e. the type of the regenerating cells depends upon the presence of JH in the same way as do the epidermis cells. This is in agreement with what has been mentioned above, but does not mean an argument in favour of the repetition theory. It appears that the increase and spread of the basal cells takes place in the early, gradient growth period of each instar, i.e. in the absence of JH, and its form depends upon whether this increase is affected by the JH at the time the effective concentration is reached or not. This conclusion, however, needs further experimental evidence.

The concept of Steinberg. Steinberg (1958, 1959a) takes a view similar to that of Zakhvatkin. On the basis of a long series of experiments (1938–57) he attempts to evaluate the mutual relationships amongst the developmental processes in the imaginal discs of wings and legs of Holometabola and reaches the following conclusions: (1) The position of the external imaginal parts of the body is determined at a very early stage of ontogenesis. The eggs are here of a mosaic type. (2) The development of the organs as a whole is, to a large extent, regulatory and is realized under a direct influence of the epidermis cells. (3) The development of the imaginal discs depends in its earlier stages only upon a mutual action of their cells, but, in the later stages, the regulatory functions are taken over by the epidermis cells.

Steinberg (1959) further studied the developmental potentialities of various kinds of tissues under experimental conditions and examined them from both ontogenetical and phylogenetical points of view. He showed a phylogenetical relationship between the mode of development of a transplanted tissue and the fate of the corresponding part of the body in phylogeny. For example, parts of the epidermis of the lateral portion of the prothorax of *Galleria mellonella* transplanted into another specimen show a tendency to develop wing buds which would correspond to the pro-thoracic paranotal outgrowths in some fossil insect orders (e.g. Paleodictyoptera), being serial homologues of the wings. These tissue potentialities are also preserved in the corresponding parts of the body in the phylogenetically higher orders where they are only realized when they obtain a new functional significance, as in the respiratory filaments of the simuliid pupae, or under experimental conditions.

The research by Steinberg (1933–56) into metamorphosis is mainly concerned with the problem of tissue differentiation, particularly with the regulation and regeneration potentials of the imaginal discs. From a large amount of experimental data, he emphasized the formative influence of the epidermis cells in the creation of the imaginal discs. He showed a clear connection between moulting and morphogenesis in the arthropods where the moulting is an indispensable condition and component of the morphogenesis. It is in this connection that he emphasizes the greater importance of embryonization compared with desembryonization in the morphogenesis of insects from the point of view of their phylogenesis.

Wigglesworth's theory of metamorphosis as an example of polymorphism. Wigglesworth (1954 etc.) criticizes the Berlese-Jeschikov theory from a different point of view. He can be agreed with in so far as he states that this conception is mainly descriptive in character when considered from the standpoint of the present knowledge of the metamorphosis hormones. This was quite inevitable at the time, when only morphological data were available. Wigglesworth himself views the metamorphosis as a special type of polymorphism. According to him each polymorphic organism 'contains within it the potentialities for its different forms', that is larva (nymph) and adult in Hemimetabola, and larva, pupa and adult in Holometabola. It is the genetic constitution of the given species on one hand and the specific factors of the environment on the other that decide which of the two (in Hemimetabola) or three (in Holometabola) potentialities is realized in the ontogenetical development. He refers to the earlier experiments of Geigy (1931) and others who have shown the mosaic character of insect eggs and argues that these observations demonstrate 'the independent existence within the embryo of two latent organisms, larval and adult'.

The following must be observed here: it is, of course, of only terminological importance whether the term polymorphism is used in its narrower sense, as is generally the case in zoological literature, or whether it is understood in its broadest sense (to include the metamorphosis), as was done by Wigglesworth and suggested, perhaps for the first time, by Swammerdam (1758), and for which the term polyeidism was suggested (cf. Lubbock, 1883). In its former sense, which is preferred in the present work, polymorphism means the occurrence of two or more different forms in one and the same morphological stage, more often in the adult animals. In this sense, of course, the metamorphosis is a more general phenomenon which has nothing to do with the polymorphism. There is one important difference between the two interpretations of the term. Whereas in the first case the polymorphic forms occur alongside each other, there is always only one of the possible forms in a given specimen. In the second case both (all) forms are present one after the other, in normal development of the same specimen, and one of the forms can only be suppressed by experimental treatment. As a matter of fact, as mentioned above, the whole morphogenesis from the egg to the adult consists of a series of stages equivalent to larva, pupa and adult, only secondarily subdivided into instars by the moults in arthropods. This meaning of the term polymorphism is therefore practically synonymous with that of morphogenesis.

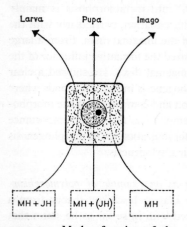

FIG. 35. Mode of action of the metamorphosis hormones according to Wigglesworth (from Wigglesworth, 1957). (JH) = a small amount of JH.

As to the influence of the metamorphosis hormones on polymorphism, Wigglesworth (1940a, 1954), using his interpretation of the term (i.e. = polyeidism), assumes that 'they serve merely to release, control and direct the inherent capacity for growth and differentiation possessed by the cells of various tissues', perhaps by activating one of the three different substrates (enzyme systems) in one and the same epidermis cell (cf. fig. 35).

Amongst other things, Wigglesworth (1934, 1940a, b, 1957, 1954b) studied very thoroughly the histological aspect of insect metamorphosis and he made a number of very important findings. Even if not all of the conclusions drawn from these are accepted, they form a substantial part of the material evidence for the conception of metamorphosis supported in this book. Wigglesworth's findings on the distribution pattern of mitoses in the presence and absence of the JH are regarded by the author as particularly important for an understanding of the mode of action of the juvenile hormone and the principle of the metamorphosis (cf. p. 117): in its presence they are uniformly distributed over the entire surface of the body, whereas in its absence they only appear in special areas of the epidermis which correspond to the surface of imaginal structures such as the wing pads, the rudiments of the genital appendages etc. Equally important are his findings on the sequence of the degeneration changes in the pro-thoracic glands of the blood-sucking bug *Rhodnius prolixus* following im-aginal moulting. Contrary to the conclusions of Bodenstein (1953a; cf. p. 162) it seems very probable that, irrespective of the specific conditions in the various tissues, these are generally true for the larval structures of metabolic insects. No doubt the two following stages of disintegration found by Wigglesworth in the prothoracic glands occur in all of them: (*a*) the stage when the JH is absent, which controls the breaking down of the gland but during which this may be prevented by the implantation of an active corpus allatum; and (*b*) the stage reached after a certain time (immediately after the ecdysis of the adult) during which the disintegration of the gland is irrevocable. It appears, however, that no other endocrine stimulus except that of the JH regulates the process of disintegration.

In a recent paper, in which he examines the effects of farnesol on the development of the last instar nymph of *Rhodnius*, Wigglesworth (1961) distinguishes two different types of differentiation during growth, referring to similar results mentioned in an earlier paper by Halbwachs, Joly, and Joly (1957) on *Locusta*: (1) The progressive increase in size of the wing lobes and the progressive differentiation of the sexual appendages con-trolled by the time of action and concentration of the MH. (2) The altera-tions in the type of cuticle and the general form and pattern of the body from the larva to the adult controlled by the JH. A qualitative difference between the two is claimed. This conclusion, however, needs further evidence in regard to the sequence of morphogenetical changes in the absence of the JH and the results of what has been called progressive metathetely (Novák, 1951b, 1956), caused by the acceleration of the moult-ing process by MH.

The hypotheses of metamorphosis as the result of a temporary inhibition of the growth of the imaginal structures. Several authors see the origin of the metamorphosis in a temporary suppression of the growth of the imaginal parts of the body. They attempt, therefore, to find the cause of this inhibition. For example, according to Anglas (1901a, b) the imaginal discs are kept in a latent stage by the products of excretion of the active larval parts of the body and only when these degenerate can the growth and development of the imaginal parts start. According to Perez (1902, 1910a, b), the latent imaginal discs are activated by a secretion from the gonads; Kopeć (1924) assumed that their development is controlled by secretions from the brain. Kovalevskyi (1887) and Rees (1888) saw the reason for this inhibition in a secretion by the larval tissues which inactivates the phagocytes of the haemolymph; this secretion is assumed to cease at the end of the larval period, which leads to the disintegration of the larval parts by phagocytosis and the development of the imaginal discs in their place. Other authors see the reason for histolysis of the larval parts in a physical restricting of their ability to obtain nourishment by diffusion from the haemolymph (Tiegs, 1922 etc.) or in their asphyxia (Bataillon, 1893). There are others who attempt to explain the activation of the imaginal discs by the action of an oxidase associated with melanin formation which reaches a maximum at the time of pupation (Dewitz, 1916; cf. Agrell, 1951 etc.).

If, however, the growth of the imaginal parts of the body during the larval period is studied, it is seen that not only is their growth not suspended during that time, but that they even grow relatively more than the larval parts, due to the allometric growth period at the beginning of each instar, before the effective concentration of the juvenile hormone is reached (cf. p. 157). The growth inhibition of the imaginal parts of the body during the larval period is, therefore, only apparent and only appears when the increase during the larval period is compared with that during the metamorphosis. There is therefore no reason for looking for a factor which suppresses them during the larval period (except the juvenile hormone), but far more for looking for a factor which stimulates their growth during the metamorphosis but which itself is not the cause of the metamorphosis (cf. p. 116). Regarding the histolysis or phagocytosis of the larval parts, this is not the reason but the consequence of their decline. Neither of the enzymatic factors affecting the histolysis can therefore be viewed as the cause of metamorphosis.

The theories of tissue specific determination. The Swiss authors Geigy (1941) and Hadorn (1942) examine the problem of the principle of metamorphosis from still another point of view. Its advantage lies in that it is not confined to metamorphosis in insects, but includes the results of experiments in amphibians and the findings in other groups of animals where metamorphosis occurs. Geigy refers to his classical experiments with the UV irradiation of the eggs of *Drosophila* as the result of which the imaginal parts of the body (legs, wings) were affected, whilst the larval ones remained unchanged. He concludes that the body of metabolic animals is formed by a mosaic of the following three different parts: (1) Larval structures which are histolysed during the metamorphosis. (2) Adult structures which remain undifferentiated in the embryonic stage until the onset of the metamorphosis and only then start to differentiate. (3) Larvo-adult structures which are well developed in the larval period and which survive the metamorphosis without any noticeable change and are fully active in the adult (cf. p. 164).

The determination of the various parts of the body into these three groups takes place in the early embryonic period or, in some cases such as *Drosophila*, before the segmentation of the egg. From the experiments mentioned, together with those of Lüscher (1944) on *Tineola bisselliella*, Geigy concludes that the determinative processes controlling the later differentiation start in the larval structures and continue only subsequently and separately in the imaginal structures. As such a process, Geigy also views the period of secretory activity in each of the endocrine glands which he compares with an alarm-clock mechanism that causes the clock to ring at a given moment. In spite of the limitations due to the state of knowledge at that time, this conception provides an important contribution towards a better understanding of the principle of metamorphosis.

Hadorn (1942) examined the problem of metamorphosis from a similar point of view. Later (1953, 1954) he concentrated his attention on the genetic aspect of the question and was particularly concerned with genetic disturbances of the type in the category of lethal mutations (lethal-translucide, lethal-giant etc.). Many of his collaborators, such as Grob (1952), Vogt (1947), Chen and Hadorn (1955), Ursprung (1959), Faulhaber (1959) etc., continued to work in this direction.

The metamorphosis hormone theories. A completely new point of view has been reached and a considerable amount of experimental evidence has accumulated regarding the principle of metamorphosis in the work on the metamorphosis hormones which has increased enormously during the last two decades. The publication of these works, however, caused a certain confusion in the whole subject at the outset, due to the subjective approach of most of the authors and their preoccupation with the mechanics of development. Latterly, however, the majority of the incomplete theories proposed have been abandoned by their authors, and theories more generally applicable because of the increasing mass of comparative material have been evolved. As most of these incomplete theories are discussed in connection with the hormones concerned in the appropriate parts of this book, only the most important of them are briefly mentioned here in so far as they provide new ideas regarding the principle of metamorphosis.

The growth and differentiation hormone conception of B. Scharrer (1948, 1952a, b, 1953 etc.) and Williams (1952 etc.) is worth discussing. According to this, the prothoracic gland hormone is a principle which actively induces growth and differentiation. Irrespective of the objections that can be raised against it, the theory is preferable to the other hypotheses in several respects (cf. p. 71) (it explains, for instance, pupation without any JH action). It does not, however, avoid the fallacy of using the term differentiation hormone for the MH, as mentioned above.

The successful isolation of the prothoracic gland hormone by Butenandt and Karlson (1954) is very important for a better understanding of the mode of action of this factor. A theory of metamorphosis has been formulated in a series of papers by Karlson (1956, 1957 etc.) and Bückmann (1956, 1957 etc.) which attempts to correlate the findings regarding ecdyson and its mode of action with the data on other metamorphosis hormones. It may be illustrated by the diagram in fig. 36. It is, however, chiefly concerned with ecdyson and to this extent it practically agrees with the present author's conception (Novák, 1951a, b, 1956 etc.), discussed below.

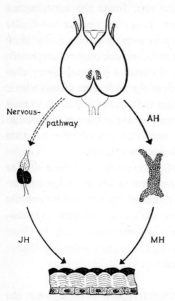

FIG. 36. Mode of action of the metamorphosis hormones according to Karlson (after Karlson, 1956).

A point of view intermediate between the two theories mentioned has developed from the view first taken by Piepho (1951). According to this, the difference between the pupal and the imaginal moulting depends on the presence of a small amount of the JH in the former. This view was later adopted by Wigglesworth (1957) and by Schneiderman and Gilbert (1961); cf. Schneiderman (1961 etc.). Nevertheless it contradicts the fact that the implantation of active pupal prothoracic glands induces normal pupation in ligatured abdomens of *cecropia* larvae (Williams, 1952), i.e. in the complete absence of the JH, and the finding that ecdyson can cause both pupation and the subsequent imaginal moulting when injected into ligatured *Calliphora* larvae. On the other hand, the various findings regarded as supporting this conception may be explained equally well in other ways (cf. p. 69). To summarize, it can be concluded for all the metamorphosis hormone theories that although they produced a rich mass of experimental data they are only partial and, in themselves, unable to provide a complete solution of the metamorphosis problem.

Morohoshi's hypothesis of hormonal balance by antagonism. The conception of Morohoshi (1957) provides an interesting contribution to the problem of the principle of metamorphosis. From the abundant data obtained by the Japanese authors on the inheritance of the moltinism (number of instars) and voltinism (number of generations in a year) in the different industrial races of the silkworm (*Bombyx mori*), and on the basis of his own interesting transplantation experiments, Morohoshi attempts to combine these data with the findings on the effects of (*a*) various environmental factors such as photo-periodism, temperature, humidity and (*b*) the endocrine factors such as AH, MH, JH and the hormone produced by the suboesophageal ganglion (cf. p. 199). His conception may be briefly summarized as follows:

The corpora allata produce a growth stimulating hormone (?JH) which is assumed to suppress diapause in the eggs of the next generation (cf. p. 200), to shorten the length of the larval and pupal instars and to reduce the number of moults (instars). An antagonistic growth inhibitory hormone is assumed to be produced by the suboesophageal ganglion. This is said to prolong the length of the larval and pupal instars and to induce diapause. A genetically governed balance of both these hormones determines the number of moults, i.e. the 'moltinism', the number of generations per year,

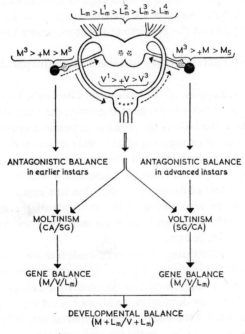

FIG. 37. Diagram of Morohoshi's hypothesis of the antagonistic hormonal balance (after Morohoshi, 1957, modified).

i.e. the voltinism, and the size of the body in a given silkworm race, as well as a number of other characters, such as the length of the instars, the body weight, and the weight of the cocoons etc. The production of each hormone is regulated by the brain through the nervous system via the nervi corporum cardiacarum and nervi allati on the one hand and the circumoesophageal connectives on the other, as well as by the gene complex. Of the complicated gene complex which influences these features, the maturing genes, some of which are sex-linked, should be taken into account first of all. They are said to affect the production of the two hormones by influencing the nervous activity of the brain. The 'major gene' affects the moltinism and acts by increasing the secretion from the corpora allata, whilst the 'minor gene', which affects voltinism, acts by regulating the secretory activity of the suboesophageal ganglion. The various environmental factors produce their activity by affecting the mechanisms mentioned.

Although the hypothesis contains several marked contradictions (such as the supposition that the growth-inhibiting hormone causes an increase in weight) and needs further clarification in many respects, as well as a comparison with the present stage of knowledge of the factors concerned and further experimental proof of its conclusions, it provides, nevertheless, several new aspects on the problem of insect metamorphosis.

The Gradient-Factor Theory of Insect Metamorphosis

The principle and outline of the conception. The above hypothesis of the existence of a tissue factor necessary for growth, the inactivation of which in certain parts of the body is the principle of gradient growth (cf. p. 124), led the author to an explanation of the mode of action of the metamorphosis hormones and also of the principle of metamorphosis (Novák, 1951a, b, 1955, 1956b etc.). It not only agrees fully with the earlier, purely morphological theory of Berlese-Jeschikov, but confirms and explains this. It also suggests an explanation of the principle of the morphogenetic activity of all three metamorphosis hormones which was previously not fully understood (cf. p. 117).

The gradient-factor theory of metamorphosis is as follows: the morphogenesis of the embryonic period is the result of gradient growth during which various parts of the body lose the ability for further growth. They are partly or completely decomposed whilst the other parts continue growing so that the shape of the body changes continuously. In Apterygota this type of development continues in the postembryonic period with decreasing morphological changes, interrupted periodically by the moulting processes, until the adult shape is reached. This method of development is modified by the intervention of the juvenile hormone from the phylogenetically recent organ, the corpora allata. The hormone activates growth in the larval parts of the body, which lost the ability for it towards the end of the embryonic period due, according to this hypothesis, to the inactivation of their gradient-factor. Through the action of the juvenile hormone the gradient growth is converted into an isometric one which is characteristic of the whole larval development. During this period morphogenesis is suspended. The juvenile hormone reaches its effective concentration late in the embryonic period in lower Hemimetabola, but the time when it becomes active morphogenetically occurs increasingly early in the morphogenesis with the phylogenetical accomplishment of the gland. It may, therefore, be shifted to the polypod and even to the protopod stage in some of the Holometabola. In the corpus allatum hormone we thus have the factor the activity timing of which can completely explain the main assumption of the Berlese-Jeschikov theory.

Morphogenesis can only take place when the juvenile hormone concentration falls below its effective level. As previously mentioned, this occurs for a short period at the beginning of each larval instar because

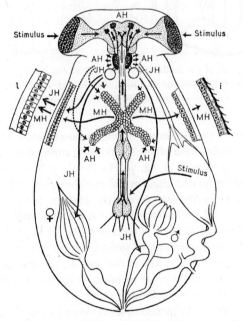

FIG. 38. Diagram of the action of the metamorphosis hormones. *l* – larval type of integument; *i* – imaginal type.

of the break in the production of the hormone at the time of ecdysis. These periods of gradient growth increase in length at the expense of the subsequent isometric growth periods with each successive instar. Sooner or later, this must lead to an instar where there is no isometric growth. The larval parts of the body then suffer a partial or complete disintegration connected with their prolonged inactivity, whilst the activity of the imaginal parts increases. This results in a marked change in form, from

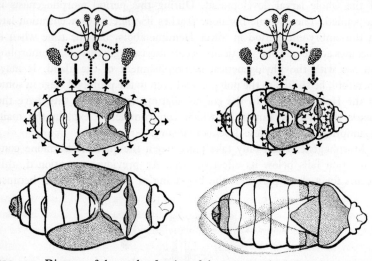

FIG. 39. Diagram of the mode of action of the metamorphosis hormones according to the gradient-factor theory (after Novák, 1956). Dotted area – structures containing the GF; short arrows – growing parts of the body. Left-hand side – with JH; right-hand side – without JH.

larva to adult, which is known as the metamorphosis and which is no more than a continuation of the temporarily suppressed gradient growth of the embryonic period (cf. fig. 39). In Hemimetabola this takes place in one intermoulting period alone as the morphological differences between the full-grown larva (the nymph) and the adult are not very large, but two stages are necessary in Holometabola for the adult differentiation to be accomplished (cf. p. 162). It is therefore not gradient growth which is peculiar to the metamorphosis of insects, but the isometric growth of the larval period. Gradient growth is common to all animals but isometric growth is a special evolution of metabolous insects. On the basis of the gradient-factor theory the following previously incompletely understood phenomena of the insect metamorphosis may be explained.

The effect of the metamorphosis hormones on the epidermal cells. Most of the cells of the body (those composing the larval structures) lose their activity and disintegrate during metamorphosis, whereas others simultaneously develop from the undifferentiated gradients of imaginal growths. There are, however, special types of cells which are fully developed and function in the larval period, and which do not die but change markedly during the metamorphosis, preserving all their potentials in the adult stage. This happens with many of the epidermal cells, at least in the Hemimetabola. Histological analysis of an adequate series of transitions between the larval and imaginal type of epidermis shows that these changes may be interpreted as a gradient growth of some parts of the cell, whilst the other parts remain unchanged or are decomposed, with a corresponding change in the character of their secretion, the new cuticle.[1] The connection between each of these cells and the juvenile hormone thus corresponds to that of the insect body as a whole. The changes may be completely inhibited at any time by the juvenile hormone. The epidermal cells, therefore, are the most sensitive test object for juvenile hormone activity. Although, however, they are very suitable for studying the mode of action of the juvenile hormone, they are less suitable for studying the reaction of the body as a whole towards this hormone.

The effect of the juvenile hormone on the epidermal cells lies in a total or partial suppression of their imaginal differentiation. It must, however, be kept in mind that, as with other morphological changes, variation in the action of any of the other metamorphosis hormones may have similar results, as shown by Fukuda (1944) and others. An acceleration of the moulting process compared with imaginal differentiation by premature injection of the moulting hormone may cause a partial suppression of imaginal characters. The same effect can, however, be caused indirectly by the activation hormone causing premature production of the moulting hormone. Correspondingly, a slowing down of the moulting process during the larval period due to a variation in the action of either of these hormones may result in an opposite effect, i.e. in accelerated differentiation. It is by a differential action on these two processes (moulting and differentiation), either directly or by means of the metamorphosis hormones, that the various external conditions, such as temperature and humidity, influence the morphogenesis in the way shown by Wigglesworth (1952).

The dependence of the type of cuticle laid down by the epidermis on the hormones acting is shown by fig. 40 (in Hemimetabola) and by fig. 41 (in Holometabola). The difference between the pupal and the imaginal cuticles which are both deposited in the same hormonal environment, seems to depend partly on the stage of differentiation of the epidermis, which is

[1] V. J. A. Novák, unpublished observation.

different at the beginning of the last larval and the pupal instars, and partly
on the length of the intermoulting period and other factors. The experiments by Piepho and Meyer (1951) and by Wiedbrauck (Meyer) (1953)
show that a pupal or imaginal epidermis transplanted into a new larval
host develops a new form (without scales and thicker than that of the adult)
which may sometimes appear larval in parts of the epidermis bladder.
This seems to be due not only to differences in hormonal influences, but to

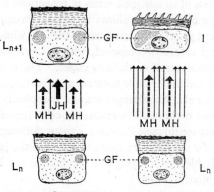

FIG. 40. Diagram of the supposed mode of action of the metamorphosis hormones on the epidermis cells in Hemimetabola. L_n – epidermis cell of the last instar
nymph; L_{n+1} – of supernumerary giant nymph; I – imaginal; thin arrows – the
average external factors influencing morphogenesis, food, temperature, length of the
arrows indicates the relative length of action of the corresponding factor; GF – part
of the cell supposed to be conditioned by the gradient-factor. (From Novák, 1956.)

differences in the length of the instar and in the internal environment. The
experiments of Williams (1947, 1952) and other authors, in which isolated
abdomens of last instar larvae, implanted with active prothoracic glands
alone, later produced a normal pupal and imaginal cuticle, clearly show that
there are no differences in the hormonal conditions between the last instar
larva and the pupa. This in no way contradicts the finding of Nayar (1954),
that the integument of young caterpillars transplanted into freshly moulted
pupae may develop imaginal scales without the intervention of a pupal
stage. It does not, however, mean that any of the morphogenetical stages
would be omitted in the absence of the pupal moult.

The question of a partial reversal of metamorphosis. Examination of the
behaviour of epidermal cells affected by the juvenile hormone provides a
reasonable explanation, in terms of the gradient-factor theory, of the
influence of this hormone on the reappearance of some of the juvenile
characters in experimentally induced moultings of the adult integument.

It was shown by Wigglesworth (1939, 1940b), that when a *Rhodnius* adult was caused to moult again in the presence of an effective concentration of the juvenile hormone, the cuticle showed several features of a larval nature in the pattern and structure, and even in some of the morphological characters. Similar results were obtained by Piepho (1939), Piepho and Meyer (1951) and Wiedbrauck (Meyer) (1953), by implanting pieces of pupal integument into young larvae of *Galleria mellonella*. After the next

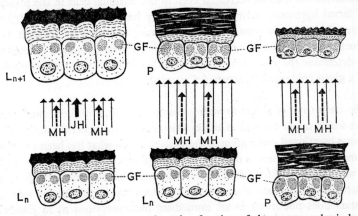

FIG. 41. Diagram of the supposed mode of action of the metamorphosis hormones on the epidermis cells in Holometabola. P – pupal epidermis cells. Other explanations cf. fig. 40. (From Novák, 1956.)

moult, these laid down a cuticle without scales, resembling that of the larvae. Imaginal integument implanted into young larvae gave rise to an atypical cuticle with some larval characters, which was followed by a pupal and finally by an imaginal cuticle, in agreement with the type of moulting in the host. These changes, however, do not affect elaborately differentiated structures, such as the genitalia (cf. Wigglesworth, 1954). Bodenstein (1953a–d), on the other hand, was not able to obtain any juvenilizing effect in similar experiments with *Periplaneta americana*. The fragments of imaginal cuticle transplanted into young larvae did not show any larval characteristics even when caused to moult as many as four times in the presence of the juvenile hormone. The observed juvenilizing of the adult integument was one of the most important arguments of Wigglesworth in favour of his polymorphism theory (cf. p. 149). The observed facts may, however, be just as probably explained as follows:

As mentioned above, the character of the epidermal cells and the type of cuticle secreted depends not only on which of the metamorphosis hormones is present but also on the length of the intermoult period during which the cuticle is formed, and probably also on the character of the nutrition obtained from the haemolymph (which differs, for example, in the last larval and pupal instars). The specific characteristics of the larval integument are thus only partly due to the stage of differentiation of the given cell, which is genetically conditioned. They are also controlled by a physiological reaction of the corresponding cell to the juvenile hormone, which is independent of its stage of differentiation. These characteristics may be recreated even in the imaginal cells in the presence of larval hormonal environment and may be the cause of their 'partial reversal of metamorphosis' without having anything to do with their genetically governed differentiation process. Further research is necessary to determine the exact proportion of either influence in the morphology of a given epidermal structure (cf. p. 159).

The competence of tissues to undergo metamorphosis. Another experimental fact which might be used as an objection against the general validity of the above-mentioned conception of metamorphosis is what has been called the competence of tissues to undergo metamorphosis (cf. Wigglesworth, 1954). It was found by Pflugfelder (1939) in *Carausius morosus* and by B. Scharrer (1946) in *Leucophaea maderae*, that allatectomy in the earlier nymphal instars does not result in an immediate metamorphosis as in *Rhodnius*, various Lepidoptera or other holometabolous insects. Instead, two further moults are necessary after allatectomy for the adult characters to develop. The first moult leads to what has been called a 'preadultoid' with incomplete imaginal differentiation, and only the second results in a practically complete, miniature adult.

The author's attempt, mentioned above, to explain these observations by claiming that the tissues in the young larvae are not yet competent to undergo the metamorphosis and an extra moult is necessary for this ability to be gained. Wigglesworth (1954), on the other hand, concludes, on the basis of a comparison with other insects, that 'it seems more probable that the delay in metamorphosis in *Carausius* and *Leucophaea* results from the blood already containing some juvenile hormone when the corpora allata are removed'. There is, however, another apparently more probable explanation, which agrees in all respects with the gradient-factor theory. This is based on the fact that both the species mentioned belong to the phylogenetically lowest groups of Hemimetabola (Phasmida and Blattoptera).

It is well known that Apterygota continue to moult in the adult stage, so that their prothoracic glands are not larval in character. In contrast to those of metabolous insects they act independently of the presence of the juvenile hormone. It is therefore quite natural that the dependence on this

factor is less complete in the lower Hemimetabola. An extra moult sub-
dividing the precocious metamorphosis into two instars is the only thing
that really happens in the cases mentioned. This is also understandable
in the terms of the Berles-Jeschikov theory: The Apterygota, such as
Thysanura, reach the adult stage in the oligopod stage of morphogenesis.
The supposed inactivation of the gradient-factor of the prothoracic glands
which results in their disintegration occurs somewhere between the

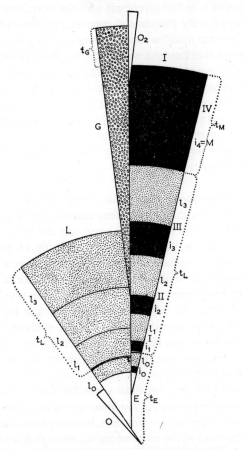

FIG. 42. Diagram of interrelationships in the growth of the various parts of the
body during the ontogenesis of insects. O – growth of the egg; O_2 – the egg of the
next generation; L – growth of larval parts of the body; l_0–l_3 – periods of proportionate (larval) growth; I – imaginal parts of the body; i_1–i_2 – periods of allometric
surplus increase of the imaginal parts; M ($= i_4$) – growth during the metamorphosis, growth of the gonads; t_E, t_L, t_M, t_G – period of embryogenesis, of larval
development, metamorphosis, gonad development; 1st–4th – 1st to 4th larval instar.

oligopod and the advanced postoligopod stage (judging from its occurrence during the last larval instar in Hemimetabola and in the pupa of Holometabola). This stage is, obviously, not reached in allatectomized younger nymphs of Phasmida and Blattodea before the next moult is induced by the moulting hormone, which at the same time suspends the rest of the imaginal differentiation. Hence the extra moult and the preadultoid instar results in these groups.

This explanation is in full agreement with the experimental findings of Bodenstein (1953a–e) for *Periplaneta americana*. He found that gonopods from 8th or 9th instar nymphs undergo metamorphosis with the new host when transplanted into the 10th instar, whereas those from the 4th instar nymphs remain nymphal. A similar explanation may apply to the differentiation of transplanted imaginal discs in *Drosophila* and other insects (cf. Bodenstein, 1939b, 1941a, 1943b, 1946) and transplanted larval ovaries (Kopeć, 1911, Fukuda, 1939, Vogt, 1940). Further examination along these lines of the rudiments of various organs in different species will no doubt throw more light on the problem of the gradient-factor and the method of its inactivation.

The course of gradient-factor inactivation during ontogenesis. As mentioned above (p. 156) two main types of tissue may be distinguished by their behaviour in the metamorphosis: the larval and the imaginal structures. The larvo-imaginal structures have been defined by Geigy and Hadorn (cf. p. 129) as an intermediate category. Even though most of the insect tissues can undoubtedly be placed in one or other of these categories, there are a number of other important structures which cannot be placed in any of the three groups. The following eight groups can be distinguished according to the time of the inactivation of their gradient-factor in ontogeny. It is very probable that further research will reveal still more groups.

(*i*) *Embryonic structures*, the GF of which is inactivated before the onset of juvenile hormone action so that they do not survive into the postembryonic period (e.g. the abdominal appendages of the polypod stage).

(*ii*) *Larval structures* already differentiated and losing their GF in the embryonic period. They survive, however, because of the juvenile hormone activity, until the onset of the metamorphosis, when they are usually partly or completely decomposed. They constitute the most characteristic parts of the larval body (e.g. the pseudopods of the caterpillars).

(*iii*) *Late larval structures*, the differentiation of which continues in the larval period (in the gradient-growth periods at the beginning of each larval instar). They lose their GF and survive until the onset of the metamorphosis, where they are partly or completely disintegrated together

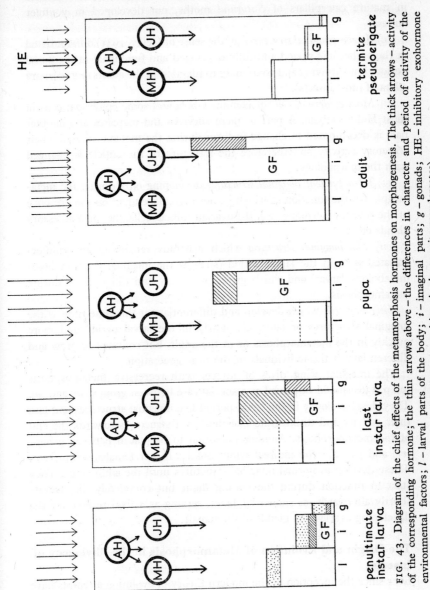

FIG. 43. Diagram of the chief effects of the metamorphosis hormones on morphogenesis. The thick arrows – activity of the corresponding hormone; the thin arrows above – the differences in character and period of activity of the environmental factors; *l* – larval parts of the body; *i* – imaginal parts; *g* – gonads; HE – inhibitory exohormone (causing stationary moultings in the termite pseudergates).

with the other larval structures (e.g. the various integumental structures in mature caterpillars of *Saturniid* moths, not developed in younger larvae).

(*iv*) *Larvo-imaginal structures* (in the sense of Geigy, 1941) differentiated in the embryonic period and fully developed and functional in the larval period, but surviving and continuing to function in the adults (e.g. corpora allata of most insects).

(*v*) Most *epidermal cells* of Hemimetabola and some epidermal cells in most Holometabola. A part of them survives and increases and another part is decomposed to change in form during the metamorphosis. Their secretory activity and therefore the structure of the cuticle is changed with the morphology.

(*vi*) *JH-dependent imaginal structures* developing only during the metamorphosis, the function of which is, however, dependent on the presence of the juvenile hormone (e.g. the ovarian follicle cells, the male accessory glands etc.).

(*vii*) *The imaginal structures* which generally remain in an undifferentiated state in the larval period (such as the imaginal discs in holometabolous larvae) and which grow intensively and differentiate during metamorphosis.

(*viii*) *Sex cells* which develop and differentiate at the same time as the imaginal structures or later, i.e. slowly in the larval period and more quickly in the metamorphosis or in the adult, but continue to grow and differentiate in the individuals of the next generation.

The imaginal wing discs of insects with regressive metamorphosis (cf. p. 136) should be placed as a special case between groups (*iv*) and (*v*). They develop slowly in the larval period like imaginal structures and lose their activity and disintegrate like the larval structures towards the end of the metamorphosis. Another exception to be placed between groups (*vi*) and (*vii*) are the indirect wing muscles in ant females (cf. p. 129). These develop as normal imaginal structures until the adult stage. They start to function during the mating flight but completely disintegrate shortly afterwards, as shown by Janet, serving as a food reserve for the developing ovaries and glands of the female.

The Origin and Evolution of Metamorphosis in the Phylogeny of Insects

Ever since the inception of the modern theory of evolution attempts have been made to explain the origin of the phenomenon of insect metamorphosis and how it gradually developed into its present different types during the phylogeny of insects. The first attempts, which were largely based on speculation, were followed by others based on morphological and rather incomplete paleontological data. The recent findings on the metamorphosis hormones have opened a new and very important source of information on this subject which has hitherto been very little used for this purpose.

The following is an attempt to formulate a uniform conception of the phylogeny of insect metamorphosis which is based mainly on the author's gradient-factor theory but takes into account all the available facts. Even though this may perhaps be no more than a more or less perfect logical scheme until a complete series of fossil remains is available, it may be useful as a comprehensive synthesis of the present information on the problem. The morphological basis of the present theory does not differ very much from the Berlese-Jeschikov concept.

The conception of the phylogeny of metabolous insects discussed depends on three main phylogenetical mechanisms: (1) the epigenesis though which the postoligopod and winged stages of nymphs and adult Exopterygota (Hemimetabola) develop from the oligopod stage of Apterygota (Thysanura). (2) The temporary replacement of the embryonic gradient growth by the larval isometric growth period. (3) The desembryonization together with the internal development of the wings and the origin of the pupal instar. The phylogenetically oldest of these three which is obviously closely connected with the appearance of the winged adult stage appears to be the larval isometric growth caused by the action of the JH.

The incomplete metamorphosis of Hemimetabola. The isometric growth of the larval period is therefore the chief characteristic and really new feature of metabolous insects. The gradient growth of the metamorphosis stage is simply a continuation of the embryonic gradient growth, which in principle is common not only to Apterygota but to all other arthropods. As shown experimentally, the isometric growth of the larval stage is wholly due to the action of the JH. The artificial removal of this may cause the metamorphosis to start in the 1st larval instar and conversely its artificial induction (corpora allata implantation) may prevent metamorphosis in the last larval instar (cf. p. 89).

The phylogenetical origin of the JH. The occurrence of the JH is necessarily connected with the presence of the secretorily active corpora allata. All that has been so far discovered regarding the phylogenesis of this organ and its occurrence in Apterygota appears to be in full agreement with this conclusion. Corpora allata occur in only the phylogenetically highest

Apterygota such as Japygidae (Cazal, 1948), Lepismatidae (Yashika, 1961), and Machilidae (Bitsch, 1962), and even if they produce active JH here they do not cause any isometric growth.[1] Although it has not yet been shown experimentally this can only be explained by the fact that production of this hormone only commences in the adult insects. It may therefore be concluded that its primary function is that of activating development of the gonads (the function of the ovarian follicle cells in the female and of the accessory glands in the male). This appears to be its function in the Thysanurans mentioned (cf. p. 169).

Under these conditions where JH is necessary for adult insects a selection pressure developed which promoted and increased the secretion of this hormone by the corpora allata. With the increase in its production thus caused, its active concentration was necessarily reached progressively earlier in ontogenesis. Whilst it had no morphological effects in the adults it stopped morphogenesis when it reached the larval stages. A period of larval isometric growth followed by a metamorphosis therefore necessarily appeared in the early Pterygota. No example of this initial stage of morphogenetical activity of the JH is known among recent insects. There is, however, a remnant of this type of development where the JH action does not commence until the second or third larval instar so far as may be concluded from the occurrence of morphogenetical changes up to this period. It is observed in the Order Ephemeroptera (may-flies). Here the insect hatches as the so-called larvula, which subsequently changes into a normal ephemeropterid nymph. This at first continues to moult without morphological changes except those at the beginning of each instar (before the effective level of the JH is reached, cf. p. 107).

The majority of the present-day insects are at a stage where the development in this direction has advanced to reach the end of embryogenesis. Here, therefore, the larvae hatch in their definitive form which is maintained almost unchanged throughout the whole larval stage until the beginning of metamorphosis. This phylogenetical process of shifting the isometric growth period towards the earlier stages of embryogenesis continues in Holometabola where the JH reaches its active concentration still earlier so that the larvae hatch in an early oligopod or polypod stage of morphogenesis, in some cases even in a protopod stage (cf. p. 172). At the same time the process of desembryonization proceeds which may cause the hatching of larva before the active concentration of the JH is reached.

---

[1] There is no true isometric growth during the postembryonic development in Apterygota in constrast to the larval period of winged insects, even though the amount of morphogenesis and allometric increase is very limited in each instar and tends to decrease towards the adult stage.

Then two further types of larvae appear as in the case of hyper-metamorphosis and the protopod larvae of some parasitic hymenoptera.

The following hypothesis has been drawn up regarding the phylogenetical origin of the JH in the corpora allata (Novák, 1951, 1955, 1956). It is based on the possibility of a complete replacement of the hypothetical GF by JH, assuming that the JH is nothing more than the original GF of the corpora allata which has become soluble in the haemolymph and produced in an increased quantity. The paired invaginations of the lateral parts of the head between the mandibular and the maxillary sclerites, are the remnants of the ectodermal parts of the original tubules of annelid nephridia, from which the corpora allata have perhaps evolved. These were a very suitable site for this change which could depend on a very small alteration in a part of the supposed GF molecule which made it soluble in haemolymph. This is, of course, a secondary hypothesis depending on the supposed relationship between the JH and GF. As mentioned above the ability of the JH to make the larval parts capable of further development could also depend on the reactivating in some way of the GF in these parts of the body.

Whatever the true character of the JH and its relationship to the GF, no doubts appear to remain regarding the environmental conditions which led to its origin. According to paleontological data, the first appearance of metabolous insects from the paleozoic Ametabola coincides with the beginning of the Carboniferous period. The warm Carboniferous marshes and primeval forests created very suitable environmental conditions for accelerating the phylogenetical development. One of the changes brought about was undoubtedly the production of JH in the invaginations mentioned. Its high selective value led subsequently to the development of the corpora allata. In this way, the dependence of the ovarian follicle cells on the JH appeared first (cf. p. 90), and the interdependence between the JH and morphogenesis developed only later. The promotion of proteosynthesis by the JH was, doubtless, also the leading internal factor regulating the evolution of wings from the paranotal outgrowths of the mesothorax and metathorax and it also had a general positive effect on the rate of evolution. These two factors controlled the role of the JH in the evolution of the Pterygota as the group by far the most abundant as regards the number of species not only in the class Insecta but amongst all animals. The occurrence of the JH in the newly formed corpora allata has the same phylogenetical importance as that of the hypophysis and thyroid hormones in the phylogeny of vertebrates, or as homoiothermy in the phylogeny of birds and mammals, or vivipary and milk glands in that of mammals. Its origin may be classified as a typical aromorphosis in the sense of Sewertzoff (1931) (cf. Novák, 1955, 1956).

The phylogenesis of the MH. The origin of the moulting hormone is at present less clear. The experiments with ecdyson (Karlson, 1957; cf. p. 77) as well as a series of experiments with different species of Crustacea show that such a hormonal control of the moulting process is not limited to insects. As regards the Decapoda, recent findings suggest the source of the MH in the so-called rostral glands or Y-organ (Gabe, 1955; Carlisle and Knowles, 1959). Even though it has not been shown in other classes of arthropods there remains little doubt that this is a common principle in the whole Phylum. It therefore seems very probable that MH already occurred in the highest groups of their annelid ancestors and it may be assumed that it will also be found in some of the recent Annelida. From this point of view the suggested homology between the prothoracic glands and the ectodermal portion of the nephridian tubuli of annelids, so suggested by B. Scharrer (1948), is very interesting. On the basis of the previously mentioned dependence of the MH production on the presence of the AH, as well as the phylogenetical relationship, it may be concluded that the MH did not appear in the phylogeny until after the AH system was fully developed. The absence of moulting in adult metabolous insects due to the degeneration of the prothoracic glands, the source of the moulting hormone, on account of their larval characteristics (lack of the GF), appears to have evolved after the appearance of the winged stage in the phylogeny of insects. The selective value of this lack of moulting in adult insects depends on the difficulty, if not the impossibility, of successful moulting of such membranous structures as the wings. The chief selective value of the MH seems to be in synchronizing the process of moulting over the whole surface of the body. This is very important with the hard, adherent cuticle. The other effects of the MH, both direct and indirect (cf. p. 69), appear to be of a secondary nature from the phylogenetical point of view.

The phylogenesis of the AH. The occurrence of groups of neurosecretory cells similar to those found in the pars intercerebralis of insects and the frontal organs of crustaceans, in various groups of Annelida and even in some Turbellaria, appears to show the very ancient character of the AH. This conclusion is further corroborated by the fact that the AH is the first of the metamorphosis hormones to appear in the embryogenesis, as well as by the dependence of the production of the other two hormones on its presence. Of its various effects, the activating of the prothoracic glands

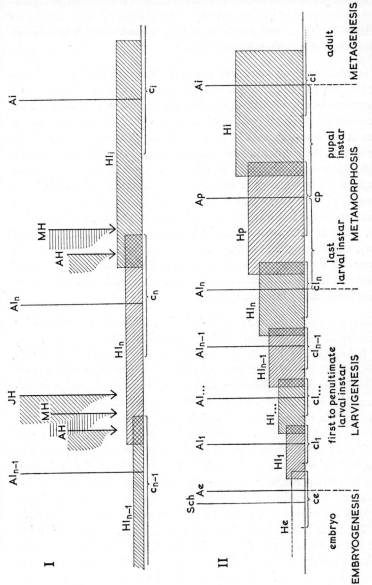

FIG. 44. The interrelationships of the subsequent moulting processes in the penultimate and last larval instars of Hemimetabola (I) and in the ontogenesis of Holometabola (II). A – moment of ecdysis; Sch – hatching of larva; H – moulting process; c – cuticle; e – embryo; l_1–l_n – first to last instar larva; p – pupa; i – adult.

or the corresponding sources of moulting hormone in other Articulata[1] seems therefore to be secondary in character. Little is known so far regarding the occurrence of the dependence of the midgut protease activity on this hormone (cf. p. 209) which might be a primary effect. The selective value of both these effects is very high.

The interrelationships in the morphogenesis of Articulata. Here the relationship between the ontogenetical development of metabolous insects and other groups of arthropods and annelids must first of all be compared. To understand the morphological relationships between the morphogenetical stages in the embryogenesis of insects and those in the ontogeny of the other groups, the primary features must be distinguished from those which are phylogenetically secondary in character. Amongst the latter are all changes of the type known as adaptiomorphoses (in the sense of Schmalgauzen, 1946 = idioadaptations in the sense of Sewertzoff, 1931) which are adaptations to the living conditions and habits of the given ontogenetical stage. They do not, however, change its general level of organization and vitality. Considering the primary features alone, it immediately becomes evident that they have much in common and the recapitulation law of Darwin and Haeckel[2] becomes fully evident. These interrelationships are evident from table 3 on page 173.

The morphogenesis and hormones in Articulata. In the diagram the period of activity of the individual single metamorphosis hormones is given. The following five morphogenetical stages may be distinguished in the morphogenesis of metabolous insects to say nothing of the early embryonic one (i.e. the morphogenesis from the commencement of the segmentation of the fertilized egg until the protopod stage), and have their counterparts in the morphogenesis of the other groups.

The *protopod* stage occurs in insects (besides the protopod larvae of some of the parasitic Hymenoptera) as well as in most other arthropods in the embryonic period. It corresponds, in its general level of organization, to the free living nauplius of some crustaceans and to the early metatrochophores of Archiannelida. Its chief characteristic is the occurrence of embryonic appendages and segmentation in the anterior part of the body only. The same general level of morphogenesis occurs in principle in the larvae and adults of Acarina. Here, of course, it must be assumed to have the character of a secondary phylogenetical simplification of a neotenic type so that the ancestors of this group reached the more advanced polypod stage.

---

[1] Term used in the sense of Cuvier to include both Annelids and Arthropods.
[2] Usually, though less correctly, referred to as 'the biogenetic law of Haeckel'.

TABLE 3

SYSTEMATIC GROUP	STAGE OF MORPHOGENESIS					
	Early embryonic	*Protopod*	*Polypod*	*Oligopod*	*Post-oligopod*	*Winged*
Annelida (Polychaeta)	embryos trochophores	larvae	adults	—	—	—
Crustacea	embryos	nauplii	zooeae adults	adults	—	—
Arachnoidea	embryos	embryos	embryos	adults	—	—
Myriapoda	embryos	embryos	adults	—	—	—
Apterygota	embryos	embryos	embryos	adults	—	—
Hemimetabola	embryos	embryos	embryos	embryos	nymphs	adults
Holometabola	embryos	embryos larvae	embryos larvae	larvae	pupae	adults

············ activation hormone
‒ ‒ ‒ ‒ ‒ ‒ moulting hormone
─────── juvenile hormone
thin line – the presence of hormone may be assumed
thick line – the presence of hormone has been proved

The polypod stage is the level of organization of the adult annelids, characterized by a more or less uniformly segmented body and undifferentiated appendages in all segments. In this morphogenetical stage Trilobita also reach their adult form as do Onychophora and Myriapoda. In insects it is reached either in the embryonic (Hemimetabola) or the larval (some Holometabola) period. As regards the majority of crustaceans with differentiated appendages in all segments of the body, these may be viewed either as an advanced polypod or early oligopod stage.

The oligopod stage is characterized by a secondary, partial or complete, suppression of the abdominal appendages which eventually reappear partially or completely in the adult insect as the copulatory appendages. In addition to being reached in Crustacea, the oligopod stage appears in some adult Arachnoidea and in Apterygote insects, this being perhaps for the first time in arthropod phylogeny. In metabolous insects it occurs in either the embryonic or larval period. The embryonic appendages may here be completely suppressed in some specialized cases, as in the apodous larvae of higher Diptera and Hymenoptera. In such cases the thoracic appendages also disappear temporarily. In other cases some of the abdominal appendages may occur in a reduced stage in the form of special styli as in many Thysanura or differentiated into structures with special functions as in Collembola. These are characteristic of the polypod stage but from the general shape of the body as well as the much more developed thoracic appendages these forms clearly belong to the oligopod stage. The campodeiform larvae of some Holometabola are also oligopod.

The postoligopod stage, as described by Jeschikov (1936), is the stage in which the nymphs of most of the Hemimetabola (except e.g. the larvula of Ephemeroptera) hatch. It may be characterized by the fully differentiated legs and mouth parts of the adult type. The mature nymph with wing pads and the pupa of the Holometabola must also be classed as a late postoligopod stage. It is subdivided by moults into several instars with gradually increasing differentiation. It occurs in the postembryonic development of metabolous insects and perhaps in adult spiders.

The winged stage is the morphogenetical structure of adult metabolous insects, developed through epigenesis (in the sense of Severtzov, 1931), from the oligopod Apterygota. Pterygota are the only group of arthropods where it occurs.

A comparison of morphogenesis in insects with that of other arthropods, as shown in the diagram on p. 173, allows the following conclusions regarding the phylogenetical origin of metamorphosis: The various consecutive morphogenetical stages are, in principle, identical in all metabolous insects. A special characteristic of metabolous insects is that they produce JH during larval development. As a result of this the completion of embryogenesis is temporarily suspended so that it cannot occur until the last larval stage when there is a temporary absence of an effective quantity of this hormone. JH, and thus metamorphosis, appear in the phylogeny of insects concurrently with winged forms. It may therefore be assumed that it was this delay in the completion of morphogenesis, due to the JH, which created the conditions for the development of wings. It would be difficult to imagine their development in the embryonic period with the subsequent moults. This appears to be the chief selective value of the JH in the phylogeny of insects.

The Origin of the Pupal Instar in the Phylogeny of Holometabola

The explanation of the mode of action of the metamorphosis hormones also throws some new light on the phylogenetical origin of the pupal instar as well as other features of the subclass Holometabola. As opposed to the views expressed by Hinton, Snodgrass and other authors who, in principle, accept Poyarkoff's theory (cf. p. 142), the author prefers an explanation based on the Berlese-Jeschikof theory of the necessity of moulting in the course of the metamorphosis as a condition for the normal development of the internal imaginal discs of wings in the larvae of Holometabola (End-opterygota) (Novák, 1956b, d). All the other characteristics of the pupal stage, such as the position of head and appendages, immobility and cocoon spinning etc., are phylogenetically of a secondary nature.

The connection between the internal position of the imaginal discs and the origin of the pupal instar. The GF theory discussed above allows a simple and probable hypothesis for the origin of the internal position of the imaginal discs. It has been shown that the time the minimum effective concentration of the JH was reached became gradually earlier in the morphogenesis during the phylogeny of Holometabola (cf. p. 168). In consequence the larva hatched in increasingly earlier morphogenetical stages. When the first rudiments of the imaginal discs are developed before the effective minimum concentration of the JH has been reached, as is usual in the nymphs of Hemimetabola, the precursors of the imaginal tissues (e.g. wing pads) may develop freely on the surface of the body. When, however, the morphogenetical effect of the JH starts before the differentiation of the imaginal discs, this cannot commence until the next gradient growth period at the beginning of the first larval instar. At this time, however, unlike the embryonic period, the chitinous cuticle is well developed, and this favours the internal development of the discs. Their undifferentiated state and so-called embryonic character until the beginning of metamorphosis is thus a natural consequence of their internal position isolated from the majority of outside stimuli, their lack of any physiological function, and the optimum conditions for obtaining food from the haemolymph by diffusion.

Two metamorphosis moults are necessary for the development of functional wings in the adult; in the first, the undifferentiated internal discs evaginate on the surface of the body. This evagination is only possible in a rather undifferentiated stage before the wing has reached its definitive length and membrane-like structure. It can, however, only occur in a rather advanced stage of the moulting process when a sufficiently large exuvial space, filled with exuvial fluid, has been formed. The complete formation

G

of the functional adult wings cannot therefore be realized in one and the same instar. This means that the internal position of the imaginal wing discs was necessarily a major obstacle to a successful development before the other metamorphosis moult, the pupal moult, was evolved. A prerequisite for the development of a pupal moulting is that the amount of morphogenesis during metamorphosis was prolonged by the same factor that caused the internal positioning of the imaginal discs, i.e. the extension of the period of JH activity further into embryogenesis. Only then can such a prolonged development, which enables amongst other things a more complete attachment of the muscles, as supposed by Poyarkoff and Hinton, have any selective value. Another selective value of this more marked metamorphosis with a difference between larva and adult lies in their ability to utilize, in each ontogenesis, two quite different living media consecutively, such as water and air, earth and air, plant tissues and air, etc.

The secondary features of the pupal instar. The principal internal cause of the origin of Holometabola thus appears to depend on a slight quantitative change in the secretory activity of the corpora allata, i.e. its extension into the earlier stages of embryogenesis. The other features of the pupal instar, such as the lack of mobility, the cocoon spinning, the specific position of head and appendages, etc., are phylogenetically secondary. On the other hand, several of these characteristics of the pupal stage may be found, in a rudimentary state, in the postembryonic development of some Hemimetabola. For instance, a short period of immobility precedes each ecdysis and may be prolonged for as long as eight days in some cases, e.g. in the nymphs of *Rhinotermes taurus* (cf. Imms, 1946). Similarly, the characteristic position of the pupa with the head flexed downwards on to the thorax and the appendages pressed close to the central surface of the body appears, at least momentarily, at each ecdysis even in Hemimetabola. The spinning of a cocoon less complete in form is also not of an exclusively pupal character, but occurs in a number of species at the time of each larval ecdysis. Sometimes the larvae spin silk tubes before each ecdysis even in species where pupal cocoons are regularly produced, as in the moths *Ephestia* and *Galleria*. On the other hand, a second metamorphosis instar, as in Ephemeroptera, occurs in the form of the so-called subimago, without any other pupal characteristics. In some cases, as in the pupae of Thysanoptera and males of Coccidae and Aleurodidae, several of these characteristics develop in the last larval instar of Hemimetabola. In general, however, they have developed gradually, even if in a complicated interdependence, for example, the immobility of pupa is a prerequisite for cocoon. In this way, without doubt the improved attachment of the muscles brought about by the second metamorphosis moult has also contributed to the selective value of the pupal stage (cf. p. 142).

On the basis of what has been mentioned the often discussed question of whether the Holometabola developed from Ametabola through the intermediate stage of Hemimetabola or whether they developed independently can be examined. Irrespective of what could be said in favour of the second conception, it seems obvious that the phylogenesis of the recent Holometabola must necessarily have included a stage which would have to be classified as belonging to the recent Hemimetabola (unlike the views of Zakhvatkin (1933), Sharov (1953), and others). This does not however necessarily mean that the development of Holometabola went through some of the recent orders of Hemimetabola. What has been said above regarding the internal factors of the metamorphosis also in no way contradicts the primary importance of environmental factors in the phylogenetical changes leading to the origin of metamorphosis, such as those assumed by Ghilyarov (1949 etc.) in his paper on the importance of the soil in the origin and development of metabolous insects. The findings and conclusions mentioned simply show the existence of factors and mechanisms through the action of which morphological development is controlled by environmental influences.

F. GENERAL CONCLUSIONS ON MORPHOGENESIS

From the findings on the metamorphosis hormones and their mode of action there may be drawn a series of conclusions on morphogenesis and its principles in animals in general. Such generalizations have been attempted by several students of this problem and conclusions of general importance for the question of growth and differentiation in animals in general obtained.

The organism as a chemical continuum and as an integrated discontinuous community. When examining the different systems of chemical co-ordinations inside the organism, Wigglesworth (1948) reached the conclusion that the animal body is an integrated system, a chemical continuum, the essential continuity of which is independent of the cells. He compares the animal body as a whole with a giant molecule: the differentiated parts of the organism arise as active centres within this molecule, the polarity and the symmetry of the body deriving from the polarity and symmetry of the molecule. The segments of this molecule are formed by cells which are superimposed upon the chemical system which is the essential organism.

The animal hormones act on this system influencing the reaction of the cells.

At the same time the organism may be compared with a community of individuals at the cell level or lower, the integration of which is realized by a complicated system of hormones and nerves (Wigglesworth, 1959). As suggested by Wigglesworth, there is no necessary contradiction between these two conceptions: the original chemical system differentiates into a community of cells which becomes more and more integrated through the development of complicated systems of correlation during phylogeny. The living organism may be thus interpreted as 'a hierarchy of integrative mechanisms rising from those of simple chemistry to those of the most complex physiology, with no break in the chain'.

The gradient hypothesis of Child and Wigglesworth. On the basis of his experiments on the determination of small epidermal differentiations such as the plaques, dermal glands and sensilla, in the bug *Rhodnius prolixus*, Wigglesworth formulated a conception of one of the above-mentioned correlating systems which he identifies in principle with the 'gradient hypothesis' of C. M. Child (1941). This can be briefly summarized as follows: When an area in an undifferentiated part of the body absorbs a specific substance, the 'inductor' or 'modifier', from its surroundings, it unites with it and becomes determined to form a particular structure (e.g. a bristle). By this it drains the inductor substance from the surrounding region and therefore inhibits the determination of the same structure in its nearest vicinity. A gradient of determination thus results in the given part of the body. This process may be repeated again and again inside the gradient which thus subsequently differentiates into a given structure or organ. Wigglesworth's gradient hypothesis, which must be distinguished from the gradient-factor theory discussed above, shows and satisfactorily explains the principle of determination and mutual co-ordination of the growth gradients, both of microstructures formed by several cells, such as the epidermal differentiations mentioned above, and of complex organs such as appendages or head, and may have a quite general application in the morphogenesis in animals generally. It is, however, only concerned with one aspect of morphogenesis, the determination of growth gradients. A possible explanation of the mechanism of their development is provided by the gradient-factor theory[1] (cf. p. 156).

[1] The term theory seems to be justified here as the concept includes a series of further laws and hypotheses, apart from the hypothesis of the GF, the validity of some of them being independent of whether or not the primary supposition will be completely confirmed.

The Gradient-Factor Theory of Morphogenesis

As shown above, insect metamorphosis is no more than the completion of the embryonic morphogenesis which has been delayed by the action of JH until the end of the postembryonic development (cf. p. 174). The metamorphosis, therefore, wholly corresponds in principle with all other periods of morphogenesis. Its chief principle, the anisometric growth, is thus also necessarily the principle of all other morphogenetical processes. It may, therefore, be supposed that the chief mechanism of all cases of morphogenesis depends on a gradual inactivation of a generally occurring growth factor with the characteristics and mode of action of the GF. It will be further shown below that a series of useful assumptions may be drawn from this generalization, which might be called the gradient-factor theory of morphogenesis. This forms a useful working hypothesis whether or not the existence of the gradient-factor is confirmed chemically. Only then can it be decided whether the effect of the gradient-factor is due to only one substance, a chemical individuum, or whether it is, perhaps more probably, a common feature of a group of substances with a common configuration of atoms.

The justification for the assumption of a general principle of morphogenesis in animals. The following main reasons seem to justify the above-mentioned generalization of the GF-theory (cf. Novák, 1955):

(*i*) As shown by the experiments with allatectomy in the early larval instars (cf. p. 89), inactivation of the GF in larval parts of the body occurs in the late embryonic period. There is thus no reason for assuming a different mechanism of morphogenesis in the embryonic period from that in the metamorphosis. And as there is no major difference in the embryogenesis in insects and all other animals from this point of view, the same mechanism may be assumed to be present here also.

(*ii*) Tumour growth or blastomogenesis may be interpreted as a failure of the mechanism of morphogenesis. Recent findings show that tumour growth occurs in all groups of animals. When, therefore, the same result occurs in all cases from the failure of a mechanism of morphogenesis, the existence of a more or less identical mechanism in all the groups may be assumed.

(*iii*) That such biologically active catalysts are of general occurrence in animals is in no way remarkable. In fact, biochemical results appear to show that the most important biologically active substances are of very common occurrence. For example, the nucleic acids seem to be quite indispensable for all animals, plants and micro-organisms. Some of the enzymes of tissue respiration are very common in animals, as are the chlorophylls or auxins in plants. Therefore the assumption of the gradient-factor as a substance (or group of substances) common to all animals also cannot be viewed as a priori improbable.

Anisometric growth as a principle of morphogenesis. The differential (anisometric) growth of living matter may be viewed as a quite general principle through which morphological structures arise in organisms. Very few other principles of limited importance are known, such as the morphogenetical movements in the early embryonic period of some groups. As shown above, anisometric growth occurs in two forms, as an allometric growth in which the different parts of the body grow at a different rate and as a gradient growth in which various parts of the body gradually lose their growth potential. The second of these two types is far more important for morphogenesis. Whilst allometric growth may depend either on a differential growth potential of different parts of the body or on a differential inhibitory effect of its various specifically localized components, gradient growth seems to be caused by a gradual loss of the growth potential of some parts of the body and retention of this by others. With the loss of growth potential there is usually associated a decrease of vitality which may result in a partial or complete removal of the parts of the body concerned by histolysis or phagocytosis. By the interaction of these, the changes in form become more rapid and conspicuous. A further consequence of the elimination of the rather extensive parts of the body which lose the capacity for further growth is the increase in the share of the growing, activated parts in the total foodstuff reserves which are at the disposal of the body in the given period (cf. the law of the correlation in consumption, p. 116). These reserves increase as further tissues are histolysed. Anisometric growth of each type usually includes both differentiation in form and increase in size (weight), even if differentiation may predominate in some periods and growth in others. In the embryonic period the growth of the embryo occurs at the expense of the yolk (included inside the body in the more advanced period of the insect embryo), and differentiation without growth also occurs in the postembryonic period in some cases, e.g. during starvation. The isometric growth of the larval period in insects under the influence of the JH is a special case of growth without differentiation. This is rather rare in other animals.

The general gradient-factor, gf. The reasons mentioned above allow the conclusion that a common principle of the common phenomenon exists also in the anisometric (gradient) growth of other animals. This means that the inactivation of a specific common factor indispensable for growth is the reason for gradient growth in all cases where it occurs, i.e. in practically all animals. The factor appears to be a substance or, perhaps more probably, a group of related chemical substances with a common effective atomic configuration which is necessarily one of the most important components of tissue metabolism and may be one of those known for a long time by its biochemical characteristics. The nucleoproteins or some of the indispensable links of their autoreproduction deserve, first of all, to be taken into consideration. Their gradient-factor character depends on nothing but the tendency of the corresponding substance to be inactivated by various internal and environmental factors with morphogenetical activity which are released in different parts of the animal body during ontogenesis. All the various effects which regulate the specific growth pattern of the given species could thus depend on only one influence, i.e. in the local inactivation of this general gradient-factor, the gf of morphogenesis, a special case of which is the GF of insect metamorphosis. Morphogenesis could thus be explained as a series of concentric processes of gf inactivation ranging from the molecular level to that of the type of insect metamorphosis which includes the whole body. The origin of a new individual from the sex cells of adults with the subsequent decline of the other (adult) organism (cf. fig. 45) can be viewed as a process which is, in the main, of the same type.

The relationship between the gf and the organizers, inductors and other morphogenetically active factors. A series of factors with marked morphogenetical effects has been described in experimental embryology and in the physiology of postembryonic development. Many of these are chemical in character, amongst them the organizers and inductors (cf. J. Needham, 1946), the templates and antitemplates (Weiss and Kawanau, 1957), the morphogenetically active hormones and many other substances with similar activity. The gf theory shows a simple and widely applicable mechanism for their morphogenetical activity. This may now be explained as a regular species-specific and space-specific inactivation of the hypothetical gf in various parts of the body, which determines the gradient growth. The mode of action of different environmental factors such as air (oxygen) on the surface of the body by its reacting with these substances, humidity etc. can be explained in a similar way. All these factors may affect morphogenesis in a species-specific way either directly by inactivating the gf or indirectly by converting some of the chemical components of the body into a morphogenetically active substance which inhibits the gf.

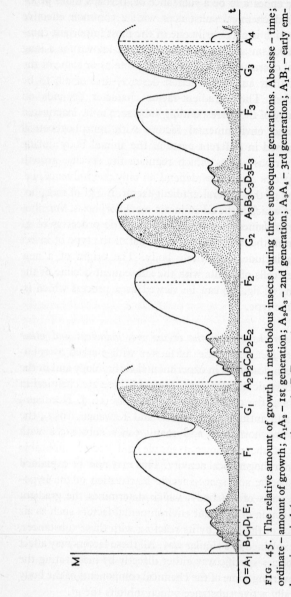

FIG. 45. The relative amount of growth in metabolous insects during three subsequent generations. Abscisse – time; ordinate – amount of growth; A_1A_2 – 1st generation; A_2A_3 – 2nd generation; A_3A_4 – 3rd generation; A_1B_1 – early embryonic period (egg segmentation etc.); B_1E_1 – embryonic morphogenesis (composed of a series of morphogenetical processes: B_1C_1, C_1D_1, D_1E_1); E_1F_1 – larval period; F_1G_1 – period of metamorphosis; G_1A_2 – period of gonad development in adults; A_2B_2 – early embryonic period in second generation, etc. Each of the morphogenetical processes depends on that part of the body losing the ability for further growth and disappearing (white area), whereas the remaining parts continue to grow (dotted area). (From Novák 1955.)

The Mechanism of Tumour Growth

Tumour growth both benign and malignant in character is known in all chief groups of animals including insects, as shown in a series of reviews covering the last twenty years (cf. Finkelstein, 1944; B. Scharrer and Szabo-Lockhead, 1950 etc.). A large number of papers deal with tumours in insects, many of them from an experimental point of view (see among others B. Scharrer, 1945, 1949a, b; Demeretz, 1947; Hadorn and Niggli, 1946; Hartung, 1949a, b; Rapoport, 1939; Russell, 1940a, b; Pflugfelder, 1948b; Thornton, 1947; Wilson, 1949; Woolf, 1950; etc., etc.). Tumorous growth, generally speaking, may be interpreted as a changing of the normal gradient growth into an abnormal unrestricted isometric growth. The fact that this pathological reversal of growth is possible practically everywhere that morphogenesis occurs is important evidence in favour of the existence of a simple uniform mechanism of gradient growth in all animals, as supposed by the gf theory. On the other hand, the gf theory provides a simple hypothetical explanation of the principle of tumorous growth consistent with this theory.

As shown above, the function of the hypothetical gf depends on it being gradually inactivated in various parts of the body, presumably by reacting with organizers or other morphogenetically active factors and thus losing its character as a growth factor. A very tempting explanation of the changing of gradient growth into tumorous growth would be a change in the molecule of gf which would not deprive it of the ability to induce further growth, but which would, nevertheless, make it resistant to inactivation by factors which would otherwise inhibit it. In this way the part of the body containing the changed gf would necessarily give rise to unlimited growth resulting first in subsequent de-differentiation and then in permanent isometric growth, as in malignant tumours. A change of this type in the gf would be the simplest possible mechanism of action of chemical carcinogens or blastomogens.

The reaction could be illustrated by the following equation in which bg is the chemical blastomogen (carcinogen) and bf the changed gf, which causes the tumorous growth, i.e. the so-called blastomofactor (cf. Novák, 1955, 1962):

$$gf + bg = bf \qquad (1)$$

This change may be explained as a monotopic chemical reaction between the molecules of the corresponding substances, i.e. a change which originally occurs in one tissue, or even in one cell. The subsequent spreading of the bf takes place either by its autoreproduction which results in the tumorous growth or by means of blood-transported individual cells or groups of cells containing bf (metastases).

This could be an explanation of the mechanism of chemical blastomogenesis. The mechanism of blastomogenesis induced by irradiation or other physical factors may be slightly more complicated, depending on a two-step chemical reaction:

$$bx + pg = bg \qquad (2)$$

where bx is the corresponding external factor inducing blastomogenesis, through the action of which a specific component (chemical) of the body, the problastomogen (pg), is changed into the internal blastomogen (bg) which then reacts in the way mentioned with the gf to give the blastomofactor.

Even though the real conditions of blastomogenesis in the body may be much more complicated, both quantitatively and qualitatively, the sense of this so-called gf theory of blastomogenesis depends in that it shows the simplest possible model mechanism which could completely explain the known facts. It has often been realized that Nature prefers simplicity wherever possible.

CHAPTER FOUR

Hormones and Diapause

Definition of diapause. Diapause is one of the features of insect development which has attracted the greatest interest among research workers in the field of insect physiology in recent years. It may be defined as a temporary interruption of development which, in a given species, would occur even if the insects were kept under optimum conditions, and a period of adverse conditions of a definite character is necessary before development can continue. The opposite of diapause is quiescence, where inhibition of development is the immediate consequence of adverse conditions at the end of which development is immediately renewed. It has been mentioned that the beginning of a 'true' diapause is independent of current environmental conditions; this does not mean that environmental conditions play no part at any point in the development of a given species in determining the occurrence of diapause. The occurrence of diapause in the most unfavourable conditions for the development of the species, for example the low temperatures of winter or summer drought, and its adaptive value for the species clearly show the role that environment has had in the evolution of a given species. Apart from this common 'phylogenetic' adaptation, in so-called 'facultative' diapause the ambient conditions during earlier stages of the life-history of the species concerned have been found to determine whether the genetically conditioned 'facultative' diapause will actually occur or not.

Diapause development. The length of the period of adverse conditions (coldness) necessary for the re-commencement of development varies with the species from two or three weeks to several (4–5) months. This period of arrested morphological development does not involve a complete rest in the physiological sense of the word; it is rather the time required for specific physiological changes to occur, which make it possible for the insect organism to re-commence development. It is, therefore, called the period of diapause development (cf. Andrewartha, 1952).

The diapause development of a given species has a definite minimum length at a particular temperature. In most species where this aspect has so far been studied, the optimal temperature for diapause development is around 5 °C. With both decrease or increase of temperature there is a

185

marked increase in the length of diapause development, ranging from several weeks to several years as the temperature approaches the 'living' optimum (20–25 °C), while development practically ceases at low temperatures below 0 °C.

The stage at which diapause occurs. Diapause occurs at the most varied stages of ontogenetical development in different insects. For any one species, however, it is connected with a particular stage of development. There are many cases of embryonic diapause occurring at early embryonic stages (as in *Orgia antiqua* or *Bombyx mori*), near the middle of embryonic development (as in *Locusta migratoria*, other Orthoptera and some of the Lepidoptera), or at the end of embryogenesis in a fully developed larva prior to hatching (as in *Lymantria dispar*). Similarly, diapause can occur in any instar of larval development, for example the first instar in *Cacoecia fumiferana*, the second in *Euproctis chrysorrhoea*, the third in *Gastropacha quercifolia*, the penultimate in *Grillus campestris* or the last larval instar in *Macrothylacia rubi*. Very often diapause occurs in the pupal instar, as in *Saturnia pyri*, *Hyphantria cunea* etc. Imaginal diapause mainly involves those parts of the body which continue to develop during adult life, primarily the ovaries of female insects (e.g. *Anopheles maculipennis* or *Pyrrhocoris apterus*). Cases where diapause occurs at two separate stages within one generation are rather infrequent (e.g. in *Dendrolimus pini* or *Cephaleia abietis*; see later).

Obligatory and facultative diapause. In some insects, diapause occurs in each generation independently of the environmental conditions the animals experience. In others, it occurs only in some generations, when specific environmental conditions prevail or have prevailed at an earlier stage. The former type mainly occurs in insects with a long period of postembryonic development lasting one or more years. If it must occur in each generation, the diapause is termed obligatory. The second type, however, occurs in insects with two or more generations a year, and appears at the appropriate stage only in those generations which bridge the period of unsuitable conditions, e.g. the overwintering generations. In such cases diapause is facultative and is dependent on the appropriate conditions. Special mechanisms are usually developed in some of the stages preceding diapause when it may be determined by specific conditions of, for example, photoperiod and temperature. Whereas obligatory diapause is mainly associated with univoltine species, facultative diapause occurs in polyvoltine ones, i.e. bivoltine, trivoltine, tetravoltine or multivoltine. Transitions between obligatory and facultative diapause are also known where, for example, development can continue without a break for many generations under suitable conditions, but may easily be interrupted when unsuitable conditions appear. When induced in such species, the arrest in development has the character of a true diapause, but may relatively easily be broken by specific environmental conditions, e.g. long photoperiod, and thus occupies an intermediate position between diapause and quiescence. Such a type of development has been observed in *Lucilia sericata* (Cragg and Cole, 1952), *Calliphora erythrocephala* (Cousin, 1932), and *Dendrolimus pini* (Geyspitz, 1949 etc.; cf. Lees, 1955, and Danilevski, 1961).

The physiology of diapause. The arrest of growth, which is the principal feature of diapause, is connected with many biochemical and physiological changes in the insect organism. These demonstrate the adaptive nature of diapause, as they increase the ability of the insect to survive the adverse conditions (winter, drought, etc.). Some physiological characteristics have been observed in all types of diapause:

(*i*) *Overall metabolism.* The beginning of most types of diapause is correlated with a marked decrease in oxygen consumption. The respiration curve falls to a characteristic very low level – about one-tenth of the normal oxygen consumption of the particular stage – and this level is maintained practically unchanged throughout diapause. Diapause often coincides with the bottom of the oxygen consumption curve for non-diapausing insects (cf. p. 48).

(*ii*) *The respiratory enzymes.* Various authors have demonstrated a series of changes in the activity of the respiratory enzymes. From the observed increase in the resistance to HCN and CO as well as a resistance (seventy times higher) to organic poisons which block the cytochrome system (i.e. pilocarpin and diphtheria toxin), it was concluded that the cytochrome system is inactivated during diapause and replaced by a particular cytochrome, b_5. Further research, however, has led to different conclusions. Investigations on the resistance to cyanide and CO of the heart beat of diapausing *cecropia* pupae, which is able to work for $5\frac{1}{2}$ hrs. in the complete absence of oxygen, showed a large surplus of cytochrome oxidase in comparison with cytochrome c, producing the observed increase of resistance (Williams and Harvey, 1958a, b). Kurland and Schneiderman (1959) attempted to generalize from these results for other types of diapause, including embryonic diapause, on the basis of their studies on the respiration of diapausing pupae of several saturniid silkworms (*Cecropia, Cynthia, Promethea, Polyphemus*).

They considered that cytochrome c would be the factor limiting respiration during diapause, and that changes in respiratory metabolism would be the result of the lack of this factor as a direct or indirect consequence of the MH.[1] The distribution of cytochrome oxidase and succinic oxidase in adults of the Colorado-beetle (*Leptinotarsa decemlineata*) in the course of the diapause period was studied in detail by Ushatinskaya (1957b). The results of her work and those of other Soviet authors are included in her monograph on cold-hardiness of insects (Ushatinskaya, 1957a). The physiology of diapause in sawflies was studied in detail by Sláma (1959a, b, c) in a series of papers. The physiology of the imaginal diapause in two coccinellid species (*Semiadalia undecimnotata* Schneid., and *Coccinella septempunctata* L.) was studied by Hodek and Čerkasov (1958, 1959).

(*iii*) *The utilization and accumulation of reserves*. An important physiological feature during diapause is the reduced utilization of reserve materials (protein and fats) connected with the reduced metabolism. Prebble (1941) showed that, in the sawfly *Gilpinia polytoma*, no more than about 2% of the reserve materials (dry matter) was consumed during the whole winter period. Similar results have been obtained with other species (Slifer, 1946). This seems to be one of the most important selective advantages of diapause. Where reduced metabolism occurs during suitable living conditions so that the diapausing insect is able to accept food, as is the case in the so-called pre-diapause of the imaginal diapause (cf. p. 197), there is an accumulation of fats and other reserve materials in the fat body.

(*iv*) *Water balance*. An increased proportion of dry matter is another important feature of diapausing insects making them more resistant against cold. The previous water balance is usually restored following the resumption of growth. The lack of a suitable humidity may markedly prolong diapause in some cases. In summer diapause, as in locust eggs, and less frequently in winter diapause, as in codling moth, diapause can be broken by immersing the insect in water. It is important to note that changes in the water balance as well as all the previously mentioned features of diapause seem to be the consequence of changes in the humoral balance of one particular endocrine factor, the AH, which controls, amongst other things, the water balance of the body (cf. p. 50).

(*v*) *Digestion during diapause*. Many insects are able to move freely and to accept food during diapause. This is particularly true of imaginal diapause, in so far as it occurs during suitable environmental conditions. It has been observed, however, that mostly they are not able to utilize the food either for the development of the gonads or for restoring their fat-body reserves, so that they die of exhaustion within a few days (cf. Hosek, Čerkasov, 1958, 1959). This can also be interpreted as an AH-deficiency syndrome, now

[1] Moulting hormone.

that its role in the activity of the digestive enzymes has been demonstrated by Thomsen and Möller (1959) and by Strangways-Dixon (1960, 1961) (cf. p. 49).

The determination of diapause. As shown above, diapause usually co-incides closely with the period of adverse environmental conditions for a given species.

In multivoltine species, a special mechanism is required to ensure such synchronization. Usually the insect has a hereditary make-up which will respond with diapause to particular environmental conditions which normally precede diapause, such as a certain day-length (photoperiodism) or a change in temperature. Just as diapause itself is strictly attached to a particular stage of development, so is its period of determination, which is therefore hereditary. As suggested by Novák (1958b), the phylogenetic origin of this genetic mechanism can be explained as the result of selection for a tendency which perhaps occurs in all insects to a very small extent at certain stages of development. Thus it has been shown in bivoltine races of *Bombyx mori* that optimal conditions during the embryonic period and during the first part of larval development (1st and 2nd instar) tend to produce egg diapause in the next generation (cf. p. 200). The same conditions during the third instar produce no effect on diapause. On the other hand, in the second half of larval development (4th and 5th instar) these same conditions (long photoperiod and higher temperature) tend to induce development without diapause and the converse also applies (cf. Emme, 1953). By specialization through selection for the early instar effect short day photoperiodism[1] results, while specialization on the latter effects result in long day photoperiodism. The role of selection in the evolution of this type of dependence seems obvious from the markedly adaptive character of all the mechanisms.

Similar to photoperiodism, but less pronounced, is the action of temperature during the determining period of facultative diapause. It is interesting that the influence of temperature in a given species works in the same direction as photoperiodism: in short day species a low temperature has a positive effect in the same way as a short photoperiod while higher temperatures induce diapause; in long day species the temperature and photoperiodism act in the opposite direction. It is important to note that

[1] I.e. short days favour development, whereas long days inhibit it. This is the way the term short or long day photoperiodism is understood in plant physiology. In some papers, however, perhaps accidentally, the opposite terminology has been applied: using short day for the second mentioned type of dependence and long day for the first (cf. Emme, 1953).

in both cases the temperature response has a clear adaptive value, e.g. a low temperature together with a short photoperiod during embryonic development causes the deposition of non-diapausing eggs in the bivoltine race of *Bombyx mori*. It is also well known that the first spring generation of silkworms hatches in the early spring (March or April in China) when low temperatures and relatively short days are the normal conditions. The females of this generation thus deposit non-diapausing eggs of the second generation which hatch in about June, when the days are long and the average temperature is high. In this way the females of the second generation are conditioned to lay diapausing eggs which are able to survive the winter period, whereas a hatch in autumn would automatically lead to death through cold and lack of food. The interaction of the effects of photoperiod and temperature when the conditions are varied experimentally has been shown to be very complicated (Geyspitz, 1949 etc.; Danilevski 1949a etc., cf. 1961).

Beside the effects of photoperiod and temperature an influence of humidity on diapause has also been observed in several species, e.g. *Bombyx mori*. Again the effect of humidity is aligned with the influences of the other two factors; with short day species conditions of lower humidity induce development without diapause and higher humidity induces diapause. The influence of humidity in the summer type of diapause in insects from tropical and subtropical countries appears to be rather more involved, though not yet fully understood. The influence of food and its composition on the determination of diapause is also not yet fully clear. Many results in the literature have proved to be unreliable when repeated with a controlled photoperiod. In other cases it is still doubtful whether the observed effect is specific or merely very generally affects the development, e.g. suboptimal nutrion might make the insect more susceptible to factors inducing diapause. There is, however, a definite case of an influence of lack of food on diapause determination in blood-sucking insects. Here a special mechanism has developed which synchronizes development with periods of food abundance and induces a state corresponding to a diapause during periods of starvation (cf. p. 48). Lack of food also seems to be a stimulus inducing diapause in some plant-feeding insects, e.g. in *Diatraea lineolata*, a subtropical maize-borer (cf. Lees, 1955).

Termination of diapause. As described above, temperature during diapause development may produce a profound effect on length of diapause. Nevertheless, no change of temperature within ecological limits is able to break diapause at any given moment and re-induce development. There are, however, a number of other factors including experimental treatments which may be able to induce normal development in animals already determined for diapause. Perhaps the best known are the various treatments which suppress diapause in diapausing *Bombyx mori* eggs (cf. e.g. Kogure, 1933, Mikhailov, 1950). It is important to note that most of these factors are only likely to break diapause during a definite, relatively short sensitive period; this is usually just before or at the beginning of diapause. For example, a short immersion of silkworm eggs determined for diapause in concentrated HCl can prevent diapause completely if performed during the first 48 hours after oviposition, i.e. before the eggs have their normal grey-blue colour. After this moment the acid treatment is completely ineffective. A similar effect on diapause as the HCl treatment can be obtained by increasing the temperature to about 46°C for ten minutes in the same sensitive period (Austarov, 1940, 1943; cf. Mikhailov, 1950).

Diapause in larvae of the fly *Lipara lucens* can be broken by a pin prick or by contact with a glowing pin. Similar stimuli will also break easily the relatively feeble diapause in flies of the genus *Lucilia*. Diapause in eggs of the grasshopper *Melanoplus* can be broken at any time in its duration by immersing the eggs in xylol or another wax solvent. It has been shown that the effect of the xylol is to remove the waterproof wax layer which covers the hydropyle during diapause and prevents water penetration, this being the fundamental cause of diapause. Removing both cuticular envelopes (the yellow and white cuticle) and immersing the eggs in insect Ringer has the same effect as xylol (cf. Lees, 1955). It may be suggested that the effect of strong mineral acids on breaking diapause, e.g. in silkworm eggs, lies in producing a particular temperature, which is the fundamental cause of the breaking of diapause, on the surface of the eggs.

The reason for the break of diapause induced in various examples of postembryonic diapause by irritation of the nervous system seems to lie in the renewed secretory activity of the neurosecretory brain cells. The only treatment which is able to break postembryonic diapause at any stage of its development is experimentally to induce production of the AH (by implantation of an active brain) or the MH (by implantation of prothoracic glands or by the injection of ecdyson).

The Hormonal Principle of Diapause

A series of different theories has been formulated to explain the mechanism and the origin of diapause. The more important of these can be divided into three groups after Andrewartha (1950):

(1) Diapause is the result of an accumulation of a specific inhibitory substance 'acting through the inhibition of the life processes', and slowly decomposed during diapause development (Raubaud, 1920; Bodine,

1932). This category also includes the concept of a general diapause hormone supposed by Hinton (1953). However, no experimental evidence of a substance with such characteristics has so far been obtained except the findings on the humoral conditioning of embryonic diapause in *Bombyx* (cf. p. 199).

(2) Diapause is the result of a decrease in water content in the tissues caused, among other things, by the accumulation of reserve materials, primarily fats. This leads to a decrease in metabolism and to the other features of diapause (Slifer, 1946). Diapause is, however, much more probably the cause rather than the effect of all these changes, as Andrewartha (1960) has suggested, or perhaps the result of one and the same cause as these changes (cf. p. 48).

(3) Diapause is hormonally conditioned, either as a result of the lack of metamorphosis hormones indispensable for development, or, in the case of embryonic diapause, the result of the action of a special humoral factor. A suggestion that such is a role of the brain hormone can already be found in Kopeć's (1917, 1922) papers based on his experiments with *Lymantria dispar*. The first clear formulation of this concept was given by Wigglesworth (1936a) in his study of the hormonal system of the bloodsucking bug *Rhodnius prolixus*.

All the experimental evidence which has accumulated up to now unambiguously supports the hormonal theory of diapause. The changes in the hormonal system, however, cannot be viewed as a primary cause autonomously determining the onset of diapause in a given individual. It should rather be considered merely a mechanism which realizes the effect of environment on the principal functions of the insect organism. The environmental conditions affect these functions either directly in the same generation by means of the nervous system and neurosecretory cells, or indirectly through the previous phylogenetic stages, via the genetic mechanism under the continual pressure of natural selection. Three main types of diapause can be distinguished on the basis of their hormonal mechanism: *i*. Diapause caused by a lack of the AH and (therefore) of the MH. To this category belong all cases of larval and pupal diapause known so far and, doubtless, also late embryonic diapause. *ii*. Diapause caused by a lack of the AH and the JH; this mechanism is concerned in imaginal diapause. *iii*. Diapause caused by the action of the neurosecretory factor produced by the suboesophageal ganglia of the female, and affecting the development of the eggs. This category comprises early embryonic diapause.

A. DIAPAUSE CAUSED BY A DEFICIENCY OF THE ACTIVATION AND
MOULTING HORMONES

This is the most common type of diapause, and the type so far most
thoroughly investigated. It consists of an arrest of growth and development,
due primarily to the absence of the MH, itself a consequence of an inhibition of AH production. It was originally supposed by most authors that
the lack of the MH was the only internal cause of this type of diapause.
Recent findings on the role of the AH in digestion (cf. p. 49) and water
balance (cf. p. 50), however, make it very probable that, besides the
indirect effect of the AH in activating the prothoracic glands, there also
exists a direct effect the lack of which is the cause of an important part of
the diapause syndrome.

1. *Pupal diapause.* The first and most complete study of pupal diapause
was carried out by Williams and his school, using the giant silkworm
Hyalophora (= *Platysamia*) *cecropia*. The main facts about this type of
diapause may be briefly summarized as follows:
Diapause starts practically at the same time as the moult to pupa. The
characteristically low metabolism of diapause starts somewhat later,
however, at about the bottom of the U-shaped curve. The metabolism is
highly resistant to the metabolic poisons HCN and CO and to toxins of
bacterial origin such as diphtheria toxin, and differs from normal metabolism in a variety of other features which disappear when development
is renewed. Pupal diapause is often obligatory as in *H. cecropia* and the
middle-Eastern saturniids (*Saturnia piri*, *S. spini*, *Eudia pavonia*), but may
also be facultative as in the bivoltine *Antherea pernyi*.

Experiments with extirpation, transplantation, sectioning of pupae, injection of extracts etc., have shown that the primary internal cause for the
inhibition of development in pupal diapause lies in an interruption of
secretory activity in the neurosecretory cells of the pars intercerebralis, and
most probably entails a blocking of the passage of neurosecretory granules
into the haemolymph.[1] By implanting an active brain into the diapausing
insect it is possible to break diapause at any stage of diapause development.
The effect of chilling on the termination of diapause is especially concerned
with the brain. This is shown by the fact that the implantation of the brain
alone from a chilled specimen is able to break the diapause in another
unchilled pupa, whereas the chilling of a decerebrated unchilled pupa has
no effect on diapause. Adding the AH source is, however, only effective
when the host specimen retains its own prothoracic glands or when they

[1] This may be concluded from the presence of neurosecretory material in the
diapausing brain and corpora cardiaca visible in dark ground observations (cf. later).

are implanted at the same time. The implantation of one or more active brains into an isolated abdomen has no effect, whereas the implantation of active prothoracic glands breaks the diapause and development continues (Williams, 1952a, b). The same effect is produced by injecting the MH in the form of ecdyson prepared by the method used by Butenandt and Karlson (Williams, 1954). From this it may be concluded that interruption of development during diapause is caused by external stimuli on the nervous system. Little is known about which of the other known characteristics of diapause are the direct effects of the lack of MH, which of them are the results of growth inhibition and which are perhaps caused by the lack of AH. Similar results to those from the work on *H. cecropia* were obtained by other authors using diapausing pupae of other insects. Thus, in *Hyphantria cunea*, *Antherea pernyi* and *Eudia pavonia*[1] the implantation of either an active brain or prothoracic glands results in breaking the diapause.

A detailed histological study of diapausing pupae of the moth *Mimas tiliae* was carried out by Highnam (1958a, b). He showed that the neurosecretory cells of the brain are inactive in the diapausing pupa at room temperature, but that they produce intracellular material during the first 3 weeks of chilling (at $3\,^{\circ}\mathrm{C}$). The material (granules) passes to the corpora cardiaca and towards the end of diapause development the neurosecretory cells again become inactive. A similar period of activity was observed in the corpora allata. The removal from specimens of both corpora cardiaca and corpora allata, however, had no effect on the duration of diapause. Such specimens had a notably thicker epidermis and their fat bodies contained a much smaller number of inclusions than the controls. The author supposes that the corpora allata play some role in maintaining diapause, perhaps by controlling the metabolism of the fat body in some way. No signs of secretory activity were observed during subsequent development at $25\,^{\circ}\mathrm{C}$. This was probably due to the partial reconstruction (histolysis and phagocytosis) of the gland. The possibility that these observations may have general application is a matter for further research.

A series of papers has been published on the effects of AH and MH deficiency on the metabolic enzyme system during pupal diapause. Apart from the work mentioned above, Shapirio and Williams (1957a, b) studied the cytochrome system in various tissues of late larvae and pupae of *H. cecropia* using low temperature spectroscopy and a DU spectrophotometer. They report the presence in last instar larvae of a complete cytochrome system with moderate to high concentrations of cytochromes a, a_3, b, c, and b_5, whereas in diapausing pupae no b and c were detectable

[1] V. J. A. Novák, unpublished observations.

by the methods used. When development continued after the termination of diapause, the activity of the original complete system reappeared. The explanation of the observations given by the authors must, however, be compared with the later findings of Williams and Harvey (1958) and of Kurland and Schneiderman (1958), which have been mentioned previously (cf. p. 187).

Little is known about the mechanism by which the external conditions produce their influence on the neurosecretory function of the brain. The first light on this question appears to come from a paper by van der Kloot

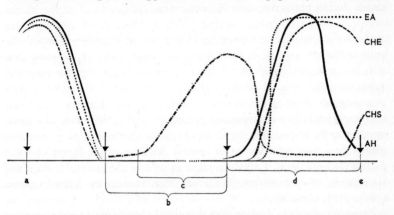

FIG. 46. The interrelationships in the activation hormone production (AH), electrical activity of brain (EA), choline esterase content (CHE), cholinergic substances (CHS) in *Hyalophora cecropia* during the pupal instar. *a* – beginning of cocoon spinning; *b* – period of diapause; *c* – period of low electrical activity; *d* – period of development; *e* – maginal moulting (ecdysis). (After van der Kloot, 1955.)

(1955). He studied the sequence of changes in the electric activity of the brain, i.e. the titre of the cholinesterase (ChE), the electric activity (EA) and the amount of cholinergic substances in connection with the observed AH production in *H. cecropia*. He found that all these changes are closely connected with AH secretion and, together with the latter, closely connected with diapause. Thus the electric activity drops together with AH and cholinesterase activity, remaining practically at zero throughout diapause with a steep rise afterwards. The cholinergic substances, however, follow an almost exactly opposite pattern (cf. fig. 46). Their amount steadily increases during diapause development and reaches its maximum at the point when diapause ends. At this time the electric activity reappears and rapidly increases together with the titre of the cholinesterase (cf. fig. 46). It appears that the observed accumulation of the cholinergic substances forming a substrate for cholinesterase is the direct internal cause of the effects of chilling, because it is optimal at low temperatures. It is concluded that such a surplus of cholinergic substances as a substrate for the renewal of cholinesterase activity is necessary for the production of AH and the renewal of electrical activity. In the brain of the non-diapausing *Galleria mellonella* the cholinesterase content and the amount of cholinergic substances is constant during metamorphosis. In the medial neurosecretory cells of *Bupalus piniatus*, neurosecretory material seems to be produced and correspondingly the spontaneous electrical activity of the brain continues during pupal diapause (Schoonhoven, 1962).

2. *Larval diapause.* Our knowledge of the various examples of larval diapause is far less complete. From what is known, however, it seems clear that larval diapause does not differ fundamentally from pupal diapause. It has been observed, by Sellier (1949, 1951) for example, that in diapausing pentultimate instar larvae of *Gryllus campestris* the histology of the prothoracic gland shows a reduced secretory activity and that the brain appears to be responsible for these changes. The brain and prothoracic glands have also been shown to control diapause in the larvae of *Sialis lutaria* (Rahm, 1952). Larval diapause in ants of the genus *Myrmica* and its relation to cast polymorphism has been studied in detail by Brian (1959, 1961, cf. 1960).

Most of the papers dealing with diapause in larvae have been concerned with the diapause which occurs in sawflies. This, however, is not a true larval diapause but rather the diapause of an instar in metamorphosis occurring between the true larva and pupa. The existence of neurosecretory cells in the brain of the sawfly *Diprion pini* has been demonstrated by L'Hélias (1953a, b, c). Church (1953, 1955) has shown that diapause in *Cephus cinctus* is caused by a temporary interruption of the neurosecretory activity of the larval brain, and that the renewal of this activity requires a certain period of chilling. The same author later showed that certain prothoracic glands described by him are necessary to terminate diapause. Two periods of diapause, separated by a period of limited interdiapause development, have been found in the prepupal stages, the eonymph and pronymph of another sawfly, *Cephaleia abietis* (Pamphilidae) (Novák, 1951). In this insect the normal length of development is two years. The first diapause period, which occurs at the eonymph stage, needs a distinctly longer period of chilling (not less than four months) than the second period in the pronymph. This usually takes place in the second winter, and is shorter under the same conditions. The interdiapause development normally occurs in the summer months between the first and second hibernations.

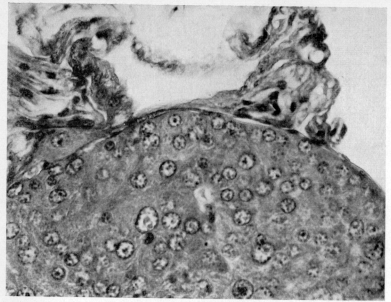

PLATE VIII. *Above:* Part of a median section through the corpus allatum of an adult female *Oncopeltus fasciatus*, stained with Dobell's ammonium molybdenate – haematoxylin method. × 1000. *Below:* Sagittal section through the epidermis of a diapausing pronymph of *Cephaleia abietis*.

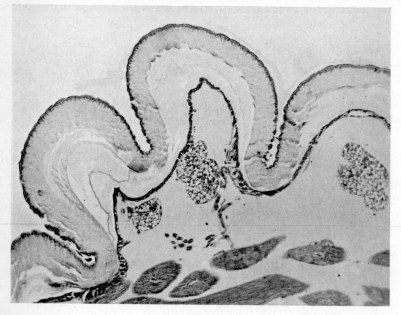

The pronymphal diapause can be broken by the implantation of an active brain. Ligaturing experiments have shown a distinct dependence on the brain and prothoracic centres in this sawfly, as in other species (cf. Sláma, 1959a, b, c).

3. *Late embryonic diapause.* No experimental evidence is available concerning the diapause which occurs in more or less completely formed larvae before hatching, as is found in *Lymantria dispar*. The fact that active neurosecretory cells and prothoracic glands can be demonstrated in embryos (cf. Jones, 1953, 1956) leaves no doubt that the same hormonal mechanism as in larval diapause is at work at this stage, though this is not the case in younger embryos (see later).

B. ADULT DIAPAUSE AS A RESULT OF THE DEFICIENCY IN BOTH ACTIVATION HORMONE AND JUVENILE HORMONE

In imaginal diapause a quite similar mechanism operates as in the abovementioned cases of true diapause, but with the difference that it is a lack of JH, not of MH, which is the main factor in adult insects. Moreover the neurosecretory mechanism of the JH is not fundamentally different from that of the MH. The hormonal mechanism of imaginal diapause has been most thoroughly studied in Coleoptera, for example in *Dytiscus marginalis* (Joly, 1945a, b) and *Leptinotarsa decemlineata* (de Wilde, 1953, 1958a, b, 1959, 1960 etc; Ushatinskaya 1952, 1958, 1959, 1961a, b), and in Diptera, for example in *Calliphora erythrocephala* (E. Thomsen, 1952, 1955; E. Thomsen and Moeller, 1960, 1961) and in the mosquitoes *Anopheles maculipennis* (Detinova, 1945, 1954), *Culex pipiens, C. molestus* and *Aedes aegypti* (Larsen and Bodenstein, 1959). The same mechanism operates in the imaginal diapause of Heteroptera as has been shown by Johansson (1958) with *Oncopeltus fasciatus* and by Sláma (1962) with *Pyrrhocoris apterus*. Little is known about imaginal diapause in Lepidoptera, such as occurs in most of the common butterflies which overwinter as adults; but a similar mechanism may well be assumed.

Morphologically, imaginal diapause is only evident in the interruption of growth of the ovaries and in the suppression of the functions of the accessory glands of both males and females. As has been shown by the experiments of E. Thomsen (1952) with *Calliphora erythrocephala*, this seems to involve a complex syndrome of both AH and JH deficiency. The implantation of corpora allata can induce the ripening of some of the eggs, but a quantitatively complete termination of diapause is only possible by the simultaneous action of both JH and AH. Apart from this, presence of the AH seems indispensable for the corpora allata to function normally. The most important physiological effect of a lack of AH in diapausing adults is that on proteinase activity in the gut (cf. p. 49), which is probably also the cause, either directly or indirectly, of a variety of other physiological changes in species with imaginal diapause.

A stage which has been described by some authors as 'prediapause' has been observed before hibernation in most examples of imaginal diapause in insects. It is said to be a period of preparation for hibernation, and during it various biochemical changes occur in the body which make the insect more resistant to cold and other adverse conditions, e.g. an increase of reserve materials (fat), a decrease of water content in the tissues increasing resistance to freezing, etc. Individuals of diapausing generations grow less quickly than those with continuous development, and related to this is the fact that they usually reach a greater weight and size during their periods of development.[1] Many authors have tried to explain these changes as caused by an internal factor (conditioned by environmental conditions) which induces diapause. This supposition was made in the so called 'food mobilization' theory (cf. Andrewartha, 1950). There is, however, weighty evidence against this supposition. In many cases, perhaps even in most, of imaginal diapause, diapause starts without such earlier changes in the organism, and appears to be fundamentally identical to 'prediapause'. In addition, diapause following a preparative prediapause can be terminated equally well by the AH or the JH.

A much simpler explanation of this stage seems likely: there is no difference in physiological conditioning between 'prediapause' and the subsequent diapause; both are due to a deficiency of AH and JH[2]. When this deficiency occurs within normal environmental conditions, feeding and the other functions of the body continue but the ovaries and accessory glands are inactive. Food utilization is therefore limited to energy and basal metabolism, with the result that surplus food accumulates in the form of reserve materials. Other changes are probably caused by the lack of the AH effect on the activity of the gut proteinases. The effect of the brain neurohormone on water balance is apparent from what has already been stated in chapter III A (cf. p. 50). All the processes continuing uninterrupted during prediapause are arrested by the adverse conditions of winter. Prediapause is therefore without doubt true diapause, whereas what is regarded as proper diapause by the adherents of the 'food mobilization' theory is diapause (of the ovary and accessory gland tissues) combined with quiescence

---

[1] It is, however, difficult to decide whether this is connected with the occurrence of diapause or, as is more probable, connected with the lower temperature at which the diapausing generations develop.

[2] Or, perhaps more probably, to only a JH deficiency.

of all the other parts of the body. The results of Hodek (1962) suggest, however, that in 'prediapause' the syndromes of AH and JH deficiency seem to be combined with inherited instincts for hibernating – such as the instinct for flight to hibernation sites in Coccinellidae. In agreement with these conclusions on the nature of 'prediapause' is the fact that the occurrence of a prediapause is almost limited to imaginal diapause and only affects a small part of the body while other tissues continue their functions. In this connection it should be noted that in many insects diapause ends before the start of the winter, sufficient chilling resulting already from the cold days and especially the cold nights of autumn. In other cases diapause may be ended at the beginning of winter simply by placing the insects in optimal conditions for further development. Although the state of such insects in winter corresponds in most respects to true diapause, it differs by corresponding with quiescence in that it may be broken by transferring the insects to laboratory conditions. As regards the other biochemical characteristics of imaginal diapause, it should be remembered that, apart from the direct effect of a lack of AH on proteinase activity, only the diapause of the ovarian tissues corresponds to a diapause caused by AH–MH deficiency but that their condition affects all the growing tissues of the body.

Besides winter diapause, a summer dormancy in *Leptinotarsa decemlineata* has been described by Ushatinskaya (1961) as occurring in a proportion of the beetles surviving from the previous year. The beetles creep into the soil in the hot summer months (June, July) and remain there for about one month, after which they continue to feed. It is very probable that this summer diapause has the same hormonal mechanism as the winter one. In the autumn some of the 'old' beetles of the previous year enter another 'winter diapause' which has some features distinctly different from that of the first year (cf. Ushatinskaya, 1961).

C. EMBRYONIC DIAPAUSE CONNECTED WITH THE NEUROHORMONE
OF THE SUBOESOPHAGEAL GANGLION OF THE FEMALE

The principal difference between embryonic diapause (except late embryonic diapause mentioned earlier) and the preceding two categories is that in the former type determination usually takes place in the females of the previous generation, so that it must be assumed that the determination is transmitted via the eggs. The other important feature of this type of diapause is that it occurs at a stage of ontogeny before any of the metamorphosis hormones become active. The relatively low number of species in which the hormonal mechanism of embryonic diapause has been adequately studied precludes any broad generalizations from what has been observed.

However, the biochemical features of embryonic diapause have much in common with those of diapause in later stages of ontogeny.

For example, diapausing embryos of the grasshopper *Melanoplus differentialis* show not only a U-shaped respiration curve which is quite similar to that in the pupa, but also a reduced susceptibility to HCN and CO which again disappears with the onset of development (Bodine, 1932, 1934 etc.). Similar characters have been found by Wolsky (1941) in diapausing eggs of *Bombyx mori*. Diapause in the eggs of migratory locusts, as of *Locustana pardalina* (Matthee, 1951, Jones, 1953, 1956a, b), is of a markedly different character, perhaps more similar to the type associated with AH–MH deficiency.

We are indebted to Fukuda (1952a, b, c, 1953a, b, c) and Hasegawa (1951) for the first reliable data on the hormonal mechanism of embryonic diapause. These papers are, however, not concerned with diapause itself, but with the way it is determined in the mother organism. For a long time it has been known that the occurrence of diapause in the bivoltine races of the silkworm is determined by the environmental conditions under which the egg of the parent generation developed (cf. p. 155). However, the environmental conditions do not, as might perhaps be expected, affect the rudiments of the gonads directly, but indirectly via the secretory functions of the nervous system which is not yet formed when determination occurs. The appropriate stimulus to the ovaries does not occur till the subsequent pupal period, as Umeya (1936) showed for the first time in his ovary transplantation experiments. The complicated mechanism whereby this transmission occurs was first discovered, however, by the systematic research work of the two earlier mentioned authors. Their findings may be summarized briefly as follows:

It can be shown that the incidence of diapause in eggs is conditioned by the endocrine activity of special neurosecretory cells in the suboesophageal ganglion of the mother specimen. The extirpation of this ganglion at the beginning of the pupal instar causes eggs which were determined for diapause through their mother to develop without diapause. In the same way univoltine females can be caused to lay non-diapausing eggs, a thing which they never do under normal conditions. Conversely, if, up to a critical point in time, a female pupa which has been conditioned to lay non-diapausing eggs receives a suboesophageal ganglion from a female which would have laid diapausing eggs, it also will lay diapausing eggs. The same effect can be produced by the implantation of suboesophageal ganglia from either females or males of a univoltine race. That the relevant 'diapause hormone' is non-specific for species, genus or family was shown by implantations of the suboesophageal ganglia from other Lepidoptera.

The ability to induce diapause was found not only in the ganglia of other species with an embryonic diapause such as *Antherea yamamayi*, *Dictyoploca japonica* and *Lymantria dispar*, but also in the ganglia of *Antherea pernyi*, a species with a pupal diapause. Ganglia from pupae of *Philosamia cynthia* and *Dendrolimus pini* had no effect.

The mechanism of transmission is, however, still more complicated. A female conditioned to lay non-diapausing eggs can be made to deposit diapausing eggs by decerebration or simply by cutting the circumoesophageal connectives before a certain moment. From these and a further series of experiments it was concluded that the endocrine activity of the suboesophageal ganglion which conditions diapause in the eggs is inhibited by a nervous stimulus from the brain transmitted via the circumoesophageal connectives.

It has since been reported by Hasegawa (1957) that he has succeeded in isolating an effective diapause hormone extract from *Bombyx mori* pupae which had been conditioned to lay diapausing eggs (univoltine race). The suboesophageal ganglia together with the brains of about 15,000 pupae were dissected and homogenized in 80% methanol. After centrifugation,

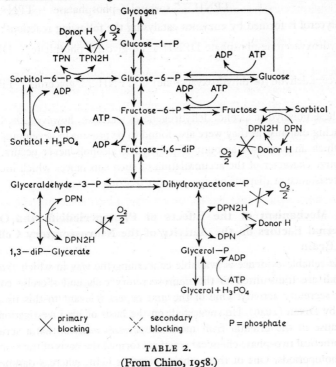

TABLE 2.

(From Chino, 1958.)

the supernatant fluid was evaporated under vacuum, diluted with water and washed with ether. The aqueous layer was then extracted with chloroform. The evaporated chloroform extract yielded a fluid which showed a high diapause inducing activity when it was injected into female pupae conditioned to lay non-diapausing eggs. An extract with a similar activity was obtained from the heads of adult females.

A further stride in the investigation of the mechanism of embryonic diapause development in silkworms was recently made by Chino (1957, 1958, 1961). It was shown that almost all the glycogen present in the eggs of *Bombyx mori* before the onset of diapause was rapidly decomposed by a complicated enzymatic reaction, the end products of which were the two polyhydric alcohols sorbitol and glycerol. A resynthesis of glycogen started at the moment when diapause ended (cf. table 2). It was further shown that sorbitol is formed by dehydrogenases catalysing the following two reactions:

$$\text{glucose} + \text{TPNH} \rightleftarrows \text{sorbitol} + \text{TPN}^+ \tag{1}$$

$$\text{glucose (or fructose)-6-phosphatase} +$$
$$\text{TPNH} \rightleftarrows \text{sorbitol-6-phosphatase} + \text{TPN}^+ \tag{2}$$

Glycerol is formed by enzymes catalysing the following reactions:

$$\text{dihydroxyacetone phosphate DPNH} \rightleftarrows \alpha\text{-glycerol phosphate} + \text{DPN}^+ \tag{1'}$$

$$\text{glyceraldehyde (or dihydroxyacetone)} + \text{TPNH} \rightleftarrows \text{glycerol} + \text{TPN}^+ \tag{2'}$$

These polyhydric alcohol dehydrogenases were not, however, the factor inducing diapause as they were also found to be present in developing eggs in which an increased amount of polyhydric alcohols never occurs. The adaptive character of the accumulation of such substances which increase the resistance of diapausing eggs against freezing is evident.

The Mechanism of the Effects of Photoperiodism and Other External Factors on the Activity of the Neurosecretory Cells in the Brain

Little reliable evidence is available concerning the way in which external stimuli are transmitted to the neurosecretory cells and thereby control their secretory activity. One of the first papers relevant to this problem was by Dixon (1949). He suggested, on the basis of his investigations on diapause in the oriental fruit moth *Laspeyresia molesta*, that a series of hypothetical two-phase chemical reactions formed the basis of the response to photoperiods. One of these phases requires light, whereas darkness is necessary for the other. Ushatinskya (1961c) suggested that in this context cytochrome oxidase might play an important part. Its inhibition by CO is prevented by light, this being a photosensitive reaction of a type which could be the basis of such a mechanism.

The perception of photoperiod by *Leptinotarsa decemlineata* has been investigated in a series of papers by de Wilde *et al.* (1956, 1958, 1959 etc.). The Colorado beetle is a typical long day species, diapausing in a photoperiod of less than 14 hours of light. The threshold intensity of white light is less than 0·1 lux. Experiments aimed at localizing the site of perception have not as yet yielded clear-cut results. Removal of eyes or preventing them functioning does not affect the photoperiodic reactions. The eyes are therefore probably not the only sites of perception. Unlike Dixon and Ushatinskaya, de Wilde suggests a possible effect of feeding, perhaps connected with a rhythm of feeding activity. A review on the problem of photoperiodism in insects has been produced by Lees (1959). Quite recently a monograph by Danilevski (1961) on the photoperiodism of insects has appeared.

The Synchronization of the Diapause of Parasites with that of the Host

Many authors (the reviews of Salt, 1941; Lees, 1955; Hinton, 1951; Doutt, 1959; Zelený, 1961; Schoonhoven, 1962 etc.) have observed that the endoparasitic larvae of entomophagous insects have a life-cycle closely synchronized with that of the host. With small entomophagous parasites such as some Braconids and Tachinids, if the host larva is to survive and develop to an adult, such a synchronization appears to be essential. A special internal mechanism must be supposed in cases where both parasite and host undergo diapause. In this connection several authors (Schneider, 1951; Lees, 1955; Buck and Keiter, 1956) have suggested an intervention by some of the metamorphosis hormones. This possibility has recently been studied experimentally by Schoonhoven (1902) in *Bupalus piniarius* L. (Geometridae) and its parasite *Eucarcelia rutilla* Vill. (Tachinidae). A series of experiments involving chilling, decerebration and parabiosis of diapausing host pupae has provided evidence that one of the two metamorphosis hormones associated with pupal diapause (the AH and MH) is responsible for activating the parasite when the imaginal development of the host starts. Schoonhoven gives reasons why this hormone must be the MH. The development of the parasite seems to respond to the hormone more readily than that of the host.

Similar results were obtained by Maslenikova (1961) working on the development of the Chalcid, *Pteromalus puparum*, and its hosts *Pieris brassicae* and *Pieris rapae*. Maslenikova concluded, on the basis of a large number of experiments, that the physiological influence of the host on the parasite larva is exerted via the metamorphosis hormones, most probably the MH.

Artificial Diapause

Wigglesworth (1936), using *Rhodnius prolixus*, was the first to show that the artificial elimination of the source of AH results in a condition which in many respects resembles true natural diapause. For example, decapitated *R. prolixus* nymphs, though unable to move or accept food, may live several times longer than normal nymphs. The same is true for decerebrated *Hyalophora cecropia* pupae and isolated pupal abdomens, as has been shown by Williams (1947, 1952 etc.). Investigating the physiology of such an experimentally produced diapause in *Bombyx mori* pupae has shown that it is identical with natural diapause in many respects, although no natural pupal diapause occurs in *Bombyx*. There is a marked decrease in oxygen consumption and an increase in resistance to HCN, although to a lower degree than in the natural diapause of the saturniid *Eudia pavonia* with which it was compared (Novák, 1959, 1961). It may be concluded that the enzyme system working in natural diapause is also operating in the experimentally induced case, even though it may be much less developed. This favours the concept that the origin of diapause was the result of a gradual evolution (see later), under the action of natural selection and resulting in an adaptation to adverse environmental conditions.

The Evolution of Diapause

The discoveries concerning the close interrelation between diapause mechanisms and the action of the metamorphosis hormones make it possible to produce a fairly likely theory of the origin of diapause in the phylogeny of the insects. In this connection, five important facts should be emphasized: (1) Diapause is also known to occur in other groups of Arthropods such as the Acarina and probably also the Crustacea, Arachnida and Myriapoda. (2) The primary internal cause of diapause is an interruption of the production of a neurohormone secreted by the neurosecretory cells of the brain. (3) Even intraspecific closely related forms often differ in their possession of diapause (cf. sibling species). (4) Diapause always has a clear adaptive character. (5) Although the tendency to show diapause at a particular stage of ontogenesis in a given species is genetically conditioned, the appearance of diapause in a given specimen is determined by stimuli during ontogenesis. From this it can be concluded that the basis of the origin of diapause (basically dependent on the metamorphosis hormone system) is phylogenetically very ancient, both in insects and in other arthropods. From this basis special mechanisms have developed in various insects, enabling them to achieve a rapid adaptation within onto-genesis to the particular environmental conditions.

This conclusion is in full agreement with the view expressed by Ghilyarov (1949) and Emme (1953) on quite different grounds. According to this view, diapause developed during the adaptation of the originally soil-dwelling insects to the relatively low humidity on the surface of the ground. The original diapause was most probably rather more similar to the present hot climate type, and only subsequently was the cold type developed from it, connected with the penetration of insects into the temperate regions of the earth with a cold winter period.

On the basis of the present state of knowledge of the different types of diapause in recent insects as reviewed above, the following four hypo-thetical phylogenetic stages may be supposed to have occurred in the evolution of insect diapause:

I. The development of an interdependence between the moulting process, the process of ovarial development etc. on the one side and a specific hormonal function on the other. As regards the AH, on the basis of what is known about the distribution of the neurosecretory cells of the brain, this stage may be supposed to have originally developed at a period before the arthropod level was reached (cf. p. 170).

II. The development of a secondary temporary interruption of the secretion of one or more of the metamorphosis hormones and the activity of the corresponding enzyme system under adverse environmental con-ditions. In connection with this the various other physiological characters of diapause developed (perhaps at the Apterygote level).

III. The development of a genetically stabilized interruption of AH production under adverse environmental conditions, directly caused by these conditions, e.g. drought or a hot or cold period. This interruption would then of necessity occur only after such conditions had appeared (at the species level).

IV. The evolution of a correspondingly specific dependence (determina-tion) of the existing AH mechanism on specific and often quite different environment factors, e.g. photoperiod, temperature, humidity, expansion of the abdomen etc., which usually signal the appearance of adverse con-ditions in the life cycle (at the subspecies level).

CHAPTER FIVE

The Neurohormones

Neurohormones and Neurohumoral Factors

Neurohormones, in the broad sense of the word, comprise all the physiologically active products of the nerve cells. Irrespective of the quantity of its secretion, each nerve cell is secretorily active in this sense, at least at its nerve ending, synapses etc. The enzymatic synthesis and decomposition of specific materials such as acetylcholine and noradrenaline at both sensory and motor nerve endings and synapses is the source of changes in the electric potential. These changes form the basis of nervous activity. In the older literature these substances produced by the normal nerve cells are mentioned under the term neurohormones. In the last two decades, however, the term has been given a new and narrower meaning (cf. e.g. E. and B. Scharrer, 1954a), to exclude the above-mentioned ultramicroscopic secretions, for which the term neurohumoral factors is used (cf. Gersch, 1958), in the nerve endings of normal nervous cells. The neurohumoral factors are not true hormones for the purposes of this book (cf. p. 1), as they produce their effect at the place of their origin and thus belong to the category of protohormones. The neurohormones *sensu stricto*, on the other hand, are a special group of true hormones combining the characters of both tissue hormones, being produced in tissues with other functions than hormonal, and gland hormones, originating in specialized secretory (neurosecretory) cells. From the true neurosecretory cells there can further be distinguished those cells of nervous origin which have become completely specialized to endocrine neurosecretory activity and have lost their nervous function during this phylogenetic adaptation, e.g. the cells of the medullary part of the adrenal bodies producing noradrenaline. There is, however, a clear phylogenetic link between these three types of cells which is also evident from their development in ontogeny (cf. p. 267).

The true neurosecretory cells may be defined as a special type of nerve cells characterized, in addition to their nervous function, by the production of a secretion with specific properties. This secretion originates in the cytoplasm of the neurosecretory neurones in the form of granules of variable size, characterized by their reaction to particular staining methods (cf. p. 30) and by their shining white appearance under dark ground

206

(cf. p. 31) illumination. Another important feature of the neurosecretory granules observed in most of the known neurosecretory cells is their movement along the axons of the neurosecretory cells, usually to a place where they are accumulated, e.g. the corpora cardiaca of insects, the neurohypophysis of vertebrates or the sinus glands of crustaceans. From the site of accumulation they pass into the circulatory system at specific periods (cf. p. 52). This movement of neurosecretion has been shown experimentally in the neurosecretory cells of various animals, including insects. As mentioned above (p. 44) the cutting of one of the nervi corporum cardiacarum results in the accumulation of the neurosecretory materials in the cut end of the proximal part of the nervus, whereas it gradually disappears in the distal part including the corpus cardiacum and corpus allatum. The movement of granules has also been observed in living cells in tissue cultures (Hild, 1954). A speed of movement of about 3 mm. in 24 hours was observed in one instance.

The carrier substance. No clear data are yet available concerning the chemical composition of the neurohormonal granules. It has, however, been adequately substantiated that the granules are not pure neurohormone; they are composed of a stainable material, the carrier substance, on which the corresponding neurohormone is bound either chemically or perhaps only physically, e.g. adsorbed (cf. E. and B. Scharrer, 1954a). The neurohormones appear to be first freed from the carrier substance when passing into the blood (haemolymph), perhaps freed by the enzymolytic activity of the haemocytes (cf. p. 56). Several types of neurosecretory cells (cf. p. 41) can be distinguished by the staining properties of the carrier substance. No data are available on the connection between these differences in the carrier substance and differences between the neurohormones in the different neurosecretory cells. In contrast to its original concept, the carrier substance is now supposed to be insoluble in lipoid solvents and is probably polypeptide or protein in character (neurophysine) (cf. B. Scharrer, 1959). The molecules of the neurohormone seem to be attached to the large protein molecules of the carrier substance. The neurohormones themselves seem to have rather different chemical properties. Some of them have been said to have a lipoid character, e.g. a substance with the effect of AH was recently claimed identical with cholesterol (cf. p. 55 and Kobayashi, Kirimura and Saito, 1962, cf. p. 78). This has now been questioned by the results of Gersch (1961) on the identity of AH with the neurohormone D_1. Other neurohormones have been shown to be substances soluble in water and alcohol with acid or alkaline properties (e.g. neurohormones C and D, cf. Gersch, 1960). There is indirect evidence

H

that some of the neurohormones in the eye stalks of crustaceans are of polypeptide character (Perez – Gonzales, 1957; Edman, Fange and Ostlund, 1958). It has recently been suggested by Novák and Gutmann (1962), that the carrier substance is closely related with the so-called gliosecretion (gliosomata of B. Scharrer, 1939) of *Periplaneta* and other arthropods. This independent phylogenetic origin of the carrier substance and the neurohormones suggests that the carrier substance probably represents the original secretory activity of the primary ectoderm cells (cf. p. 229).

The occurrence of neurohormones. Typical neurosecretory cells have recently been found by their histological characters in all the main Phyla of Metazoa except the Porifera and Coelenterata. At least in the latter group, the lack of neurosecretory cells seems due to the insufficient stage of our present knowledge and more profound research in the future may well reveal their existence, as has been suggested by Gersch (1960). In insects, they have been found in all groups where they have been seriously looked for. This also applies in crustaceans and other arthropods. There is now no doubt that at least three or four different neurohormones occur in all arthropods.

The general significance of neurosecretion in the organism. On the basis of the specific and uniform nature of neurosecretion in the animal organism as well as with regard to its importance and general occurrence, E. Scharrer (1952) views the neurosecretory system as a special third system of integration in the animal organism in addition to the systems of nervous and endocrine integration. This third system is a mediator between the short term (nervous) and the long term (endocrine) adaptation of the organism to the environmental conditions. The justification of this approach may be questioned, e.g. it seems reasonable to include the neurohormones within the general category of tissue hormones as having the character of primary hormones (cf. p. 268), but it remains indisputable that the unique character of neurosecretion forms a special type of humoral activity. This unique character of the system lies not only in its location in the nervous system but also in its form of intracellar granules moving inside the axons of the neurosecretory cells and again in the role of the neurosecretory system in the transformation of nervous impulses into hormonal activity (E. Scharrer, 1952). Neurohormones act either directly on the effector organs, as in myotropic or chromatophorotropic effects, or indirectly by the secretion of another secondary regulating hormone (e.g. the MH, cf. p. 46), or again by influencing the production of a tertiary hormone regulated by the secondary, dependent hormone. This last applies to the control of the

adrenal hormone in vertebrates by the ACTH of the adenohypophysis which is itself under the control of the hypothalamus (cf. B. Scharrer, 1959). Several examples of environmental influences mediated in such a way have been described in insects, e.g. the influence of the distension of the abdomen on AH production in *Rhodnius* (cf. p. 52), and the corresponding influence of photoperiodism in diapausing insects (p. 189) etc. Doubtless the various cyclic phenomena in the production of myotropic and chromatophorotropic effects observed in various insects by Gersch *et al.* (1960) (cf. p. 211 and p. 215) are also of this type.

The effects of neurohormones. Ignoring the neurohumoral factors concerned with the nature of nervous activity, the following categories of effects caused by neurohormones can be distinguished: (1) Myotropic effects (influences on the frequency and amplitude of the spontaneous rhythmic activity of muscle, e.g. in the heart, Malpighian tubules, oviducts, gut etc.). (2) Chromatophorotropic effects (influence on pigment movements, i.e. dispersion and concentration, in epidermal cells and chromatophores; also the development of various pigments in the epidermis). (3) Daily activity pattern. (4) Influences on water balance (cf. p. 50). (5) The activation of enzymes (midgut proteinase activity, cf. p. 49). (6) The activation of the secretion of other endocrine glands. (7) The induction of diapause (the humoral effect of the suboesophageal ganglion in the female moth pupa on the diapause of the embryos of the next generation (cf. p. 199)). (8) Influences on the development of the gonads and related effects (e.g. the suboesophageal castration cells in females of *Leucophaea maderae* (cf. p. 226)). There remains little doubt that several of these activities are due to one and the same hormone. Thus, for example, the myotropic neurohormones C and D of Gersch have been shown to produce corresponding effects on pigment movements in *Carausius* and *Corethra* (cf. p. 215). It seems probable that one of these hormones (D_1) is identical with the AH of the pars intercerebralis. But as there is still little clear evidence regarding the other activities it seems preferable to discuss the various activities separately irrespective of whether they are due to different hormones or to the same hormone.

Neurohumoralism

The most widely occurring and the earliest known type of secretory activity of nerve cells is the so-called neurohumoralism, i.e. the production of physiologically active substances such as acetylcholine and noradrenaline in the nerve endings. The definition of hormones applies to these substances in that they are produced by specific cells, they are physiologically

active and they produce their effect inside the organism. The definition does not apply, however, in that the substances work in their site of origin (in the nerve endings and synapses) without entering the body fluid under natural conditions. They thus correspond to the concept of protohormones (cf. p. 268) as used in this book. Even though they should not be included among neurohormones in the strict sense, it seems useful to include them in this chapter because at least some of them are closely related, if not identical, with some of the neurohormones in their chemical composition. Also probably most, if not all, of the neurohormones have passed through such a stage in the course of their phylogenetic development. In some instances it is as yet difficult to decide whether a given active substance isolated from nervous tissue (e.g. acetylcholine) has the character of a neurohumoral factor or perhaps that of a neurohormone produced by neurosecretory cells.

The function of most of the neurohumoral factors known so far consists of their share in the transmission of nervous excitation in the synapses. This seems to apply to acetylcholine, known from the nervous endings (synapses) of the parasympathetic nerves and the preganglionic parts of the sympathetic nerves of vertebrates. Bykow and Kibjakov succeeded in demonstrating that acetylcholine was also present in the nerve endings of the central nervous system. In the postganglionic parts of the sympathetic nerves the function of acetylcholine is replaced by noradrenaline (sympathin). The reactions in the synapse can be regarded as consisting of the following stages. The electric current reaching the synapses from nerve processes starts complicated chemical reactions. These result in acetylcholine being liberated, and this produces a similar change in the electric potential in the nerve fibre (axon or dendrite) of the next nerve cell. This change is transmitted to the other pole of this nerve cell in the form of an electric current. Similar but more complicated chemical reactions occur in the sensory and effector nerve endings.

In insects, acetylcholine has occasionally been found in very high concentrations, e.g. up to fifteen times more acetylcholine was found in the nervous system of the cockroach *Periplaneta americana* than in the central system of vertebrates (Mikalonis, 1941; Tobias, 1948). The question remains whether acetylcholine does not occur, as well as in the nerve endings, also as a true neurohormone inside the neurosecretory cells. Besides acetylcholine, acetylcholine esterase has also been found in large quantities within insects, again in *Periplaneta americana* (Richards and Cutkomp, 1945) and also in *Apis melifica* and *Melanoplus differentialis* (Means, 1942). There are indications that a series of other neurohumoral factors besides those mentioned occur in the nerve endings of insects and

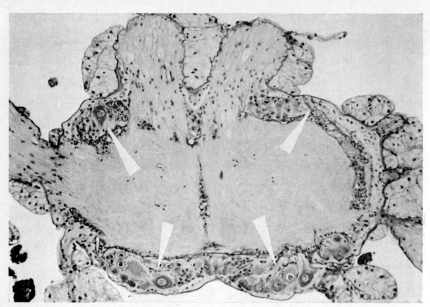

PLATE IX. Gliosecretion in *Periplaneta americana*, Xth instar nymph. *Above:* Frontal section of the mesothoracic ganglion. Arrows indicate the main accumulations of the gliosecretion. 120 : 1. *Below:* Detail from the above, 1500 : 1. Interneuronal gliosecretion around gliocyte nuclei and trabeculocytes with trabeculae.

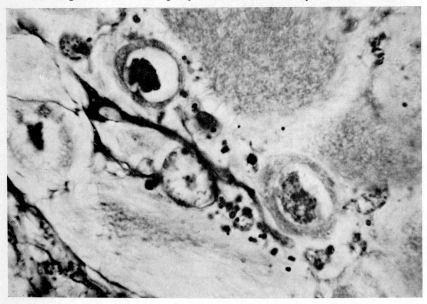

are so far partly or perhaps completely unknown (cf. Pringle and Hughes, 1948).

A. MYOTROPIC EFFECTS

The starting point for experiments on the myotropic effects of neurohormones are Loewi's classic experiments. In insects such effects may be demonstrated on organs with a spontaneous rhythmic activity such as the heart, Malpighian tubules, oviducts and gut. One of the first authors to show the hormone dependence of the pulsations in isolated Malpighian tubules, oviducts and gut was Koller (1948). He showed that extracts of brains and corpora cardiaca accelerate the contractions of isolated Malpighian tubules in insect Ringer solution, whereas the same extracts reduce the peristaltic movements of the gut under similar conditions. In contrast, stimulation of gut pulsation is caused by extracts of the gut and corpora allata. Enders (1956) has found the opposite effect of extracts from brains, corpora cardiaca and corpora allata on the peristalsis of the oviducts in the stick insect *Carausius morosus*. Brain extract had a positive effect, whereas the effect of extracts of corpora cardiaca and corpora allata was negative.

Experiments with Corethra. A detailed account of research into myotropic effects in the transparent larvae of Corethra (*Chaoborus crystallinus*) has been given by Gersch (1952, 1955, 1960a, b etc.) and his co-workers (Füller, 1960 etc.). This species has the great advantage for this kind of work that the effect of various extracts on the gut can be made visible by the use of various vital stains and can easily be observed *in vivo* owing to the transparency of the larva's body. A characteristic feature of the species is the strong antiperistaltic movements which follow each food acceptance. The function of these movements is to bring the digestive enzymes into the pharynx, where the process of digestion in this insectivorous species commences. The mechanical or thermal irritation of the brain and of single ganglia in the ventral nerve cord has demonstrated the dependence of these antiperistaltic movements on specific ganglia. There were three indications in favour of a humoral character for this effect: (1) The effect of the irritation only appeared after a definite 'latent' period; it subsequently increased and continued to affect the movement for about one hour. (2) The observed effect was in no way reduced when the adjacent ganglion on either side had been destroyed by burning so that the connectives were interrupted. (3) No nervous branches entering the gut walls could be found arising from these ganglia, the only nerve supply to the intestine being the stomatogastric nervous system arising from the brain. A similar effect was obtained by irritating the cerebral ganglion, with the only difference that in this case the rise in the rate of peristaltic movement was preceded by a wave of increased activity of short duration. This was no doubt due to a nervous impulse from the stomatogastric system. The proof of a humoral action of the ganglia via the haemolymph was obtained by experiments with extracts, not only from the various ganglia of the nervous system of the same species (*Chaoborus*), but also from ganglia of the cockroach *Blatta orientalis* and the stick insect *Carausius morosus*. These extracts were equally active on the isolated gut in insect Ringer. The relevant active substances were obtained from all parts of the nervous system, and were specific neither for species nor order. Later research has shown that they affect the heartbeat not only in other arthropods but even in other animal Phyla such as molluscs and vertebrates.

The isolation of neurohormones. The above-mentioned effects were investigated further by Gersch's co-worker Unger (1956) who used isolated hearts of *Blatta orientalis* and *Periplaneta americana* as test material. Insect Ringer extracts from various parts of the nervous system were used. The heart of insects is known to be innervated partly by the stomatogastric system and partly by thin nerve branches from the corresponding abdominal ganglia. The pulsation may therefore be influenced directly by either of the nervous paths (cf. Florey, 1952). However, it was shown in the insect Ringer preparations that the heartbeat could be stimulated by means of the same extracts as had been found to influence gut peristalsis. In contrast, extracts of the corpora allata subdued the heartbeat. This effect also showed a very wide non-specificity; the cockroach heart preparations were influenced not only by extracts from cockroaches but also by extracts from stick insects, dragonfly larvae and blowflies (*Calliphora*).

The detailed analysis of such extracts and their separation by paper chromatography has revealed that no less than three physiologically different substances can be isolated. One of these substances, found in all parts of the ventral nerve cord but missing in the brain and the retrocerebral glands, was shown to be identical with acetylcholine. It stimulated the heart beat and gut peristalsis. Another substance occurring in the brain and the corpora cardiaca as well as in the ventral nerve cord was called neurohormone D by Gersch and Unger (1951). This equally stimulated the frequency of the heart beat but at the same time also increased its amplitude. At high concentrations it stopped the heart beat during diastole. Its characteristic fluorescence was later shown to be due to a mixture of pterins which it is very hard to separate. A third substance, partially antagonistic to neurohormone D and denoted neurohormone C by the same authors, was found in all parts of the nervous system and in the corpora cardiaca like neurohormone D, but was also found in the corpora allata. It equally increased the frequency of the heart beat, but also decreased its amplitude and, at higher concentrations, stopped the heart during systole. In this respect the effect of neurohormone C is antagonistic to the effect of neurohormone D. All these three substances were also isolated from the haemolymph.

Further research along these lines enabled Gersch and his collaborators (Gersch, Fischer, Unger, Koch, 1960; cf. Gersch, 1960 etc.) to separate the original neurohormone D into two different substances D_1 and D_2 and the original C into hormones C_1 and C_2. These were extracted from 3200 lyophilized central nervous systems of *Periplaneta americana* with a succession of petroleum ether, ethyl ether, ethyl acetate, ethanol, water, acetic acid, and pyridine. The largest amount of the physiologically active component was obtained from the water fraction, and was found identical with the ethyl alcohol fraction. Paper chromatography of the water soluble fraction with butanol-pyridine-water ($1 : 2 \cdot 5 : 2 \cdot 5$) clearly showed two substances: one with the activity of neurohormone C (at an RF of $0 \cdot 17$) and the other with the activity of neurohormone D (at an RF of $0 \cdot 33$). They were eluted with water and shown to correspond with the previously described hormones in biological tests. The substance with the physiological action of neurohormone D was recrystallized several times to yield about 50 μg. of fine spheroid crystals with a fairly constant form. This substance was designated as neurohormone D_1 and some of its physical properties were determined. The absorption peaks in the infra-red were found at 1140, 1400, 1480, 1640, 3400 and 3600 cm.$^{-1}$. In this relatively pure form it was slightly soluble in water, hardly soluble in ethyl alcohol, and insoluble in organic solvents. When peptides are added, however, it readily dissolved in water. The second substance recrystallized in needles which showed a tendency to fuse, corresponded with neurohormone C in physiological activity and was designated as neurohormone C_1.

Two further substances with similar, though distinctly different features were obtained from the ethyl acetate fraction by paper chromatography with butanol-ethanol-acetic acid-water. One of them, occurring at an RF of 917, was designated as neurohormone C_2 and agreed with C_1 in its positive effect on the frequency of the heart beat without inducing systolic contraction. The other substance D_2 occurred at an RF of $0 \cdot 25$, corresponded (approximately) with D_1 in its crystal form, and showed a similar stimulation of the heart beat. Unlike C_1 and D_1, neither C_2 nor D_2 produced any effect on colour change. The possibility must be taken into account that they may be either decomposition products or intermediate compounds in the C_1 and D_1 synthesis of the body. None of the four substances could be identified with either adrenaline, noradrenaline or histamine (Unger, 1956). On the other hand, a series of substances of synthetic or vertebrate origin have proved to be active in isolated gut or heart experiments. For example acetylcholine, doryl, physostigmine and histamine have been found to stimulate antiperistaltic movements, the most active being acetylcholine which is still active at a concentration of 10^{-7}. In contrast, the effect of adrenaline and pilocarpine is distinctly negative, damping the movement (cf. Gersch, 1960). Extracts of the nerve ring and the ventral ganglion of *Ascaris* also affect the peristalsis of the gut in *Chaoborus* and the heart beat of the snail *Helix pomatia*. Similarly, extracts from the snail *Aplysia* affect the heart beat of *Chaoborus*. This shows the marked un-specificity of neurohormones.

Gersch (1962) made a detailed study of the possible identity of some of these neurohormones with the AH produced by the medial neurosecretory cells of the brain, using last instar larvae of *Calliphora erythrocephala* and *Lymantria dispar*. A series of experiments involving the injection of brain extracts, injection of the isolated neurohormones C_1, D_1, C_2 and D_2, as well as implantation of immature ring glands suggested that the neurohormone D_1 was identical with the AH. It was possible to induce pupation in brainless *Lymantria dispar* larvae by injecting the purified neurohormone D_1. Similar results were obtained in *Calliphora*. The neurohormone C_1, however, showed no such activity either in *Lymantria* or, with two or three exceptions, in *Calliphora* (cf. p. 283).

Six factors having an accelerator action on the isolated heart of *Periplaneta* were extracted in ethyl acetate, ethylacetate-ethanol mixtures, and ethanol from the corpora cardiaca-allata of the cockroach by Ralph (1962). Another accelerator soluble in saline solutions was found in all neural structures examined. Factors, possibly five in number, that caused heart deceleration were found by the same solvent extraction method in the brain suboesophageal and ventral cord ganglia.

B. NEUROHORMONES AND THE COLOUR CHANGE

Two types of colour change occur in animals in general. In one of them the change of colour, or in insects mostly only the change in intensity of colour, results either from the concentration or the dispersion of pigment granules contained in special pigment cells (or in all epidermal cells as in *Carausius morosus*) or from the contraction or expansion of melanophores as occurs in the tracheal air sacs of Corethra larvae (*Chaoborus crystallinus*). This type of colour change is a short-term process which is usually periodic, mainly with a 24-hour period. It results in a rapid adaptation by the insects to the colour or light intensity of the environment. This type of adaptation is called physiological colour change. By contrast, the term morphological colour change refers to long-term or irrevocable changes in the colour of the integument. These are produced in the course of onto-genetical development, often as a response by the organism to specific conditions of temperature, humidity, light or other conditions. Such changes have an equally adaptive character. There are, of course, examples of colour changes which are intermediate between these two types. In any case, both physiological and morphological colour changes are regulated by hormones.

1. *Physiological colour changes*

Colour change of the stick insect epidermis. Relatively few cases of physiological colour change occur in insects by comparison with crustaceans, where it is a very common feature. Only two cases have so far been described in some detail. One of these is the 24-hour change in the intensity of coloration in *Carausius morosus*. This colour change is caused by the movement of the pigment granules inside the epidermal cells. Four different pigments are found in *Carausius*: a green and a yellow pigment which are distributed uniformly in the cytoplasm of the epidermal cells, an orange pigment dispersing and concentrating horizontally on a plane with the nucleus, and a dark brown pigment moving in vertical direction.

By day the dark brown pigment is found at the internal end of each epidermal cell while the orange pigment is concentrated around the nucleus. This explains the light coloration of the insect in day-time. At night, the dark brown pigment moves towards the outer end of the cell and the orange granules spread out evenly, horizontally across the cell. As a result the integument of the insect darkens (cf. fig. 47).

This movement of pigments is related to the light conditions. If stick insects are illuminated at night they become lighter and, by contrast, stick insects kept in darkness during the day become darker in colour. These changes, however, only become apparent after a while. If the insects are kept in constant darkness the rhythm of colour change takes several weeks to disappear completely. About the same length of time is necessary to reverse the rhythm by keeping the insects in the dark by day and in the light at night. The reactions of the insects to humidity are comparable with their reactions to changes in illumination. In a high relative humidity the coloration becomes darker, and becomes lighter in a low humidity. The colour change is clearly adaptive. Stick insects, sitting on the twigs of a shrub and with a remarkably cryptic body form and behaviour, are very much less noticeable to their enemies if they are lighter by day and darker at night.

The possibility of a humoral mechanism for the colour change in *Carausius* was first suggested by Giersberg (1928) and later by Atzler (1930). A detailed study of the problem was carried out by Janda (1934, 1936) who showed histologically that there was no connection between the nerve endings and the epidermal cells. In this way he proved that a direct nervous influence on the colour change was impossible. In addition, he carried out a series of ligature experiments. When a nymph was ligatured at the middle of the body so as to prevent haemolymph passing from the

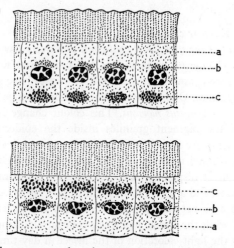

FIG. 47. *Carausius morosus* – the pigment movement in the epidermis cells. *Above* – light adaptation; *below* – dark adaptation, *a* – green and yellow pigment (motionless), *b* – orange-red pigment, moving in the horizontal level, *c* – brown pigment, moving vertically. (After Giersberg, 1928.)

anterior to the posterior part of the body, the diurnal colour change continued only in the anterior part of the body while the posterior part remained constantly light in colour. The ligature caused no apparent harm to the insect even after many days. When the ligature was loosened, the rhythm of colour change re-appeared. After extirpation of the brain the whole body became evenly light in colour. Janda concluded from this that the colour change is initiated by a substance which is released from the brain and transported by the haemolymph. This was confirmed by experiments in which a piece of integument darkened when transplanted from a light-adapted to a dark-adapted insect and, conversely, a piece from a dark-adapted to a light-adapted specimen became lighter in colour (cf. fig. 48).

The conclusions of Janda were confirmed and extended by the work of

Dupont-Raabe (1951a, b, cf. 1959). She showed that specimens made light in colour by extirpation of the brain became very dark if implanted with the brains of dark-adapted individuals. The same effect could be caused by injecting extracts prepared from such brains. The high activity of the extracts was evident from the discovery that even one-twentieth of the amount obtained from a single brain was sufficient to induce darkening. The effect of an extract of the suboesophageal ganglion was equally intensive. A similar, but less intensive, effect was caused by extracts of the corpora cardiaca and of the ganglia of the ventral nerve cord. Removal of various parts of the brain has demonstrated the interesting fact that the active principle is produced neither by the neurosecretory cells of the pars intercerebralis nor by those of the lateral groups of the protocerebrum, but by specific neurosecretory cells in the tritocerebrum. The existence of these cells was shown by a special histological technique. Raabe (1959) named this substance neurohormone C and concluded that the active substance could not be considered identical with the AH. This conclusion, how-

FIG. 48. *Carausius morosus*, penultimate in star nymph. The ligatured abdomen is pale, the fore part containing the neurohormones is dark.

ever, conflicts with results obtained by Gersch (1961) and described later (cf. p. 218).

Another active substance with a similar but weaker effect was obtained, also by Raabe (1949–58), from the corpora cardiaca and was designated substance (neurohormone) A. Its identity with the A substance obtained from the eye stalks of various Crustacea by Carlisle and his co-workers

(1955 etc.) has been suggested (Raabe, 1959), but this is still inconclusive (Carlisle and Knowles, 1959). It does, however, seem to be identical with an active substance obtained from the corpora cardiaca of various insects by Hanström (1936, 1940) and M. Thomsen (1943). This latter substance activates the chromatophores of crustaceans. The relationship of these active substances to the C and D neurohormones of Gersch is not yet clear, because of the inadequacy of the technical data; although according to Raabe (1959) it seems possible to distinguish between at least some of them.

In a series of papers, Gersch and his collaborators have been able to show that the myotropic substances C and D mentioned above (cf. p. 212) are identical with the substances affecting the colour change in *Carausius*.

A very sensitive in vitro test was developed, which made possible a detailed analysis of chromatotropic activity. Small pieces of *Carausius* integument in insect Ringer proved to respond readily to neurohormone extracts in far lower concentrations than produced a response in whole animals. With this technique it could be shown that neurohormone C_1 causes an intense darkening of the integument whereas D_1 produces less intense darkening at low concentrations and a lightening at higher concentrations (Gersch and Mothes, 1956).

The term 'normal solution' was employed to refer to the quantity of both neurohormones obtained from ten specimens (i.e. from the cerebral ganglion including the corpora cardiaca and corpora allata, from the sub-oesophageal ganglion, the whole ventral nerve cord and as much haemolymph as possible from each specimen) dissolved in 1 ml. of Ringer solution. The term 'biological unit' was used to refer to the smallest quantity of either hormone which, dissolved in 1 ml. Ringer solution, still produced a darkening of the integument. About 1000 biological units of the two hormones together were found in one specimen of *Periplaneta americana* (tested with *Carausius* integument). As 50 μg. of crystallized neurohormone D_1 were recovered from an extract of 3200 cockroaches, each specimen appears to contain 0·015 μg.

The in vitro test was used to show that neurohormone D_1 is located in the pars intercerebralis (although lower quantities occur also in other parts of the nervous system) whereas C_1 is found in the deutocerebral and tritocerebral parts of the brain. This would suggest that C_1 and D_1 are respectively identical with C and A of Raabe (see above). The lack of an effect of extracts from the pars intercerebralis in Raabe's experiments (see above) is possibly explained by the fact that at high concentrations its effect is to lighten the integument (Raabe used darkening as a measure of activity). As already mentioned above, neurohormones C_2 and D_2 were found to have no effect on colour change.

Colour change in Corethra larvae. Another example of a physiological colour change which has been thoroughly investigated occurs in the larvae of Corethra (*Chaoborus cristallinus*). In these transparent aquatic larvae the colour change is limited to the surface of the so-called air-sacs. There are two pairs of kidney-shaped sacs (in the thorax and in the seventh abdominal segment) of tracheal origin and with a hydrostatic function. All four sacs are covered with cells containing a black pigment and capable of considerable distension and contraction. Against a dark background (e.g. the bottom of the pool in which the larva lives) the chromatophores are distended so that they cover the entire surface of the air-sac. When a larva is transferred to a light background the chromatophores quickly contract, becoming rounded to form only small black spots on the surface of the bladders. In this way the colour change is caused by the movement of whole cells, the melanophores. Research during the last decade has shown that, in this case also, a humoral control is involved (Kopenetz, 1949; Hadorn-Fritzi, 1949 etc.; cf. Raabe, 1959).

Methodical research on the mechanism of the colour change in *Chaoborus* was carried out by Gersch (1956; cf. 1960a, b etc.) and his school. A series of experiments, involving the irritation and removal of individual ganglia in the nerve cord as well as the injection of extracts from various parts of the nervous system, have shown an interaction of at least three neurohormones with partially antagonistic effects. Subsequent separation of extracts with paper chromatography and electrophoresis has shown that the principal substance concerned is identical with neurohormones C_1 and D_1 and acetylcholine. The effect of these substances on the melanophores corresponds with their effect on the movement of pigment in *Carausius*. Neurohormone C_1 causes expansion of the melanophores and therefore a darkening of the air-sacs. The effect of acetylcholine is very similar, whereas neurohormone D produces a lightening of the bladder colour (cf. fig. 49).

Although physiological colour change is a common phenomenon in Malacostraca, in some Cephalopoda and in vertebrates, it has only been observed in a few additional species of insects. In none of these has the physiology yet been studied. Thus it has been found in some grasshoppers (Acrididae) including *Kosciuskola tristis* (Key and Day, 1954), in the family Oedipodidae, in some mantids and in many other phasmids besides *Carausius*. There is little doubt that neurohormones are again involved in the colour change of these species (cf. p. 215).

2. *Morphological colour change.* Examples of morphological colour change are much more numerous in insects than physiological colour change. In

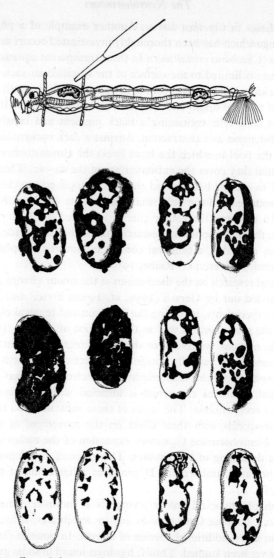

FIG. 49. The effect of the neurohormones on the melanophores of the tracheal sacs in corethra larvae. *Above* – diagram of the larva into the ligatured thorax of which the hormone is injected, the untreated hind pair of sacs serves as a control (right pair in each series). Upper series – insect Ringer control; middle series – neurohormone C (left pair of bladders); lower series – neurohormone D. (After Gersch, 1957.)

addition to the clearly adaptive true colour change occurring in some Orthoptera and Lepidoptera changes in the size and form of the pigment (melanin) pattern which occur in many insect groups such as grasshoppers, bugs, moths, beetles, and wasps may also be included. It can be supposed that hormones are involved in these changes also, even though not all have yet been studied from this angle.

Some examples of morphological colour change have already been mentioned in connection with the metamorphosis hormones which control them indirectly. For example, the complicated colour change preceding metamorphosis in *Cerura vinula* caterpillars is a part of morphogenesis and controlled indirectly by the activity of the MH (cf. p. 74). Similarly, the colour changes connected with the phase polymorphism of migratory locusts are conditioned by the JH (cf. p. 93).

A quite different mechanism appears to be involved in the adaptive coloration of some butterfly pupae. This phenomenon takes the form of a partial adaptation to the background colour. Thus it has been known for a long time that the colour of the pupal cuticle in some species of the families Papilionidae and Pieridae is dependent on the background colour experienced by the individual immediately prior to pupation (cf. Dürken, 1923; Brecher, 1923). Ohnishi and Hidaka (1955) have recently shown that a similar phenomenon in several East Asiatic species of the genus *Papilio* is humorally conditioned. For example, pupae which formed on young green twigs are also green whereas those which formed on older twigs with a brown bark (on the plant *Poncirus trifoliata*) are brown.

In a series of experiments involving ligaturing, extirpation of individual ganglia and nerve interruptions with caterpillars before pupation, Hidaka (1956) found that colour adaptation was conditioned by optical sensations requiring an undamaged cerebral-prothoracic-suboesophageal ganglionic complex.

The basic colour of the pupa is green, which may or may not be supplemented by brown depending on the colour of the background. If any of the above-mentioned ganglia are removed or their connection broken, the brown colour fails to develop even in pupae determined for brown. Both a nervous (optical) impulse and a neurohormonal mechanism are therefore necessary for the appearance of the brown coloration; this is similar to the conditioning of embryonic diapause (cf. p. 199). Recently Hidaka (1960, 1961) has claimed to have found the source of the pupal brown colour hormone in the prothoracic ganglion of *Papilio xanthus* L. and several other species. In contrast, the brown pupae of several other species in the genera *Nymphalis* and *Malacosoma* which do not show morphological

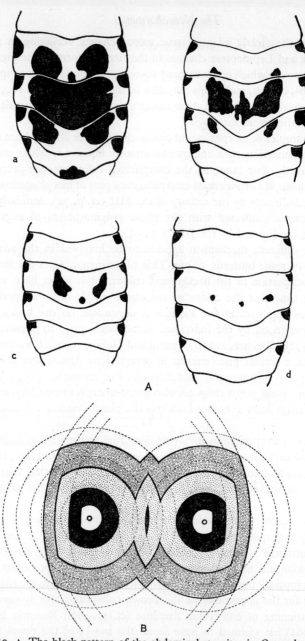

FIG. 50. A. The black pattern of the abdominal sternites in *Oncopeltus fasciatus* females in four different rearing temperatures: *a* – room temperature; *b* – 25 °C; *c* – 28 °C; *d* – 32 °C. **B.** Diagram of the geometrical pattern produced by two factors spreading from two foci with equal and proportionate velocity, inhibited laterally. The areas with equal concentration of the factor are marked in the same way. Compare with the figure above. (From Novák, 1955d.

colour changes, make no similar response to the removal of the prothoracic or other ganglia.

There is little doubt that a hormonal mechanism is also responsible for controlling the morphological colour changes in the caterpillars of *Laphygma exigua* and *L. exempta* (cf. Faure, 1943) and *Spodoptera* (Mathee, 1945) as well as the seasonal dimorphism in *Araschnia levana* (Süffert, 1924a, b, H. J. Müller, 1960), even though such a mechanism has not yet been experimentally demonstrated.

A connection has been shown to exist between JH activity and the shape and size of the ventral black spots on the abdomen of the lygaeid bug *Oncopeltus fasciatus* (Novák, 1955d). Symmetrical black pigment spots develop on the ventral side of the abdomen of adult insects round two foci which correspond in position to the centres of the paired gonads. The differences between male and female in the shape and size of these spots correspond to the differences in the shape and size of the gonads. The size of the spots decreased in insects kept in a high temperature and their change in shape was consistent (cf. fig. 50A).

The spots were largest at room temperature and practically disappeared at 30 °C. Low doses of JH, or supplying the JH by the implantation of corpora allata at the last larval instar, were found to produce the same effect at high temperature. The effect both of increased temperature and the hormone can therefore be explained as a very weak form of progressive metathetely (a delay in the development of the imaginal characters produced by the positive influence of other larval parts of the body, including the product of the prothoracic glands). The hypothesis was suggested that the black spots are controlled by the two sources of a determining substance, which spread out from the parts of the gonads where ripe sex cells first appear. However, castration experiments showed that removal of the gonads at the beginning of the last larval instar had no effect on the development of the spots.

C. THE RHYTHM OF ACTIVITY

A series of recent papers has shown a causal connection between cyclical, seasonal and diurnal activity and the activity of the neurosecretory cells. Klug (1958) has shown that there is a correlation between winter and summer diapause and the volume of the nuclei of the corpora allata. Also the neurosecretory cells of the pars intercerebralis were found to be full of secretion at noon, but were almost empty at 4 o'clock in the morning.

Oezbas and Hodgson (1958) have shown that an extract of the corpora cardiaca decreases the 'spontaneous' electrical activity in isolated ganglia of the ventral nerve cord in *Periplaneta americana*, whereas extracts of the brain, abdominal ganglia and corpora allata have no effect. Cutting the nerve between the brain and corpora cardiaca made extracts of the latter less effective. When the corpora cardiaca extracts were injected into living animals, movements became unco-ordinated and stereotyped locomotor behaviour appeared several hours after the treatment and lasted for between one and three days.

Harker (1955, 1956, 1958, 1959, 1961 etc.) studied the endocrine control of the activity rhythm of the same species, using parabiosis and transplantation experiments. Her results showed that suboesophageal ganglion was the source of the active substance involved. Injecting extracts of this ganglion into decapitated insects produced a period of increased activity, the duration of which depended on the time of day when the injection was carried out (cf. p. 300).

Mothes (1960) carried out a detailed study of diurnal activity and the rhythm of colour change in *Carausius morosus*, using the in vitro colour change test already mentioned (cf. p. 218). The quantities of neurohormones C_1 and D_1 in Ringer extracts of the brain, the suboesophageal ganglion, the ventral nerve cord, the corpora cardiaca and corpora allata, and the haemolymph were calculated. These experiments produced the following results: The concentration of both hormones in the haemolymph was very high at night and low by day (cf. Gersch, 1960b). Gersch (1960b) considers his earlier view, that neurohormone C caused darkening and neurohormone D lightening of the body, to have been disproved. Rather the period of decreased activity and light cuticle (cf. p. 216) is when the quantity of the neurohormones in the haemolymph is low (i.e. by day), while the night is the period of high activity and dark cuticle.

Brain extracts prepared from individuals at the end of the night (early in the morning) showed low activity, whereas the activity of extracts increased during the day (cf. fig. 47).

Extracts of the suboesophageal ganglion and the ventral nerve cord showed the same activity (high at night and low by day) as the haemolymph, whereas extracts of the corpora cardiaca and corpora allata showed no diurnal change in activity.

Several weeks in reversed conditions of day and night caused the animals to change their rhythm of activity, the activity of extracts also became reversed; i.e. low in the cerebral ganglion while high in the haemolymph and ventral ganglia by day and vice versa at night (cf. fig. 47). The activity of extracts of the corpora cardiaca and corpora allata again remained unchanged.

D. INFLUENCES ON THE WATER BALANCE

As suggested by van der Kloot (1960), the close analogy between the insect neurosecretory system of the pars intercerebralis-corpora cardiaca and the vertebrate neurosecretory centres of the hypothalamus-neuro-hypophysis make it probable a priori that the neurosecretory cells of the insect brain have a role in water metabolism. This has actually been shown by a number of authors. From what is now known there is little doubt that the AH itself influences the water balance. Little attention has so far been paid to the possibility that other neurohormones have a role with regard to water metabolism. Perhaps the only suggestion for this may be found in the papers by Altmann (1956a, b). It seems justified to consider all known humoral relations with water balance as forming one of the effects of the AH (cf. p. 50). Even if this were the only neurosecretory product influencing water metabolism, the recent view of Gersch (1961) on the identity of the AH and the neurohormone D_1 (cf. p. 214) would lead one to expect similar effects in the individual ganglia of the ventral nerve cord. Other effects of the AH could perhaps depend on its particular effect on water metabolism, primarily by an activation of the secretion of the prothoracic glands.

E. EFFECTS ON GUT PROTEINASE ACTIVITY

The importance of the neurosecretory products from the brain for normal activity of the gut proteinases in *Calliphora* has been clearly demonstrated (see above, p. 49). It is not known whether a special hormone is involved or, as is perhaps more probable, this is again an effect of AH.

F. ACTIVATION OF THE PROTHORACIC AND OTHER ENDOCRINE GLANDS

Perhaps the most familiar and most fully analysed effect of neurohormones in insects is the effect of AH on the activity of the prothoracic glands (cf. p. 46). The recent findings of Gersch (1961) have produced a new view on this effect, whereby AH would be identical with the previously described and isolated neurohormone D_1. Although not yet fully proved, this conclusion is supported by the following findings: Isolated larval abdomina of *Calliphora erythrocephala*, prepared as for the *Calliphora* test (cf. p. 25), could be induced to pupate by injecting a purified extract of neurohormone D_1 with the simultaneous implantation of inactive ring glands from younger larvae. The neurohormone extract was prepared from *Periplaneta americana* (cf. p. 214). When the neurohormone was injected without the simultaneous implantation of the ring gland, partial pupation occasionally occurred.

That the neurohormone D_1 has been shown to be a water soluble compound, probably a polypeptide, contradicts the findings of Kobayashi and Kirimura (1958, cf. p. 78). These authors succeeded in isolating a lipoid fraction from silkworm brains which induced pupation when injected into brainless pupae. Recently Kirimura *et al.* (1962) identified this fraction with cholesterol. The most likely explanation of this contradiction is that the lipoid fraction of Kirimura and his co-workers is not the true hormone but a substance which imitates its effects by an entirely different principle, perhaps by having a very general stimulating effect. However, one cannot exclude the possibility that the two factors are ontogenetically closely related (cf. p. 284).

If the conclusions of Gersch (1961) prove to be correct, it would necessarily follow that AH is present in other parts of the nervous system, i.e. in all those where neurohormone D_1 has been found. This would agree with the fact that type A neurosecretory cells occur in all ganglia of the ventral nerve cord (cf. Füller, 1960).

G. EFFECT ON DIAPAUSE

A temporary break in AH activity in the neurosecretory cells of the brain has been shown to be the primary internal cause of the most common type of diapause (cf. p. 195). In the early embryonic type of diapause, as occurs in silkworm eggs, it is the neurosecretory cells of the suboesophageal ganglion which have been shown to produce the humoral factor which actively induces diapause. Kobayashi (1957) found that females determined for laying diapausing eggs had larger (more than 30 μ) neurosecretory cells than females laying non-diapausing eggs. Whether the humoral factor involved is identical with any of the other suboesophageal neurohormones (cf. p. 199 and p. 227) has not yet been investigated.

H. EFFECT ON THE GONADS

That AH is necessary for the development of ovaries in *Calliphora*, and no doubt also in most other insects, has been shown by E. Thomsen (cf. p. 48). An increase in the amounts of neurosecretory granules in the neurosecretory cells of the pars intercerebralis in the period shortly before and during egg laying has been observed in several insect species, e.g. the stick insects *Carausius* and *Clitumnus* (Dupont-Raabe, 1951, 1952), *Bombyx mori* (Arvy, Bounhiol and Gabe, 1953), *Calotermes flavicollis* (Noirot, 1957) and in *Iphita limbata* (Nayar, 1958). The role of a brain-hormone in the development of the gonads therefore seems to be quite definite (cf. Raabe, 1957).

Another interesting relationship between the neurosecretory cells and the ovaries has been demonstrated by Scharrer (1955a, b) in the cockroach *Leucophaea maderae*. Normally the following three types of neurosecretory cells occur in the suboesophageal ganglion of the females: four cells of type A with abundant neurosecretory granules staining purple with paraldehyde fuchsine, two cells of type B lying ventromedially and with their granules, also staining red, occurring only on the surface layer of the

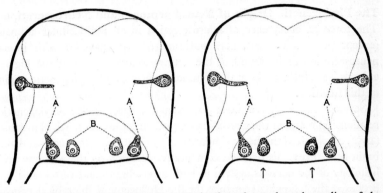

FIG. 51. Diagram of the castration cells in the suboesophageal ganglion of the cockroach *Leucophaea maderae*; on the left – in presence of the ovaries; on the right – after the ovariectomy. A – normal neurosecretory cells; B – castration cells. (From B. Scharrer, 1955.)

cytoplasm, and two cells of type C, which are smaller and again have red-staining granules. A striking change in the appearance of the type B cells occurred in adult females which were castrated between the 3rd and 7th instars. In these cells the granules increased in size and number and stained green with paraldehyde fuchsine and Masson-Foot. The neurosecretory material in the other cells remained unchanged. Scharrer concluded that there was a humoral relationship between the cells of type B and the ovaries, and therefore named them castration cells or ovariectomy-cells. No corresponding effects of castration were observed in males (cf. fig. 51).

The effects of castration were also analysed by Gersch, Fischer, Unger and Koch (1960) in *Periplaneta americana* and *Blatta orientalis* (cf. Gersch, 1960). Following castration, neurosecretory cells of type B with granules staining green were also found in other ganglia of the ventral nerve cord. Similar cells were also found in the ventral nerve cord of *Chaoborus* larvae. There remains little doubt that they are of general occurrence in insects. The observed effects are not necessarily a proof of a specific endocrine principle of the ovaries influencing the neurosecretory cells concerned. It is much more probable that the changes observed in the 'castration' cells are the result of a falling off in the consumption of their secretion by the ovaries. The phenomenon is therefore probably similar to the observed hypertrophy of the corpora allata following ovariectomy. In this connection it is very interesting that Noirot (1957) has observed the appearance of new neurosecretory cells in the suboesophageal ganglion of functional reproductives in termites.

The Phylogenetic Origin of Neurohormones and Neurosecretion

The common occurrence of neurosecretion in all multicellular animals (except perhaps Coelenterata) and the striking analogies with insect neurosecretion to be found in the neurosecretory system of the higher animals leave little doubt of the common principle and phylogenetic origin of this function.

Several theories have been formulated regarding the phylogenetic relationship between the neurosecretory cell and the nerve cell. Hanström (1954) emphasized the basic similarity of the neurosecretory cells and the brain cells. From his detailed comparative research on the anatomy and histology of the nervous system in both invertebrates and vertebrates, he proposed the following sequence for the phylogeny of the typical neuro- secretory cell: (1) typical neurone, (2) neurone with all the characteristics of a nerve cell but containing a limited number of neurosecretory granules, (3) neurosecretory cell with axon, dendrites and all other characteristics of a typical nerve cell, (4) typical neurosecretory cell with axon but without dendrites and the other properties of a nerve cell, and (5) secretory cell of neurosecretory origin without any of the characteristics of a nerve cell from the medulla adrenalis of the higher vertebrates.

Clark (1956) based his theory on his investigations of the brain in the polychaete families Naphthidae and Nereidae. He supposes that secretory activity was phylogenetically the primary function of the neurosecretory cells, and that these were only secondarily included into the mass of the brain. He regards the cerebral organs of the Nemertini, the frontal organs of Phyllopoda (Copepoda) and the X-organs of Malacostraca as evidence supporting his theory.

Gersch (1960), on the basis of his co-worker Uhde's work showing the existence of neurosecretory cells in Platyhelminthes (*Dendrocoelum* sp.), agrees with Hanström that the nervous system is primary. The neuro- secretory cells developed only secondarily from the nerve cells and parallel with the development of the gland cells from the original ectodermal cells. Only after this did they gradually acquire the functional importance they now possess in the neurosecretory system of higher animals.

Important evidence of the secondary character of the neurosecretory cells is their occurrence in very varied parts of the nervous system and in different histological units.

A theory reconciling the two contradictory concepts of Hanström and Gersch on the one hand and Clark on the other has recently been put forward by Novák and Gutmann (1962). They have shown that the secretory granules found in the glia cells in the nervous system of cockroaches (earlier described as gliosomata by B. Scharrer, 1939) agree in all their staining properties with the typical neurosecretory granules of the type A cells. The granules in the glia cells, of course, lack the other physiological features of neurosecretion and do not show any signs of cyclicity and hormonal activity. The authors suggest the term 'gliosecretion' for this particular type of secretory activity. They assume that the gliosecretory granules have the same chemical composition as the carrier substance in neurosecretion but lack the physiologically active neurohormones. Both gliosecretion and neurosecretion are assumed to have developed from the secretory activity of the primary ectoderm cells. The same origin is shared by the so-called trabeculae, a network produced by a particular layer of glia cells round the neuropile of the ganglia, as well as by the perineural lamella produced by the perineurium cells. The primary secretory product inside the cytoplasm of particular nerve cells then became the carrier substance for the phylogenetically later neurohumoral factors (specific to nerve cells) which thus developed into true neurohormones (cf. fig. 58.) A detailed cytochemical and electronmicroscopic study of gliosecretory granules (gliosomata) has been made quite recently by Pipa *et al.* (1961, 1962).

One component of the neurosecretory material, the carrier substance, would therefore be phylogenetically earlier than the generalized nerve cells, whereas the other, i.e. the neurohormones themselves, would be phylogenetically secondary having developed from the neurohumoral factors of the nerve cells as supposed by Hanström and Gersch.

CHAPTER SIX

The Protohormones

One of the most characteristic features of hormones is that they produce their effects in parts of the body different from the place where they are secreted and reach their site of action by means of the body fluid. This should, however, be regarded as phylogenetically secondary and the result of a long and gradual process of evolution. Apart from all the different true insect hormones so far considered, there have been found in arthropods a series of physiologically active substances which have their site of action at the place where they are produced and are only occasionally carried in the body fluid when they may produce their effect elsewhere.

Thus these substances no doubt represent a stage through which all the present hormones of all animal groups had to pass in their phylogeny. It therefore seems useful to classify them as a special group of physiologically active substances, giving them the term protohormones or prehormones. They may be regarded as hormones *in statu nascendi*. Most of the present protohormones are substances, the evolution of which has stopped at this level and which carry out their particular functions in the body of present-day animals just as, for example, rudimentary light sensitive spots instead of complex eyes are found contemporaneously with the very complicated compound eyes of arthropods, or as the primitive protozoans appear alongside the most complicated and phylogenetically advanced vertebrates.

The protohormones known at present may be divided into two groups: A, *the neurohumoral factors* which have been considered together with the neurohormones in the previous chapter, and B, *the gene hormones*. The latter may be defined as substances which depend on particular genes and condition particular genetic features, but can produce their effect by means of the circulation of body fluid, even when introduced into animals where the appropriate genes are absent.

Gene hormones

Gene hormones in the eye-colour of Ephestia kuehniella. Perhaps the first gene hormone discovered was the one which conditions the development of black colour in the compound eye of *Ephestia kuehniella* (Caspari, 1933; Plagge, 1936a, b). A red-eyed mutation has been isolated in cultures of this

230

moth, whereas the eyes of the wild type are black. Genetical analysis has shown that red eye colour is recessive to black. The wild form AA is further characterized by dark pigment spots on the testicles and black pigmentation of the larval epidermis and of the ganglia of the nervous system. These features are all missing in the aa form.

It has been shown that the coloration peculiar to the wild form AA may equally develop in the red-eyed mutant if testicles from normal males are

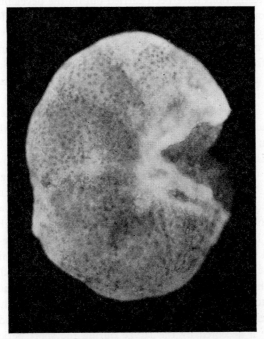

FIG. 52. Testis of *Ephestia kuehniella* in the pigmented surface membrane.

implanted within a particular sensitive period before pupation. Transplantation of the ovaries, of the brain and even of individual eggs from the AA form produce the same effect as transplanting the testes. This effect has further been shown not to be species specific: implantation of ovaries from the moth *Acidalia virgulata* and transfusion of haemolymph from pupae of *Galleria mellonella* and even from the flies *Drosophila melanogaster* and *Calliphora erythrocephala* have the same effect (cf. Plagge, 1936a, b; Ephrussi, 1942a, b). It is interesting to note that the effect is not directly proportional to the amount of the gene A. It has been shown that the tissues of the hybrid race Aa have the same effect as those of the AA form. From this it was concluded that the effect is not due to the gene itself but to a substance produced in the tissue when it is present. It has further been shown by Plagge that the presence of AA tissue for 24 hours is sufficient to produce the effect whether the implant is then removed or not. A possible explanation of this is that the pigment may catalyse its own further synthesis once it has developed in the new medium (the aa host).

Gene hormones in the eye-colour of Drosophila melanogaster. Even more detailed investigations have been carried out on the development of eye-pigmentation in *Drosophila*, where a similar protohormone effect has been demonstrated. Genetical experiments with *Drosophila* have produced numerous mutations differing in slight degrees of tone in their eye-coloration from the dark red of the wild type to pure white. Some of these colorations are effected autonomously by genes, while in others a hormonal effect very similar to that described for *Ephestia kuehniella* has been found. The difference between these two groups of coloration is evident in gynandromorph individuals of *Drosophila* from the fact that, whereas in the former group each eye can have a different colour tone, in the latter group, if one eye is of the wild type (w^+), the other necessarily shows the same coloration. Of the many mutations described the following have been shown to be hormonally controlled: vermilion (v^+), cinnabar (cn^+), cardinal (cd^+) and scarlet (st^+). The substances controlling these colour tones are again present in various parts of the body such as the Malpighian tubules and the fat body. By transplanting these tissues the given eye-colour may be induced in the mutants lacking the relevant gene. Similarly, if an imaginal eye disc with a particular gene missing is transplanted into a larva which has that particular gene, the eye which develops from the disc shares the colour tone of the host. It has been shown that these gene hormones produce their effects even when they are administered in food, though of course only if accepted by the larvae during the short period of about 70–65 hours before pupation (Beadle and Law, 1938).

The chemistry of the gene hormones. Much attention has been given to the chemical composition of the gene hormones which affect eye-coloration. The careful investigations of Butenandt, Weidel and Becker (1944) and Tatum and Beadle (1938) have shown that the gene hormone A of *Ephestia kuehniella* and the gene hormone v^+ of *Drosophila* are identical. Moreover, their effect can be repeated with l-kynurenine, which has some physical and chemical features in common with the gene hormones. In contrast, d-kynurenine and kynurenic acid have no effect on eye-coloration.

L-kynurenine is a substance formed by the enzymatic oxidation of the amino-acid tryptophane. The gene hormones concerned have been shown to work as oxidation enzymes in such a way as to continue the reaction till the particular colour substance has been formed. The following diagram shows how, according to Beadle (cf. B. Scharrer, 1942), the various eye-pigments develop in this way:

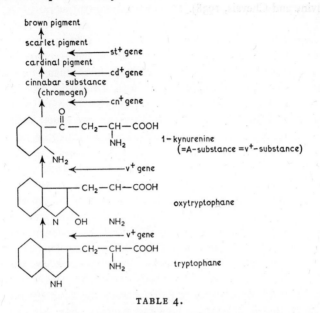

TABLE 4.

The brown eye-pigment of *Drosophila* is a substance of the ommochrome group (Becker, 1942). The cinnabar pigment (cn+) may be regarded as the chromogen for the black eye-pigment (Kikkawa, 1941). Quantitative investigations on the formation of eye-pigment in *Ephestia* have shown that the amount of pigment is directly proportional to the amount of the injected pigment.

Other gene hormones. Apart from the gene hormones affecting the pigmentation of the eyes and various other parts of the body, a humorally transmissible factor which conditions the number of facets of the eye has been shown in *Drosophila*. In *Drosophila melanogaster* a mutation known as 'bar' occurs, which differs from the wild type in that its compound eyes have 50–60 facets instead of the normal 600–650 facets. It is said to lack the gene B+. When mutant larvae receive an extract of wild type larvae in their food, however, the number of facets shows a significant increase (Chevais, 1943, 1944; Ephrussi, Chevais and Khouvine, 1938). An extract of *Calliphora* pupae is equally effective. The active substance concerned, known as 'anti-bar substance', seems to be very common in insects. Its chemical composition has not yet been determined, although the same effect can be obtained using imidazole derivatives such as histidine, creatinine and methylhydantoin, which is especially active (Khouvine and Harnly, 1936; Khouvine and Chevais, 1938).

CHAPTER SEVEN

Incompletely Known Substances with Allegedly Hormonal Characteristics

Apart from the groups of insect hormones considered in the previous chapters, the existence has been reported of several other phenomena with an alleged hormonal character in a variety of insect species. It seems useful to give them a brief mention in this chapter, although there is still insufficient proof of a hormonal character for most of them, and the hormonal character of others has been irrefutably disproved.

The Problem of Sex Hormones in Insects

The first attempts to demonstrate humoral substances of a hormonal nature were concerned with the gonads. The reason for this was probably that the first and most striking endocrine effects in vertebrates had been found to be those of the morphogenetically active sex hormones. The lack of success which followed such research with insects was probably the main reason why the first discoveries of hormones in insects were so delayed in comparison with the hormones in vertebrates. Today it is considered proved that there are no substances in insects equivalent to the morphogenetical sex hormones which influence the secondary sexual characters of vertebrates. One of the most convincing reasons for this conclusion is the existence in insects of several types of gynandromorphs (mosaic, transverse and longitudinal), i.e. specimens which combine the secondary sexual characters of males and females. Such individuals are not found among vertebrates. As all parts of the insect body are permeated by one body fluid (haemolymph), they would of necessity all come in contact with all substances discharged into it. Were any of these substances to influence differentiation towards either male or female, all parts of the body would necessarily be affected in the same way. Therefore no sharp transition between male and female parts could exist.

This evidence is supported by the almost entirely negative results produced by work with experimental castration. The few exceptions of which the results were inconclusive are discussed in more detail below. Numerous experiments carried out by a number of authors in a variety of insect groups, and involving the removal of the gonads, have not resulted in any appreciable changes in the secondary sexual characters (Kopeć, 1910a, b, 1911a, 1912, 1914; Oudemans, 1899; Meissenheimer, 1908; Regen, 1909, 1910 etc.). Some authors refer to the results of experiments by Prell (1915) with the moth *Cosmotriche potatoria* as demonstrating an exceptionally positive effect of castration. Prell found that the castration of male caterpillars produced the pigment pattern characteristic of females in some of the resulting moths. In addition, females with the ovaries removed developed to moths with green haemolymph, which is colourless in normal specimens. Similar experiments by the same author with *Lasiocampa quercus* were, however, without any effect.

Ignoring the possibility of the presence in the *Cosmotriche* material of intersexes, which are quite common and would appear independently of the experimental treatment, the most probable explanation of Prell's results appears to be an artifact produced by the experimental treatment. Such treatment might have interfered with the factor correlating the reaction rates of the various developmental processes (cf. Goldschmidt, p. 117). This factor probably affects the development of secondary sexual characters in this species by influencing the individual morphogenetical processes differentially.

Often quoted as strong evidence in favour of the existence of special sex hormones are the numerous cases of morphological effects resulting from the stylopization, mermithization and internal parasitism by larvae of entomophagous insects. For example, stylopized females of solitary bees of the genera *Andrena* and *Halictus* lack various secondary sexual characters, such as the pollen brushes and pollen baskets on the third pair of legs. In addition, the shape and pattern of the clypeus more or less completely resemble the male condition. Similarly, parasitized males resemble females in some particulars. There is, however, a simple explanation of these phenomena without supposing a special sex hormone; it is the result of a decrease caused by the parasite in the amount of the food taken by the host. This explanation is supported by observations quoted by Schwanvich (1949) that stylopization can only affect the normal course of morphogenesis if the host larva is unable to replace the quantity of food consumed by the parasite. This is just what occurs in solitary bees and wasps, but not in the social species. In solitary Hymenoptera, e.g. the genera *Andrena* and *Halictus* mentioned above, the larva is in a mud cell and is supplied with a certain quantity of pollen and nectar by the mother bee. The cell is then closed, so that the larva is restricted to a particular amount of food, much of which may subsequently be used by the parasite. In contrast, the larvae of the social bees and wasps are fed directly by mouth-to-mouth feeding from the workers. As the amount of this feeding depends on the needs of the larvae throughout their development, no deficiency in parasitized individuals can occur. In fact, no morphological effects have so far been observed in stylopized specimens of the social species, although the occurrence of stylopization is quite frequent.

The various results of internal parasitism of ant females lead to the same conclusion. With ants, the caste differences between the reproductive females (queens) and the sterile workers or soldiers are modified by parasitism in a similar way. It has recently been shown that the differences between castes are influenced by differences in the quality and quantity of food during particular periods. Females of *Lasius niger* parasitized by the nematode *Mermis* and known as mermithogynes have their abdomen almost entirely filled by the worm, and are distinctly smaller and have a narrower thorax and shorter wings than normal females. Similarly, the mermithized workers of the Texas ant *Pheidole commutata* described by Wheeler, approach the female condition in having developed ocelli and a broader thorax. This does not necessarily mean, however, that the usual interpretation given, i.e. that the parasite induces female (queen) characters in the worker larva, is correct. It is much more probable that the queen larvae are so strongly affected by the reduced nutrition that their adult appearance resembles that of workers more than that of productive females. In all these examples the secondary sex and caste characters are controlled by a morphogenetical mechanism which is based on the quantity or quality of the food taken by the insect during a critical period as a larva. Such a mechanism is therefore easily affected by parasitism.

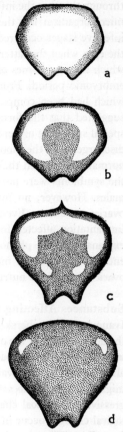

FIG. 53. The effect of stylopization on the form, size and pattern of clypeus in the wasp *Odynerus perennis*: *a* – clypeus of normal male; *b* – stylopized male; *c* – stylopized female; *d* – normal female. (After Salt, 1931.)

Buchner's observations on the sexual differences in female leaf-hoppers of the genera *Euacanthus* and *Solenocephalus* likewise cannot be regarded as evidence for the existence of a special sex-hormone, though they were claimed as such by Koller (1938). Buchner showed that the mycetomes of the female leaf-hoppers in these genera differed from those of the males by a special protuberance, which he called the infection-protuberance. It was through this that the infective stages (analogous to spores) of the symbiotic micro-organism left the mycetomes. Coincident with the protuberance, infective stages occurred only in the females. These stages penetrate into the eggs when the latter ripen and form a special globular structure from which the mycetomes of the new individual develop in the course of the embryonic period. From observations on three females, the ovaries of which had been completely destroyed by a dipterous parasite, Buchner suggested that the formation of the protuberance was determined by a special substance or perhaps several substances which the ripening ovaries discharged into the blood. Although the mycetomes of these females were normally developed they lacked protuberances and the infective stages of the symbionts were not formed; thus the mycetomes resembled those of males. However, no humoral effect of any substance produced by the ovaries was shown. Even if it were possible to show that castration or ovary implantation affected formation of the protuberance etc., a more probable explanation of the phenomena would still be that it was the result of differences in the internal medium (the requirements of the quickly growing ovaries altering the nutrient balance otherwise available to the mycetomes).

Substances Affecting the Ovarian Cycle in Insects

Ivanov and Mescherskaya (1935) carried out a detailed investigation on the development of the ovaries, egg-laying and the shedding of the oothecae in females of the cockroaches *Blattella germanica* and *Blatta orientalis*. They also studied the equivalent periods of time in the ovarian cycle of the migratory locust (*Locusta migratoria*). They found that, besides the progressive histological changes associated with egg ripening, rapid physiological changes occur in the ovaries of adult females. These changes were reversible and were primarily recognized by a change in the permeability of the follicular epithelium found between the individual oocytes.

The immature ovaries, as found in the nymphs of *Blatella germanica*, can be recognized by the impermeability of the follicular epithelium to various vital stains such as neutral-red and haemoglobin, to some salts and to hydrogen peroxide. However, at a later stage, the permeability is especially marked with the above-mentioned vital stains, which even penetrate into the oocytes and stain the cytoplasmic granules. This stage lasts until the ootheca is formed, when the permeability of the follicular epithelium again decreases. The increase in permeability does not reappear until after the ootheca has been shed and, correlated with its reappearance, further eggs ripen.

The substance from the fat bodies which affects ripening of the ovaries. The same two authors found that ovarian maturity and its associated permeability characteristics could be induced artificially in immature nymphal ovaries by transplanting them into the body cavity of a female with maturing eggs. In vitro experiments showed that this was in fact a humoral effect carried in the haemolymph. By testing extracts of various organs from mature females it was shown that, besides the haemolymph, extracts of the fat body were also active. The authors concluded that the fat body produces a hormone which induces maturity of the ovaries. At the same time, however, they showed that the effect is unspecific, extracts of the hypophysis having a similar effect when injected into the body cavity of a female with immature ovaries. The fact that maturity of the ovaries depends on the increased permeability of the follicular epithelium led the authors to suppose that a similar effect might be produced by various substances which lower surface tension. Saponin and sodium taurocholate were tested and proved active, both in vitro and when drunk in an aqueous solution by females with immature ovaries. Unlike extracts of the fat body and the hypophysis, however, the action of these substances did not induce the normal maturation of the eggs. Although growth of the ovaries was accelerated by the substances, maturation ceased at a certain point so that no mature eggs ready for oviposition were obtained.

The substance from the 'corpus luteum' inhibiting maturation of the ovaries. The temporary return to immature conditions is characteristic of those species in which the female carries the eggs in an ootheca until they hatch,

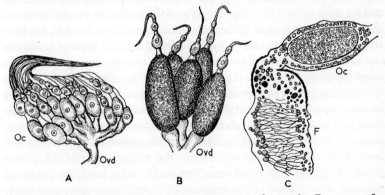

FIG. 54. *Blattella germanica.* A – immature ovary of nymph; B – ovary of a sexually mature female; C – longitudinal section of an ovariole of a female with ootheca; Oc – oocyte; F – empty follicle with corpus luteum; Ovd – oviducts. (From Ivanov and Mescherskaya, 1935.)

I

which include the cockroaches studied by Ivanov and Mescherskaya. In such species, maturation of additional eggs during this period would be useless and might even be harmful. Transplantation of a mature ovary into the body cavity of a female with an ootheca has shown that here also the return to immaturity is due to a substance carried in the haemolymph. The search for the source of this substance has shown that it originates at the posterior ends of the ovarioles, where the 'corpora lutea' form in the emptied follicles. The substance affects the ovaries within 30–60 minutes. Again the effect is not specific to the one substance, but can be reproduced by an extract of thyroidea or by pure thyroxin, by free iodine and also by substances such as cholesterol which increase surface tension.

It is interesting that, in spite of the numerous references made to the paper by Ivanov and Mescherskaya, there is as yet no data to show whether corresponding substances occur in other groups of insects.

In order to demonstrate whether such substances are really hormonal it would be necessary to show that they are of general occurrence and that they are indispensable for normal development of the ovaries. It would further be necessary to determine their relations to the two metamorphosis hormones, i.e. the AH and the JH, which several authors have recently shown to affect the ovarian cycles of other insect species.

The Humoral Activity of the Oenocytes

For a long time the oenocytes have been the centre of a great deal of attention by workers interested in the endocrine functions of insects. Although most authors are agreed that the oenocytes are in some way connected with humoral activity (cf. Wigglesworth, 1953), their function is still far from clear. The cycle of their activity during the successive instars in the larval development of the chironomid *Syndiamesa branicki*, has been studied in detail by Zavřel (1953a). He found that the cycle of activity of the imaginal oenocytes (synoenocytes) was closely connected with the moulting process and with the development of the gonads. In this species the synoenocytes do not appear until the last larval instar and then rapidly increase in volume. At the same time spindle-like vacuoles appear in their basophilic cytoplasm. Towards the end of metamorphosis the synoenocytes decrease in size and form syncytia-like structures with indistinct cell boundaries. This cycle corresponds to the activity cycle of the Verson gland (cf. fig. 55). The larval oenocytes, on the other hand, are connected with the development of the imaginal discs and disintegrate completely during metamorphosis together with most of the other larval tissues (cf. p. 306).

As regards the larval oenocytes, several authors have suggested that they produce a hormone which induces moulting (Koller, 1939, cf. Wigglesworth, 1953a). This is supported by the fact that, in silkworms, the oenocytes are the first cells to show any activity during the moulting cycle of normal specimens, whereas they show no activity in a mutant strain which

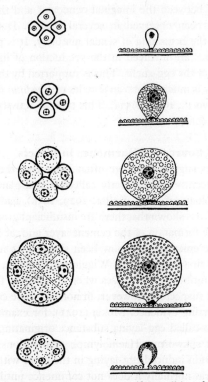

FIG. 55. Secretory cycle of an oenocyte group (four cells) and a Verson gland in the epidermis of the chironomid *Syndiomesa branicki* in five consecutive periods of the last larval instar (after Zavřel, 1935b).

fails to moult. In the bug *Rhodnius*, however, the oenocytes do not reach the peak of their activity until long after the moulting cycle has begun (Wigglesworth, 1933). In this species a definite relation of the oenocytes to the deposition of the cuticular layer of the epicuticle has been observed. Immediately before the deposition of this layer, the oenocytes become greatly enlarged and lobulate. At this time they stain deep grey with osmium tetroxide and stain diffusely with fat stains. As the oenocytes discharge their contents and subsequently shrink in size, these staining reactions are shown successively by the epidermal cells and the newly formed cuticulin layer of the epicuticle. From these observations Wigglesworth

(1948b, 1949) suggested that the oenocytes should be regarded as epidermal cells which have become specialized for the production of the lipoproteins forming the cuticular layer and perhaps the wax layer in some other insects.

A connection between the imaginal oenocytes and the development of the gonads has been observed in several species. Definite changes are associated with the beginning of sexual maturity. It is probable that here also the oenocytes are involved in the production of lipoprotein forming part of the eggs or the egg-shells. This is supported by the observation that oenocyte activity is much greater in females of *Rhodnius prolixus* than in the males (Wigglesworth, 1933, 1953a). This type of activity seems to be of a humoral nature (cf. p. 270).

Other Alleged Sources of Hormones in Insects
In earlier papers suggestions were often made that the so-called Verson glands, more recently and correctly called dermal glands as in Verson's original terminology (cf., e.g., Koller, 1929, 1938), had a secretory function. Later work has shown that there are insufficient grounds for this view. Their role in the formation of the cement layer and, at least partly, of the wax layer of the epicuticle has now been shown in a number of species. Such a role was first suggested by Wigglesworth (1934, cf. 1939).

There are a number of other cases where a secretory function of various tissues has been suspected. However, in none of these cases is there as yet sufficient supporting evidence. Mokia (1941), for example, suggested the existence of a so-called egg-laying substance originating after fertilization in female adult silkworms. Haemolymph transfusions from a fertilized female into a virgin induced egg-laying in the latter within the first day of adult life, whereas normally it does not commence until several days after the imaginal moult. The myotropic effects of the neurohormones C and D mentioned previously (cf. p. 211) must also be considered in this connection.

Also falling into this category is Yakhontov's (1945) suggestion that sexual maturity and the flying instinct in some beetles are humorally connected. There is also a regulating factor in the timing of the degeneration of the indirect flight musculature of female ants with regard to fertilization and egg laying.

There is little doubt that future work will reveal a number of further humoral relationships in insects.

CHAPTER EIGHT

The Exohormones

The exohormones are of hormonal character in that they are produced by the organism and are physiologically active at extremely small concentrations. However, they do not act solely, if at all, in the individual which produces them, but instead affect other individuals in the same colony of social insects. For this reason some authors have called them 'sociohormones'. The term 'ectohormones' has also been used, but this is less apt because not all exohormones occur on the body surface of the individuals producing them and scarcely any are produced there.

Karlson and Lüscher (1959a, b) recently proposed a new term 'pheromones'[1] for this kind of active substance, the term to include substances 'secreted by an individual and received by a second individual of the same species in which they release a specific reaction, for example, a definite behaviour or developmental process. The principle of minute amounts being effective holds. They function as chemical messengers among individuals.'

Apart from the exohormones as defined above, however, the authors also include in the term pheromones (later changed to pherormones by Pain, 1961) sexual attractants and other olfactorily active substances which reach their site of action through the air, such as marking scents and warning substances. The authors further include orally active substances such as the alleged determining substance in royal jelly.

In another paper reviewing this category of substances Karlson and Butenandt (1959) suggest the 'possible future necessity' of distinguishing between substances which act sensorily, for which the term telomones is suggested, and those which act biochemically, to which the term pheromones would be restricted.

There are major reasons against including both the sensorily and biochemically active substances under the same heading, within which one may separate the biochemically active substances working inside the body (hormones) from those working outside the body (exohormones). First of all, a basic phylogenetical difference exists between the two groups. Those substances which act sensorily, indirectly and by means of the nervous system have secondarily acquired a physiological action on a particular function (e.g. copulatory movements) after that function had been fully

[1] From the Greek 'pherein' = to carry, and 'hormon' = to stimulate, to excite.

developed phylogenetically. By contrast those substances which act bio-chemically and directly have an activity which is phylogenetically primary. From this a more complicated function (e.g. inhibition of ovary develop-ment by the queen inhibiting substance of the honey bee, or inhibition of morphogenesis in permanent nymphs by inhibitory substances of the reproductives in *Kalotermes*) has developed secondarily. This sharp dis-tinction between the exohormones and substances acting sensorily exists even though both types of substances seem to work together in the control of honey-bee workers by the queen. The distinction furthermore holds even though there may exist a group of substances which control neuro-secretion and which seem to combine both an indirect (sensory) and a direct (biochemical) effect but are nevertheless of a definite sensory character.

Further clear evidence that there is a close relationship between exo-hormones and hormones in the restricted sense is provided by the extremely interesting effects that exohormones of the honey bee have on the develop-ment of the ovaries in crustaceans (the work of Carlisle and Butler; cf. p. 259) and the similarity of their physiological effects to those of particular neurohormones (emphasized by Noirot; cf. p. 257).

The fundamental affinity of exohormones with hormones is even clearer if we view the social insect colony as the beginnings of an organism of a higher order. Then one may regard exohormones as substances circulating and producing their effects inside the organism (colony).

It therefore seems preferable to restrict the use of the term pheromones to those substances which act via the nervous system and to reserve the term exohormones for substances with a direct biochemical activity being transmitted within the colonies of social insects. This is the sense in which the term has been used in the earlier editions of this book.

As far as the active substances contained in royal jelly are concerned, it seems justifiable to consider them as a special group of 'milk' (or nourish-ing) substances which are neither pheromones or exohormones as they work mainly nutritionally. In this connection the term 'milk' is used in its widest physiological sense to include the pharyngeal products of bees, i.e. the royal jelly and worker food as well as the milk of mammals (cf., e.g., Brian, 1957). We thus reach the diagram on page 245 for classifying physio-logically active substances.

Of these substances only the hormones, including the exohormones, belong within the scope of this book. However, a few of the pheromones of bees (p. 252) and termites (p. 247) have also been included, as they are produced together with the exohormones and have not yet been clearly separated.

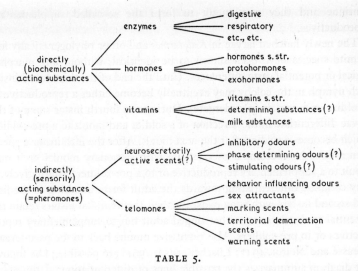

TABLE 5.

The Exhormones of Termites

Polymorphism. In spite of the low phylogenetical level of the termites, the highest level of caste polymorphism and division of labour has been reached. The diversity of types shows a substantial increase over the social Hymenoptera with the occurrence in termites of all the castes. Not only reproductives, but also workers and soldiers of various kinds are produced in both sexes. This is, no doubt, connected with a much higher phylogenetical age of the polymorphism here than in the phylogenetically younger Hymenoptera.

A normal termite colony has one pair of reproductives, the king and queen, which were originally winged and only lost their wings during the foundation of a new colony after the mating flight. The proportion of workers and soldiers in a normal well-developed colony of a given termite species appears to be more or less constant. In many phylogenetically low termite species, however, there are no true adult workers, and their position and function is occupied by the so-called pseudergates (Grassé, 1947). These are larvae whose development has been arrested at a particular morphogenetical stage prior to metamorphosis. Their prothoracic glands remain intact and active, however, so that they continue moulting at regular intervals, but without any growth or differentiation. These moults have been called stationary moults (Lüscher, 1961). The pseudergates are therefore permanent larvae in the full sense of the word. If the reproductive pair is removed from the colony, the development of the pseudergates may continue and they may moult to form the so-called supplementary reproductives.

The newly hatched larvae in *Kalotermes* and other phylogenetically low termite species have been shown to be identical, without any morphological or potential caste differences. Until the end of the third larval instar each nymph in the colony may eventually become either a reproductive or a soldier or a worker (pseudergate). During the fourth instar some of the larvae differentiate in the direction of a soldier and moult to a pre-soldier, which becomes a soldier after the next moult. After the fifth instar a specimen may either become a pseudergate with stationary moults or it may moult to a supplementary reproductive or to a pre-soldier. Alternatively, it may continue differentiating towards the adult form, moulting to the first and second instars with wing pads. Further, the nymphal instars retain the potential to develop not to the winged adult but to supplementary reproductives or to pre-soldiers. Also regressive moults back to the pseudergate (Grassé and Noirot, 1947; Lüscher, 1952, 1961) are possible. The following diagram summarizes the possible lines of differentiation:

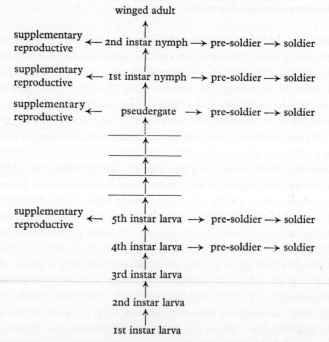

TABLE 6. Polymorphism in *Kalotermes flavicollis* (modified from Lüscher, 1961). Each arrow represents a moult, the broken line indicates the possibility of several moults.

In higher termites the situation is more complicated and several authors (cf. Brian, 1957) have alleged that genetic and histogenetic determination is involved. As evidence for genetic determination, the fact that some termite species form their soldiers from one sex and their workers from the other has been stressed. Whereas both sexes are able to produce both castes in other species, particularly in the lower termites, each sex in the higher termites seems secondarily to have lost the potential to produce one or other caste. Caste determination in these species is therefore controlled by sex and consequently also controlled genetically.

In many species of the family Termitidae differences in internal structure between winged and apterous adults are said to occur already in the first instar. In *Tenuirostritermes tenuirostris* (Desneaux) the inhibitory effect of reproductives on the formation of further reproductives has been observed at the moment of hatching and, according to Weesner (cf. Brian, 1961), may occur even earlier.

The inhibitory substances. Research over the last few years has shown that inhibition of the growth and differentiation of pseudergates (e.g. in *Kalotermes*) is caused by the effect of a particular chemical substance produced by the functional reproductives. It has been shown that in certain species the functional reproductives produce a specific substance or substances, the so-called queen inhibitory substance and probably also a king inhibitory substance, the effect of which inhibits the development of ovaries and doubtless at the same time inhibits growth (including differentiation) of the imaginal parts of the body and of the body as a whole. By the action of the inhibitory substances the development of the majority of the larvae in a colony is arrested at the pseudergate level. When the reproductive pair dies or is artificially removed from the colony the inhibitory effect disappears and many of the pseudergates change to supplementary reproductives at the next moult. The pseudergates which change are those which are in a suitable physiological state when the inhibitory effect disappears, i.e. at the appropriate stage of the intermoult period. The same applies to larvae in the appropriate stage of the fifth larval instar and to those in the first and second nymphal instar (cf. the diagram on p. 246). As soon as the first pair of supplementary reproductives starts to reproduce, further supernumerary reproductives are killed by the workers and the inhibitory substances produced by the new king and queen inhibit further differentiation of reproductives in the colony.

The recent papers by Lüscher (1961 etc.) suggest the existence of four different inhibitory substances concerned with regulating the development of the supplementary reproductives. The effect of at least two of them seems to be amplified by the workers (pseudergates) through a remarkable sex-linked effect: the male pseudergates seem selectively to inhibit the development of female supplementaries and vice-versa. Further evidence, both experimental and comparative, is necessary before these conclusions can be fully confirmed and the effects understood (cf. Lüscher, 1956).

The source of the inhibitory substances has not yet definitely been discovered. Experiments have been carried out in which a wire mesh has prevented pseudergates reaching either the anterior or the posterior parts of the body of living reproductives. Other experiments have involved the use of extracts from various parts of the body. These various experiments suggest that the active substances originate either in the head or thorax of the specimen and that they leave the body via the intestinal tract, most probably with the faeces (Light, 1944, Lüscher, 1953, Hinton, 1955/6). The inhibitory substance or substances produced by females is said to differ from that produced by males. The substances produced by the king and queen are complementary in such a way that the full effect is only obtained if both reproductives are present. The inhibitory effect of the female by itself is feeble and that of the male is virtually nil (cf. p. 307).

The chemistry of the inhibitory substances is as yet almost unknown. It has been shown, however, that the active principle can be extracted from the queens with methanol or just with pure water, and that there is little difference in the activity of the two extracts (Light, 1944). The substance is still active several months after the death of the animal yet the effect of the reproductives disappears within 24 hours of their removal from the colony. This has been interpreted as a rapid inactivation of the inhibitory substance (Lüscher, 1952/6). An alternative explanation is that the substance is quickly removed from the circulatory system by the Malpighian tubules and may perhaps be inactivated during its passage through them. Büchli (1956) has shown that the substance (substances) is only active when applied during the first third of a given instar but that the state of the fat body (quantity of reserve materials) also seems to be important. It is not yet clear whether the substance can also be produced by specimens which are unable to reproduce (cf. Hinton, 1955/6) though some of Lüscher's experiments (1956b, c) seem to show that this is so. The results of Lüscher's (1955) experiments appear to suggest that these substances are exohormones. When a sexual pair and pseudergates were separated by a double barrier of wire gauze which prevented any contact but allowed the passage of odours, the result was equivalent to the complete removal of the reproductives: a pair of functional reproductives was produced and they survived. When only a single barrier allowing antennal contact was used, all developing supplementary reproductives were eliminated. It is not clear from the experiments whether the substance (or substances) perceived by the antennae is identical with the substance (exohormone) inhibiting the development of reproductives or whether it merely affects the behaviour of the pseudergates and causes them to eliminate the excess reproductives. In the latter case the substance would be a pheromone in the sense used in this book. Such a parallel action of an exhormone and a pheromone has been found in work on bees (cf. p. 254).

The stimulating substances. As well as the inhibitory substances in both winged and supplementary reproductives, Lüscher (1956b, c) claims to have found one or perhaps two substances having a stimulating effect on the development of supplementaries. He was able to extract this substance from the heads of supplementaries with methanol, and strips of filter paper soaked with the extract proved to be active. Compared with control experiments, application of the extract produced a definite positive effect, though only if the reproductives were removed. This showed that the stimulating effect is weaker than the inhibitory one. Lüscher assumes that one of these different sex-specific substances is produced by the females which stimulates the production of males, and the other substance by males stimulating the production of females. In the natural colony these substances would assume importance if one of the reproductive pair were lost. The presence of the remaining reproductive would then stimulate the replacement of its mate by a supplementary of the appropriate sex. The selection value of the stimulating substances would perhaps be in the acceleration of the replacement process and it seems to be all the more important as the loss of only one reproductive is much more frequent in natural conditions than the simultaneous loss of the pair.

Exohormones and the metamorphosis hormones. Several authors have tested the possibility that exohormones modify the secretion and activity of the metamorphosis hormones in termites. One of the first papers on this subject was by Kaiser (1955). The results of Kaiser's work may be summarized as follows: differentiation from the pseudergate level in the lower termites involves a different number of moults for different castes, i.e. three for a normal winged reproductive, two for a soldier and one for a supplementary reproductive (cf. the diagram on p. 246). These differences suggest corresponding differences in the production and action of the metamorphosis hormones, and histological differences were in fact found in the ventral glands and the corpora allata. In the higher termites, the development of workers has been found to be correlated with low functioning of the ventral glands while the development of soldiers is correlated with a notable increase in size of the ventral glands and corpora allata. The ventral glands degenerated following the imaginal moult. A big increase in the size of the corpora allata was observed in each instar during the development of supplementaries, but this increase was not found during the development of normal reproductives where the increase occurs at the time of egg-laying. During stationary moults (see above), the ventral glands of the pseudergates about doubled their size from that of the intermoult period.

Lüscher (1957a) and Lüscher and Springhetti (1960) studied the influence of implanting corpora allata from different donors into pseudergates in normal colonies and colonies which had lost their reproductive pair. In most cases, the implantation of the corpora allata resulted in moults to pre-soldiers. Under some conditions moults to intercastes between pre-soldiers and supplementary reproductives and between pseudergates and pre-soldiers resulted. The authors concluded that at least three factors influence the type of differentiation which follows implantation of corpora allata. These factors are (1) the physiological state of the recipient specimen; (2) the physiological state of the colony; and (3) the physiological state of the implanted gland (i.e. the physiological state of the donor specimen).

The authors went on to develop a theory based on the assumption that there are two different corpus allatum hormones, one with a juvenilizing effect and the other with gonadotropic activity. According to the theory, the 'juvenile hormone' favours the differentiation of supplementaries while the 'gonadotropic hormone' favours the differentiation of pre-soldiers. This theory needs to become rather complicated to explain, even in part, the various experimental results obtained by the authors. A more simple theory, however, can be suggested which agrees with the GF theory. Such a theory involves the assumption of only one corpus allatum hormone, which does not disagree with anything known about the JH. In the presence of the inhibitory substances (i.e. in the presence of the reproductives) growth (both isometric and gradient growth), as well as production of JH, are more or less completely inhibited. Under these conditions a low dose of JH favours development towards supplementaries while increasing doses (prolonged period of action) result in intercastes and eventually the differentiation of pre-soldiers. If the exohormones are absent, supplementaries will develop. This prothetelic effect seems to be entirely due to a reduced proportion of nutrients for the imaginal parts by the accelerated growth of the ovaries in the absence of the inhibitory factor, in accordance with the law of correlation of consumption (cf. p. 116). In the presence of the inhibitory factor the application of JH will again induce the formation of pre-soldiers with possible intercastes at the expense of the supplementaries. A further piece of evidence in favour of the GF theory is that the ventral glands do not degenerate until a definite level of differentiation, as in supplementaries and adults, has been reached. They remain active both in pseudergates, where differentiation is inhibited by the exohormones, and in pre-soldiers, where differentiation is delayed by the JH.

The phylogeny of social life in termites. The discovery of exohormones has clarified the picture of the origin of social life in the Isoptera. As Kaiser (1955) pointed out, the termites differ from the Hymenoptera in that no examples are known of a solitary way of life or of transitions between this and social life. The first signs of a development towards a social life can, however, often be seen in the orders Dictyoptera (in the suborder Blattodea) and Dermaptera which are closely allied to the ancestors of the termites. In these orders it is a frequent phenomenon that nymphs in various instars live together with the female or with the parent generation. Under such conditions the appearance in phylogeny of an inhibitory substance of an exohormone character would necessarily prolong the situation by keeping the morphogenetical stage of the nymphs static. This would automatically keep the stage of development of the brain unchanged and thus preserve the nymphal instincts. The selection value of each of these effects as a step towards social life is clear. These first stages would prepare the way for the development of trophallaxis and other features of social life (cf. Schneirla, in Roeder, 1953). Such conclusions are confirmed by the wide un-specificity and doubtless also wide distribution of the exohormones shown by several authors (Carlisle and Butler, 1956; Hrdý and Novák, 1960 etc.).

Exohormones in the Hymenoptera

Polymorphism in the Hymenoptera is fundamentally quite different from that in termites. The main difference is that (apart from perhaps a few un-important exceptions) only the female sex is involved. Usually only one caste besides the reproductive females and males is found; i.e. the female workers, which may in some cases be polymorphic. A second sterile female caste, the soldier, is only found in some species of ants. In the colonies of the honey bee (*Apis mellifica*) only one extra caste exists. These are females with reduced ovaries which are known as workers. The first differentiation to worker or queen larvae does not start till the third day after the larva hatches. Up to this moment any larva may develop in either direction. The determining factor involved is the quality and quantity of the food supplied

by the workers (Rhein, 1952). Under normal conditions, however, the fate
of each individual is already decided at the time of egg laying, as the eggs
from which the queens develop are laid into special large and distinct
queen cells. In adult bees the ovaries of workers in colonies with queens are
reduced and functionless, whereas in queenless colonies the ovaries of the
workers become functional and the workers start laying eggs. Recent work
has established that both ovarian development in the workers and the
consequent instinct of workers to construct queen cells are controlled by
definite substances produced by the queen which are similar to the exohormones and pheromones already mentioned in termites. Unlike the
lower termites, however, both the bee and ant workers are adult insects
with disintegrated prothoracic glands and are therefore unable to moult
and develop further. There is, however, a major difference between the bees
and ants: whereas the queen bee is only slightly neotenic in comparison
with the worker bees, the wingless ant workers are strongly neotenic in
comparison with the winged sexual females.

The inhibitory substance of the honey bee. The inhibitory substance is produced by the fertilized queen. The first effect of removing the queen from
the colony is that the workers construct emergency queen cells. These
queen cells are constructed above some of the original worker cells in which
eggs or young larvae are still present. If neither eggs nor larvae are available
to the workers in the colony when the queen is lost, the ovaries of many of
them (of about 10% of the workers within a week of removing the queen)
start developing. After some time the workers begin to lay eggs, but of
course these remain unfertilized and only drones develop. Both the construction of queen cells and the development of ovaries in workers are the
symptoms of absence of the inhibitory substance, i.e. the absence of the
queen. There is also, however, a definite positive effect of the substance (or
group of substances) which results in the queens (alive or dead) or extracts
prepared from them being highly attractive to the workers. There is still
doubt expressed in the literature, whether Butler's original assumption
(1954) is correct that only one queen-inhibiting substance produces all the
effects mentioned, or whether there are at least two substances as suggested
by Pain (1952, 1954a, b, 1954), Grost and Voogd (1954) and Voogd (1955),
one substance being the inhibitor of ovarian development and the other
Butler's 'Queen Substance', which Brian (1957) has called a hormone and
a signal.

Pain (1961) recently made a detailed study of all three aspects of the
effects of the queen on the workers. From her work Pain suggested that the
inhibitory substance is complex and a mixture of several acids:

1. The substance isolated by Barbier (1958) from active extracts of queens and workers in colonies with queens; a substance also isolated by Callow and Johnston (1959) from the heads of fertilized queens. Both groups of authors simultaneously synthesized this acid: Barbier (1960) synthesized it from cycloheptanone and Johnston (1959) from azelaic acids. It has the following formula:

$$CH_3—C—(CH_2)_5—C = C—COOH$$

(with H above the first carbon of the C=C, O double-bonded below the second carbon, and H below the C=C)

and is α, β unsaturated 9-oxydec-2-enoic acid. Pain called this acid pheromone I. The acid forms white flakes and has the following effects on queenless workers:

(a) It inhibits the construction of queen cells – at a concentration of 0·13 μg. per bee according to Butler and at 0·5 μg. according to Pain (1961a).

(b) It is an indispensable component of the queen odour but is not itself attractive to the workers (Barbier and Pain, 1960).

(c) It does not inhibit the formation of eggs in the ovaries of workers, either when injected or in food or when licked from the body surface of the dead queen.

2. A second substance which Pain (1961) called pheromone II was isolated in the form of highly volatile esters by distillation from the active pentane soluble fraction (pentane acids). Two of these esters were identified by gas-chromatography as methyl phenylacetate and methyl phenyl-propionate (Pain, Hijel and Barbier, 1960). This substance is not attractive to workers by itself, but when mixed with 'pheromone I' gives the characteristic queen odour (Barbier and Pain, 1960).

Both pheromone I and II were found to occur in the mandibular glands of fertile queens. Only traces of exohormone I were present in emerging queens, and pheromone II appeared later. This agreed with the lack of attractivity of freshly emerged queens. The rate at which the pheromone complex (I and II) was produced appeared to depend on, apart from the age of the queen, the number of workers accompanying her, i.e. the state of nutrition of the queen seems to be the important factor.

Basing her argument on an analysis of Müsbichler's (1952) work, Pain went on to claim that the substance causing the inhibition in ovarial development of the workers was not identical with the inhibitor of queen cell construction. She was certainly also right in attaching importance to the effect of what she calls nutritional castration of the workers by the queen which causes the inhibition of ovarian development. A number of earlier workers (cf., e.g., Hess, 1947) have shown that the queen influences the development of ovaries in the workers, first by herself consuming a quantity of the pharyngeal gland secretion (royal jelly) of her attendant bees, and then secondarily, and what is much more important, by producing larvae which are the main consumers of royal and/or worker jelly. This alimentary mechanism, which works parallel with the inhibitory substance, is without doubt quantitatively the main cause of suppression of ovarian development in workers.

Pain's conclusions (1961) on the olfactory character of the queen inhibitory substance, which she suggested worked by inhibiting the secretion of the corpora allata, seem to be less convincing. Her conclusions in no way invalidate the existence of a special inhibitory substance of the exohormone type, which directly and biochemically suppresses the development of the ovaries. Such a substance has been suggested in the papers of Butler (1954, 1957), Carlisle and Butler (1956) and Hrdý, Novák, and Škrobal (1961) etc. Thus the honey-bee queen probably produces at least two pheromones (I and II of Pain) and one exohormone. These three substances work together to produce the inhibitory effects.

Apart from the views expressed by Pain (1961) and mentioned above, other authors seem entirely to agree that actual contact is necessary for the substance inhibiting ovarian development to be transmitted. This has been shown by the fact that a double wire screen between the queen and the workers prevents this inhibition occurring. That the effect of the substance is weaker when taken with food than when licked from the body surface of a dead queen is in no way contradictory of the purely direct biochemical action that Butler (1957, cf. Karlson and Butenandt, 1959) suggested. Both the amount taken per specimen as well as the concentration of the substance seem to be important in producing the inhibition, and both these were probably lower in the food than on the body surface. Thus the grounds for Voogd's 'psychic stimulation' hypothesis (1955, 1956) do not seem to be sufficient.

In contrast to Hinton's conclusions (1955b), the worker bees appear to play an important part in the transmission of the exohormone and the pheromone. It has been shown that if the queen substance, in the form of an aqueous solution of an alcohol extract, is given to worker bees, ovarian development and queen cell construction are suppressed not only in these workers, but also in others which had not originally drunk the extract.

The occurrence of exohormones in other Hymenoptera. Little is still known on exohormones in Hymenoptera other than honey bees. According to

Sakagani (1954) the effect of the queen substance (or substances) in the Japanese bee *Apis indica japonica* seems to be much weaker than in *Apis mellifica*, for fully developed ovaries were found in seventeen out of twenty workers accompanying the queen. This seems to be at least partly due to the workers taking some of the royal jelly, i.e. the secretion of the pharyngeal glands which is fed to the queen. In this species the stimulating effect of the jelly appears to be stronger than the inhibitory effect of the queen substance.

Cumber's (1949) observations suggest that substances with an inhibitory effect on ovarian development also occur in bumble-bees. He found that the sterility of auxiliary females was not determined by the quantity of food available to the bumble-bee colony but by the presence of the queen, for removal of the latter resulted in development of the ovaries of the auxiliary females. Similarly the loss of the queen in colonies of *Polistes gallicus* resulted in egg-laying by the 'workers' within about 24 hours (cf. Hinton, 1955–6). Similar effects have been found in some species of the genus *Halictus* (Qué, 1958).[1]

Stumper (1956) has found an exohormone system, similar to that in bees, in a number of ant species. This system appears to control the following behaviour patterns: (1) crowding of the queen by the workers; (2) extensive licking of the queen; and (3) carrying the queen.

Similar effects are caused by the same substance in various Hymenoptera, and are especially pronounced in *Lasius alienus* and *Pheidole pallidula*. Petroleum proved the most suitable solvent for extracting this exohormone. A dead *Lasius* worker impregnated with an extract of a *Pheidole* queen was accepted as a queen by an orphan *Pheidole* colony. Bier (1956, 1958; cf. Karlson and Butenandt, 1959) has shown that the presence of a functional queen inhibits ovarian development in workers of the species *Leptothorax unifasciatus* and *Formica pratensis*.

The influence of the metamorphosis hormones on caste differentiation has been studied by Brian (1958a) in the ant *Myrmica rubra*. He has shown that there is a critical period in the last larval instar of all female larvae during which the functioning of the corpora allata may be prevented by the neurohormone (AH?) of the neurosecretory cells of the brain. When this happens only sterile workers develop. In the absence of this inhibition the increase in secretory activity of the corpora allata promotes the growth of the imaginal wing and ovarial discs and the ovaries, so that sexual females

---

[1] Those female wasps and bumble-bees which do not lay eggs are not true workers as occur in bees and ants. They are merely unfertilized females of reduced size and with undeveloped ovaries, and are morphologically identical with the 'queen' in every respect, including the activity of gonads.

(queens) develop. Development, however, is also dependent on the state of nutrition as well. Starvation causes a more or less limited development of the wing discs at a critical period, resulting in intercastes of various grades.

In a later paper the same author (Brian, 1961) suggests the following hypothesis. When the MH (ecdyson) concentration increases quickly the relatively small ovaries and wing discs do not have enough time to respond, and workers develop. On the other hand, when the MH concentration increases gradually, as in diapausing larvae, the corpora allata are active and the ovaries and the imaginal discs of the wings grow and develop normally so that winged sexual queens are produced. The determination of diapause which in its turn influences the type of neurosecretory activity of the brain cells thus also affects determination of the female caste.

Brian (1959) has also discussed the possible existence of a special substance with the character of an exohormone which would simultaneously suppress the development of ovaries and other female features and influence the instincts of the workers. He assumed that it would also suppress the secretory activity of the larval corpora allata at the same time.

Concerning the Phylogenetical Origin of Exohormones

The occurrence of hormonal substances inhibiting ovarian development and other growth processes in arthropods is not limited to the social insects. It has been known for a long time that neurohormones produced by the eye stalks of many Decapoda have an inhibitory effect on moulting and growth (Scudamore, 1942; cf. Carlisle and Knowles, 1959). It is therefore extremely interesting that Carlisle and Butler (1956; cf. Carlisle and Knowles, 1959) found that the ovary-inhibiting hormone in the eye stalks of Decapoda produced a similar effect as the queen substance on the ovaries of honey-bee workers in the absence of the queen. The same result was obtained on ant and termite workers. Similarly, the queen substance has been shown to suppress moulting and the functioning of the ovaries in prawns. It has been suggested (Carlisle and Butler, l.c.) that these substances are steroids (cf. p. 259).

The wide un-specificity of the queen-bee inhibitory substance has been further confirmed by Hrdý, Novák and Škrobal (1961; cf. Hrdý and Novák, 1961). An aqueous solution of an evaporated alcohol extract of fertile honey-bee queens was tested on groups of *Kalotermes flavicollis* workers. The extract caused a significant delay in the development of supplementaries compared with control groups. Moreover, whereas the workers in the controls allowed one pair of supplementaries to remain, the workers in the experimental series destroyed the reproductives as they appeared.

Another inhibitory humoral effect is that of the so-called diapause hormone. This is produced by the suboesophageal ganglion of female pupae in those Lepidoptera which show embryonic diapause (cf. p. 200).

It is a rather tempting hypothesis that such humorally active substances were the phylogenetic origin of the various inhibitory exohormones of social insects mentioned above. Such substances probably attained the position of exohormones in one of several ways: (1) by removal from the blood via the Malpighian tubules and then leaving the body with the faeces (as in termites); or (2) by accumulating in glands such as the mandibular glands of the honey bee; (3) by reaching the alimentary canal or perhaps the salivary fluid (cf. Noirot, 1955).

It is therefore very interesting that, according to Noirot (1955), various groups of neurosecretory cells occur in the cerebral and suboesophageal ganglia of the ventral nerve cord of termites. A paired group of neurosecretory cells in the posterior part of the pars intercerebralis, which are not identical with the cells producing the AH, are of particular interest in this respect. These cells stain more deeply in adult insects than in larvae.

An alternative possibility has been suggested by Novák (1961) who emphasizes the similarity in the mode of action of the inhibitory exohormones and the so-called pseudo-juvenilizing effects of some substances like the unsaturated fatty acids (cf. p. 124).

CHAPTER NINE

The Effects of Insect Hormones on Other Groups of Animals and the Effects of the Hormones of Vertebrates and Other Animals on Insects

One of the characteristics of hormones as a group of active substances is the very wide un-specificity of their effects. It has been known for a long time that most of the mammalian hormones produce their effects in birds, amphibians and other groups of vertebrates. Conversely, most of the hormones in all other classes of vertebrates have proved to be active in mammals. The same un-specificity seems to apply to insect hormones and the hormones of the few other groups of anthropods where this aspect has been studied. Besides this wide effect over classes of animals, there are indications that at least some of the insect hormones have a still wider inter-phylum effect and that at least some of the vertebrate hormones are active in insects.

The Effects of Insect Hormones on Crustaceans

Effects on colour changes. In spite of the comparatively close relations of the endocrine systems of insects and crustaceans, particularly as regards the neurohormones, relatively few papers have as yet appeared which deal with the mutual effects of the hormones. That insect neurohormones affect the colour changes in Decapoda has been known for some time from the earlier papers of Hanström (1936, 1938). Hanström studied the effects of various extracts from the nervous system and corpora cardiaca of insects. He found that corpora cardiaca extracts from *Carausius morosus* and several Orthoptera (Saltatoria) caused the concentration of pigment granules in the red and yellow chromatophores of *Palaemonetes vulgaris* and *Leander adspersus*. Kalmus (1936) obtained a similar effect on the chromatophores of *Astacus vulgaris* with extracts from the heads of *Carausius*, although only when the extracts had been boiled. Moreover, the effect was stronger if the insects had been killed during the day than if they had been killed at night. These effects of insect corpora cardiaca were studied in detail in numerous Decapoda by M. Thomsen (1943), and positive results were consistently obtained. The extracts were found to have a very high sensitivity, being effective at a dilution of 1 : 100,000 (tissue to water). The identity of these active substances with any of the known insect hormones has not yet been clarified.

The effect of the queen-bee exohormone on ovarian development. The various similarities in character and effects of the inhibitory exohormone of queen bees with the Decapod neurohormones inhibiting growth of the ovaries led Carlisle and Butler (1956) to test the effects of the exohormone on ovarian development in *Leander serratus* (cf. p. 256). An alcohol extract of a queen bee was emulsified in water using a small quantity of palmitic acid and injected into thirteen female prawns with their eye stalks and sinus glands (i.e. the source of the hormone inhibiting growth of the ovaries) removed. A week later the ovaries were weighed. The weight of the ovaries in the experimental series (an average of 0·72 g.) was lower than in controls injected with palmitic acid (an average of 3·39 g.) by a factor of several times. The authors concluded that both the insect and Decapod substances were closely related if not identical, and suggested they might be steroids.

Effects on the moulting process. Karlson's (1957) discovery of an effective quantity of ecdyson (MH) in the shrimp *Crangon vulgaris* and in several species of crabs was in itself strong evidence that insect MH would induce moulting in crustaceans (Novák, 1959). This effect has recently been shown experimentally by Karlson, Skimmer and Carlisle (unpublished; cf. note in Carlisle and Knowles, 1959). It now seems to be established that an endocrine system (X organs–sinus glands–Y organ) analogous to that in insects (pars intercerebralis–corpora cardiaca–prothoracic glands) controls the moulting process in Crustacea and that there is a close relationship between the hormones (AH and MH) in both groups.

The Effects of Insect Hormones on Vertebrates

The metamorphosis hormones. Peredielsky (1940) studied the effects of homogenates prepared from the bodies of *Pieris brassicae* and *Lymantria dispar* caterpillars and pupae on the progress of metamorphosis of *Rana temporaria* tadpoles. Homogenates from caterpillars at different stages of development were tested. The homogenates of the younger (last instar) caterpillars and the older pupae produced little or no effect on the tadpoles in comparison with control specimens, whereas the homogenates of caterpillars immediately before the pupal moult or of young pupae soon after moulting produced a significant acceleration of metamorphosis. These experiments do not show conclusively whether this effect is specific to the AH or to the MH or whether a less specific effect controlled by some other substance is involved. From the account of the experiment it does seem clear, however, that the effect is not a general effect of feeding and that it is produced by a substance the presence of which is determined by the stage of development of the insect.

Burdette (1961) carried out a series of in vitro experiments on mice sarcoma cells to demonstrate an effect of the MH (ecdyson). The basis for the experiments was that the MH might have a negative effect on the malignant growth and it was founded on the observation that in some cases atypical growths in *Drosophila* showed a definite regression at metamorphosis which was thought due to the increasing concentration of ecdyson. This supposition was suggested by the discovery that removal or damaging of the ring gland resulted in increased atypical growth (Burdette, 1954, 1960; cf. p. 94).

The observations are, however, much more likely to be explicable by both the lack of the GF due to the larval condition of the tissues where the growths were located and the increased histolytic activity occurring during metamorphosis. Nevertheless, in Burdette's (1961) experiments, an inhibiting effect of an ecdyson extract on the growth of tumour cells in mouse tissue culture was demonstrated and the effect was found to increase with the concentration of ecdyson. Burdette interpreted this as probably being a hormonal effect.

Effects on the gonads. A number of less recent authors claimed to have succeeded in obtaining extracts from the bodies or ovaries of insects, which affected the sexual cycle in mammals. Thus Stefani (1931) obtained an extract from the caterpillars and pupae of a silkworm (*Bombyx mori*) which caused the corpus luteum of guinea-pigs to persist after littering, whereas normally it soon degenerates. This effect is similar to that produced by the embryonic extract of vertebrates. Steidle (1930) extracted a substance from bees which caused castrated female mice to be on heat for a prolonged period, three to five days after injection. A similar effect has been obtained with extracts of spiders and scorpions, and Schwerdtfeger (1931) found a substance which also had such effects present in hornets (*Vespa crabro*). The work of Loewe *et al.* (1922) is the most convincing of such observations. These authors prepared an extract from the ovaries and oviducts of freshly moulted females of *Attacus atlas*. This extract produced an effect similar to that of the female sex hormone of vertebrates. The substance was present in Lepidoptera ovaries at about the same concentration as in those of mammals (about 90 to 130 mice units per 1 kg. of fresh ovaries).

Myotropic effects. Wense (1938) obtained an extract from mealworms (*Tenebrio molitor*) which affected an atropinized frog heart in the same way as adrenaline. He succeeded in obtaining a pure crystalline substance from the extract which differed only slightly in optical rotation from the crystallized vertebrate hormone.

Gersch and Deuse (1957) studied the effect on frog hearts of extracts prepared from various parts of the nervous system of *Periplaneta americana* and *Carausius morosus*. Of the two neurosecretory insect hormones isolated (cf. p. 212), neurohormone D in rising concentrations progressively increased the amplitude of the heart beat and neurohormone C also increased the amplitude although its effect in insects on the pulsation of the heart and colour changes is antagonistic. In contrast, acetylcholine produced an instantaneous inhibition or cessation of heart activity.

Effects on colour change. In comparison with the numerous papers on the effects of crustacean neurohormones on the chromatophores of vertebrates, data on similar effects of insect hormones are rather scarce. Such data include the results of Pflugfelder (1941), Hanström (1936c) and M. Thomsen (1943) concerning the effect on the melanophores of fishes of extracts of corpora allata and corpora cardiaca. A more recent paper by Florey (1951) has shown that extracts of *Pieris brassicae* caterpillars immediately prior to moulting produce the maximum dispersion of pigment in the melanophores located in the fins of *Phoxinus laevis*.

Pautsch (1952) has shown that extracts from various parts of the insect body and haemolymph not only affect the melanophores of crustaceans such as the isopod *Idothea* and the shrimp *Crangon*, but also affect those of various amphibians, e.g. *Rana esculenta*, *Rana temporaria* and *Amblystoma mexicanum*. Although the effects of extracts from the head differed from those of the body and haemolymph in dispersing or concentrating the pigment in Crustacea, the melanophores of all amphibia species tested reacted to all the extracts by dispersion of the pigment.

The Effects of Crustacean Hormones on Insects

From the relatively close affinity of the two groups of animals as well as the activity of insect hormones in crustaceans mentioned earlier, it can be concluded that crustacean hormones also produce their effects in insects. That this occurs has already been demonstrated in several instances.

Effects on moulting. Karlson (1951) succeeded in preparing a hormone extract from shrimps which showed the same effect in *Calliphora* tests as ecdyson (the MH). The fact that the hormone was obtained by the technique used to extract ecdyson (cf. p. 77) suggests that there is a very close chemical affinity if not an identity between the two substances. The shrimp extract, however, was distinctly less active than an extract from silkworm pupae (cf. p. 78). Also the concentration in crustaceans seemed to be lower than in insects (500 kg. of silkworm pupae yielded 25 mg. of ecdyson whereas 1,000 kg. of shrimps provided only 15 mg.).

Effects on colour change. Although there are some papers which deal with various aspects of the effects of insect neurohormones on colour change in crustaceans, there are practically no papers which describe such an effect of crustacean hormones in insects. The similarities in growth of the two groups and the close affinity of their endocrine systems leave little doubt that at least some of the crustacean hormones have such an effect (cf. Gersch, 1957b). Carlisle and Knowles (1959) go even further and suggest that the A-substance is identical in various groups of Crustacea (Natantia, Reptantia, Brachyura, Stomatopoda) and insects (cf. p. 256).

Effects on ovarian development. In a paper mentioned earlier, Carlisle and Butler (1956) showed, amongst other things, that not only does the queen-bee exohormone have an inhibiting effect on crustacean ovaries, but also that extracts from the sinus glands of crustaceans have a similarly striking inhibitory effect on the ovaries of bee workers. The evidence for this was as follows: The sinus glands and eye stalks of 20 prawns (*Leander serratus*) were homogenized in 67% sugar syrup; the syrup was then mixed with pollen powder and fed to a group of freshly moulted queenless bees. The experiment was carried out at a constant temperature. After nineteen days the ovaries of the bees were compared with those of control bees fed with sugar and pollen only. The results were quite striking. Thirty out of the thirty-four control workers had developed ovaries whereas ovaries were suppressed in fifteen of the thirty-two treated specimens.

The Effects of Vertebrate Hormones in Insects
Papers on the effects of vertebrate hormones in insects are numerous when compared with those on the effects of crustacean hormones, especially in the early literature of 20 to 30 years ago. Nevertheless, the results are far from being unambiguous. The time over which the problem has been investigated can be approximately divided into three periods: (1) the earliest period during which both negative results and numerous positive results were obtained, even though the latter were mainly not fully proved; (2) a period following in which more thorough and analytical papers were published, and when the results were entirely negative, and most workers

began to doubt that vertebrate hormones showed activity in invertebrates; (3) the present period in which a more thorough knowledge of insect hormones and their times and modes of action has become available. Although recent work still confirms that the original optimism on effects of vertebrate hormones in insects was unfounded, the activity of particular hormones under specified conditions is nevertheless being demonstrated. Even though the validity of most of the negative results obtained earlier cannot be doubted in the context of the experimental conditions described, there is now the need for a thorough revision of all the accumulated evidence based on the criteria now available for assessing the activity of insect hormones.

Only the most important works are mentioned below, especially as in a comprehensive review by Wense (1938), an almost complete survey of the literature is available.

The hypophysis hormones. In most of the earlier experiments pure hormone preparations were not used. Usually crude extracts prepared by simple techniques or merely powdered glands were employed. These were mainly supplied together with the food so that it is often difficult to decide if the effect obtained was indeed a specific effect of the hormone. It is perhaps more probable that the observed effects were un-specific effects of feeding with the gland constituents. If the gland tissue tended to produce the same effect as the hormone the effect would be enhanced, and conversely the effect might be antagonized and suppressed. With hormones of a polypeptide or protein nature, e.g. somatotropine of the adenohypophysis, there is the additional possibility that they may not be able to pass through the digestive tract without losing their activity. This is especially likely in insects which feed on dead animals and other protein materials such as *Calliphora* larvae and the larvae of Dermestidae. These have often been used in such experiments. Where a delay or an inhibition of growth was obtained, it may have been due to a direct or indirect (by inducing infection) negative effect of the application. Such effects are difficult to avoid, especially in animals such as most caterpillars which are very susceptible to bacterial infections resulting from the unusual meat diet. A positive result with caterpillars was claimed at an early date by Abderhalden (1929), who used a partial hydrolysis to break down the protein components of the hypophysis extraction. Caterpillars of *Deilephila euphorbiae* which he fed with these materials became noticeably large moths, some of them having partially reduced wings. From the author's descriptions this was clearly a juvenilizing effect (progressive metathetely). This becomes very interesting when one considers recent results on the close similarity of somatotropine and the insect corpus allatum hormone (cf. p. 275), especially as this could hardly have been suspected at the time of Abderhalden's experiments. However, one cannot exclude the possibility that some lipoid material, perhaps activated by hydrolysis, was having a pseudo-juvenilizing effect (cf. p. 121).

In the rather numerous papers by other authors on this subject, the results were mainly negative or contradictory (cf., e.g., Patterson, 1928) or the effects shown were not specific. The results of Ivanov and Mescherskaya with a hypophysis extract, mentioned earlier, may have some bearing on this, as its effect was completely un-specific and could be reproduced using many other physiologically active substances. No evidence is available about the activity of the three neurohypophysis (hypothalamus) neuro-hormones. One can assume, however, that [their action is widely un-specific, especially as it has recently been shown that the insect neuro-secretory mechanism has a close analogy in vertebrates, e.g. in amphibian metamorphosis.

Effects of the thyroid gland. The negative results obtained with the thyroid gland (Zavřel, 1927, 1930, 1931; Hahn, 1928; Dobkiewicz, 1928; Janda, 1930 etc.) are more convincing. This is primarily because pure thyroxine injections have been used in addition to pulverized glands and crude extracts. Furthermore, there is no evidence in insects of a substance analogous to thyroxine in its accelerating effect on metamorphosis.

It is interesting that doses of thyroxine which are toxic to mice are completely harmless to *Celerio vespertilio* caterpillars, from which thyroxine is quickly removed in the form of inactive compounds (cf. Wense, 1938). Whereas thyroxine activity is still quite evident five minutes after injection, it disappears completely after twenty-four hours. However, the objections mentioned against negative results for hypophysis effects again apply, for the injected hormone must be at a suitable concentration for a definite length of time to have any effect on growth or morphogenesis. This is rather difficult to achieve with thyroxine, as shown by these experiments.

Claims of positive results with the thyroid gland have also been made, the first of these again being in Abderhalden's (1922) paper. The results were obtained using extensively hydrolysed thyroid tissue. These hydro-lysates were fully active when tested on frogs' hearts. Abderhalden claims that they produced conspicuously small yet fully developed moths with an aberrant wing pattern and under-developed wings when applied to *Deilephila euphorbiae* larvae. Other workers observed an increase of meta-bolism in insects treated with thyroxine. Thus Ashbel (1935) observed a thirty-fold increase in the oxygen consumption of silkworm eggs, and an eighty-fold increase during the first twenty minutes in suspensions of powdered tissues of various invertebrates. A similar increase in the oxygen consumption of diapausing pupae, but not found in developing pupae, was reported by Romeis *et al.* (1920, 1932). This was without doubt, however, not an effect of the injected hormone, but an effect of the injection itself. This phenomenon was later described by Williams (cf. p. 298) as 'injury metabolism'.

The hormones of the suprarenal glands. Abderhalden also obtained positive results when caterpillars ate leaves sprayed with hydrolysates of the supra-renal glands. As with thyroxine small moths were produced, but they were not completely developed. It is possible that this effect as well as the similar effect of thyroxine may have been the expression of unsuitable rearing con-ditions, especially as other authors (e.g. Farkas and Tangl, 1926) have been unable to repeat these results with similar experiments.

Medvedeva (1935, 1939) observed hyperglycaemia in silkworm cater-pillars following the application of adrenalin, though the effect only occurred in the earlier instars. Fifth instar larvae, pupae and adult moths did not show any reaction. This may be explained by the extensive reconstruction of the nervous system which occurs at the pupal stage and by a lack of glycogen reserves in the adults. Hykeš (1926) found that the addition of adrenalin at a concentration of 1 : 1,000,000 increased the heart-beat frequency in chironomid larvae. The effect was particularly striking in larvae with a low heart-beat activity. Adrenalin also had the effect of making the heart-beat more regular. In this connection reference should be made to the results of Gersch (1955a, b) and his collaborators (Gersch and Mothes, 1956; Gersch and Deuse, 1951) on the effects of acetylcholine.

Data on the effects of other vertebrate hormones in insects are very scarce, incomplete and often contradictory (cf. Wense, 1938). (Cf. p. 308.)

CHAPTER TEN

The Theoretical and Practical Significance of Insect Hormones

The exceptional interest of insect physiologists in insect hormones, best demonstrated by the accumulation of more than 2,000 references in only two decades, has arisen for the following reasons. Data on insect hormones are not only of primary importance in insect physiology but are equally important for a deeper understanding of the problems of endocrinology in general, both from the comparative and the physiological point of view. It has been shown in some of the previous chapters how useful an analysis of the action of insect hormones may be in apparently difficult problems such as the problems of morphogenesis and blastomogenesis. Lastly but no less important, findings on the morphology of the endocrine glands are very welcome and important contributions for improving our knowledge of the phylogeny and taxonomy of insects. Furthermore the possibility of direct practical applications must not be ignored, even if we have as yet only a glimpse of the future along such lines. Basically, of course, all data on the physiology as well as the morphology and ecology of such an eminently important group as the insects are of practical importance.

The Importance of Insect Hormones in the Study of Endocrinology in General

In insects, hormones are present in the most diverse phylogenetic stages. As a result of the very wide phylogenetic spectrum of insects there is a range in the phylogenetic level of hormones starting with the protohormones and culminating in the secondary glandular hormones and exohormones. This phylogenetic range extends from the crustacean or even annelid level in some of the Apterygota to perhaps the highest level reached in the invertebrates in termites and the social Hymenoptera. Comparative research into insect hormones, even at its present initial stage, may thus be extremely helpful for a better understanding of how hormones have originated and developed and how they each act. As has been stressed throughout this book, several new lines of thought seem to have developed from research on insect hormones which may also be of great importance in vertebrate endocrinology, e.g. the relationship between implants and the host endocrine gland, the minimum active concentration of a humoral substance, the law of correlation in consumption and its implications, the phylogenetic stages in the evolution of hormones, etc. A very important practical feature of research on insect hormones lies in the short developmental period of insects as well as the low cost of rearing them. This makes it possible to use ten or more times the number of animals in each experimental series than would be possible with vertebrates given the same facilities, i.e. number of workers, laboratory equipment and financial support.

The evolution of hormones and endocrine systems. The phylogenetic aspect is one of the most neglected in the endocrinological literature. Only a few authors have attempted to discuss the hormonal system as a complex developing unit and to consider its phylogenetic history. These include Laufberger (1925a, b), Medvedeva (1939), B. and E. Scharrer (1944, 1948 etc.), Hanström (1936, 1952) and more recently Gersch (1957, 1960). These authors discuss either the phylogenetic development of particular hormones or the phylogeny of the neurosecretory system in a particular group of animals such as insects, Crustacea and vertebrates.

The increasing amount of knowledge about insect hormones and comparisons between these and vertebrate hormones nevertheless allows some new generalizations to be made and gives a better understanding of the origin and evolution of the endocrine function not only in insects but in animals in general (cf. p. 274).

In order to be able to consider the phylogenetic origin of hormones, it is first necessary to divine the advantage of a given hormone at a given stage in phylogeny under conditions of natural selection. The eventual improvement of a hormone would depend on this selective advantage. The hormonal system is usually assumed to correlate the individual physiological processes in the organism. It is therefore often identified as the system of chemical correlation inside the organism. This is perhaps true of all vertebrate hormones, but the generalization becomes less accurate if one includes the insect hormones and their overall diversity. Correlation is perhaps the main selective advantage of the moulting hormone as it synchronizes the process of moulting over the entire body surface, but this applies less to the JH, the chief value of which is an extension and intensification of differentiation, and even less to the genehormones and the other protohormones. In any case, correlation cannot have been the primary phylogenetic characteristic of any hormone, as this function has only developed secondarily. The function of correlation presupposes two earlier stages of the given substance. (1) The phylogenetic stage at which a given substance of some specific value to the organism started to enter the blood circulation and thus be carried to almost all parts (cells) of the body. (2) The stage at which the given substance began to be indispensable to a certain part of the body, because the latter had lost its own source of the equivalent substance (enzyme). The dependence of the prothoracic glands on the JH is an example of this. It is only after these stages have been completed that the function of correlation of the new hormone could start to have a selective advantage for the organism.

There is, however, another important selective value of each hormone which applies from the earliest stage of its evolution, i.e. the moment when it started to be discharged into the haemolymph, assuming that the substance is required for one of the necessary functions of the organism. This value is that it supplies the substance to the other parts of the body from the haemolymph and enables them to become independent of their own production of the substance. This independence in turn produces a marked increase in the potential genetical mutability of the organism's body. Up to this moment in phylogeny any change in the organism, no matter how advantageous from the point of view of natural selection, would be a lethal mutation (in the broadest sense of the word) unless it was linked with the ability to produce the given substance.

The following phylogenetic stages may be theoretically supposed in the evolution of a glandular hormone:

o. *The prehormonal (desmohormone) stage.* Here the given active substance is produced in sufficient quantities for normal life for which it is a necessity in all parts of the body.

1. *The protohormone stage.* The active substance is produced in surplus amounts by some part of the body and passes into the haemolymph at an active concentration. The other parts of the body may then be affected by it without being dependent on it for their normal development.

2. *The tissue (non-glandular) hormone stage.* The production of the active substance becomes limited to only a part of the tissue for which it is necessary and the other parts become dependent on it for their supply via the body fluid. The tissue producing the hormone, however, retains its original function and does not show any morphological adaptation for endocrine function.

3. *The primary (independent) glandular hormone stage.* Because of the high selective advantage of its new function, the tissue producing the hormone becomes specialized and develops into a special organ, the endocrine gland, by increasing its secretory activity and by special adaptations for accumulating the hormone and discharging it into the body fluid, eventually under nervous regulation. However, the gland remains unaffected by the production of any other hormones.

4. *The secondary (dependent) hormone stage.* The part of the body (tissue or gland) producing the hormone becomes dependent, in the same way as any other part of the body, on the occurrence of another, primary hormone in the body fluid.

5. *The tertiary (double dependent) hormone stage.* The part of the body (tissue or gland) which originally produced the secondary hormone becomes dependent, either directly or indirectly, on the production of a further secondary[1] hormone.

Most of the secondary and tertiary hormones known so far are glandular

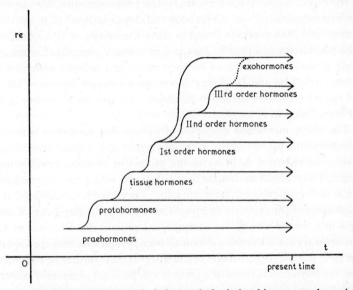

FIG. 56. Diagram of the supposed phylogenetical relationships among the various types of hormones: abscissa – time (t); ordinate – relative phylogenetical level.

in character. Secretin as a tissue hormone is perhaps an exception, though it can be assumed that it is dependent on the neurohormones of the hypothalamus, even if this has not yet been shown conclusively.

A further phylogenetic stage in the above series is that of exohormone. Theoretically, this may develop from any of the five hormonal stages or from active substances of non-hormonal character. If we are correct in assuming a neurohormonal origin for the termite exohormones, then the stage from which they developed is most probably the primary or perhaps

---

[1] As is the case with vertebrate sex hormones, the production of which is dependent on gonadotropine from the adenohypophysis, which is itself dependent on the neurohormones of the hypothalamus.

Insect Hormones

tissue hormone stage. This also applies to the exudates of the mandibular gland of *Apis* (cf. p. 252).

All the above-mentioned developmental stages can be found among the known insect hormones. Thus at least some of the neurohumoral factors provide an example of the prehormonal stage, while others are intermediate between this and the protohormonal stage. The hypothetical gradient-factor shares this intermediate position, according to the second hypothesis of its hormonal (desmohormonal) character (cf. p. 156). The genehormones and perhaps also some of the neurohumoral factors found in the blood, e.g. acetylcholine, are typical protohormones. We can regard the two substances (from the fat body and corpus luteum; cf. p. 239) which Ivanov and Mescherskaya found to affect the ovaries as tissue hormones. The neurohormones may be regarded as primary glandular hormones, or some of them as transitional between tissue and primary glandular hormones. The MH and JH, being dependent on the production of the AH, are typical secondary glandular hormones. No tertiary hormones have so far been found in insects.

The above-mentioned examples of present-day hormones which correspond to the various stages in the phylogeny of hormones should not, of course, be regarded as being in the process of evolving towards higher stages. They should be thought of as substances which have stopped evolving at their particular phylogenetic stage. They have been stabilized at this stage due to their function and importance in a particular group of organisms in a similar way as, for example, the present-day Protozoa or Coelentearata are not developing mammals even though they may correspond to the early developmental stages of the latter It must further be remembered that the phylogenetic level of a given hormone is not necessarily correlated with the level of its chemical complexity—sometimes exactly the reverse is true. For example, the MH of insects and thyroxine in mammals are at a phylogenetically advanced level, but they consist of a small, simple, nitrogen-free molecule (cf. p. 285). In contrast some of the protohormones, for example some of the neurohumoral factors, are complex proteins or polypeptides. From this we can conclude that although some of the hormones at the most advanced phylogenetic stages are highly complex proteins or polypeptides others have passed through the lower stages without changes in their chemical composition or with only slight changes which resulted in an increased physiological activity.

The question of a mutual interaction of endocrine glands. An early discovery by Pflugfelder (1939a) and later confirmed by other authors is very important for a better understanding of the general laws of hormone action.

This was that implantation of active corpora allata resulted in the inhibition of growth and the degeneration of the host's corpora allata. Pflugfelder's explanation of this phenomenon was that the corpora allata of younger specimens were more active and thus suppressed the humoral activity of the older glands of the host. There is, however, a more probable explanation—namely that the stage of activity of the recipient's gland is the all important factor determining the effect of implantation. If the recipient's gland has not yet started to produce its secretion in full when the implantation is made, the concentration of JH in the haemolymph produced by the implanted gland may become higher than in the cells of the gland of the recipient. This prevents any further diffusion of hormone from this gland into the haemolymph, suppresses secretion of the hormone and later causes shrinkage of the gland. When a similar reversal of the concentration gradient of the hormone takes place while the gland is fully active, as occurs in castrated females, diffusion is again prevented and the hormone accumulates inside the gland resulting in hypofunctional hypertrophy (cf. p. 109). Effects on the secretion of endocrine glands similar to the above will occur wherever similar conditions apply, i.e. primarily the absence of a special mechanism for discharging secretion into the body fluid against a concentration gradient. This condition seems to apply to all the insect endocrine glands with perhaps one exception – the prothoracic glands in those species where a central muscle fibre occurs together with a nerve fibre inside the gland. The contraction of this muscle fibre is probably a special mechanism for this purpose.

The overall significance of the implantation effect is that it suggests the most probable mechanism whereby a particular part of the body could start to become specialized for the production of a particular active substance indispensable for life and originally produced by all tissues for their own requirements. Progress in this direction would be favoured by natural selection. An acceleration of hormone production by one part of the body would increase hormone concentration in the blood, and would automatically inhibit the production of the substance in all other parts of the body.

The parts of the body predetermined for such an acceleration of secretory activity would be those which, at a given phylogenetic stage, did not have any important physiological function and which retained their secretory potential from an earlier phylogenetic stage. An example of such structures are the paired lateral ectodermal invaginations of nephridial origin in the head and body from which the corpora allata and the ventral and prothoracic glands developed (cf. p. 87).

The problem of hormone consumption by the affected tissues. This is a problem

K

of general importance, for the solution of which insects provide much more suitable material than vertebrates. The papers by Bounhiol (1952a, 1953), which demonstrate the role of the Malpighian tubules in removing hormones from the haemolymph, are a first step towards a solution. Bounhiol showed that ligaturing the Malpighian tubules in silkworm caterpillars resulted in an increased level of JH in the blood. This was manifested by morphological effects in the last larval instar. Even though the experiments are open to criticism, they do seem to show that the Malpighian tubules play a major part in the active removal of the hormone from the body.

The Contribution of Hormone Research to the Natural Classification and Phylogeny of Insects

Discoveries about insect hormones are very important for a better understanding of phylogenetic problems for two main reasons, one objective and the other subjective:

(1) Hormones constitute a very uniform group of compounds and are present, though with specific modifications, not only in all animals but in almost all groups of higher multicellular organisms. (2) Our knowledge about insect hormones is very recent; it is quite a new aspect of comparative morphology and physiology and thus provides a criterion for examining our existing ideas.

The hormonal system and Martinov's scheme of insect phylogeny. Cazal's (1948) monograph on the comparative morphology of the retrocerebral endocrine system in various orders of insects provides a concrete example of the application of research on insect hormones to problems of insect phylogeny.

The numerous conclusions of Cazal on this subject are still little known and are interesting as they agree very well with a new concept of evolution of insects based on papers by Martynov (1938 etc.) and modified by Jeannel (1947), and Rohdendorf (1959 etc.). Cazal's conclusions agree so well with Martynov's scheme, though this was based on quite different material—palaeontological data, particularly wing venation—that they may be regarded as evidence for its validity.

Phylogenetical relationships between insects and both crustacea and vertebrates based on endocrine systems. There is a very interesting morphological and physiological relationship between the endocrine system of the insects and that of the Crustacea and vertebrates. The first author to draw attention to this was Hanström (1939, 1941, 1949, 1952, etc.). The question was dealt with in more detail by B. and E. Scharrer (1944, 1948b etc.) particularly with respect to neurosecretion. Hanström was the first to emphasize the close relationship and agreement in the position of the neurosecretory cells of the brain in all these groups, in the way their secretory products reach the body fluid and, at least to some degree, in the effects of these products and their influence on other endocrine glands.

That the relationship of the neurosecretory system in all these groups has its common origin as low as the annelid level has recently been shown by Clark (1956). The relationship is without doubt more than a mere analogy. In his paper showing the homology of the neurosecretory cells in the Polychaete genus *Nereis* with the mucous protostomial cells in the phylogenetically older genus *Nephthys*, Clark concludes that the secretory activity which forms the basis of neurosecretion is an original feature of all nerve cells as part of the original ectoderm from which they develop during both phylogeny and ontogeny. Novák and Gutmann (1962; cf. p. 229) have recently shown that this conclusion does not necessarily contradict Hanstrom's view that the neurosecretory cells are secondary and derived from normal neurones.

In the above-mentioned paper, Clark (1956) goes on to show definite agreement, based on comparative studies, in the origin and formation of the neurosecretory centres in the head region of the central nervous system in various groups of animals: the neurosecretory cells of the frontal organs in Nemertini; the groups of neurosecretory cells in the head of Polychaeta referred to earlier; the neurosecretory cells of the frontal organs of some Crustacea (Entomostraca) and the X-organs of Decapoda; the Tömösváry organ of Acarina; the neurosecretory cells of the pars intercerebralis of Insecta; and the characteristic osphradium cells of Lamellibranchs and the corresponding structures in other Mollusca. The most interesting aspect of this work is the probable homology of all these structures with particular cells in the neural gland of Ascidians. These cells are regarded by most authors as homologous with the hypophysis of vertebrates. There appears to be a striking agreement in the origin and structure of the main neurosecretory system in nearly all groups of multicellular organisms (with the exception of perhaps the Coelenterata and possibly also the Echinodermata).

As already suggested, the same agreement exists in the way in which the neurosecretory material reaches the body fluid, and in its special physiological activity (i.e. affecting water metabolism and thus the secretory activity of other endocrine glands). A similar agreement also exists in the other two main sources of insect hormones, that of the MH and the JH. Hanström has shown that there is a particularly close relationship between the metamorphosis hormone system of insects and the X-organs–sinus glands–rostral glands (Y-organs) system of crustaceans on the one hand, and the system of neurosecretory cells in vertebrates, hypothalamus–neurohypophysis–adenohypopophysis, on the other. Just as in insects, the neurosecretory material from the brain in these two other systems

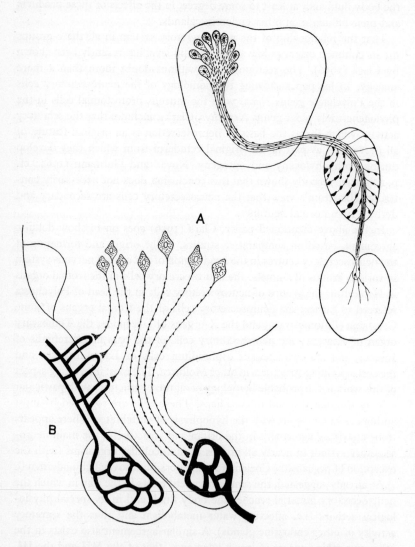

FIG. 57. Comparison of the neurosecretory system of insects (brain, corpora cardiaca, corpora allata) with that of vertebrates (hypothalamus, neurohyophysis, adenohypophysis). A – after M. Thomsen, 1951, B – after E. and B. Scharrer, 1954.

reaches special organs (sinus glands, neurohypophysis) where it is accumulated and passed into the body fluid. The identity of the corpora allata with the adenohypohysis is equally fundamental, and agreement exists between the hormones of the two glands – the JH of the corpora allata and somatotropin, the most important product of the adenohypophysis. B. Scharrer (1948a, b etc.) described another close agreement of insect and vertebrate glands, namely the prothoracic glands of insects (as described in cockroaches, for example) and the thymus gland of vertebrates in their phylogeny, their relation to the nephridia, their degeneration in adult animals, and their histological structure, etc.

It is therefore already clear from the still very incomplete state of our knowledge, that a basic unity can be found in the endocrine system of all animals. At first such homologies and close agreements among such diverse organs may appear rather surprising. It must, however, be remembered that such agreements in embryonic origin, structure and function of equivalent organs are quite a general phenomenon and are apparent in other organs and organ systems. For example, the nervous system is another organ system developed in all groups of multicellular animals and has the same phylogenetic origin in them all (arising from the invaginated median strips of the embryonic ectoderm). The general structure (at both the micro- and macro-level) of the nervous system is also of the same pattern in the various animal phyla as is the function of the system ensuring rapid co-ordination of the various parts of the body by the transmission of impulses. This overall unity of the nervous system is also seen in the muscular system, the digestive system, the reproductive system and other systems, provided we do not restrict our criteria to the narrow classical concept of homology. These basic similarities appear quite natural if we consider the unity of function and phylogenetic origin of the various animal phyla. From such considerations, there is little difficulty in appreciating the unity found in the hormonal system.

The Significance of Hormones in Problems of Morphogenesis and Heredity

The special importance of insect hormones for a better understanding of the laws of morphogenesis in these animals has been adequately discussed in Chapter Three (p. 127) and in part in Chapter Six (p. 232). This importance lies in the possibility of interfering with the actual nature of morphogenesis by means of substances such as the JH. By the same token they are also important for a better understanding of problems of blastomogenesis (malignant growth), as has already been suggested by Wigglesworth (1946).

A short survey of the main functions of the so-called gene hormones and their role in the development of various features in the course of morphogenesis has been given in Chapter Six. From this emerges a clearer picture of the material basis of genetics and of what are called, though not always unambiguously or rationally, genes. The metamorphosis hormones are similarly important for an understanding of the mechanism of inheritance, as they have far-reaching morphogenetic effects. In this connection the series of papers by Hadorn (1942, 1948a, b, 1954 etc.) and his numerous collaborators (Hadorn and Butani, 1948; H. and Gloor, 1946; H. and Stumm-Zollinger, 1953; H. and Fritz, 1950 etc.) are of great importance, as well as the papers by El Shatoury (1955c, 1957). These show, for example, the connection between a particular lethal mutation in *Drosophila* and the lack of one of the metamorphosis hormones. Wigglesworth (1948, 1954 etc.) has produced some interesting additional suggestions about the genetical aspects of hormones and the endocrinological aspects of genetics.

The insect hormones, particularly the JH, provide a mechanism for interfering with the very principle of morphogenesis and for producing genetical environments in insects resulting in what are known as phenocopies. The most obvious example is the possibility of inducing experimental neoteny (progressive metathetely) by the action of the JH at a suitable stage of development (cf. p. 79) and under various temperature (raising or lowering the temperature) or surgical treatments etc. A similar morphological effect can be induced by the other metamorphosis hormone, the MH, when prematurely introduced into the organism (Fukuda, 1944). Such possibilities for genetical research are as yet nowhere near fully utilized theoretically.

Further Aspects of Research in Insect Hormones

Another equally promising future possibility is that of using particular hormones to interfere with various functions of an animal without affecting its other functions and thus without affecting its normal life and its physiological balance. Only the first steps have as yet been taken in this direction (the work of Wigglesworth, Williams, Thomsen, B. Scharrer, etc.).

With the above-mentioned examples of the far-reaching theoretical importance of research on insect hormones, the future possibilities are still far from exhausted (and will increase as our knowledge of these substances increases). It can be said without exaggeration that insect hormones are an important method of interfering experimentally with all the various processes taking place in the insect body in which they are involved to any extent. It would indeed be difficult and probably impossible to find a living process or feature of the insect organism which is not affected in some way or other by the hormones known at present, even though this number is still incomplete.

The Outlook for the Use of Insect Hormones in Applied Entomology

As well as the many possibilities of using insect hormones in research on more or less theoretical problems, future practical uses in applied entomology are beginning to become apparent. There are at least three distinct possibilities along these lines.

1. *Metamorphosis hormones and viability.* The effect of the metamorphosis hormones, particularly the JH, on the viability of the bug *Eurygaster integriceps* has been studied by Teplakova (1947) as part of a complete investigation of this serious pest of grain in eastern Europe. By studying the size of the corpora allata in insects collected from different environmental conditions, she found a close correlation between macro- and microclimatic conditions and the functioning of the gland. Teplakova's work shows that the effect of the secretion of the corpora allata is one of the most important internal influences on viability and the physiological state of the insect organism. The hormone thus has a profound effect on those features of the insect organism which are of economic importance both in the control of pests and the rearing of useful species.

2. *Metamorphosis hormones and susceptibility to insecticides.* The idea that viability and internal secretion are directly connected has been amplified by Mednikova (1952) in a paper on the retrocerebral glands of mosquitoes (Culicidae) which includes several suggested practical applications. From the connection between the appearance of the endocrine glands (as judged by their volume and histology) and the susceptibility of female mosquitoes to DDT, Mednikova points to the necessity of ascertaining the state of the endocrine glands when planning the timing and dosages of spray applications. In this way it would be possible to apply the insecticide when the majority of a given population was most susceptible. This aspect deserves consideration with respect to the control of agricultural pests by the large-scale application of insecticides.

3. *The possibilities of applying insect hormones as insecticides.* Williams (1957) suggested the interesting possibility of applying the metamorphosis hormones directly as insecticides. He emphasized their possible importance through being produced by the organism itself, and therefore unlikely to lead to the appearance of resistance. Williams reached his conclusions from his experiments on the pathological effects of surface applications of a

cecropia extract. Even though this substance does not appear to be identical with the true corpus allatum hormone, the whole idea is capable of broader application and deserves further attention and testing. In addition, substances in the insect body which are not hormonal in character should also be considered, though resistance in insects is not primarily immunological in character. (Cf. p. 296.)

CHAPTER ELEVEN

Additions for the Years 1963–1965

Methods and Techniques

A simple and effective *micro-injection apparatus* for *Drosophila* larvae was described by Rizki (1953). He used a glass micropipette fixed in a rubber plug by means of a hypodermic needle. The hypodermic needle B-D 17 was forced through the plug. A glass micropipette was then inserted into the bore of the needle and the needle was then carefully withdrawn leaving the micropipette in the plug. This was fitted into a glass tube about 8 cm. long with a hole at the side near one end. The other end was attached to a rubber bulb by means of rubber tubing about 1·5 m. long. The rubber bulb was pressed by foot and the pressure in the micropipette was controlled by opening and closing the hole in the glass holder with a finger.

Removal of the gland. A special apparatus was constructed by Strong (1963) for removing the corpora allata of locusts and for certain other operations within the head capsule. A simplified method used by de Wilde and his colleagues (cf. p. 18) was used by Sláma (1964) for allatectomy in *Pyrrhocoris*. He removed the gland through a transverse split in the cervical membrane using microforceps which he himself prepared from very small entomological pins. A special apparatus for the application of concentrated u.v.-rays (the 'Strahlenstich-Mikroskop' produced by Carl Zeiss, Jena) was used by Rohdendorfová (1965) to destroy the corpora allata and other tissues in *Thermobia domestica*. The technique of *intra-specific and interspecific transplantations* of the salivary glands in chironomid larvae was described by Panitz (1964). He implanted the extirpated glands in a special funnel-shaped case prepared from aluminium foil to prevent damaging by the treatment. The capsule was implanted into a lateral incision near the end of the abdomen and the body was ligatured in front of the incision immediately afterwards to prevent bleeding.

An improved method for *isolating the neurohormones* from the nervous system of insects and crustaceans by means of paper chromatography was described by Gersch, Unger, Fischer, and Kapitza (1964). After storing in absolute alcohol, the brains, eye stalks, etc. were homogenized. The homogenate was applied to chromatographic paper (Schleicher and Schüll 2043b) and developed by the ascending method using a n-butanol/

ethanol/acetic acid/water – 8 : 2 : 1 : 3 – mixture, or by paper electro-phoresis in phosphate buffer at a pH of 7·5 using 110 V, 3·0 mA for 3 hours. Ninhydrin (0·2% in 95% n-butanol + 5% acetic acid) dipicrylamine solu-tion (Augustinsson)[1] and hydroxylamine ferric chloride (Whittaker)[2] were used for detection.

A very useful method of *handling insect eggs* for micromanipulation is described by Rizki (1950). He embeds the eggs in agar by the following procedure: (*i*) The eggs are dechorionated either by peeling off the chorion or by treatment with sodium hypochlorite; (*ii*) A few drops of melted agar solution (2·5 – 5%) are placed in a Syracuse watch glass; (*iii*) When the agar is about to set, an egg is quickly inserted with a blunt glass needle, the latter being withdrawn with a slight jerk while the egg remains in the solidifying agar; (*iv*) the watch glass is placed in ice-cold water for 30 sec.; (*v*) the solidified agar block is removed and trimmed with a razor blade on all sides, so that the egg can be oriented as desired for the opera-tion or observation. The agar should be trimmed as close to the micropyle as possible to allow the larva to hatch. After the operation the block is left in a wet chamber. With eggs of *Drosophila* the author obtained a survival rate of 90 to 95%.

A quite original method of *softening insect cuticle* for paraffin sections was developed by Carlisle (1960). He used chitinase solutions prepared by extracting mushrooms with salt solution (in 35% w/v NaCl steeped over-night). Before use it was diluted to an appropriate salt concentration (about 1 : 10) with acetate buffer at pH = 5. Fixed specimens washed overnight with running tap-water were incubated for 12 to 24 hrs. at 37°C. A small amount of toluene was added to prevent bacterial infection when longer incubation was necessary. This method does not work with heavily sclerot-inized cuticle which has a high protein content.

A new highly specific method for *staining neurosecretion* was elaborated by Sterba (1963, 1964 etc.). He used a very weak pseudoisocyanin solu-tion in distilled water (0·02%) after having oxidized the sections with $KMnO_4$ as in Gomori chromalumhaematoxylin-phloxin or with per-formic acid as in Sloper's performic acid-alcyan blue method (cf. p. 30).

The construction of a home-made *cytophotometer* used for quantitative determinations of the amount of neurosecretion in the neurosecretory cells was described by Gersch, Tappert, Meussinger and Drawert (1964) and Gersch and Drawert (1964). The authors used paraldehyde-fuchsin for

---

[1] Augustinsson, K. B. and Grahn, M. 1953. 'The separation of choline esters by paper-chromatography.' *Acta chem. scand.*, **7**, 906.

[2] Whittaker, V. B. and Wijesunera, S. 1952. 'The separation of esters of choline by filter-paper-chromatography.' *Biochem. J.*, **51**, 348.

staining the granules. The criteria of activity of a neurosecretory cell have been discussed by a number of authors and recently summarized by Highnam (1965) (cf. p. 299).

Further improvements in *electron-microscopic techniques* for the study of insect endocrines have been made by B. Scharrer (1963, 1964) in her study of the ultrastructure of the corpora cardiaca and corpora allata. Special methods were used by Brosemer, Vogell, and Bücher (1963) in electron-microscopic reserch on the indirect flight muscles in *Locusta migratoria*.

A number of authors used *autoradiographic methods* in the investigation of insect tissues, especially of the developmental changes in the ovaries (Telfer and Melius, 1963; Ramamurty, 1963; Bier, 1963).

A method of *oscillographic study* of the effect of neurohormones inducing nervous impulses in the phallus nerve in *Periplaneta americana* has been described by Gersch and Richter (1963). The effect on the autorhythmic activity of the thoracic ganglia *in situ* has been studied by Haskell and Moorhouse (1963) in *Locusta migratoria*, and the effects on isolated thoracic ganglion by Strejčková, Servít and Novák (1965) in *Periplaneta americana*.

The influence of hormones on *the respiration of body fragments* of *Pyrrhocoris apterus* adults has been studied by Sláma (1965b) using a special method. The method for determining the oxygen consumption of living specimens in the same species following various treatments was described by the same author (Sláma, 1964c) and applied in a number of studies (Sláma, 1964d, 1965a).

Colorimetric determination of blood proteins using the Folin reagent micro-method after precipitating the blood proteins with trichloracetic acid was employed by Orr (1963a, b) in the blow-fly *Phormia regina*. The same, simplified method was used by Sláma (1964e) and by Brettschneiderová and Novák (1965) to study the effect of the JH on the concentration of proteins in the haemolymph of *Pyrrhocoris apterus*.

Tissue culture of the gonads of *Galleria mellonella* and ovaries of *Periplaneta americana* was carried out by Duveau-Hagege (1963, 1964 etc.) and Leander and Duveau-Hagege (1962) who obtained survival for 7 days and differentiation of the explanted organs. Saline of the following composition was used: KCl 5·5 g., CaCl 0·6 g., MgCl$_2$ 1 g., MgSO$_4$.7H$_2$O 5·5 g., NaH$_2$PO$_4$ 1 g., trehalose 1·6 g., H$_2$O dist. 1000 ml., 1·5% gelose. The solution was sterilized and two volumes of an extract of chicken embryos (9 days) diluted 1 : 1 with saline containing 2% of meat peptose (Merck), 1 volume of horse serum (Inst. Pasteur, Paris), 5000 I.U. of penicillin and 0·5 mg. streptomycin per 25 ml of the culture medium were added to 10 volumes of the saline. The pH ranged from 6·5 to 6·9.

The technique of incubation of the salivary glands of chironomid larvae in vitro was described by Panitz (1964) in his study of hormone effects on the chromosomes. He used larval haemolymph with a small amount of penicillin as the culture medium. The cultures survived up to 48 hrs. without the medium being changed.

The Metamorphosis Hormones

The problem of the hormonal regulation of insect development has been discussed in detail by Laufer (1963). Considering his own and other authors' experiments on the effect of the MH (ecdyson) on the puffing patterns in the polytene chromosomes of the salivary glands in Chironomidae and the interrelationships with enzymatic activities in the glands, he discusses the question of the processes by which hormones influence the action of genes. He concludes that the action of hormones can be either at the level of the chromosomes or on the DNA template itself, or it may be more indirect, affecting some of the extrachromosomal regulator substances in the nucleus, the mitochondria, or the endoplasmic reticulum. Alternatively, they may affect the key enzymatic reactions and only subsequently force a shift in metabolism in new directions.

Another approach to this question was made by Novák (1963) in further developing his *gradient-factor theory* (cf. p. 156). Here especially the question of the transformation of chemical changes into changes in the structure and shape of the insect body is discussed. Reasons are given for assuming this principle to be generally valid in the morphogenesis of animals. An alteration of the earlier conception of the biochemical aspects of endocrine mechanisms in insects by L'Hélias (cf. p. 99) is made by this author (L'Hélias, 1964).

The morphology of *the cephalic endocrine system of Thysanura* was described in detail by Watson (1963) using *Thermobia domestica*. He distinguishes: (*i*) Medial and lateral groups of neurosecretory cells in the brain. (*ii*) A pair of corpora cardiaca each consisting of two parts, storage and glandular. (*iii*) A pair of primitive, vesicular corpora allata innervated principally from the suboesophageal ganglion, but also from the corpora cardiaca. (*iv*) A pair of ventral glands at the base of the labium.

A histological and histochemical investigation of the corpora cardiaca and *corpora allata* during the developmental changes of their secretory activity was carried out by Belyaeva (1964) in *Gryllus domesticus*. She found the first signs of secretory activity in the glands in the embryonic period. She observed the release of the secretion both through the membrane of the glands and through the adjacent wall of the aorta dorsalis. In addition, transport of material is claimed to take place through the branches of the nervus allatus from the corpora allata to the suboesophageal ganglion, hypocerebral ganglion, etc. The possible function of the club-shaped processes of the nervi allati is discussed.

The Activation Hormone (AH)

The influence of the neurosecretory cells of the pars intercerebralis on the *development of the ovaries* has been studied by a number of authors. Highnam (1962) has shown that in *Schistocerca gregaria* they exert a positive control over oocyte development and that copulation as well as electrical stimulation, drastic wounding, or enforced activity may all bring about a release of material from the neurosecretory cells of the pars intercerebralis and accelerate the development of the terminal oocytes in 14-days-old females reared without males. In the same species a positive control of *haemolymph protein concentration* by neurosecretion during ovarian development was found by Hill (1962). The presence of mature males is shown to speed up *the release of material* from the female neurosecretory system, with consequent rapid development of terminal oocytes and an increase in the number of eggs (Highnam and Lusis, 1962). A positive effect of the pars intercerebralis on the development of the ovaries, as well as on the postembryonic development, on the *function of the ventral glands* and *the corpora allata*, and on *metabolism, water balance,* and *chromatic adaptation* was described by Girardie (1964) in *Locusta migratoria*. Similar results were obtained by Mordue (1965a, b, c) with adult females of *Tenebrio molitor*.

Carlisle and Ellis (1963) injected ivth instar nymphs of *Locusta migratoria migratoroides* with cholesterol dissolved in ether. The purified preparation and one of two samples of commercially available crystalline cholesterol were without effect whereas the other sample of commercial substance hastened the moulting by about 18 hrs. (P < 0·01). The authors concluded that cholesterol as such has no prothoracotropic effect which they assume to be derived from some impurities present in the sample concerned. They suppose that the active ingredient is a steroid related to cholesterol, and that the natural brain hormone is likewise a steroid of this group, or possibly a triterpenoid of related configuration.

In a similar way, Gilbert (1964) expressed his opinion in favour of the steroid character of the brain hormone in his review of the question. He also joins the earlier authors in assuming 'a number of neurosecretory substances produced by the brain, the prothoracotropic effect being produced by one of them and the other effects of the brain neurosecretion by others'.

A different standpoint has been accepted by the author (Novák, 1963, 1964). He agrees with Gersch (1962, cf. 1964 etc.) in his assumption of a polypeptide character of the AH and claims that most of the known effects of the brain secretion could well be produced by one and the same substance influencing the membrane activity and thus the water metabolism and secretory activity of the cells. The only exceptions are the neurosecretion of the lateral neurosecretory cells shown to be engaged in inducing the circadian rhythms of activity (cf. Harker, p. 224) and the effects of the neurohormone C (cf. Gersch, p. 213). The effect of cholesterol would be that of a vitamin supplying the steroid skeleton necessary for the production of ecdyson. This is necessarily lacking in decapitated or decerebrated insects unable to accept food. In such cases its supplying by injection can re-induce the production of MH when at least a small amount of AH is present. This, however, is not the case later in the diapause when no AH is present.

The Moulting Hormone or Ecdyson (MH)

The nature of the action of the MH (together with that of the JH) at the cellular level was studied in detail by Wigglesworth (1963c) in the epidermal cells of *Rhodnius prolixus*. He concludes that the MH is not a necessary ingredient for growth in insects in general. It is necessary for the activation of the epidermal cells to produce their secretion (the moulting fluid and the chitinous cuticle) and to grow and divide. But precisely the same response is obtained by 'wound hormones' from injured tissue (cf. Wigglesworth, 1937). And the cells of the fat body and haemocytes do not need the MH at all – their activation and mitotic activity is brought about by nutrition alone. The finding of the first visible effects of the MH in the nucleolus of the epidermis cells is discussed and compared with the effects on the puffing patterns in the salivary glands in *Chironomus*.

An investigation of *enzymic activities* such as those of cathepsin, alkaline phosphatase, acid phosphatase, amylase and cytochrome oxidase and the determination of adenosine triphosphate and nitrogen contents in the course of the first and second larval instars of *Gryllus bimaculatus* was carried out by Krishnakumaran (1962a) who deduced conclusions regarding the biochemistry and the MH-action. It is suggested that the activation of the ribonucleic acid and/or cytochrome oxidase synthesis might be the primary function of the MH. To substantiate this conclusion the same author (Krishnakumaran, 1962b) gives a survey of the knowledge of the endocrine control of metabolism in arthropods. This might be true, however, only of the epidermal cells, and perhaps some other tissues of ectodermal origin (cf. p. 79, and the above results by Wigglesworth).[1]

A series of papers by the Karlson school deals with the question of

[1] Author's comment.

the chemistry of the MH and of the biochemistry of its production (cf. p. 75). On the basis of their work the definitive solution of the chemical structure of ecdyson was recently made by Karlson (1965). As suggested previously, it has a steroid molecule of the following structure:

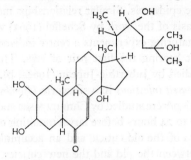

It is a $2\beta.3\beta.14\alpha.22\beta F.25$-pentahydroxy-$\Delta 7$-$5\beta$-cholestenon-(6). The C20 has the normal steric configuration, i.e. $20\beta F$-methyl, 6-keto $- \, o = o - 1$; $14\alpha - o = o - 2$, $2\beta - o = o_3$, $3\beta o = o - 4$, $25 - o = o - 5$, $22 - o = o - 6$.

Five different biologically active fractions of ecdyson are said to have been obtained by chemical treatment of *Bombyx mori* extracts, three of them being undescribed and two known from the work of Karlson and his colleagues and earlier from that of Burdette and Bullock (1963). A positive effect on tissue growth in mammals is claimed together with stimulation of proteosynthesis in the cytoplasm.

The correlation between the prothoracic (= ventral) glands and phase development in *Schistocerca gregaria* and *Locusta migratoria* was studied by Carlisle and Ellis (1962). The prothoracic glands which normally disappear in adults were found to survive for a longer period in the solitary than in the gregarious phase. Apart from this the corpora allata are larger in solitary than in gregarious nymphs. Extirpation of the greater part of one of the pair of the prothoracic glands in solitary nymphs resulted in the assumption of gregarious habits. It is supposed that a complex interaction exists among all three metamorphosis hormones in influencing phase differences.

A comparison of the activity of the pericardial glands in normal and regenerating (with the mesothoracic legs removed) 1st instar nymphs of *Carausius morosus* was made by Vietinghoff, Penzlin and Spannhof (1964). A statistically significant difference in the volumes of nuclei was found between the glands of regenerating and normal specimens. The decrease in volume connected with the onset of the moulting process occurring in normal specimens was delayed by two days in the regenerating individuals.

Control of moulting by AH and MH closely resembling that in the pterygotes has recently been shown by Watson (1964a) for *Thermobia domestica*. There is a critical period for the secretion of the AH here, shortly followed by maximum activity of the ventral glands which coincides with the activation of the epidermis. Similar relationships may be assumed for *Chilopoda* on the basis of the work by Scheffel (1963) who has shown by decapitation and ligaturing experiments a centre indispensable for moulting in the segment bearing the first pair of legs. The relationships in *Symphyla* were studied by Juberthie-Jupeau (1964a, b).

The effects of thiourea injections into silkworm (*Bombyx mori*) larvae on moulting and pupation were studied by Chmurzyńska and Wojtczak (1963). Injections made up to 24 hours before larval moulting or cocoon spinning resulted in retention of the old cuticle and an accumulation of a haemolymph-like fluid between the old and the new cuticles. Partial inhibition and a delay in the sclerotizing of pupal cuticle was observed in histological sections.

A number of new papers deal with the question of MH effects on the puffing patterns of the giant chromosomes in the salivary glands of *Chironomidae* (Clever, 1963, Karlson, 1963, Panitz, 1963, etc., cf. Gilbert, 1964). It seems to be well shown that specific patterns of puffing and Balbiani rings appear soon after the application of ecdyson. They are the first changes to be observed in the insect body after the application of the hormone. They appear within the first hour after injecting the ecdyson into the freshly moulted last instar larvae of *Chironomus* as shown by Clever (1963). Theories on gene activation by hormones, gene activities, and their interrelationships were elaborated on this basis. On the other hand, it has been shown that similar changes in puffing patterns can be obtained by the application of many chemicals such as ions of heavy metals (e.g. zinc or cadmium), various narcotics, etc. (Kroeger, 1963). It has been concluded that the MH does not affect the chromosomes directly but only by means of a control system depending on the sodium/potassium ratio inside the nucleus (Cf. Gilbert, 1964).

The distribution of labelled ecdyson injected into the insect body was studied by Karlson and Sekeris (1963).[1] They found that soon after injection the hormone accumulated in the epidermis and later in the fat body. The nuclei of the epidermal cells exhibited the greatest activity. The authors conclude that the sites of action of the MH are the nuclei of the epidermal cells and that microsomes of the fat body eliminate the excess of the hormone from the haemolymph.

A detailed study of effects of the metamorphosis hormones on the puffing

[1] *Z. physiol. Chem.*, quoted from Gilbert, 1964.

patterns of the polytene chromosomes in larvae of the chironomid *Acricotopus lucidus* was performed by Panitz (1964), both in vivo by transplantaions of the salivary glands and in vitro on the explanted glands using the haemolymph of various developmental stages.

The Juvenile Hormone (JH)

A difference between corpora allata from adult females which inhibited metamorphosis (induced 'supernumerary' larval moults) and those from adult males, which failed to produce this effect, was found by Fukuda (1963) in the silkworm (*Bombyx mori*). This sexual difference in the activity of the corpora allata persisted after gonadectomy, after both gonadectomy and reimplantation of the gonads of the opposite sex, and even in corpora allata which were transplanted into another specimen after the beginning of the pupal period. The activity of the female corpus allatum was not inhibited by decerebration at the beginning of the pupal period.

The effect of the JH on the growth and morphogenesis of internal organs was studied by Sehnal (1956a, b) in *Galleria mellonella*. Complete agreement with its effect on surface structures was found. The implantation of three complexes of brain–corpora cardiaca–corpora allata at the beginning of the last larval instar completely inhibited metamorphosis. Later implantation resulted in a series of transitions between the larval and imaginal shape of the brain and other organs.

The endocrine function of the corpora allata in the development of termites was studied anew by Lüscher (1963, 1964) in *Kalotermes flacicollis*, by transplantation of the glands. He concluded that the corpora allata played a crucial part in development and caste differentiation. He assumed that a high JH titre in 1st instar nymphs induced regressive development, that a low titre allowed progressive development to winged forms, and that an intermediate titre could lead to stationary moults. He also claimed the existence of another corpus allatum hormone, secreted only by the glands of soldiers, replacement reproductives, nymphs and winged adults, supposed to induce the development of soldiers (cf. p. 249). A 'soldier hormone' effect was also obtained by implantation of the corpora allata from the cockroach *Leucophaea maderae*. A similar effect to that of the JH was obtained with farnesol and its derivatives.

The question of the biochemical and morphogenetic activities of the JH was studied by Stegwee (1963, 1964) in preparations of isolated flight muscles (sarcosomes) from diapausing adults of *Leptinotarsa decemlineata*. Here the normal sarcosomes almost completely disappeared in association with reversible degeneration of the flight muscles. This author stated that the administration of *cecropia* extract in high concentrations (which he supposed was identical with the corpus allatum hormone) increased oxidative phosphorylation, together with partial regeneration of the respiratory system and the morphogenesis of sarcosomes and muscle fibrils, during diapause development. Complete regeneration, however, was observed only after the termination of diapause.

The influence of the JH on the chemical composition of the body in *Pyrrhocoris apterus* adults was studied by Janda jr. and Sláma (1965). The amount of glycogen, fats, and nitrogen (total nitrogen content and urea) was determined in the following normal and experimental insects: (*i*) normal freshly moulted adult females; (*ii*) normal females 5 days after moulting, immediately before the first egg-laying; (*iii*) normal females 15 days after moulting, which had performed at least three ovarian cycles; (*iv*) allatectomized females 15 days after moulting and operation; (*v*) females castrated at the beginning of the vth instar 15 days after adult moulting; (*vi*) cardiacallatectomized females 15 days after adult moulting; (*vii*) diapausing females 15 days after adult moulting; (*viii*) females 10 days after adult moulting, completely starved during this period; (*ix*) females 11 days after moulting, starved for 10 days and then fed for 24 hours; (*x*) females determined for diapause immediately after adult moulting; (*xi*) freshly moulted adult males; (*xii*) normal adult males 15 days after imaginal moulting; (*xiii*) males determined for diapause 15 days after imaginal moulting. The authors concluded that the changes found in the chemical composition of the body in these groups were secondary and that they depended on the amount and physiological stage of the tissue engaged in metabolism. They supposed that the AH stimulated digestion, the resorption and synthesis of proteins and possibly other components of nutrition, whereas JH determined the utilization of the available nutrients by specific parts of the body, such as the ovarian follicle cells or the larval tissue.

The effect of the JH on the protein concentration in the haemolymph was studied by a number of authors. It was shown by Hill (1962, 1963) and Highnam, Lusis, and Hill (1963a, b) that allatectomy in *Schistocerca gregaria*, unlike removal of the source of the activation hormone (cf. p. 97), resulted in a big increase in the haemolymph protein concentration. The authors concluded that the haemolymph protein concentration was regulated by direct hormone action. On the other hand, Sláma (1964), on the basis of a detailed investigation of adults of *Pyrrhocoris apterus*, concluded that the effect of hormones in the haemolymph protein concentration was indirect. He supposed that the JH reduced the protein level only by stimulating the process of egg maturation, thus facilitating consumption of the reserve material. Similar conclusions were reached by Brettschneiderová and Novák (1965) for the post-embryonic development of the same species. It must be taken into account that the protein level at a given moment is dependent both on the rate of induction of proteins into the haemolymph from the gut and fat body and on its removal from the haemolymph by growing tissue. Both processes are influenced by the metamorphosis hormones in a rather complicated way. On the other hand, Orr (1964a, b), from a comprehensive investigation of the action of various nutritional and hormonal factors on the chemistry of the fat body, blood, and ovaries of the blowfly *Phormia regina*, claims that the primary action of the corpus allatum is to regulate body lipid metabolism. His conclusions, however, need revising on the basis of data from the above papers and other available findings on the juvenile hormone. Engelmann (1965), in agreement with the conclusions of Sláma (see above), found specific cyclicity in both the quantity and quality of the haemolymph proteins of *Leucophaea maderae*.

The effect of JH on the synthesis of proteins and nucleic acids in Rhodnius prolixus was studied by means of autoradiography by Wanderberg (1963). The results of the incorporation of tritium-labelled precursors into DNA, RNA, and protein in nymphs deprived of their corpora allata by decapitation and on decapitated controls, have shown that there is little or no effect on DNA synthesis whereas RNA and protein syntheses were 'drastically inhibited in all tissues studied' by removing the corpora allata. The question whether it is a direct or indirect effect of JH was not answered.

The influence on reproduction has been dealt with by a large number of authors. The question of the endocrine control of reproduction was reviewed by Doane (1962), by Highnam (1963) and by Nayar (1964). Nervous control of egg maturation by specific neurones along the ventral nerve cord was demonstrated by Engelmann (1964) in pregnant females of viviparous cockroaches, *Leucophaea maderae*. These neurones are supposed to inhibit the corpora allata by influencing specific regions of the brain. The author assumes that a humoral factor released by the brood sac affects these neurones, but his experimental evidence does not seem to prove this. The role of hormonal factors in the control of ovarian development in *Schistocerca gregaria* was investigated in a series of papers by Highnam (1962), Highnam and Lusis (1962), Lusis (1963), and Highnam, Lusis, and

Hill (1963a, b). In *Locusta migrataria* castration in the last larval instar does not seem to affect the cellular volume of the corpora allata in either males or females (L. Joly, 1964). Allatectomy in a highly autogenous strain of *Aedes taeniorhynchus* inhibited egg maturation when carried out within one hour after adult moulting; yolk deposition was stimulated by the implantation of one pair of active corpora allata (Lea, 1964). Similar results were obtained in other aedine mosquitoes (Lea, 1963).

The question of hormonal influences on sexual behaviour in various species of the order Saltatoria was discussed by Loher (1964). In some species, allatectomy influences the males, while in others the females are affected, and there are species which are not influenced by the corpora allata at all (e.g. *Gryllus campestris*). No effect of either allatectomy or the implantation of additional corpora allata was found by Röller, Piepho, and Holz (1963) in *Galleria mellonella*. On the other hand, Beetsma, de Ruiter, and de Wilde (1962) report that the injection of *cecropia* extract shifts the balance between photopositive and photonegative orientation tendencies in larvae of *Smerinthus ocellata* towards a positive response. The implantation of active prothoracic glands had the reverse effect.

The question of the existence of one or more corpus allatum hormones was recently approached by Sláma and Hrubešová (1963) using *Pyrrhocoris apterus*. On the basis of the complete identity of the effect of larval and imaginal corpora allata implantations into adult females on respiration these authors came to the conclusion that there was no reason to assume the presence of more than one corpus allatum hormone, the juvenile hormone, in this species. They suppose that this state applies to insects in general. (Cf. p. 105.)

The control of the function of the corpora allata. In the last few years much attention has been paid to the question of the innervation of the corpora allata and the form of the supposed nervous and neurosecretory control of their secretory activity. The relevant papers were reviewed by Highnam (1963). The existence of a fine nerve connecting the corpus allatum with the suboesophageal ganglion, demonstrated by Engelmann and Lüscher (1956) in *Leucophaea maderae*, was also found in *Periplaneta* (Harker, 1960; Füller, 1960), in *Schistocerca* (Highnam, 1961a; Strong, 1963), and in *Locusta* (Staal, 1961). Neurosecretory granules were detected in this branch of the nervus allatus. When this nerve is ligatured, neurosecretory material accumulates on the corpus allatum side of the ligature (Harker, 1960). Three various forms of control of the activity of the corpora allata were suggested:

1. *Nervous control*, assumed to be of an inhibitory character in some insects, e.g. *Leucophaea* (B. Scharrer, 1952; Engelmann and Lüscher, 1956; Engelmann, 1957 etc.), while possibly having a stimulatory effect in others, e.g. in *Oncopeltus* (Johansson, 1958) or *Schistocerca* (Highnam, 1962b; Strong, 1963), in which removal of the brain neurosecretory cells by cautery or extirpation prevents the corpora allata from attaining their full size. The possible cause of this contradiction was recently pointed out by Strong (see below). The nonspecific effect of regeneration of the operation injury must, however, also be taken into account. It was found, for instance, in *Schistocerca*, that the development of the eggs can be considerably advanced by wounding, as shown by the experiments of Norris (1954), Highnam (1961b, 1962a, b), etc.

2. *Local effect of neurosecretory granules* from the neurosecretory cells of the brain reaching the corpus allatum via the nervus allatus. Granules of Gomori-positive materials were found in the corpora allata of various species by a number of authors (cf. p. 73). B. Scharrer (1958) assumed that 'the restraining influence on the corpora allata takes place by nervous activity, whereas the stimulatory affect is brought about by a substance present in the neurosecretory material'. Khan and Fraser (1962), who found neurosecretory granules in the corpora allata of newly moulted adults of *Periplaneta americana*, believed, contrary to B. Scharrer (l.c.), that they were responsible for the restraining influence there. Mordue (1963) observed neurosecretory material in the corpora allata of female pupae of *Tenebrio molitor* before imaginal moulting; after mating, it disappeared from the corpora allata, remaining, however, in the allatic nerves in close proximity to the gland. The corpora allata were found to grow more rapidly in mated than in unmated females. Here again there is no unequivocal evidence of a local physiological function of the neurosecretion in the gland, and on the basis of what we know of neurohormones and their way of reaching the target organs, it seems that it probably has none.

3. *Humoral activation* by the activation hormone of the brain, corresponding to the activation of the prothoracic glands. It seems that activation or inhibition of the production of AH by nervous stimuli from other parts of the body (e.g. the ovaries, ootheca, etc.) or by various external factors (e.g. photoperiodism) might be the only way of control of the corpora allata activity (cf. Highnam, 1962a; Haskell and Highnam, 1963; Highnam, 1963). Among other findings, this is shown by the fact that the imaginal diapause in *Leptinotarsa* (de Wilde and Stegwee, 1958), aphids (Lees, 1959) and *Pyrrhocoris* (Sláma, 1964), which is an AH deficiency syndrome, can be completely abolished by implanting active brains and/or

corpora cardiaca, whereas the implantation of active corpora allata is not fully effective in the absence of AH (in brain and cardiacectomized specimens), as recently shown by Sláma (1964) for *Pyrrhocoris*.

The role of the nervous system in the activation of the corpora allata was studied by removing parts of the brain and by sectioning the innervation of the glands in female adults of the Central American locust (?*Schistocerca paranensis* Burm.) and by an histological investigation of neurosecretory activity with the following results (Strong, 1965a, b): striking changes in the volume and appearance of the corpora allata were found during maturation, whereas only slight changes occurred in the amounts of neurosecretion at the same time; no material from the median neurosecretory cells was found in the nerves which innervate the corpora allata, but granules from the lateral cells with different histochemical properties from those of the median cells were found in these nerves; extirpation of the cerebral neurosecretory cells resulted in reduced volume and inhibited the activation of the corpora allata. Unlike other experiments (cf. p. 90), the implantation of corpora allata did not restore oögenesis in allatectomized females. The implanted glands could only become and remain active when they retained intact connections with the central nervous system. Nerve sections and cautery of the neurosecretory centres of the brain showed that the activation of the corpora allata was mediated through the lateral neurosecretory cells in the adjacent half of the brain. Transsection of the nervi corporum cardiacarum II. resulted in inactivity and reduction of the volume of the corpus allatum on the corresponding side. The contradiction between the supposed inhibitory effect of the neurosecretory cells of the brain and their stimulatory effects (cf. p. 106 and p. 117) seems to be due to a disregard of the possible breaking of this connection. No clear distinction, however, has been made as to whether the effects of the lateral neurosecretory complex upon the corpus allatum are mediated through nervous or neurosecretory stimuli, or, perhaps more probably, through the humoral action of the activation hormone (cf. p. 47). No function could be attributed to the nervous connections between the corpora allata and the suboesophageal ganglion.

A number of papers are concerned with the effects of *juvenile hormone-like substances*. Several new chemicals have been found to influence (inhibit) metamorphosis in the *cecropia* silkworm and other insects. Bowers and Thompson (1963) showed that effects similar to those obtained by earlier authors with *cecropia* extracts, farnesol and its derivatives, various fatty acids, etc., are also produced by various isoprenoids and straight-chain alcohols such as neralidol, decanylmethylether, dodecanylmethylether, etc., following both surface application and injections.

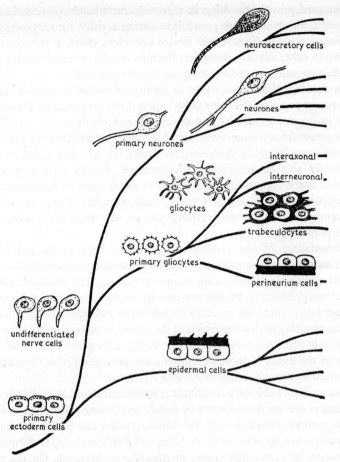

neurosecretory cells

neurones

primary neurones

interaxonal

interneuronal

gliocytes

trabeculocytes

primary gliocytes

perineurium cells

undifferentiated
nerve cells

epidermal cells

primary
ectoderm cells

FIG. 58. Supposed phylogenetical relationship of the Gomori-positive structures in insects.

Similar results were obtained by Schneiderman and Gilbert (1964), who claimed, on the basis of their experiments, that the JH and *cecropia* extract were, in principle, identical and assumed that the other active substances acted in a similar way. A similar standpoint is accepted by most of the other authors dealing with this question (see below).

Quite the opposite view is taken by Novák (1963, 1964a, 1965a, b, c) who emphasizes an earlier finding by Sláma (1962; cf. Novák, 1961), according to which the action of JH consists of an activation of growth of the larval parts of the body and results in progressive metathetely (Novák, 1951b), whereas that of the pseudojuvenilizing substances consists of the inhibition of imaginal growth, resulting in regressive metathetely (Novák, l.c.). In principle, substances with pseudojuvenilizing activity are supposed to be growth antimetabolites. Their limited stimulant effect, if it were really shown to exist, might perhaps, in principle, consist of regeneration caused by their injuring the tissue in a space-specific pattern.

Doubts regarding the character of the juvenile hormone are also implied in a recent paper by Williams (1963), even if not expressed by the author, who found in *cecropia*: (*i*) that the morphogenetically active *cecropia* extract comes from the moth abdomen; (*ii*) that in closely related species of saturniid moths (*P. polyphemus, A. pernyi, A. orizaba*) neither sex is ordinarily able to accumulate the hormone, despite their very active corpora allata; (*iii*) adult moths caused to moult again by joining them to developing pupae form a new adult cuticle, even in the presence of high concentrations of *cecropia* extract, without any sign of a reversal of metamorphosis.

Maintenance of the prothoracic glands by both crude and highly purified male *cecropia* extracts was demonstrated by Gilbert (1962). This substance can thus induce a supernumerary moult. The persistence of the glands may, however, be due not only to the direct effect of the *cecropia* extract but perhaps far more to its inhibitory influence on the imaginal tissue, resulting in decomposition of the glands in other ways and the production of histolytic enzymes (note by V. N.). This might be also the principle of the effect of farnesol methyl ether on regeneration observed by O'Farrell and Stock (1964) in *Blatella germanica*.

Contradictory evidence is submitted by various others regarding the induction of ovarian development by pseudojuvenilizing substances. A number of authors claim to have found definite positive effects, e.g. Larsen and Bodenstein (1959) in mosquitoes, Chen and Robbins (1962) in *Periplaneta americana*, Wigglesworth (1961) in *Rhodnius prolixus*, etc. On the other hand, negative results were obtained by E. Thomsen (1959) with *Calliphora*, de Wilde (1959) with *Leptinotarsa*, Weirich (1963) with *Aedes*, and Sláma (1962, 1965) with *Pyrrhocoris*. Little or no effect was observed by Weirich (1963) and Highnam, Lusis, and Hill (1963a, b). In the light of Wigglesworth's results, this might have been due to the low activity of the substance used, or because the amount used was insufficient. Taking into account that the requirements for juvenile hormone in various groups of insect range from nought (e.g. *Bombyx*, etc.) to absolute necessity (e.g. *Calliphora, Rhodnius, Dytiscus*, etc.) it seems possible that in some species a slight upset of the balance among tissues may result in a stimulant effect of the substance, based on the principle of regeneration (see above), or act in some other way, which may not occur in other species.

From the point of view of the above conclusions on the inhibitory action of the pseudojuvenilizing substance, mention should be made of the observation of Dearden (1964) who found that farnesol, when incorporated in *Drosophila melanogaster* culture medium, caused delay in puparium formation and emergence of adults, when larvae were reared on the medium from the time of hatching. The greater the concentration of farnesol in the medium, the greater the delay. The seemingly contra- dictory observation that the average number of facets in the Bar-eye mutant is markedly increased in specimens reared on medium containing 1% farnesol (v/v) can be readily explained by assuming that the reduction in the number of facets in normal mutants occurs on the principle of regres- sive metamorphosis (cf. p. 233). In that case, farnesol would simply inhibit the morphogenetic process of reduction of the number of facets, in agree- ment with its general inhibitory effect on growth and morphogenesis (growth antimetabolite, cf. p. 294).

However, the most important fact in the whole matter is that the existence of substances which selectively inhibit growth without affecting any of the other body functions gives us a well-founded hope of finding a chemical which will suppress tumerous growth without any injurious effect on the human organism. Lipids of the same type as the inhibitory substance mentioned in social insects are the first to call our attention from this point of view.

The juvenilizing effects of parasitism by Microsporidia were analysed in detail by Fisher and Sanborn (1964). They obtained as many as six supernumerary moults and doubled the normal weight in *Tribolium* larvae infected with *Nosema* sp. The same effect was obtained in allatectomized nymphs of *Blaberus craniifer* and *Byrsotria fumigata*. The juvenilizing effect was unchanged when the parasite was confined to a small chamber com- municating with the host's haemocoele through a Millipore filter but pre- venting it from passing into the haemolymph of the insect. Ether extracts of the parasite prepared in the same way as *cecropia* extracts (cf. p. 120) did not, however, have a comparable effect. The authors conclude that *Nosema* is capable of replacing the hormone normally produced by the host's corpora allata. The earlier findings by Fisher (1961) thus seem to be confirmed.

A substance contained in paper materials of American origin was shown to produce a strong morphogenetic effect in the bug *Pyrrhocoris apterus* by Sláma and Williams[1] recently. It is active by contact in extremely low con- centrations. Its effect depends in preventing normal adult morphogenesis

---

[1] Sláma, K., and Williams, C. M., 1965. 'Juvenile hormone activity for the bug *Pyrrhocoris apterus*.' *Proc. Nat. Acad. Sci.*, **54**, 411-14.

and thus also the sexual activity. However, its alleged relation to the juvenile hormone does not seem probable. Unlike JH, its effect is highly species specific. It is completely inactive in other insects, including other families of the Heteroptera, its effects being restricted to *Pyrrhocoris* and, perhaps, a few other genus of the family Pyrrhocoridae. The substance was shown to be contained in extracts of a number of American coniferous trees, the most active being those of balsam fir (*Abies balsamea*), hemlock (*Tsuga canadensis*), and yew (*Taxus brevifolia*). The authors suggest the possibility of its practical application as a highly active and selective insecticide. The possibility of finding other substances of this type which would affect various insect pests seems to be rather tentative.

Morphogenesis of the insect integument under both normal and experimental conditions was studied in a number of papers by Locke (cf. 1964). He described the gradient organization of the epidermis cell and the segmental organization of the integument in *Rhodnius prolixus* and reached conclusions of general importance.

The Gradient-Factor (GF) and Morphogenesis

A number of papers have appeared dealing with various aspects of morphogenesis in insects, bringing new data concerning the histology, cytology, ultrastructure, etc., of insect development, approached both descriptively and experimentally. The course of the differentiation of imaginal structures (wing pads) and the influence of JH on this was studied by Sláma (1964a) in normal 4th and 5th instar nymphs of *Pyrrhocoris apterus*. In both series, allatectomized specimens and those with reimplanted corpora allata were investigated at comparable time intervals and the morphogenetical effects of the metamorphosis hormones were discussed. The changes in ultrastructure in the course of the formation of the imaginal structures and the development of the interrelated enzymatic pattern were investigated in detail by Brosemer, Vogel, and Bucher (1963) in the indirect flight musculature of *Locusta migratoria*. The sequence of histolysis of the larval tissue (i.e. lacking active GF) and its dependence on various internal and external factors was investigated with the same thoroughness by Lockshin and Williams (1964, 1965).

The macromolecular patterns in the development of insects and other arthropods were studied, by means of immunochemical methods, by Laufer (1964). Specific changes in the haemolymph proteins were found in the course of postembryonic development, the pattern being characteristic for a given species. The phylogenetical conclusions were discussed. The role of carnitine (-amino-hydroxybutyrobetain) in the diet on the development of *Tribolium destructor* was studied in a series of papers by

Naton. A number of pathological changes in the tissues were found following a carnitine-free diet. The cells of the corpora allata were found to be especially sensitive to the lack of carnitine which, in its turn, resulted in serious physiological disturbances (Naton, 1963a, b). The release of lipids from the fat body was studied by Chino and Gilbert (1964) in *Hyalophora cecropia*. Diglycerides in the form of a complex with haemolymph proteins were found to be the most probable means by which the lipids are transported in this species.

The growth of the compound eye and the influence on this of MH and AH was studied by Schaller (1963, 1964) in the larvae of *Aeschna cyanea*. The phase differences in *Schistocerca gregaria* reared under crowded and isolated conditions were studied with special reference to oxygen consumption, and the possible interaction of the endocrine system was discussed by Pener (1963). Photoperiodism was shown to be the main factor in the determination of the seasonal dimorphism of the butterfly *Polygonia c-aureum*, a relative of the European *Vanessa io*.

Mathematical relationships in the allometric growth of arthropods and their evolutionary aspects were studied by Matsuda in a number of papers (Matsuda, 1961a–1962c) which were summarized by the author (Matsuda, 1963).

Two types of pathological effects were observed by Biellmann (1963) following X-ray irradiation of *Locusta migratoria* (4th instar nymphs): localized direct effects affecting pigmentation and growth, and general effects manifested by a disturbance of the moulting cycles and an increase in mortality. Larvae in the period of maximum mitotic activity at the beginning of the intermoulting period were the most sensitive.

A series of papers by Penzlin (1963, 1965 etc.) deals with the regeneration capacity in an insect (*Perplaneta americana*) and its influencing by the nervous and endocrine system. Removal of the source of the AH (both pars intercerebralis and corpora cardiaca) produced a negative effect on regeneration (incomplete regeneration) whereas extirpation of the corpora allata had little if any effect. The effect of replacing the metathoracic legs by the prothoracic legs was studied by Urvoy (1963a, b).

Transmission of tumours by the injection of haemolymph or by cell-free filtrates of homogenized tumours was shown by Matz (1963) in *Locusta migratoria*. The active factor was destroyed by heat.

In summarizing the results of all the available papers dealing with insect morphogenesis, the author concludes (Novák, 1965b) that none of them is contradictory to the GF-theory and some of them bring new evidence in its favour. From the contemporary data the assumption that the substance responsible for GF activity should be looked for in some of the links in the chain of proteosynthesis, between DNA and protein, seems the most feasible.

Insect Hormones and Diapause

A number of new papers deal with the endocrine basis of diapause. Hasegawa (1963) and Yamashita and Hasegawa (1964a, b) further examine the question of the mode of action of the so-called diapause hormone in the silkworm (*Bombyx mori*). The fate of the hormone after injection into a female pupa is discussed and its effect on the penetration of 3-hydroxy-kynurenine into the developing egg is found. The latter substance is the precursor of the serosa pigment (ommochrome) determining the coloration of the diapausing eggs; it is much less abundant in the non-diapausing eggs. Further, the effect of the diapause hormone on the glycogen content of the ovaries and the blood sugar level of the female pupae were studied. It was concluded that one of the actions of the hormone was to stimulate the penetration of blood sugars into the pupal ovaries and their deposition therein in the form of glycogen, thus decreasing their content in the haemolymph.

Several authors have studied the respiratory metabolism during diapause and its influencing by the metamorphosis hormones. The oxygen consumption in diapausing adult females of *Pyrrhocoris apterus* was found to be identical with that occurring in normal (non-diapausing) specimens after removal of both corpora cardiaca and corpora allata. It also corresponded with that in normal untreated males, whereas it was distinctly higher in the females which had only been allatectomized (Sláma, 1964a, b). Typical low diapause respiration with a low water content and an increased amount of fat was found by Tombes (1964) in aestivating curculionids *Hypera postica* (Gyll.). DNA synthesis during metamorphosis and diapause was studied by the incorporation of tritiated timidine in *cecropia* and cynthia silkworms. In diapausing pupae, the incorporation of timidine was limited to spermatogonia, haemocytes, and a few other cells. In the diapausing epidermal cells, DNA synthesis appeared only following a large epidermal injury and was limited to the immediate vicinity of the wound. On the other hand, a generalized incorporation was observed after the termination of the diapause at the beginning of adult development. This is said to be the only criterion for distinguishing between the increase in metabolism of normally developing specimens and those following injury (cf. p. 265) (Bowers and Williams, 1964).

The mechanism breaking the diapause by increased photoperiod was studied by Williams and Adkisson (1964) in *Antherea pernyi*. They found that long-day conditions (15–18 hours light) promoted termination of the diapause whereas the short-day (4–12 hours) prevented it. The experiments showed that the brain itself is the site of the action of light, most probably by nervous control of the AH production. In this connection the transparent window in the pupal integument immediately above the brain seems to be of primary importance, as shown by Shakbazov (1961) a little earlier. A photoperiodic acceleration of the termination of diapause was also found by McLeod and Beck (1963) in *Ostrinia* (= *Pyrausta*) *nubilalis*. A similar acceleration was observed following administration of large doses of ammonium acetate or other ammonium compounds. Synergism in accelerating diapause development was found between the action of NH_4 ions and a long photoperiod. It has been shown that the effect of a long photoperiod in preventing diapause can be replaced by an additional short photophase (5–30 min.) applied daily at about the middle of the dark period, even when combined with a very short photoperiod (e.g. 10 hours) (Barker, Mayer, and Cohan, 1963). The problem of the physiology and ecology of photoperiodism in insects was summarized and considered in toto by Beck (1963).

Neurohormones

Cyclical changes in the neurosecretory cells of the pars intercerebralis protocerebri were studied in two species of Lepidoptera (*Dasychira pudibunda* L. and *Pieris brassicae* L.) during the larval period and metamorphosis, including the diapause (Kind, 1964). Accumulation of neurosecretory granules, which differed in different types of neurosecretory cells, was observed during diapause. The author concludes that some of these cells have a specific role in diapause development and that the diapause is not a simple consequence of the absence of the activation hormone (called 'growth and development hormone' by the author). Here, however, a distinction must be made between accumulation of the granules in the neurosecretory cells and actual secretory activity, including the axoplasmic movement of the materials produced and their passage into the haemolymph. As shown by Highnam (1965), the actual rate of the endocrine activity of a neurosecretory cell is affected by the following three factors, which may vary independently: (*i*) the rate of synthesis of material in the cell; (*ii*) the rate of transport of the material along the axon; (*iii*) the rate of the release of the transported material into the circulatory system. Their interaction is therefore complex.

Data on the fate and function of the neurosecretory cells in the ventral ganglia are still very scarce. The secretory products from all three types of neurosecretory cells found within the thoracic and abdominal ganglia of the roach *Blaberus craniifer* were observed inside axons in the connectives between ganglia. Ligation of the connectives between ganglia showed that the neurosecretion moved in both anterior and posterior directions from the ganglia in which it was produced (Geldiay, 1959). A detailed study of neurosecretory cells in the ventral ganglia of *Schistocerca gregaria* Forsk. was carried out by Delphin (1963). He described the location of three types of A cells (A_1, A_2, A_3), two types of B cells (B_1, B_2), and one type each of C and D cells. The axonal transport of neurosecretory material was studied by ligation experiments, in nerve sections and by autoradiographic investigations using ^{35}S-DL-cystine. The granules were shown to pass backwards and forwards along the connectives and along at least some of the nerves originating from the ganglia. Differences in the secretory activity of various cells were observed. Extirpation and reimplantation of the last abdominal ganglion suggested that a hormonal factor which helps to control egg maturation is produced. Egg-laying was notably stimulated by implanting the ganglion from a mature female into a newly moulted one. The author also claims that the A_1 neurosecretory cells of the abdominal ganglia secrete an antidiuretic factor which is released under conditions in which water conservation might be necessary for the insect.

The role of neurosecretion and the interaction of other parts of the endocrine and nervous system in controlling circadian rhythms of activity were studied in detail by Harker (1960a, b; 1961) in *Periplaneta americana*. Immediate regulation is effected by cyclical release in a circadian rhythm of secretion by paired neuro-secretory cells situated on the ventral and slightly lateral surface of the suboesophageal ganglion. The neurosecretion which induces this phase of activity is produced daily in correlation with the onset of darkness. This dependence is, however, not autonomous. It seems that another substance is involved in the maintenance of their function, and that this second substance comes from the corpora cardiaca and enters the suboesophageal ganglion via the corpus allatums–uboesophageal ganglion nerve, in the form of methylene blue-positive granules. Once induced, the rhythm of neurosecretory activity continues for a number of days, even if the nervous connections of the ganglion are broken. The transplanted ganglion is thus capable of inducing the donor's rhythm of activity in the acceptor specimen. The timing of the active phase is primarily controlled by the environmental stimulus (a change from light to darkness) received through the medium of the ocelli. The adaptive value of these two interacting systems to an animal in normal field conditions seems to be that they allow for the gradual shift in timing of the active peak with the change in day length, but prevent phase resetting by incidental changes in light intensity at abnormal times.

Midgut tumours were produced artificially by the same author (Harker, 1958, 1960b) in *Periplaneta americana,* by experimentally breaking the above rhythms. Transplantable metastasing tumours were induced by the repeated implantation of suboesophageal ganglia out of phase with the animal's own ganglion and by breaking the neurosecretory cycle through specific environmental light conditions. It has been suggested that the production of tumours by recurrent nerve severance, as shown by B. Scharrer (1945) (cf. p. 47), is also related to the timing of suboesophageal ganglion secretory activity (Harker, 1960b).

How neurosecretion reaches the target organs. As opposed to the general belief that the active principle of the neurosecretion reaches its site of action via neurohaemal organs–circulatory fluid, it was recently suggested by Johnson (1963) that neurosecretory substances coming from neuro-secretory brain cells are distributed from the corpora cardiaca along the nervous pathways leading from these structures to various internal organs. This conclusion is based on good histological evidence submitted by the author on neurosecretion in aphids, in which the granules were followed along the branches of all three nerves leaving the corpus cardiacum, right to their endings in the muscles and various other organs. Johnson attempts to generalize this finding and suggests that the failure of similar observations in other insects might be due to the fact that 'in insects other than aphids either insufficient material is normally present in the axons for it to be readily detected by histochemical means, or it does not stain differentially with the known staining procedures'. Serious evidence seems, however, to refute this conclusion. First of all, there is irrefutable experimental evidence of the interaction of haemolymph in the action of some of the brain hormones (cf. Wigglesworth, 1934, 1940 etc.; Gersch, 1962 etc.; Harker, 1960a, b etc.; cf. also p. 224 and p. 300). Secondly, organs supposed by some authors (e.g. Strong, 1965b) to be regulated by nervous import of the neurosecretory material, such as the corpora allata, show the same cyclical activity after transplantation, indicating that activation hormone is present in the haemolymph (cf. Sláma, 1964c). Thirdly, there is even less evidence of the direct utilization of the neurosecretory material in tissue than of its passage into the haemolymph. Regarding the last, the new evidence obtained by Ganguly and Banerjee (1961) in the pyrrhocorid bug *Macroceroea grandis* should be mentioned.

It seems much more likely, as suggested by Highnam (1965, personal communication), that the state found in aphids is an exception among insects, due perhaps to far-reaching changes in the amount of body fluid associated with sucking plant sap, which could otherwise unfavourably influence the hormonal balance. It might rather be deduced that the development of neuro-haemal organs such as the corpora cardiaca is a later acquisition of evolution, so that the state in aphids could simply have originated as a return to a more primitive stage (katamorphosis sensu Schmalgausen, 1946), as is done for a number of other aphid structures.

New data on the hormonal control of metabolism by neurohormones have been obtained by a number of authors in the last three years. They were recently summarized by Gersch (1964). Some of them are discussed in connection with the activation hormone (p. 283 and p. 284). Among the most important of the others, mention should be made of the finding by Steele (1963) of a diabetogenic factor in the corpora cardiaca of *Periplaneta americana*, reminiscent of that produced by the sinus gland in crustaceans. The injection of corpora cardiaca extract (even only 0·002 of the amount of one pair of corpora cardiaca) resulted in a significant increase in trehalose in the haemolymph. It is assumed that this effect depends on activation of the phosphorylase responsible for the decomposition of glycogen.

Ralph and McCarthy (1964) found an increase in the trehalose content in the haemolymph of *Periplaneta americana* adults after injecting them with saline extracts of both corpora cardiaca and brain. They conclude that the active factor of the corpora cardiaca is produced by the neurosecretory cells of the brain.

The humoral control of water balance is still far from being clear. On the basis of histological investigations of the neurosecretory system of the cockroach *Blaberus giganteus*, Wall and Ralph (1962) concluded that a diuretic factor was released by the type A cells of the pars intercerebralis and of the thoracic ganglia. Under conditions causing dehydration, these cells produced greater than normal amounts of stainable granules. A diuretic principle was also reported by Núñez (1963) in *Rhodnius prolixus* which he supposed was produced by the neurosecretory cells of the complex thoracic ganglion (cf. also Maddrell, 1963). The remaining contradictions and confusions might be due to the fact that different active principles are probably produced by different parts of the central nervous system. At all events, the role of neurohormones in the control of water balance in insects can no longer be doubted (cf. Gersch, 1964).

New data have been obtained on *the morphology, ultrastructure and cytochemistry of neurosecretory cells*. A detailed topography of the neurosecretory system in the pyrrhocorid bug *Macroceroea grandis* (Gray) was elaborated by Ganguly and Banerjee (1961). In addition to the neurosecretory cells already known, three new groups were described and their homology with the X-organ, sinus gland and epineurium of crustaceans was claimed. The term *Wigglesworth organ* was suggested for the supposed X-organ homologue and the name *Hanström organ* for the hypothetical sinus gland homologue. Both structures were later rediscovered in the brain of the adult silkworm (*Bombyx mori*) by Ganguly and Basu (1962a). A detailed cytochemical analysis of the various types of neurosecretory cells was done in the last-mentioned and several further papers (Ganguly and Basu, 1962b; Ganguly and Deb, 1960; etc.).

A detailed cytochemical study of the neurosecretory granules and other neuroplasmic inclusions in *Periplaneta americana* was carried out by Pipa (1961, 1962 etc.). In this, gliosecretion, as well as other structures, is treated (cf. p. 208). In another paper the electron-microscopic structure of the gliosecretory granules was investigated (Pipa *et al.*, 1962). The differences found between these and the neurosecretory material seem, however, to be irrelevant from the point of view of the conclusions reached by Novák and Gutmann (1962), as recently suggested by Novák (1964). (For further papers dealing with the ultrastructure of the neurosecretory system, see p. 229.)

The formation of the neurosecretory system and its connection with the diapause in the last larval instar were studied in the moth *Ostrinia* (= *Pyrausta*) *nubilalis*. No specific differences were found between the amount of neurosecretory material in diapausing and non-diapausing brains in any of the groups of cells (McLeod and Beck, 1963). A comparative cytological investigation of the brain neurosecretory cells was made by Panov and Kind (1963) in 20 different species of Lepidoptera. Six groups of these cells were found in each hemisphere of the supraoesophageal ganglion and far-reaching agreement in their structure was found in all the species studied.

Principles affecting colour change from both insects and crustaceans were isolated by the above-mentioned methods (cf. p. 75) and were tested on crustaceans and insect chromatophores and muscle contraction rhythms in a detailed comparative study by Gersch, Unger, Fischer, and Kapitza (1964). Paper chromatography and paper electrophoresis of various parts of the neurosecretory system of both crustaceans (*Leander adsperus* and *Crangon vulgaris*) and insects (*Periplaneta americana* and *Carausius morosus*) showed the same four different substances in each group: two neurohormones, C_1 and D_1, which have already been found to be of a peptide nature (cf. p. 214), acetylcholine and serotonine. The principles obtained from insects were in complete agreement with those from crustaceans, both as regards their physico-chemical properties and their effects in biological tests on chromatophores in crustaceans, on pigment movement in the epidermis of *Carausius* and on the heart rate in *Periplaneta*. On this basis, suggestions for the chemical identification of various colour change factors described in crustaceans by earlier authors were made.

A humoral factor obtained by homogenization of the corpora cardiaca which stimulates the pericardial cells to produce a heart-accelerating principle in *Periplaneta americana*, was described by Davey (1961, 1962, 1963a, b) in great detail. Pericardial cells treated with the factor in vitro show histological signs of increased secretory activity and produce a substance increasing the heart rate, which was identified as indolalkylamine. In living animals, release of this factor from the corpora cardiaca can be induced by feeding. As suggested by Gersch (1964) there are no grounds for assuming that this form of interaction of the pericardial cells is general in insects, and there is good evidence of the direct effect of the neurohormones isolated, amongst others, from the corpora cardiaca, on the heart rate. As emphasized by Evans (1962) and Gersch (1964), it would be very interesting to determine the relationship of Davey's 'corpus cardiacum hormone' to the neurohormones C_1 and D_1 and possibly to the other active principles previously shown to occur in the corpora cardiaca as well as to the secretion of the pericardial cells.

The effect of neurohormones on the electrical activity of the nervous system in insects was studied by Gersch and Richter (1963). They showed that extracts of the brain and the ganglia of the ventral nerve cord, like those of the corpora cardiaca, release specific electrical impulses in the phallus nerve of *Periplaneta americana*. The separate application of the neurohormones C_1 and D_1 isolated by paper chromatography showed that D_1 possessed strong activity, while C_1 was inactive. The effect of these two substances on the autorhythmic electrical activity of the brain of *Periplaneta americana* in situ and of the isolated mesothoracic ganglion was studied by Strejčková, Servít and Novák (1965). It was found that neurohormone D_1 evoked hyperautorhythmia in both cases, while neurohormone C_1 inhibited the existing electrical activity after first inducing a transient rise.

Several papers deal with *the general significance and origin of the neurosecretory cells*. Bern (1963) views the 'neurosecretory neuron' as a doubly specialized cell having the features necessary both for the conduction of impulses and for the production of secretion. He discusses the ultrastructural characteristics of neurosecretory cells, with special reference to the formation of elementary neurosecretory granules by the Golgi apparatus and to the fate of neurosecretory granules in nerve endings (the so-called synaptic vesicles of the neurosecretory cells). He states that since the membranes of the neurosecretory axon bulbs are consistently smooth-surfaced, there is no evidence of pores or canals which might serve as channels for the discharge of neurosecretory granules formed, and no definite evidence of the extraneuronal occurrence of neurosecretory granules. On the other hand, unlike Johnson (see above) he emphasizes the hormogenic function (in the sense of a true endocrine organ) of the neurosecretory cells as one of their unique features. He also discusses the factors possibly determining the development of specialized 'hormone-producing neurons amid their ordinary neighbours'.

A general concept of the photo-neuro-endocrine systems and the question of their evolution is discussed by E. Scharrer (1964). He emphasizes the role of light as a synchronizer of circadian and annual rhythms in many important functions of living organisms, such as reproduction, moulting, migration, metabolic adjustment, etc. He distinguishes the following steps in the evolution of complex neuro-neurosecretory-endocrine control, as known in vertebrates: (*i*) the transparent animal in which the organs are exposed to changes in illumination; (*ii*) animals with an opaque integument excluding light except through a transparent window overlying the central nervous system (in insects, for example, this is the case in the pupa of *Antherea pernyi*, cf. p. 193); (*iii*) animals in which the retinal and central neurons transmit stimuli directly to endocrines affecting the light-dependent target organs; (*iv*) animals in which the products of the neurosecretory cells intervene between the nervous and endocrine systems. He emphasizes, however, that photoperiodicity is only one of the phenomena handled by neuroendocrine mechanisms.

Various aspects of the relationship between neurosecretion in invertebrates and vertebrates, together with phylogenetical relationships, were discussed by Gersch (1963a, b, c, 1964), particularly in his monograph on the invertebrate endocrines. He emphasizes his view that the neurosecretory system was the primary hormonal regulatory system in animals (cf. p. 228). The phylogenetic conclusions of Gersch are closely approached by the concept of Novák and Gutmann (1962), which was recently further elaborated by Novák (1964) (cf. p. 229). Novák assumes that neurosecretion has a two-fold phylogenetical origin, the carrier substance being a remnant of the secretory activity of the original ectoderm cells which became secondarily a means of accumulation of the physiologically active neurohumoral factors common in small amounts to all nerve cells.

New and Incompletely Known Insect Hormones

The finding of a new hormone called *proctodone* produced by special epithelial cells of the anterior portion of the hindgut, was recently reported by Beck and Alexander (1964a, b). The ligaturing experiment performed on diapausing last instar caterpillars of *Ostrinia* (= *Pyrausta*) *nubilalis* shows that diapause development here is dependent on a blood spread factor originating in the seventh and eighth abdominal segments. The authors suppose that it is necessary for stimulation of the neuroendocrine system of the brain in order to produce the activation hormone. Under conditions of experimentally accelerated diapause development, the action of this factor seems to be required for about two days, the source of the brain hormone then being necessary for about five days, and the pro-thoracic system for about six days, in order to complete diapause and prepupal postdiapause development. The hormone was said to be produced periodically during the light hours of the 24-hour cycle. It was postulated that it played a role in nondiapausing growth, periodism, several forms of diapause and polymorphism. Its possible relationship with the factor supposed by Davey (1962) to be produced by the epithelial cells of the anterior intestine under the influence of a corpus cardiacum factor (cf. p. 304), which stimulates muscle contractions in the hindgut was discussed. It was also suggested that it occurred in the non-photoperiodic and non-diapausing species *Galleria mellonella*. Here again, it is supposed to activate the endocrine functions of the brain. A number of questions still remain to be answered, however, before this can be accepted as a general mechanism in insects. The transplantation of supposedly active hindgut into diapausing *Ostrinia* larvae has so far not yielded conclusive results.

The secretory activity of oenocytes was studied in detail by Schmidt (1961a, b) in *Formica polyctena* during post-embryonic development. Both larval and imaginal oenocytes remain attached to the epidermis during the whole of the larval period. At the beginning of internal metamorphosis in the pupa, they are loosened and accumulate at the sites where the imaginal organs develop. The larval oenocytes appear inside the midgut and are digested when body pigmentation starts. Since the imaginal oenocytes and the trophocytes are fixed in the tissue at the same time, the haemolymph afterwards becomes clear. The size of the oenocytes depends on their secretory activity (cf. p. 240); the larval oenocytes reach their maximum size shortly before pupal moulting, the imaginal oenocytes before imaginal moulting. The oenocytes are supposed to produce enzymes necessary during metamorphosis and are thus of primary importance in the formation of the imaginal organs. The imaginal organs seem to have a function in the production of eggs. It was suggested that they were controlled by the corpora allata. There is no basis for supposing that they possess hormonal or excretory functions.

Exohormones

The question of the mode of action of the *queen inhibitory substance* on the worker bees was studied by Lüscher and Walker (1963). They found that the corpora allata in workers separated from the queen increased in volume. This increase was significantly inhibited by the queen extract prepared from about 100 queen bees by Butler's method. The authors concluded that the inhibitory effect of the queen substance on the ovaries of workers was caused by the suppression of the secretory activity of their corpora allata.

The finding of *a new phenomenon in the honey bee* is reported by Butler, Callow, and Chapman (1964). They show that a synthetic substance, 9-hydroxydec-trans-2-enoic acid, caused dispersing clusters of swarming honey bees to re-form and settle down again in the same way as does the odour of the queen, i.e. her mandibular glands secretion.

The existence of two active principles in the mandibular glands of the *Myrmica rubra* queen was suggested by Brian and Hibble (1963). One of them, probably 9-oxodec-enoic acid, is supposed to produce a stimulatory effect on brood growth similar to that caused by the presence of the queen, the other, which probably corresponds to a lipoid fraction of queen mandibular glands extract, has an inhibitory effect. In another paper, the authors analysed the influence of the queen on the growth of brood in connection with the size of the larvae in *Myrmica* (Brian and Hibble, 1963b). The influence of temperature, food and the presence of queens on caste differentiation was studied by Brian (1963) in female larvae.

The specific effect of the male and female on the development of the replacement reproductives was studied by Lüscher (1963) in colonies of *Calotermes flavicollis*. Conditions under which the replacement male produces the inhibitory and stimulatory effects were analysed.

The Effects of the Hormones of Vertebrates and Other Animals on Insects and vice versa

A number of vertebrate hormones administered in food were tested as to their *effect on the neurosecretory cells* of the pars intercerebralis, on the nuclei of corpora cardiaca and nuclei of corpora allata by Voytkevich and Leonova (1964) in the cockroach *Periplaneta americana*. The following substances were tested: thyreoidine (0·05 g), diethylstilbesterol (0·001 g), cortisone

(0·025 g), AKTG (adenocorticotropic hormone) (40 units), and DOCA (desoxycorticosterone-acetate). Some of the substances produced a distinct effect upon the size of the neurosecretory cells and the diameter of nuclei in the glands suggesting a stimulation of their secretion. The most active seem to be cortisone and DOCA.

Synthetic *oxytocin* and several of its artificially *synthetized derivatives* were shown to have positive myotropic and chromatophorotropic effects in insect preparations whereas others were completely ineffective, in a systematic study by Carlise, Novák, and Rudinger.[1]

The question of the mutual *effects of the hormones of vertebrates* and other animals in insects and vice versa was discussed by Gersch (1964) in his monograph on the endocrines in invertebrates. The older papers by Peredelsky (1930, 1939a, b, 1940) should also be remembered in this connection. More experimental evidence on the present methodological level will be necessary before the question can be definitely answered (cf. p. 262).

[1] 1966, in preparation.

References

For papers published in the years 1963–1965 see the Additional References, pp. 427–40.

ABD-EL-WAHAB, A. 1959. 'A new method for delaying pupation in *Drosophila melanogaster*.' *Nature, Lond.*, **183**, 127.

ABDERHALDEN, E. 1919. 'Weitere Studien über die von einzelnen Organen hervorgebrachten Substanzen mit spezifischer Wirkung.' II. *Mitt. Pflüg. Arch.*, **176**, 236–62.

Acta Symposii de Evolutione Insectorum, Prague, 1961 (1959), Praha, NČSAV, 435 pp.

ADAMSON, A. M. 1940. 'New termite intercastes.' *Proc. roy. Soc.* (B), **129**, 35–53.

AGRELL, I. 1949a. 'The variation in activity of apodehydrogenases during insect metamorphosis.' *Acta physiol. scand.*, **18**, 355–60.

AGRELL, I. 1949b. 'Localization of some hydrogenactivating enzymes in insects during metamorphosis.' *Nature, Lond.*, **164**, 1039.

AGRELL, I. 1951a. 'A contribution to the histolysis-histogenesis problem in insect metamorphosis.' *Acta physiol. scand.*, **23**, 179–86.

AGRELL, I. 1951b. 'Pupal diapause caused by vitamin deficiency.' *Nature, Lond.*, **167**, 283.

AGRELL, I. 1951c. 'The diapause problem.' *Année biol.*, **27**, 287–95.

AGRELL, I. 1952a. 'The aerobic and anaerobic utilization of metabolic energy during insect metamorphosis.' *Acta physiol. scand.*, **28**, 306–35.

AGRELL, I. 1952b. 'Nucleic acid metabolism during insect metamorphosis.' *Nature, Lond.*, **170**, 543.

AHRENS, W. 1935. 'Die Entwicklung des "corpus luteum" der Insekten. Nach Untersuchungen an *Termes redemanni*.' *Z. mikr.-anat. Forsch.*, **37**, 467–500.

ALESHCHIN, B. V. 1935. 'Investigation of the metamorphosis in amphibians. An attempt at a metamorphosis theory' (in Russian). *Biol. Zh.*, **4**, 461–88.

ALLÉGRET, P. 1952. 'Conditionnement précoce de la métamorphose chez *Galleria mellonella*.' *C. R. Acad. Sci. Paris*, **234**, 1641–3.

ALLEN, T. H. 1940. 'Cytochrome oxidase in relation to respiratory activity and growth of the grasshopper egg.' *J. cell. comp. Physiol.*, **16**, 149–63.

ALPATOW, W. W. 1929a. 'The influence of thyroid gland feeding on the acceleration of the growth of larvae of *Drosophila melanogaster*.' *Proc. nat. Acad. Sci. Wash.*, **15**, 578–80.

ALPATOW, W. W. 1929b. 'Growth and variation of the larvae of *Drosophila melanogaster*.' *J. exp. Zool.*, **52**, 407–432.

ALTMANN, G. G. 1950. 'Ein Sexualwirkstoff bei Honigbienen.' *Z. Bienen-forsch.*, **1**, 24.

ALTMANN, G. G. 1956. 'Hormonale Steuerung des Wasserhaushaltes der Honigbiene.' *Zool. Anz.*, suppl., **19**, 107–12.

ALTMANN, G. G. and GONTARSKI, H. 1961. 'Ueber den Wasserhaushalt der Winterbienen.' *Symp. gen. Biol. ital.*, **12**, 308–28.

ANDREWARTHA, N. G. 1943. 'Diapause in the egg of *Austroicetes cruciata* Sauss. with special reference to the influence of temperature on the elimination of diapause.' *Bull. ent. Res.*, **34**, 1–17.

ANDREWARTHA, N. G. 1950. 'Diapause in relation to the ecology of insects.' *Biol. Rev.*, **27**, 50–107.

ANDRIANOVA, N. S. 1948. 'The influence of light on growth and development of the chinese oak silkworm' (in Russian). *The Culture of Chinese Oak Silkworms in U.S.S.R.* Selchosgis, Moscow, 38–47.

ANGLAS, J. 1901a. 'Quelques remarques sur les métamorphoses internes des Hyménoptéres.' *Bull. Soc. ent. Fr.*, 104–7.

ANGLAS, J. 1901b. 'Observations sur les métamorphoses internes de la Guepe et de l'Abeille.' *Bull. sci. Fr. Belg.*, **34**, 363–473.

APHANASIEV, P. V. 1952. 'Several questions of the theory of biochemical processes' (in Russian). *Adv. mod. Biol.*, *Moscow*, **34**, 328–53.

ARDASHNIKOV, S. N. 1941. 'Malignant tumours in *Drosophila melanogaster*. Influence of the left and of the sex chromosome on the development of tumours' (in Russian). *C. R. Acad. Sci. U.R.S.S.*, **30**, 344–6.

ARISTOV, M. T. 1925. 'On the question of hibernation in *Anthonomus pomonus L.*' (in Russian). *Izv. otd. prikl. ent. agr.*, **3**, 5–6.

AROS, B. and VIGH, B. 1961a. 'Neurosecretory activity of the central and peripheral nervous system in the earthworm.' *Acta Biol. Acad. Sci. Hung.*, **12**, 169–86.

AROS, B. and VIGH, B. 1961b. 'Neurosecretory changes in the nervous system of *Lumbricus rubellus* provoked by various experimental influences.' *Acta Biol. Acad. Sci. Hung.*, **12**, 87–98.

AROS, B. and VIGH, B. 1962. 'Neurosecretion as a holocrine gland function in Lumbricidae.' *Acta Biol. Acad. Sci. Hung.*, **13**, 177–92.

ARVY, L. 1954. 'Sur l'existence de cellules neurosécrétrices chez quelques Annélides Polychétes sédentaires.' *C. R. Acad. Sci.*, *Paris*, **238**, 511–513.

ARVY, L., BOUNHIOL, J. J. and GABE, M. 1953. 'Déroulement de la neurosécrétion protocérébrale chez *Bombyx mori* L. au cours du développement post-embryonaire.' *C. R. Acad. Sci.*, *Paris*, **236**, 627–9.

ARVY, L., ÉCHALIER, G. and GABE, M. 1954. 'Modification de la gonade de *Carcinides moenas* aprés ablation bilatérale de l'organe Y.' *C. R. Acad. Sci.*, *Paris*, **239**, 1853–5.

ARVY, L., ÉCHALIER, G. and GABE, M. 1956. 'Organe Y et gonade chez *Carcinides moenas* L.' *Ann. Sci. nat.*, *Zool.*, **18**, 263–7.

ARVY, L. and GABE, M. 1947. 'Contribution à l'étude cytologique et histochimique des formations endocrinnes rétro-cérébrales de la larve de *Chironomus plumosus* L.' *Rev. canad. Biol.*, **6,** 777–96.

ARVY, L. and GABE, M. 1951. 'Données histophysiologiques sur les formations endocrines rétrocérébrales chez les Ecdyonuridae.' *Bull. Soc. zool. Fr.*, **75,** 267–85.

ARVY, L. and GABE, M. 1952. 'Données histophysiologiques sur les formations endocrines rétrocérébrales de quelques Odonates.' *Ann. Sci. nat., Zool.*, **14,** 345–74.

ARVY, L. and GABE, M. 1953a. 'Données histophysiologiques sur la néurosécrétion chez quelques Epheméroptères.' *Cellule*, **55,** 203–22.

ARVY, L. and GABE, M. 1953b. 'Données histophysiologiques sur la néurosécrétion chez les Paléoptères.' *Z. Zellforsch.*, **38,** 591–610.

ARVY, L. and GABE, M. 1953c. 'Contribution à l'histologie des glandes endocrines céphaliques chez la larve de *Prosopistoma foliaceum. F.*' *Bull. Soc. zool. Fr.*, **78,** 451–62.

ARVY, L. and GABE, M. 1953d. 'Particularités histophysiologiques des glandes endocrines céphaliques chez *Tenebrio molitor* L.' *C. R. Acad. Sci.*, *Paris*, **237,** 844–6.

ARVY, L. and GABE, M. 1954a. 'The intercerebralis-cardiacum-allatum system of some Plecoptera.' *Biol. Bull., Wood's Hole*, **106,** 1–14.

ARVY, L. and GABE, M. 1954b. 'Données histophysiologiques sur la néurosécrétion chez les insectes paléoptères (Epheméroptères et Odonates).' *Pubbl. Staz. zool. Napoli*, **24,** 54–6.

ARVY, L. and GABE, M. 1962. 'Histochemistry of the neurosecretory product of the pars intercerebralis of pterygote insects.' In Heller and Clark, Neurosecretion. *Mem. Soc. Endocrinol.*, no. 12, 331–344.

ASHBEL, R. 1935. 'Action of thyroid extract on the respiration of tissues of invertebrates.' *Nature, Lond.*, **135,** 343.

ASTAUROV, M. T. 1940. *Artificial parthenogenesis in the silkworm* (Bombyx mori). *An experimental study* (in Russian). Moscow, Akad. Nauk. S.S.S.R., 240 pp.

ASTAUROV, M. T. 1943. 'Thermic activation as a phenomenon and as a method for preventing the embryonic diapause' (in Russian). *J. gen. Biol. Moscow*, **6,** 314–44.

ATZLER, M. 1930. 'Untersuchungen über morphologischen und physiologischen Farbwechsel von *Dixippus morosus*.' *Z. vergl. Physiol.*, **13,** 505–533.

AUERBACH, C. 1936. 'The development of the legs, wings and halteres in wild type and some mutant strains of *Drosophila melanogaster*.' *Trans. roy. Soc. Edinb.*, **58,** 787–841.

AUERBACH, C. 1940. 'Tests of carcinogenic substances in relation to the production of mutations in *Drosophila melanogaster*.' *Proc. roy. Soc. Edinb.*, **60,** 164–73.

AVEL, M. 1929. 'Recherches expérimentales sur les caractères sexuels somatiques des Lumbriciens.' *Bull. biol.*, **63,** 149–318.

BAKER, F. C. 1935. 'The effect of photoperiodism on resting tree-hole mosquito larvae.' *Canad. Ent.*, **67**, 149–53.

BALAZUC, J. 1948. 'La tératologie des Coléoptères et experiences de transplantations chez *Tenebrio molitor*.' *Mém. Mus. Hist. nat.*, *Paris*, **25**, 1–293.

BALACHOWSKY, A. 1937. 'La rupture expérimentelle de la diapause chez le Carpocapse ou "ver des pommes", *Laspeyresia pomonella* L.' *C. R. Acad. Sci.*, *Paris*, **204**, 294–5.

BALKASHINA, E. L. 1929. 'Ein Fall der Erbhomöosis die (Genovariation, "aristopedia") bei *Drosophila melanogaster*.' *Arch. EntwMech. Org.*, **115**, 448–63.

BARBIER, M. and LEDERER, E. 1960. 'Structure chimique de la "substance royale" de la reine d'abeille (*Apis mellifica*).' *C. R. Acad. Sci.*, *Paris*, **250**, 4467–9.

BARBIER, M., LEDERER, E. and NOMURA, T. 1960. 'Synthèse de l'acide céto-9 décéne-2-trans oique (substance royale) et de l'acide céto-8 nonéne 2-trans oique.' *C. R. Acad. Sci.*, *Paris*, **251**, 1133–5.

BARBIER, M., LEDERER, E., REICHSTEIN, I. and SCHINDLER, O. 1960. 'Auftrennung der saueren Anteile von Extrakten aus Bienenköniginnen. Isolierung des als Königinnen-Substanz bezeichneten Pheromones.' *Helv. chim. Acta*, **43**, 1682–9.

BARBIER, M. and PAIN, J. 1960. 'Étude de la sécretion des glandes mandibulaires des reines et des ouvrières d'abeilles par chromatographie en phase gazeuse.' *C. R. Acad. Sci.*, *Paris*, **250**, 3740–2.

BARBIER, M. and SCHINDLER, O. 1959. 'Isolierung von 24-Methylencholesterin aus Königinnen und Arbeiterinnen der Honigbiene.' *Helv. chim. Acta*, **42**, 1998–2005.

BARGMANN, W. 1954. *Das Zwischenhirn-Hypophysesystem*, Berlin–Göttingen–Heidelberg.

BARGMANN, W. 1960. 'The neurosecretory system of the diencephalon.' *Endeavour*, **19**, 125–33.

BARKER, A. S. *et al.* 1959a. 'Identification of 10-hydroxyl-Δ^2-decenoic acid in Royal Jelly.' *Nature, Lond.*, **183**, 996–7.

BARKER, A. S. *et al.* 1959b. 'Biological origin and configuration of 10-hydroxyl-Δ^2-decenoic acid.' *Nature, Lond.*, **184**, 634.

BARTH, R. H. 1961. 'Hormonal control of sex attractants production in the Cuban cockroach.' *Science*, **133**, 1598–9.

BARTH, R. H. 1962. 'The endocrine control of mating behaviour in the cockroach *Byrsotria fumigata*.' *Gen. comp. Endocrinol.*, **2**, 53–69.

BARTON BROWNE, L. and DODSON, L. F. 1961. 'Adrenergic properties of the cockroach corpus cardiacum.' *Gen. comp. Endocrinol.*, **1**, 232–6.

BASDEN, E. B. 1954. 'Diapause in *Drosophila melanogaster*.' *Proc. roy. ent. Soc. Lond.*, **29**, 7–9.

BASDEN, E. B. 1955. 'Egg-laying of the stick-insect (*Carausius morosus*).' *Ent. mon. Mag.*, **91**, 201–2.

BASSINDALE, R. 1955. 'The biology of the stingless bee *Trigona gribodoi* Magretti.' *Proc. zool. Soc. Lond.*, **125**, 49–62.

BATTAILON, E. 1893. 'La métamorphose du ver á soie et le déterminisme évolutif.' *Bull. sci. Fr. Belg.*, **25**, 18–55.

BATTAILON, P. C. 1927. 'Recherches sur la tératologie des insectes.' *Encycl. ent.*, **8**, 291.

BAUMBERGER, G. P. 1917. 'Hibernation, a periodical phenomenon.' *Ann. ent. Soc. Amer.*, **10**, 179–88.

BAYLISS, W. M. and STARLING, E. M. 1906. 'Die chemische Koordination der Funktionen des Körpers.' *Ergeb. Physiol.*, **5**, 664–97.

BEADLE, G. W. 1937a. 'The development of eye colours in *Drosophila melanogaster* as studied by transplantation.' *Amer. Nat.*, **71**, 120–6.

BEADLE, G. W. 1937b. 'Development of eye colour in *Drosophila*: fat bodies and Malpighian tubes in relation to diffusible substances.' *Genetics*, **22**, 587–611.

BEADLE, G. W. 1945. 'Biochemical genetics.' *Chem. Rev.*, **37**, 15–96.

BEADLE, G. W., ANDERSON, R. L. and MAXWELL, J. 1938. 'A comparison of the diffusible substance concerned with the eye colour development in *Drosophila melanogaster*, *Ephestia* and *Habrobracon*.' *Proc. nat. Acad. Sci.*, *Wash.*, **24**, 80–5.

BEADLE, G. W., CLANCY, C. W. and EPHRUSSI, B. 1937. 'Development of eye colour in *Drosophila*: Pupal transplants and the influence of body fluid on Vermilion.' *Proc. roy. Soc.* (B), **122**, 98–105.

BEADLE, G. W. and EPHRUSSI, B. 1935a. 'Transplantations in *Drosophila melanogaster*.' *Proc. nat. Acad. Sci.*, *Wash.*, **21**, 642–6.

BEADLE, G. W. and EPHRUSSI, B. 1935b. 'Différentiation de la couleur de l'œil cinnabar chez la *Drosophila*.' *C. R. Acad. Sci.*, *Paris*, **201**, 620.

BEADLE, G. W. and EPHRUSSI, B. 1935c. 'La transplantation des disques imaginaux chez la *Drosophila*.' *C. R. Acad. Sci.*, *Paris*, **201**, 98–100.

BEADLE, G. W. and EPHRUSSI, B. 1936a. 'Development of eye colours in *Drosophila*. Transplantation experiments with suppression of vermilion.' *Proc. nat. Acad. Sci.*, *Wash.*, **22**, 536–40.

BEADLE, G. W. and EPHRUSSI, B. 1936b. 'Development of eye colours in *Drosophila*.' *J. Genet.*, **33**, 407–10.

BEADLE, G. W. and EPHRUSSI, B. 1937. 'Development of eye colours in *Drosophila*.' *Genetics*, **22**, 65–75, 76–86, 419–83.

BEADLE, G. W. and LAW, L. W. 1938. 'Influence on eye colour of feeding diffusible substances to *Drosophila melanogaster*.' *Proc. Soc. exp. Biol.*, *N.Y.*, **37**, 621–3.

BEADLE, G. W., TATUM, E. L. and CLANCY, C. W. 1938. 'Food level in relation to rate of development and eye pigmentation in *Drosophila melanogaster*.' *Biol. Bull.*, *Wood's Hole*, **75**, 447–62.

BEADLE, G. W. and THIMANN, K. W. 1937. 'Development of eye colour in *Drosophila melanogaster*. Extraction of the diffusible substance concerned.' *Proc. nat. Acad. Sci.*, *Wash.*, **23**, 3.

BEAUMONT, J. DE. 1940. 'Le déterminisme des métamorphoses chez les insectes (hormones de métamorphose).' *Mitt. schw. ent. Ges.*, **18**, 49–57.

BEAUMONT, J. DE. 1944. 'Lois de la croissance larvaire chez quelques Coléoptères.' *C. R. Acad. Sci., Paris*, **218**, 331–3.

BECK, S. D. 1950. 'Nutrition of the European corn borer *Pyrausta nubilalis*: Some effects of diet on larval growth characteristics.' *Physiol. Zool.*, **23**, 353–61.

BECK, S. D. 1960. 'Growth and development of the wax moth *Galleria mellonella*.' *Trans. Wis. Acad. Sci. Arts Lett.*, **49**, 137–48.

BECK, S. D. 1962. 'Temperature effects on Insects: Relation to Periodism.' *Proc. N. cent. Brch. Am. Ass. econ. Ent.*, **17**, 1–2.

BECK, S. D., CLOUTIER, E. J. and MCLEOD, D. G. 1962. 'Photoperiod and Insect Development.' In *Insect Physiology*, Oregon State Univ. Press, pp. 43–62.

BECKER, E. 1937a. 'Extractions des bei der Mehlmotte *Ephestia kühniella* die dunkle Ausfärbung der Augen auslösenden Gen.-A-Hormons.' *Naturwissenschaften*, **25**, 507.

BECKER, E. 1937b. 'Die rotbraune Zeichnung der Wespennestmütter, eine durch mechanischen Reiz ausgelöste Pigmentalablagerung in Liesegang schen Ringen.' *Z. vergl. Physiol.*, **24**, 305–18.

BECKER, E. 1938. 'Die Gen-Wirkstoffe-Systeme der Augenausfärbung be Insekten.' *Naturwissenschaften*, **26**, 433–41.

BECKER, E. 1939b. 'Ueber die Natur des Augenpigments von *Ephestia kühniella* und seinen Vergleich mit den Augenpigmenten anderer Insekten.' *Biol. Zbl.*, **59**, 597–627.

BECKER, E. 1941. 'Ueber Versuche zur Anreicherung und physiologische Charakterisierung des Wirkstoffes der Puparisierung.' *Biol. Zbl.*, **61**, 360–388.

BECKER, E. 1942. 'Ueber Eigenschaften, Verbreitung und die genetisch-entwicklungsphysiologische Bedeutung der Pigmente der Ommatin- und Ommingruppe (Ommochrome) bei den Arthropoden.' *Z. indukt. Abstamm.- u. VererbLehre*, **80**, 157–204.

BECKER, E. 1950. 'Metatelie bei Cerambyciden-Larven.' *Zool. Jb. (allg. Zool.)*, **62**, 93–101.

BECKER, E. and PLAGGE, E. 1937. 'Vergleich der die Augenausfärbung bedingenden Gen-Wirkstoffe von *Ephestia kühniella*.' *Naturwissenschaften*, **50**, 809.

BECKER, E. and PLAGGE, E. 1939. 'Ueber die da Puparium-Bildung auslösende Hormon der Fliegen.' *Biol. Zbl.*, **59**, 326–41.

BECKER, E. and SCHÖPF, C. 1936. 'Der mikrochemische Nachweis der Pterine.' *Liebigs Ann.*, 524–549.

BEERMANN, W. 1959. 'Chromosomal differentiation in insects.' *Symp. Dev. Growth (Growth in suppt.)*, New York, **16**, 83–103.

BEETSMA, J., RUITER, L. DE and WILDE, J. DE. 1962. 'Possible influence of neotenine and ecdyson on the sign of phototaxis in the eyed hawk caterpillar.' *J. Ins. Physiol.*, **8**, 251–7.

BEKKER, E. G. 1958. 'On the problem of origin and development of the winged insects. V. A. contribution to the knowledge of ontogeny and phylogeny of the organs of flight in Orthoptera Saltatoria' (in Russian). *Ent. Obozr.*, **37**, 775–84.

BEKLEMISCHEV, V. N. 1944. *Ecology of mosquitoes – vectors of malaria* (in Russian), Medgis, Moscow, 245 pp.

BEKLEMISHEV, V. N. 1958. *Grundlagen der vergleichenden Anatomie der Wirbellosen.* VEB Deutscher Verlag der Wiss., Berlin, 1–471.

BELAIEV, N. K. 1932. 'Artificial enlivening of the diapausing silkworm eggs' (in Russian). *Trans. Centralasiat. Sericult. Inst.*, *Tashkent*, **1**, 1–40.

BELANOVSKI, I. 1936. 'Ueber Gesetzmässigkeiten in der Massenvermehrung von Schädlingen in Verbindung mit meteorologischen Faktoren' (in Russian). *Zool. Zh.*, **15**, 187–216.

BELARSH, K. 1929. 'Spermatogenese in *Chorthippus.*' *Arch. EntwMech. Org.*, **118**, 359.

BĚLEHRÁDEK, J. 1934. 'L'origine des sécretiones internes.' *Médicine pratique*, pp. 3–9.

BELJAEVA, T. G. 1960a. 'Histochemical investigation of the corpora allata secretion in *Antherea pernyi* caterpillars' (in Russian). *C. R. Acad. Sci. U.R.S.S.*, **135**, 449–52.

BELJAEVA, T. G. 1960b. 'Several data on the neurosecretion in *Antherea pernyi* caterpillars and moths' (in Russian). *C. R. Acad. Sci. U.R.S.S.*, **134**, 987–90.

BELJAEVA, T. G. 1961. 'Data on the secretion of corpora cardiaca in *Antherea pernyi* caterpillars and moths' (in Russian). *C. R. Acad. Sci. U.R.S.S.*, **140**, 692–5.

BELOV, P. F. 1951. 'The study of stage development in *Antherea pernyi* in connection with the regulation of its voltinism' (in Russian). In *Sbornik: Dubonji belkoperad*, Selchosgis, Moscow, 5–61.

BEMMELEN, J. F. 1930. 'Ergebnisse meiner Untersuchungen über die Farbenzeichnungen der Insekten.' *Tijdschr. ned. dierk. Ver.* (3), **2**, 89–108.

BENZ, G. 1957. 'Untersuchungen über die Wirkung der Letalfaktoren, Letalbluten und Letalpolymorph von *Drosophila melanogaster.*' *Z. indukt. Abstamm.-u. VererbLehre*, **88**, 78–114.

BERG, O., GORBMANN, A. and KOBAYASHI, H. 1959. 'The thyroid hormones in invertebrates and lower vertebrates.' *A Textbook of Comparative Endocrinology*, J. Wiley & Sons, New York, pp. 302–19.

BERLESE, A. 1913. 'Intomo alle metamorphosis degli insetti.' *Redia*, **9**, 121–136.

BERN, H. A. 1962. 'The properties of neurosecretory cells.' *Gen. comp. Endocrinol.*, suppl. **1**, 117–32.

BERNHARD, C. G. and OTTOSON, D. 1959. 'On the mechanism of dark adaptation in day-and-night insects.' *Acta physiol. scand.*, **47**, 383–4.

BERSIN, T. 1959. *Biochemie der Hormone.* Leipzig, Akad. Verlag.

BERTANI, G. 1947. 'Artificial breaking of diapause in *Drosophila nitens.*' *Nature, Lond.*, **159**, 309.

BIEDERMANN, W. 1914. 'Farbe und Zeichnung der Insekten.' In Winterstein, *Handb. vergleich. Physiol.*, **3**, 897–908.

BIELLMANN, G. 1959. 'Étude du cycle des mues chez *Periplaneta americana.*' *Bull. Soc. zool. Fr.*, **84**, 340–51.

BIER, K. 1954a. 'Ueber den Saisondimorphismus der Oogenesis von *Formica rufa rufo-pratensis minor* Gössw. und dessen Bedeutung für die Kastendetermination.' *Biol. Zbl.*, **73**, 170–90.

BIER, K. 1954b. 'Ueber Phasen gesteigter Protein- und Kohlenhydrateinlagerung und die Fettverteilung im Hymenopterenovar.' *Verh. dtsch. zool. Ges.*, **16**, 422–9.

BIGELOW, R. S. 1960. 'Development rates and diapause in *Acheta pennsylvanicus* (Burmeister) and *Acheta veletis* Alexander and Bigelow.' *Canad. J. Zool.*, **38**, 973–88.

BIRD, E. T. 1949. 'Tumors associated with a virus infection in an insect.' *Nature, Lond.*, **163**, 777–8.

BIRMINGHAM, L. 1942. 'Boundaries of differentiation of cephalic imaginal discs in *Drosophila.*' *J. exp. Zool.*, **91**, 345–63.

BLAKE, G. M. 1960. 'Decreasing photoperiod inhibiting metamorphosis in insects.' *Nature, Lond.*, **188**, 168–9.

BLAUSTEIN, M. P. and SCHNEIDERMAN, H. A. 1960. 'A brief survey of the effects of potential antimetabolites and enzymes on the development of giant silk moths.' *J. Ins. Physiol.*, **5**, 143–59.

BOCH, R. and SHEARER, D. A. 1962. 'Identification of Geraniol as the active component in the Nassonoff Pheromone of the honey bee.' *Nature, Lond.*, **194**, 704–6.

BOCH, R., SHEARER, D. A. and STONE, B. C. 1962. 'Identification of Iso-Amyl-Acetate as an active component in the sting Pheromone of the honey bee.' *Nature, Lond.*, **195**, 1018–20.

BODENSTEIN, D. 1933a. 'Beintransplantationen an Lepidopteren Raupen. I. Transplantation zur Analyse der Raupen- und Puppenhäutungen.' *Arch. EntwMech. Org.*, **128**, 564–83.

BODENSTEIN, D. 1933b. 'Beintransplantationen an Lepidopteren Raupen. II. Zur Analyse der Regeneration der Brustbeine von *Vanessa urticae*-Raupen.' *Arch. EntwMech. Org.*, **130**, 747–70.

BODENSTEIN, D. 1933c. 'Zur Frage der Bedeutung hormoneller Beziehungen bei der Insektenmetamorphose.' *Naturwissenschaften*, **21**, 861–3.

BODENSTEIN, D. 1933d. 'Experimentellerzeugte Doppelbildungen von Lepidopterenbeinen.' *Zool. Anz.*, **102**, 34–8.

BODENSTEIN, D. 1934a. 'Untersuchungen zur Analyse des Häutungsproblems.' *Forsch-Fortschr. dtsch. Wiss.*, **10**, 73–4.

BODENSTEIN, D. 1934b. 'Die experimentelle Erzeugung chimärer Schmetterlingsbeine.' *Biol. Zbl.*, **54**, 181–5.

BODENSTEIN, D. 1935. 'Beintransplantationen an Lepidopterenraupen.

III. Zur Analyse der Entwicklungspotenzen der Schmetterlingsbeine.' *Arch. EntwMech. Org.*, **133**, 156–92.

BODENSTEIN, D. 1936. 'Das Determinationsgeschehen bei Insekten mit Ausschluss der frühembryonaler Determination.' *Ergebn. Biol.*, **13**, 174–234.

BODENSTEIN, D. 1937. 'Beintransplantationen an Lepidopterenraupen. IV. Zur Analyse experimentell erzeugten Bein-Mehrfachbildungen.' *Arch. EntwMech. Org.*, **136**, 745–85.

BODENSTEIN, D. 1938a. 'Untersuchungen zum Metamorphoseproblem. I. Kombinierte schnürungs-und transplantations-Experimente an *Drosophila melanogaster*.' *Arch. EntwMech. Org.*, **137**, 474–505.

BODENSTEIN, D. 1938b. 'Untersuchungen zum Metamorphoseproblem. II. Entwicklungsrelationen in verschmolzenen Puppenteilen.' *Arch. Entw-Mech. Org.*, **139**, 636–60.

BODENSTEIN, D. 1938c. 'Untersuchungen zum Metamorphoseproblem. III. Ueber die Entwicklung der Ovarien im thoraxlosen Puppenabdomen.' *Biol. Zbl.*, **58**, 329–32.

BODENSTEIN, D. 1939a. 'Imaginal differentiation inaugurated by oxygen in *Drosophila* pupae.' *Proc. nat. Acad. Sci.*, *Wash.*, **25**, 14.

BODENSTEIN, D. 1939b. 'Investigations on the problem of metamorphosis. V.' *Genetics*, **24**, 494–508.

BODENSTEIN, D. 1939c. 'Investigations on the problem of the metamorphosis. IV.' *J. exp. Zool.*, **82**, 1–30.

BODENSTEIN, D. 1940. 'Growth regulation by transplanted eye and leg discs in *Drosophila*.' *J. exp. Zool.*, **84**, 23–37.

BODENSTEIN, D. 1941. 'Investigation on the problem of the metamorphosis. VII.' *J. exp. Zool.*, **86**, 87–111.

BODENSTEIN, D. 1942. 'Hormone controlled processes in insect development.' *Cold Spr. Harb. Symp. quant. Biol.*, **10**, 17–26.

BODENSTEIN, D. 1943a. 'Factors in influencing growth and metamorphosis of the salivary gland in *Drosophila*.' *Biol. Bull.*, *Wood's Hole*, **84**, 13–33.

BODENSTEIN, D. 1943b. 'Hormones and tissues competence in the development of *Drosophila*.' *Biol. Bull.*, *Wood's Hole*, **84**, 34–58.

BODENSTEIN, D. 1944. 'The induction of larval molts in *Drosophila*.' *Biol. Bull.*, *Wood's Hole*, **86**, 113–24.

BODENSTEIN, D. 1946a. 'Developmental relations between genital ducts and gonads in *Drosophila*.' *Biol. Bull.*, *Wood's Hole*, **91**, 288–94.

BODENSTEIN, D. 1946b. 'A study of the relationship between organ and organic environment in the postembryonic development of the yellow fever mosquito.' *Bull. Cornell agric. Exp. Sta.*, **501**, 100–114.

BODENSTEIN, D. 1947. 'Investigations on the reproductive system of *Drosophila*.' *J. exp. Zool.*, **104**, 101–52.

BODENSTEIN, D. 1949. *The postembryonic development of* Drosophila. New York, J. Wiley & Son.

BODENSTEIN, D. 1953a. 'Studies on the humoral mechanism in growth and metamorphosis of the cockroach *Periplaneta americana*. I–III.' *J. exp. Zool.*, **123**, 189–232, 414–33; **124**, 105–15.

BODENSTEIN, D. 1953b. 'Endocrine control of metamorphosis with special reference to Holometabola.' *Trans. VIIIth int. Congr. Ent., Amsterdam,* **2**, 58–62.

BODENSTEIN, D. 1953c. 'The role of hormones in moulting and metamorphosis.' In Roeder, *Insect Physiology*, New York, J. Wiley & Sons, pp. 879–931.

BODENSTEIN, D. 1955. 'Contributions to the problem of regeneration in insects.' *J. exp. Zool.*, **129**, 209–24.

BODENSTEIN, D. 1957a. 'Studies on nerve regeneration in *Periplaneta americana*.' *J. exp. Zool.*, **136**, 89–116.

BODENSTEIN, D. 1957b. 'Humoral dependence of growth and differentiation in insects.' In Scheer, *Recent advances in invertebrate physiology*, pp. 197–211.

BODENSTEIN, D. 1958. 'Contributions to the problem of eye pigmentation in insects studied by means of intergeneric organ transplantations in Diptera.' In Clarke *et al.*, 'Studies in invertebrate morphology.' *Smithson. misc. Bull.* **137**, 23–41.

BODENSTEIN, D. 1959a. 'The role of hormones in the regeneration of insect organs.' *Scientia, Bologna* (6), **94**, 19–23.

BODENSTEIN, D. 1959b. 'The humoral control of egg maturation in the mosquito.' *J. exp. Zool.*, **140**, 343–82.

BODENSTEIN, D. 1962. 'Humoral conditions and cellular interactions in the development in the insect eye.' In *Insect Physiology*, Oregon State Univ. Press, pp. 1–11.

BODENSTEIN, D. and ABD-EL-MALEK, A. 1949. 'The induction of aristopedia by nitrogen mustard in *Drosophila virilis*.' *J. exp. Zool.*, **111**, 95–115.

BODENSTEIN, D. and SACKTOR, B. 1952. 'Cytochrome *c* oxidase activity during the metamorphosis of *Drosophila virilis*.' *Science*, **116**, 299–300.

BÖDEWANDT, G. H. 1951. 'Untersuchungen über das Zellteilungsgeschehen in der Entwicklung der Flügelanlagen von Kleinschmetterlingen.' *Biol. Zbl.*, **70**, 31–64.

BODINE, J. H. 1932. 'Hibernation and diapause in certain Orthoptera. III. Diapause. A theory of its mechanism.' *Physiol. Zool.*, **5**, 549–54.

BODINE, J. H. 1934. 'The effect of cyanide on the oxygen consumption of normal and blocked embryonic cells.' *J. cell. comp. Physiol.*, **4**, 397–404.

BODINE, J. H. 1941. 'The cell – some aspects of its functional ontogeny.' *Amer. Nat.*, **75**, 97–106.

BODINE, J. H. and BOELL, J. H. 1934. 'Respiratory mechanisms of normally developing and blocked embryonic cells.' *J. cell. comp. Physiol.*, **5**, 97–113.

BODINE, J. H. and BOELL, J. H. 1936. 'The effect of ultracentrifuging on the respiratory activity of developing and blocked embryonic cells.' *J. cell. comp. Physiol.*, **7**, 455–63.

BODINE, J. H. and EVANS, T. G. 1932. 'Hibernation and diapause. Physiological changes during hibernation and diapause in the mud dauber wasp, *Sceliphron caementarium* (Hym.).' *Biol. Bull.*, *Wood's Hole*, **63**, 235–45.

BODINE, J. H. and FITZGERALD, L. R. 1949a. 'Effect of urea, thiourea, phenylthiourea and thiouracil on the oxygen consumption of blocked and active embryonic cells.' *Biol. Bull.*, *Wood's Hole*, **96**, 1–8.

BODINE, J. H. and FITZGERALD, L. R. 1949b. 'The effect of homologous carbamates on the respiration of blocked and active embryos.' *Physiol. Zool.*, **22**, 117–23.

BODINE, J. H. and FITZGERALD, L. R. 1949c. 'The effects of methylene blue and urethane (ethyl carbamate) upon the oxygen uptake of embryonic cells.' *Physiol. Zool.*, **22**, 283–94.

BODINE, J. H. and LU, K. H. 1950a. 'Oxygen uptake of intact embryos, their homogenates and intracellular constituents.' *Physiol. Zool.*, **23**, 301–7.

BODINE, J. H. and LU, K. H. 1950b. 'Methylene blue, 2.4-dinitrophenol and oxygen uptake of intact and homogenized embryos.' *Physiol. Zool.*, **24**, 116–19.

BODINE, J. H. and LU, K. H. 1951. 'Structure and endogenous oxygen uptake of embryonic cells.' *Physiol. Zool.*, **24**, 120–6.

BODINE, J. H. and LU, K. H. 1952. 'The action of thyroxin on the endogenous oxygen uptake of mitotically active and blocked grasshopper embryos, their homogenates and intracellular constituents.' *J. cell. comp. Physiol.*, **39**, 255–60.

BODINE, J. H., LU, K. H. and WEST, W. L. 1952a. 'Succinic dehydrogenase in mitotically active and blocked embryonic cells.' *Physiol. Zool.*, **25**, 109–22.

BODINE, J. H., LU, K. H. and WEST, W. L. 1952b. 'Reduction of triphenyltetrazolium chloride by mitotically active and blocked embryonic cells.' *Biol. Bull.*, *Wood's Hole*, **102**, 16–21.

BODINE, J. H. and ROBBIE, W. 1940. 'Physiological characteristics of the diapause grasshopper egg. I. The stability of the diapause condition.' *Physiol. Zool.*, **13**, 391–7.

BODINE, J. H. and ROBBIE, W. 1943. 'Physiological characteristics of the diapause grasshopper egg. II. Changes in density and weight during development.' *Physiol. Zool.*, **16**, 279–86.

BOER, S. 1928. 'Vergleichende Physiologie des Herzens von Evertebrates.' *Z. vergl. Physiol.*, **7**, 445–53.

BOISSON, C. J. 1949. 'Recherches histologiques sur le complexe allatocardiaque de *Bacillus rossii* F.' *Bull. biol.*, **34**, 1–92.

BOISSON, C. J. 1950. 'Mode de sécrétion des corpora incerta de *Bacillus rossii* F.' *C. R. Soc. Biol.*, *Paris*, **144**, 11–12, 784–6.

BONNEMAISSON, C. 1948. 'Remarques sur la diapause chez un hémiptère *Eurydema ornatum*.' *C. R. Acad. Sci.*, *Paris*, **227**, 985–7.

BOUNHIOL, J. J. 1936a. 'Dans quelques limits l'écerébration des larves de Lépidoptères est-elle compatible avec leur nymphose?' *C. R. Acad. Sci.*, *Paris*, **203**, 1182–4.

BOUNHIOL, J. J. 1936b. 'Métamorphose aprés ablation des corpora allata chez le ver à soie (*Bombyx mori*).' *C. R. Acad. Sci.*, Paris, **203**, 388–9.

BOUNHIOL, J. J. 1937a. 'La métamorphose des insects serait inhibée dans leur jeune age des corpora allata.' *C. R. Soc. Biol.*, Paris, **124**, 1223.

BOUNHIOL, J. J. 1937b. Métamorphose prématurée par ablation des corpora allata chez le jeune ver à soie.' *C. R. Acad. Sci.*, Paris, **205**, 175–7.

BOUNHIOL, J. J. 1938a. 'Recherches expérimentales sur le déterminisme de la métamorphose chez les Lépidoptères.' *Bull. biol.*, suppl. **24**, 1–199.

BOUNHIOL, J. J. 1938b. 'Role possible du ganglion frontal dans la métamorphose de *Bombyx mori* L.' *C. R. Acad. Sci.*, Paris, **206**, 773–4.

BOUNHIOL, J. J. 1939. 'Récentes recherches experimentales sur les insectes: les fonctions des corps allates.' *Arch. Zool. exp. gén.*, **81**, 54–64.

BOUNHIOL, J. J. 1941. 'Les conceptions modernes sur les métamorphoses des insectes.' *Rev. Zool. agric.*, **40**, 17–28.

BOUNHIOL, J. J. 1942a. 'Relations entre le sexe et le nombre des mues chez *Bombyx mori* L.' *C. R. Soc. Biol.*, Paris, **136**, 700–1.

BOUNHIOL, J. J. 1942b. 'L'ablation des corps allates au dernier age larvaire n'affecte pas, ultérieurement, la réproduction chez *Bombyx mori*.' *C. R. Acad. Sci.*, Paris, **215**, 334–6.

BOUNHIOL, J. J. 1943. 'Nymphose (partielle) localisée, chez des vers à soie divisés en trois parties par deux ligatures.' *C. R. Acad. Sci.*, Paris, **217**, 203–4.

BOUNHIOL, J. J. 1944. 'Nymphes acéphales prématurées chez le ver à soie (*Bombyx mori* L.).' *C. R. Soc. Biol.*, Paris, **138**, 418–20.

BOUNHIOL, J. J. 1945a. 'La rétention, expérimentalement provoquées dans les tubes de Malpighi entrave la nymphose des chenilles du *Bombyx mori*.' *C. R. Acad. Sci.*, Paris, **220**, 64–5.

BOUNHIOL, J. J. 1945b. 'Destin indépendant lors de la nymphose des trois parties formées dans un ver à soie par deux ligatures plus on moins espacées.' *C. R. Soc. Biol.*, Paris, **139**, 842–44.

BOUNHIOL, J. J. 1947. 'Intervention de plusieurs glandes endocrines dans la métamorphose des insectes Lépidoptères.' *Acta 66. Congr. Assoc. Fr. Avanc. Sci. Biarritz, Zool.*, 1–4.

BOUNHIOL, J. J. 1948a. 'Métamorphoses tégumentaires localisées chez les Lépidoptères.' *C. R. Soc. Lin. Bord.*, pp. 1–7.

BOUNHIOL, J. J. 1948b. 'Rapport XIV. – Apercu sur la mue et sa physiologie.' *Proc. VIIth int. Congr. Sericult.* 95–118.

BOUNHIOL, J. J. 1951. 'Voltinism expérimental (suppression de la diapause) imposé à plusieurs générations successives de *Bombyx mori* L.' *C. R. Acad. Sci.*, Paris, **232**, 2360–2.

BOUNHIOL, J. J. 1952a. 'L'achèvement de la métamorphose et la mue imaginale seraient commandés par la cerveau à la fin de la vie larvaire chez *Bombyx mori* L.' *C. R. Acad. Sci.*, Paris, **235**, 671–2.

BOUNHIOL, J. J. 1952b. 'Nature probablement sécrétoire du facteur cérébral conditionannt la mue imaginale de *Bombyx mori* L.' *C. R. Acad. Sci., Paris*, **235**, 747–8.

BOUNHIOL, J. J. 1953. 'Role du corpus allatum dans la métamorphose des insectes.' *Trans. XIth int. Congr. Ent., Amsterdam*, **2**, 63–72.

BOUNHIOL, J. J. 1955. 'Observation des cellules neurosecretrices chez le ver à soie vivant.' *Acta Congr. Assoc. Fr. Avanc. Sci.*, 1–3.

BOUNHIOL, J. J. 1957. 'La métamorphose se produit, chez *Bombyx mori*, après suppression, au dernier stade larvaire, des relations nerveuses entre cérébroïdes et corps allates, ceux-ci restant longtemps imprégnés de neurosécrétion.' *C. R. Acad. Sci., Paris*, **245**, 1087–9.

BOUNHIOL, J. J. 1961. 'La réalisation de la mue imaginale, après ablation du ganglion sousoesophagien, chez le ver à soie.' *Atti Congr. Soc. Ital. Gen. agr.*, **14**, 124–8.

BOUNHIOL, J. J. and CAVALLIN, S. 1961. 'Conséquences d'une alimenta-tion forcée chez des chenilles du Bombyx du Murier mises à jeun ou décérébrées.' *C.'R. Acad. Sci.* (Séance du 5 juin), **252**, 3884–5.

BOUNHIOL, J. J., GABE, M. and ARVY, L. 1954. 'Données histophysio-logiques sur la neurosécrétion chez *Bombyx mori* et sur ses rapports avec les glandes endocrines.' *Pubbl. Staz. zool. Napoli*, **24**, 52–4.

BOURDON, J. 1937a. 'Sur la régénération des ébauches de quelques organes imaginaux chez le Coléoptères, *Timarcha goettingensis* L.' *C. R. Soc. Biol., Paris*, **124**, 872–4.

BOURDON, J. 1937b. 'Recherches expérimentales sur la régénération chez un Coléoptère *Timarcha goettingensis* L. (*T. violaceonigra* De Geer).' *Bull. Biol.*, **71**, 466–99.

BRADLEY, W. G. and ARBUTHNOT, K. D. 1938. 'The relation of host physiology to development of the braconid parasite, *Chelonus annulipes* Wesmael.' *Ann. ent. Soc. Amer.*, **31**, 359–65.

BRANDENBURG, J. 1955. 'Corpora allata, Gonaden und Stylopisation.' *Naturwissenschaften*, **42**, 260–1.

BRAUER, A. and TAYLOR, A. 1936. 'Experiments to determine the time and method of organisation in Bruchid (Coleoptera) eggs.' *J. exp. Zool.*, **73**, 127–52.

BRAY, E. 1929. 'Alimentazione di larva di Mosca con Ghiandole endocrine a con milza.' *Scr. biol. Castaldi*, **4**, 195–214.

BRECHER, L. 1924. 'Due Puppenfärbungen des Kohlweisslings *Pieris brassicae* L. VIII. Die Farbanpassung der Puppen durch das Raupenauge.' *Arch. mikr. Anat.*, **102**, 501–16.

BRIAN, M. V. 1954. 'Studies of caste differentiation in *Myrmica rubra* L. 1. The growth of queens and males.' *Insectes sociaux*, **1**, 101–22.

BRIAN, M. V. 1955. 'Studies of caste differentiation in *Myrmica rubra* L. 2. The growth of workers and intercastes.' *Insectes sociaux*, **2**, 1–34.

BRIAN, M. V. 1957a. 'Food distribution and larval size in cultures of the ant *Myrmica rubra* L.' *Physiol. comp. Oekol*, **2**, 329–45.

322   *Insect Hormones*

BRIAN, M. V. 1957b. 'Caste determination in social insects.' *Ann. Rev. Ent.*, **2**, 107–20.

BRIAN, M. V. 1958. 'The evolution of queen control in the social Hymenoptera.' *Proc. Xth int. Congr. Ent.*, **2**, 497–502.

BRIAN, M. V. 1959. 'The neurosecretory cells of the brain, the corpora cardiaca and corpora allata during caste differentiation in an ant.' *Acta Symp. Evol. Ins.*, *Praha*, pp. 167–71.

BRIAN, M. V. 1961. 'Organ transplants between ant castes.' *Symp. gen. biol. ital.*, **10**, 169–72.

BRIAN, M. V. 1962. 'Studies of caste differentiation in *Myrmica rubra* L. 5. Social conditions affecting early larval differentiation.' *Insectes sociaux*, **9**, 295–310.

BRIAN, M. V. and CARR, C. A. H. 1960. 'The influence of the queen on brood rearing in ants of the genus *Myrmica*.' *J. Ins. Physiol.*, **5**, 81–94.

BRIAN, M. V. and HIBBLE, J. 1962. '9-oxodec-trans-2-ensic acid and *Myrmica* queen extracts tested for influence on brood in Myrmica.' *J. Ins. Physiol.*, **9**, 25–34.

BRIDGES, C. B. 1925. 'Sex in relation to chromosomes and genes.' *Amer. Nat.*, **59**, 127–37.

BRIDGES, C. B. and DOBZHANSKY, T. 1933. 'The mutant "proboscipedia" in *Drosophila melanogaster*, a case of hereditary homöosis.' *Arch. Entw-Mech. Org.*, **127**, 575–90.

BROWN, F. A. 1948. 'Hormones in crustaceans.' In Pincus and Thiman, *Hormones, physiology, chemistry and applications*, New York, Acad. Press, pp. 159–99.

BROWN, F. A. and NEGLITSCH, A. 1940. 'Comparison of the chromatophorotropic activity of insect corpora cardiaca with that of Crustacean sinus glands.' *Biol. Bull.*, *Wood's Hole*, **79**, 409–18.

BROWN, W. 1936. 'Ueber das Zellteilungsmuster in Puppenflügelepithel der Mehlmotte *Ephestia kühniella* in seiner Beziehung zur Ausbildung des Zeichnungsmusters.' *Arch. EntwMech. Org.*, **135**, 494–520.

BROWN, W. 1939. 'Contributions to the study of development of the wing-pattern in Lepidoptera.' *Biol. Bull.*, *Wood's Hole*, **76**, 226–40.

BRUN, R. 1925. 'Ein Fall von Hirntumor bei der Ameise.' *Schweiz. Arch. Neurol. Psychiat.*, **16**, 86–99.

BUCHLI, H. 1956. 'Le cycle de développement des castes chez *Reticulitermes*.' *Insectes sociaux*, **3**, 395–401.

BUCHNER, P. 1925. 'Studien in intracellulären Symbionten, V.' *Z. Morph. Ökol. Tiere*, **4**, 88–245.

BUCK, J. and KEISTER, M. 1955. 'Cyclic CO_2 release in diapausing *Agapema* pupae.' *Biol. Bull.*, *Wood's Hole*, **109**, 144–63.

BUCK, J. and KEISTER, M. 1956. 'Host-parasite relations in *Agapema* pupae (Lepidoptera-Saturniidae).' *Ann. ent. Soc. Amer.*, **49**, 94–6.

BUCKLIN, D. H. 1953. 'Termination of diapause in grasshopper embryos cultured in vitro.' *Anat. Rec.*, **117**, 539.

BÜCKMANN, D. 1952. 'Die Umfärbung von Schmetterlingsraupen vor der Verpuppung (Üntersuchungen an *Cerura vinula*).' *Naturwissenschaften*, **39**, 213–14.

BÜCKMANN, D. 1953. 'Ueber den Verlauf und die Auslösung von Verhaltensänderungen und Umfärbungen erwachsener Schmetterlingsraupen.' *Biol. Zbl.*, **72**, 276–311.

BÜCKMANN, D. 1956a. 'Die Umfärbung der Raupen von *Cerura vinula* unter verschiedenen experimentellen Bedingungen.' *Naturwissenschaften*, **43**, 43.

BÜCKMANN, D. 1956b. 'Die Wirkung des Metamorphosenhormons der Insekten.' *Ber. Hundertj. dtsch. ent. Ges.*, Berlin, pp. 238–49.

BÜCKMANN, D. 1957a. 'Die Wirkung des Prothorakaldrüsenhormons als Farbwechselhormon bei Schmetterlingsraupen.' *Verh. dtsch. zool. Ges.*, pp. 220–5.

BÜCKMANN, D. 1957b. 'A morphological color change controlled by molting hormone in Lepidoptera.' *Biol. Bull.*, *Wood's Hole*, **113**, 326.

BÜCKMANN, D. 1958. 'Farbwechsel als Teilvorgang der Metamorphose und seine Hemmung in jungen Schmetterlingsraupen.' *Verh. dtsch. zool. Ges.*, pp. 137–44.

BÜCKMANN, D. 1959a. 'Die Auslösung der Umfärbung durch das Häutungshormon bei *Cerura vinula* L.' *J. Ins. Physiol.*, **3**, 159–89.

BÜCKMANN, D. 1959b. 'Schmetterlingsraupen wechseln ihre Farbe.' *Umschau*, **23**, 715–19.

BÜCKMANN, D. 1962. 'Die Hormonalschwelle als steuernder Faktor in der Puppenentwicklung von *Cerura vinula* L.' *Verh. dtsch. zool. Ges.*, 180–9.

BÜCKMANN, D. and DUSTMANN, J. H. 1962. 'Biochemische Untersuchungen über den morphologischen Farbwechsel von *Carausius morosus*.' *Naturwissenschaften*, **16**, 379.

BUDDENBROCK, W. 1930a. 'Beitrag zur Histologie und Physiologie der Raupenhäutung mit besonderer Berücksichtigung der Versonschen Drüsen.' *Z. Morph. Ökol. Tiere*, **18**, 701–25.

BUDDENBROCK, W. 1931. 'Untersuchungen über die Häutungshormone der Schmetterlingsraupen. II.' *Z. vergl. Physiol.*, **14**, 415–28.

BUDDENBROCK, W. 1950. *Vergleichende Physiologie. IV. Hormone*, Basel, Birkhäuser.

BURDETTE, W. J. 1950. 'Studies on *Drosophila* tumors.' *Cancer Res.*, **10**, 209.

BURDETTE, W. J. 1962. 'Changes in titer of ecdyson in *Bombyx mori* during metamorphosis.' *Science*, **135**, 432.

BURDETTE, W. J. and RICHARDS, R. C. 1961. 'Alteration of growth of mammalian cells in vitro by ecdyson extract.' *Nature*, *Lond.*, **189**, 666–8.

BURTT, E. T. 1937. 'On the corpora allata of Dipterous insects. I.' *Proc. roy. Soc.* (B), **124**, 13–23.

BURTT, E. T. 1938. 'On the corpora allata of Dipterous insects. II.' *Proc. roy Soc.* (B), **126**, 210–23.

BUSNEL, R. G. and DRILHON, A. 1937. 'Étude biologique et biochemique du *Leptinotarsa decemlineata* Say à l'état d'insecte parfait.' *Ann. Sci. nat.*, *Zool.*, **20**, 229–44.

BUTENANDT, A. 1955. 'Neuartige Probleme und Ergebnisse der biologischen Chemie.' *Naturwissenschaften*, **42**, 141.

BUTENANDT, A. 1959. 'Wirkstoffe des Insektenreiches.' *Naturwissenschaften*, **15**, 461–71.

BUTENANDT, A. and KARLSON, P. 1954. 'Über die Isolierung eines Metamorphosehormons der Insekten in kristallisierter Form.' *Z. naturf.*, **9b**, 389–91.

BUTENANDT, A., KARLSON, P. and [ZILLIG, W. 1946. 'Über den 'Anti-Bar-Stoff' – einen genabhängigen morphogenetischen Wirkstoff bei *Drosphila.*' *Biol. Zbl.*, **65**, 41.

BUTENANDT, A., KARLSON, P. and ZILLIG, W. 1951a. 'Üeber das Vorkommen von Kynurin in Seidenspinnenpuppen.' *Hoppe-Seyl. Z.*, **288**, 125.

BUTENANDT, A., KARLSON, P. and HAUSER, G. 1951b. 'Üeber Dioxopiperazine aus Puppen des Seidenspinners *Bombyx mori.*' *Hoppe-Seyl. Z.*, **288**, 279.

BUTENANDT, A., SCHIEDT, U., BIEKERT, E., and CROMARTIE, R. 1952. 'Bestimmungen des Tryphano gehaltes verschiedener Rassen der Mehlmotte *Ephestia kühniella* als Beitrag zur Analyse der Gen-Wirkungen.' *Z. Naturf.*, **7b**, 80.

BUTENANDT, A., SCHIEDT, U., BIEKERT, E., and CROMARTIE, R. 1954. 'Über Ommochrome. IV. Mitteilung: Konstitution des Xanthommatins.' *Liebigs Ann.*, **590**, 75–90.

BUTLER, C. G. 1954a. 'The method and importance of the recognition by a colony of honeybees (*A. mellifera*) of the presence of its queen.' *Trans. roy. ent. Soc. Lond.*, **105**, 11–29.

BUTLER, C. G. 1954b. 'The importance of queen substance in the life of a honey bee colony.' *Bee World*, **35**, 169–76.

BUTLER, C. G. 1956. 'Some further observations on the nature of "queen substance" and of its role in the organization of honey bee (*Apis mellifera*) community.' *Proc. roy. ent. Soc. Lond.*, **31**, 12–16.

BUTLER, C. G. 1957. 'The control of ovary development in worker honey bees (*A. mellifera*).' *Experientia*, **13**, 256–7.

BUTLER, C. G. 1960. 'The source of the substance produced by a queen honey bee (*Apis mellifera*) which inhibits development of the ovaries of the workers of her colony.' *Proc. roy. ent. Soc. Lond.*, **34**, 137–8.

BUTLER, C. G., CALLOW, R. K. and JOHNSTON, N. C. 1959. 'Extraction and purification of "queen substance" from queen bees.' *Nature, Lond.*, **184**, 1871.

BUTLER, C. G. and GIBBONS, A. D. 1958. 'The inhibition of queen rearing by feeding queenless worker honey bees with an extract of "queen substance".' *J. Ins. Physiol.*, **2**, 61–64.

BUTLER, C. G. and SIMPSON, J. 1958. 'The source of the queen substance of the honey bee.' *Proc. roy. ent. Soc. Lond.* (A), **33**, 120–2.

BUXTON, P. A. 1938. 'Studies on the growth of *Pediculus* (Anoplura).' *Parasitology*, **30**, 65–84.

BYTINSKI-SALZ, H. 1933. 'Untersuchungen an Lepidopterenhybriden. ii. Entwicklungsphysiologische Experimente über die Wirkung der disharmonischen Chromosomenkombinationen.' *Arch. EntwMech. Org.*, **129**, 356–78.

BYTINSKI-SALZ, H. 1936. 'Die Ausbildung des Chitinpanzers in der Schmetterlingspuppe.' *Biol. Zbl.*, **56**, 35–61.

CAMERON, M. L. 1945. *Recent advances in endocrinology*, 5th ed., London.

CAMERON, M. L. 1953. 'Secretion of an orthodiphenol in the corpus cardiacum of the insects.' *Nature, Lond.*, **172**, 349–50.

CAMPBELL, F. L. 1959. *Physiology of insect development*, Chicago, Univ. Press, and London, Cambridge Univ. Press.

CARLISLE, D. B. 1953. 'Note préliminaire sur le structure du système neurosecréteur du pédoncule oculaire de *Lysmata reticaudata*.' *C. R. Acad. Sci., Paris*, **236**, 2451–2.

CARLISLE, D. B. 1954. 'The X-Organ-Sinus gland complex, somatotropin, the ovarian inhibiting hormone and sex-reversal in *Lysmata*.' *C. R. Pubbl. Staz. zool. Napoli suppl.*, **24**, 79–80.

CARLISLE, D. B. and BUTLER. 1956. 'The "queen substance" of honey bees and the ovary inhibiting hormone of crustaceans.' *Nature, Lond.*, **177**, 276–7.

CARLISLE, D. B. and ELLIS, P. E. 1962. 'Endocrine glands and phase in locusts.' *Symp. gen. Biol. ital.*, **10**, 219–24.

CARLISLE, D. B. and JENKINS, P. M. 1959. 'Terminology of hormones.' *Nature, Lond.*, **183**, 336–7.

CARLISLE, D. B. and KNOWLES, F. 1957. *Hormones in Invertebrates*, London.

CARLISLE, D. B. and KNOWLES, S. F. 1959. *Endocrine control in Crustaceans*, London and New York, Cambridge Univ. Press, 150 pp.

CASPARI, E. 1933. 'Ueber die Wirkung eines pleiotropen Gens bei der Mehlmotte *Ephestia kühniella* Zell.' *Arch. EntwMech. Org.*, **130**, 353–381.

CASPARI, E. 1936. 'Zur Analyse der Matroklinie der Vererbung in der a-Serie der Augenfarbenmutationen bei der Mehlmotte *Ephestia kühniella*.' *Z. indukt. Abstamm.- u. VererbLehre*, **71**, 546–55.

CASPARI, E. 1941. 'The morphology and development of the wing pattern of Lepidoptera.' *Quart. Rev. Biol.*, **16**, 249–73.

CASPARI, E. 1943. 'The influence of low temperature on the pupation of *Ephestia kühniella*.' *J. exp. Zool.*, **94**, 241.

CASPARI, E. 1946a. 'On the effects of the gene a on the chemical composition of *Ephestia kühniella*.' *Genetics*, **31**, 454–74.

CASPARI, E. 1946b. 'Oxidation of tryptophane by homogenized a + a ± + and aa *Ephestia kühniella* tissue.' *Nature, Lond.*, **158**, 555.

CASPARI, E. 1949. 'Physiological action of eye color mutants in the moths *Ephestia kühniella* and *Ptychopoda seriata*.' *Quart. Rev. Biol.* **24**, 185–99.

CASPARI, E. and PLAGGE, E. 1935. 'Versuche zur Physiologie der Verpuppung von Schmetterlingsraupen.' *Naturwissenschaften*, **23**, 751–72.

CAZAL, P. 1947a. 'Corps paracardiaques et corps allates chez les Japygidae.' *Bull. Biol.*, **80**, 477–82.

CAZAL, P. 1947b. 'L'organe décrit par Nabert chez le Collembole *Tomocerus* n'est pas un corps allate.' *Bull. Biol.*, **80**, 483–6.

CAZAL, P. 1947c. 'Recherches sur les glandes endocrines rétrocérébrales des insectes. II. Odonates.' *Arch. Zool. exp. gén.*, **85**, 55–82.

CAZAL, P. 1948. 'Les glandes endocrines rétro-cérébrales des insectes. (étude morphologique).' *Bull. Biol.*, suppl. **32**, 1–227.

CAZAL, P. and GUERRIER, V. 1946. 'Recherches sur les glandes endocrinnes rétrocérébroidiennes des insectes. I. Étude morphologique chez les Orthoptéres.' *Arch. Zool. exp. gén.*, **84**, 303–34.

CHADWICK, L. E. 1955. 'Molting of roaches without prothoracic glands.' *Science*, **121**, 435.

CHADWICK, L. E. 1956. 'Removal of prothoracic glands from the nymphal cockroach.' *J. exp. Zool.*, **131**, 291–305.

CHANG-WHAN KIM. 1959. 'The differentiation centre inducing the development from larval to adult leg in *Pieris brassicae*.' *J. Embryol. exp. Morphol.*, **7**, 572–82.

CHANG-WHAN KIM. 1960. 'On the use of the terms "larva" and "nymph" in entomology.' *Proc. roy. ent. Soc. Lond.* (A), **35**, 61–4.

CHARMIAUX-COTTON, H. 1956. 'Déterminisme endocrinienne des caractéres sexuels d'*Orchestia gammarella*.' *Ann. Sci. nat. Zool.* (11), **18**, 304–10.

CHAUDONNERET, J. 1946. 'Sur la présence d'une glande neuroendocrine dans la maxille de *Thermobia domestica* Pack.' *C. R. Acad. Sci.*, *Paris*, **223**, 292–3.

CHAUDONNERET, J. 1949. 'Apropos du corps jugal des Thysanoures.' *Bull. Soc. zool. Fr.*, **74**, 164–7.

CHAUVIN, R. 1946. 'L'effet de groupe et la croissance larvaire des Blattes, du Grillon et du Phanéroptère.' *Bull. Soc. zool. Fr.*, **71**, 39–48.

CHAUVIN, R. 1949. *Physiologie de l'insecte*, 2nd ed., Paris, 1958.

CHEFURKA, W. and WILLIAMS, C. M. 1951. 'Biochemical changes accompanying the metamorphosis in the blood of the cecropia silkworm.' *Anat. Rec.*, **111**, 3.

CHEFURKA, W. and WILLIAMS, C. M. 1952. 'Flavoproteins in relation to diapause and development in the cecropia silkworm.' *Anat. Rec.*, **113**, 4.

CHEN, D. H., ROBBINS, W. E. and MONROE, R. E. 1962. 'The gonadotropic action of cecropia extracts in allatectomized american cockroaches.' *Experientia*, **18**, 577.

CHEN, P. S. and HADORN, E. 1955. 'Zur Stoffwechselphysiologie der Mutante letal-meander (1me) von *Drosophila melanogaster*.' *Rev. suisse Zool.*, **62**, 339–47.

CHEVAIS, S. 1943. 'Déterminisme de la taille de l'oeil chez le mutant bar de la Drosophile. Intervention d'une substance diffusible spécifique.' *Bull. Biol.*, **77**, 295–364, **78**, (1944), 1–39.

CHEVAIS, S., EPHRUSSI, B. and STEINBERG, A. G. 1938. 'Facet number and the v ± hormone in the Bar eye of *Drosophila melanogaster*.' *Proc. nat. Acad. Sci.*, *Washington*, **24**, 365–8.

CHEVAIS, S. and STEINBERG, A. G. 1938. 'Relation entre la concentration de l'extrait de *Calliphora* et le nombre des facettes dans l'œil du mutant Bar de *Drosophila melanogaster*.' *C. R. Acad. Sci.*, *Paris*, **207**, 433–5.

CHICEWICZ, M. 1951. 'The structure of endocrine glands and their role in insect metamorphosis.' *Przegl. Zool.*, **2**, 29–41.

CHILD, C. M. and YOUNG, A. N. 1903. 'Regeneration of appendages in nymphs of Agrionidae.' *Arch. EntwMech. Org.*, **15**, 543–602.

CHINO, H. 1958. 'Carbohydrate metabolism in the diapause egg of the silkworm *Bombyx mori*. II. Conversion of glycogen into sorbitol and glycerol during diapause.' *J. Ins. Physiol.*, **2**, 1–12.

CHURCH, N. S. 1955. 'Hormones and the termination and reinduction of diapause in *Cephus cinctus* Nort.' *Canad. J. Zool.*, **33**, 339–69.

CLARK, R. B. 1956. 'On the origin of neurosecretory cells.' *Ann. Sci. nat. Zool.* (11), **18**, 199–207.

CLARKE, K. U. and BALDWIN, R. W. 1960. 'The effect of insect hormones and of 2:4 dinitrophenol on the mitochondrin of *Locusta migratoria* L.' *J. Ins. Physiol.*, **5**, 37–46.

CLARKE, K. U. and LANGLEY, P. 1962. 'Factors concerned in the initiation of growth and moulting in *Locusta migratoria*.' *Nature, Lond.*, **194**, 160–2.

CLEMENTS, A. N. 1956. 'Hormonal control of ovary development in mosquitoes.' *J. exp. Biol.*, **33**, 211–23.

CLEMENTS, A. N. 1959. 'Studies on the metabolism of locust fat body.' *J. exp. Biol.*, **36**, 665–23.

CLEVER, U. 1958. 'Untersuchungen zur Zelldifferenzierung und Musterbildung der Sinnesorgane und des Nervensystems im Wachsmottenflügel.' *Z. Morph. Ökol. Tiere*, **47**, 201–48.

CLEVER, U. 1960. 'Der Einfluss der Sinuszellen auf die Borsten-Entwicklung bei *Galleria melonella*.' *Arch. EntwMech. Org.*, **152**, 137–59.

CLEVER, U. 1961. 'Genaktivitäten in den Riesenchromosomen von *Chironomus tentans* und ihre Beziehungen zur Entwicklung. I. Genaktivieřungen durch Ecdyson.' *Chromosoma*, **12**, 607–75.

CLEVER, U. 1962. 'Genaktivitäten in den Riesenchromosomen von *Chironomus tentans* und ihre Beziehungen zur Entwicklung. III. Das Aktivitätsmuster in Phasen der Entwicklungsruhe.' *J. Ins. Physiol.*, **8**, 357–76.

CLEVER, U. and KARLSON, P. 1960. 'Induction von Puff-Veränderungen in den Speicheldrüsenchromosomen von *Chironomus tentans* durch Ecdyson.' *Exp. Cell. Res.*, **20**, 623–6.

CLOUTIER, E. J., BECK, S. D., MCLEOD, D. G. R. and SILHACEK, D. L. 1962. 'Neural transplants and insect diapause.' *Nature, Lond.*, **195**, 122–4.

COCKAYNE, E. A. 1941. 'Prothetely in a larva of *Smerinthus hybr. hybridus* Stephens (Lepidoptera).' *Proc. roy. ent. Soc. Lond.* (A), **16**, 55–9.

CODREANU, R. 1939. 'Néoplasie maligne dans l'hémocœle des éphemères sons l'action de *Symbiocladius rithrogenæ*, Chironomide ectoparasite.' *Arch. Zool. exp. gén.*, **81**, 1–283.

COLHOUN, E. H. 1958. 'Physical release of acetylcholine from the thoracic nerve cord of *Periplaneta americana*.' *Nature, Lond.*, **181**, 490.

COLHOUN, E. H. and SMITH, M. V. 1960. 'Neurohumoral properties of royal jelly.' *Nature, Lond.*, **188**, 854.

CORRADINI, P. 1940. 'Su sostanze ad effetto di auxine nel Bombice del gelse. Nota prelimin.' *Riv. Biol. Firenze*, **30**, 351–6.

CORTEGGIANI, E. and SERFATY, A. 1939. 'Acétylcholine et cholinestéraze chez les insectes et les arachnides.' *C. R. Soc. Biol.*, *Paris*, **131**, 1124–6.

COSTELLO, D. P. 1948. 'Ooplasmic segregation in relation to differentiation.' *Ann. N.Y. Acad. Sci.*, **49**, 663–83.

COTRONEI, G. 1918. 'Osservazioni sull' influenza della tiroide sullo sviluppa degli insetti.' *Mem. Accad. Lincei*, **32**, 260–4.

COTTRELL, C. B. 1962a. 'The imaginal ecdysis of blowflies. The control of cuticular hardening and darkening.' *J. exp. Biol.*, **39**, 395–411.

COTTRELL, C. B. 1962b. 'The imaginal ecdysis of blowflies. Detection of the blood borne darkening factor and determination of some of its properties.' *J. exp. Biol.*, **39**, 413–30.

COTTRELL, C. B. 1962c. 'The imaginal ecdysis of blowflies. Observations on the hydrostatic mechanisms involved in digging and expansion.' *J. exp. Biol.*, **39**, 431–48.

COTTRELL, C. B. 1962d. 'The imaginal ecdysis of blowflies. Evidence for a change in the mechanical properties of the cuticle at expansion.' *J. exp. Biol.*, **39**, 449–58.

COTTRELL, C. B. 1962e. 'General observations on the imaginal ecdysis of blowflies.' *Trans. roy. ent. Soc. Lond.*, **114**, 317–33.

COURRIER, R. 1921. 'Sur le déterminisme des caractéres sexuels secondaires chez les Arthropodes.' *C. R. Acad. Sci.*, *Paris*, **173**, 668–71.

COUSIN, G. 1926. 'Sur le retard de la nymphose. La limite extrème du jeune et la réalimentation possible des larves de *Calliphora erythrocephala*.' *C. R. Acad. Sci.*, *Paris*, **95**, 601–3.

COUSIN, G. 1930. 'La diapause de *Lucilia sericata* Meig.' *C. R. Acad. Sci.*, *Paris*, **190**, 651–3.

COUSIN, G. 1932. 'Étude experimentale de la diapause des insectes.' *Bull. Biol.*, **15**, 1–341.

COUSIN, G. 1933. 'La diapause chez *Lucilia bufonivora* Meig.' *Bull. Soc. ent. Fr.*, **38**, 261–4.

COUSIN, G. 1935. 'Sur les phénomènes de néoténie chez *Achaeta campestris* L. et ses hybrides.' *C. R. Acad. Sci.*, *Paris*, **200**, 970–2.

COUSIN, G. 1937. 'Les arrêts du développement chez *Lucilia ampullacea* et remarques sur la diapause.' *Bull. Soc. ent. Fr.*, 42, 218–21.

COUSIN, G. 1938. 'La néoténie chez *Gryllus campestris* et ses hybrides.' *Bull. Biol.*, 72, 80–118.

COUSIN, G. 1939. 'Étude expérimentale de la diapause des insectes.' *Titr. Trav. Sci. Laval*, Imprim. Barnéoud, 51 pp.

COUTIN, R. and GRISON, P. 1949. 'Hémichrysalides obtenues par ligature des chenilles de *Laspeyresia pomonella* L. (Lepid.) en rupture de diapause expérimentale.' *C. R. Soc. Biol., Paris*, 143, 15–17.

CRAGG, G. B. and COLE, P. 1952. 'Diapause in *Lucilia sericata*.' *J. exp. Biol.*, 29, 600–4.

CRAMPTON, H. E. 1899. 'An experimental study upon Lepidoptera.' *Arch. EntwMech. Org.*, 9, 293–318.

CUMBER, R. 1949. 'The biology of bumble-bees with special reference to the production of the worker caste.' *Trans. roy. ent. Soc. Lond.*, 100, 1–45.

DADD, R. H. 1961. 'Evidence for humoral regulation of digestive secretion in the beetle *Tenebrio molitor*.' *J. exp. Biol.*, 38, 259–66.

DANILEVSKI, A. S. 1948. 'Photoperiodical reaction of insects under conditions of artificial illumination' (in Russian). *C. R. Acad. Sci. U.R.S.S.*, 60, 481–4.

DANILEVSKI, A. S. 1949. 'The dependence of the geographical distribution of insects on the ecological peculiarities of their life cycles' (in Russian). *Ent. obozr.*, 30, 194–207.

DANILEVSKI, A. S. and GEISPITZ, K. F. 1948. 'The effect of the day and night periodicity of illumination on the seasonal cycles of insects' (in Russian). *C. R. Acad. Sci. U.R.S.S.*, 59, 337–9.

DANILEVSKI, A. S. and GLINANYAYA, E. I. 1949. 'On the effect of the correlation of the dark and light periods of the day and night on the development of insects' (in Russian.) *C. R. Acad. Sci. U.R.S.S.*, 68, 785–8.

DANILEVSKI, A. S. and GLINANYAYA, E. I. 1950. 'The influence of the rhythm of light and temperature on the occurrence of diapause in insects' (in Russian). *C. R. Acad. Sci. U.R.S.S.*, 71, 963–6.

DANNEEL, R. 1941. 'Die Ausfärbung überlebender *v*- und *cn-Drosophila*-Augen mit Produkten des Tryptophansstoffwechsels.' *Biol. Zbl.*, 61, 399.

DANTCHAKOFF, V. and VATKOVITCHUTÉ, A. 1936. 'Sur l'immunité de la *Drosophila* envers les hormones sexuelles hétérologues.' *C. R. Soc. Biol., Paris*, 121, 755–7.

DAVEY, K. G. 1961. 'The mode of action of the heart accelerating factor from the corpus cardiacum of insects.' *Gen. comp. Endocrinol.* 1, 23–9.

DAVEY, K. G. 1962a. 'Changes in the pericardial cells of *Periplaneta americana* induced by exposure to homogenates of the corpus cardiacum.' *Quart. J. micr. Sci.*, 103, 349–58.

DAVEY, K. G. 1962b. 'The release by feeding of a pharmacologically active factor from the corpus cardiacum of *Periplaneta americana*.' *J. Ins. Physiol.*, 8, 205–8.

DAVIES, R. G. 1958. 'The terms "larva" and "nymph" in entomology.' *Trans. Soc. Brit. Ent.*, **13**, 17–36.

DAY, M. F. 1940a. 'Possible sources of internal secretion in the heads of some holometabolous insects.' *Anat. Rec.*, **78**, suppl., 150.

DAY, M. F. 1940b. 'Neurosecretory cells in the ganglia of Lepidoptera.' *Nature, Lond.*, **145**, 264.

DAY, M. F. 1943a. 'The function of the corpus allatum in Muscoid Diptera.' *Biol. Bull.*, *Wood's Hole*, **84**, 127–40.

DAY, M. F. 1943b. 'The homologies of ring-gland of Diptera Brachycera.' *Ann. ent. Soc. Amer.*, **36**, 1–10.

DAY, M. F. and GRACE, T. D. E. 1959. 'Culture of insect tissue.' *Ann. Rev. Ent.*, **4**, 17.

DAY, M. F. and POWNING, R. F. 1949. 'Bestimmung der Proteinaseaktivität.' *Austr. J. sci. Res.* (B), **2**, 175.

DE BACH, P. 1939. 'A hormone which induces pupation in the common housefly, *Musca domestica* L.' *Ann. ent. Soc. Amer.*, **39**, 743–6.

DEEGENER, P. 1911. 'Zur Beurteilung der Puppe.' *Zool. Anz.*, **37**, 495–505.

DEFRETIN, R. 1956. 'La néurosecrétion des polyosides et ses rapports avec l'épitoquie chez les néréidiens.' *Ann. Sci. nat. Zool.*, (11) **18**, 208–22.

DE LERMA, B. 1932. 'Osservazioni sui *corpora allata* del *Grillotalpa*.' *Arch. Zool. Ital.*, **17**, 1105–8.

DE LERMA, B. 1933. 'I corpi fariengei degli ortotteri. Prova sicura della asistenza di glandole endocrine negli artropodi.' *Rc. Acad. Lincei*, **17**, 1105–8.

DE LERMA, B. 1934. 'Organi e fenomeni incretori negli invertebrati.' *Riv. Fis. Mat. Sci. nat.*, **8**, 460–9.

DE LERMA, B. 1936. 'L'attivita endocrina negli invertebrati.' *Arch. zool. ital.*, **23**, suppl. **2**, 83–134.

DE LERMA, B. 1937. 'Osservazioni sul systema endocrina degli insetti (Corpora allata e corpi faringei).' *Arch. zool. ital.*, **24**, 339–60.

DE LERMA, B. 1942. 'Richerche sperimentalli sulle metamorfosi dei Ditteri.' *Boll. Zool.*, **13**, 109–13.

DE LERMA, B. 1950. 'Endocrinologia degli insetti.' *Boll. Zool.*, **17**, suppl., 68–192.

DE LERMA, B. 1951. 'Note originalli e critiche sulla morphologia comparata degli organi frontali degli Artropodi.' *Annu. Ist. Zool. Univ. Napoli*, **3**, 1–25.

DE LERMA, B. 1954. 'Osservazioni sulla neurosecrezione in *Hydrous piceus* L.' *Pubbl. Staz. zool. Napoli*, **24**, suppl., 56–9.

DE LERMA, B. 1956. 'Corpora cardiaca et néurosécrétion protocérébrale chez le Coléoptère *Hydrous piceus* L.' *Ann. Sci. nat. Zool.*, (11) **18**, 235–250.

DE LERMA, B., DUPONT-RAABE, M. and KNOWLES, F. 1957. 'Sur la question de la fluorescence des substances chromactives des Crustacés et des Insectes.' *C. R. Acad. Sci., Paris*, **241**, 995–8.

DE LERMA, B. and DE VINCENTIIS, M. 1955. 'Sulla natura pteridinica di un prodotto di fotolisi da irragiamento ultravioletto del pigmento rosso degli occhi di *Drosophila melanogaster* M.' *Boll. Soc. ital. Biol. sper.*, **21**, 1606–9.

DELEURANCE, E. P. 1955. 'Contribution à l'étude biologique des *Prolistes* (Hymenopteres, Vespides). II. Le cycle évolutif du couvain.' *Insectes sociaux*, **2**, 285–302.

DEMAL, J. 1956. 'Culture in vitro d'ébauches imaginales de Diptéres.' *Ann. Sci. nat. Zool.*, (11) **18**, 155–61.

DEMEREC, M. 1947a. 'Mutations in *Drosophila* induced by a carcinogen.' *Nature, Lond.*, **159**, 604.

DEMEREC, M. 1947b. 'Production of mutations in *Drosophila* by treatment with some carcinogen.' *Science*, **105**, 634.

DENNELL, R. 1947. 'A study of an insect cuticle: the formation of the puparium of *Sarcophaga falculata* Pand. (Diptera).' *Proc. roy. Soc.* (B), **134**, 79–110.

DENNELL, R. 1949. 'Weismann's ring and the control of tyrosinase activity in the larva of *Calliphora erythrocephala*.' *Proc. roy. Soc.* (B), **136**, 94–109.

DEORAS, P. J. and BHASKARAN, G. 1962. 'Observations on the endocrine glands of *Musca nebulo*.' *Curr. Sci.*, **31**, 336–7.

DERBENEVA, N. N. 1959. 'New findings in bionomy and metamorphosis of several species of Thripsidae' (in Russian). *IV. Congr. Ent. U.R.S.S.*, **1**, 41–3.

DEROUX-STRALLA, D. 1948a. 'Recherches anatomo-histologiques préliminaires a une étude des mécanismes endocrines chez les Odonates.' *Bull. Soc. zool. Fr.*, **73**, 31–6.

DEROUX-STRALLA, D. 1948b. 'Recherches expérimentales sur le rôle des "glandes ventrales" dans la mue et la métamorphose, chez *Aeschna cyanea* Müll.' *C. R. Acad. Sci., Paris*, **227**, 1277–8.

DETINOVA, T. S. 1940. 'To the experimental research on the imaginal diapause in *Anopheles maculipennis*' (in Russian). *Dissert. Inst. malar.*, Moscow.

DETINOVA, T. S. 1945. 'On the influence of glands of internal secretion upon the ripening of the gonads and the imaginal diapause in *Anopheles maculipennis*' (in Russian). *Zool. Zh.*, **24**, 291–8.

DETINOVA, T. S. 1953. 'Mechanism of gonadotropic harmony in the common malarial mosquito (*Anopheles maculipennis* Mg.)' (in Russian). *Zool. Zh.*, **32**, 1178–88.

DEUSE-ZIMMERMANN, R. 1960. 'Vergleichende Untersuchungen über Neurosecretion bei Enchytraeidae, Tubificidae und Naididae.' *Z. Zell. Forsch.*, **52**, 801–16.

DEWITZ, J. 1902. 'Recherches expérimentales sur la métamorphose des insectes.' *C. R. Soc. Biol., Paris*, **54**, 62–9.

DEWITZ, J. 1904. 'Zur Verwandlung der Insektenlarven.' *Zool. Anz.*, **28**, 166–82.

DEWITZ, J. 1905. 'Untersuchungen über die Verwandlung der Insekten-larven. II.' _Arch. Anat. Physiol._, Lpz., 389–415.

DEWITZ, J. 1913. 'Physiologische Untersuchungen bezüglich der Ver-wandlung von Insektenlarven.' _Zool. Anz._, 41, 385–98.

DEWITZ, J. 1916. 'Bedeutung der oxydierenden Fermente (Tyrosinase) für die Verwandlung der Insektenlarven.' _Zool. Anz._, 47, 123–4.

DEWITZ, J. 1924. 'Experimentelle Untersuchungen über die Verwandlung der Insektenlarven.' _Zool. Jb._, Abt. 4, 41, 245–334.

DICKSON, R. C. 1949. 'Factors governing the induction of diapause in the Oriental fruit moth.' _Ann. ent. Soc. Amer._, 42, 511–37.

DICKSON, R. C. and SANDERS, E. J. 1945. 'Factors inducing diapause in the Oriental fruit moth.' _J. econ. Ent._, 38, 605–6.

DOANE, W. W. 1960a. 'Developmental physiology of the mutant female sterile (2) adipose of _Drosophila melanogaster_. Effects of altered environ-ment and residual genome on its expression.' _J. exp. Zool._, 145, 23–41.

DOANE, W. W. 1960b. 'Completion of Meiosis in uninseminated eggs of _Drosophila melanogaster_.' _Science_, 132, 677–8.

DOANE, W. W. 1961a. 'Effects of implanted adult corpora allata on that of host in two species of _Drosophila_.' _Science_, 134, 838–9.

DOANE, W. W. 1961b. 'Developmental physiology of the mutant female sterile (2) adipose of _Drosophila melanogaster_. Corpus allatum complex and ovarian transplantations.' _J. exp. Zool._, 146, 275–98.

DOANE, W. W. 1961c. 'Persistence of fs (2) adp in the _Kaduna_ population after four years.' _Drosophila Inform. Serv. Bull._, 35, 78.

DOBKIEWICZ, L. 1927. 'Der Einfluss von Schilddrüsenfütterung auf Ent-wicklung, Wachstum und Fortpflanzung der Taufliege (_Drosophila melanogaster_).' _Arch. EntwMech. Org._, 113, 96–122.

DOBKIEWICZ, L. 1928. 'Der Einfluss von Schilddrüsenfütterung auf Ent-wicklung, Wachstum und Fortpflanzung des Speckkäfers (_Dermestes frischii_ Kg.).' _Arch. EntwMech. Org._, 114, 458–99.

DOBZHANSKY, T. 1930. 'Interaction between female and male parts in gynandromorphs in _Drosophila simulans_.' _Arch. EntwMech. Org._, 123, 719–46.

DOESBURG, P. H. 1956. 'Einige waarnemingen betreffende de waard-parasiet relatie bij _Bupalus_ en _Carcaelia_.' _Ent. Ber._, 16, 173–5.

DOSKOČIL, J. 1957. 'Beitrag zur Kenntnis der Insektendiapause. 2. Einfluss der Beleuchtungslänge auf die Entstehung der Diapause der Eier' (in Czech). _Mém. Soc. Zool. tchécosl._, 21, 273–83.

DOSKOČIL, J., JANDA, V. and WENIG, K. 1952. 'Gesamt Stoffwechsel der Insekten. I. Die Beziehung zwischen Körperlänge, Körperoberfläche und Körpergewicht während der Post-embryonalentwicklung von Stabheu-schrecke _Dixippus morosus_ Br. et Redt' (in Czech). _Mém. Soc. Zool. tchécosl._, 16, 33–42.

DOUTT, R. L. 1959. 'The biology of parasitic Hymenoptera.' _Ann. Rev. Ent._, 4, 161–82.

DRASTICH, L. 1924. 'Neue Adaptation von Microrespirometer.' *Biol. Listy*, **10**, 1–20.

DRESCHER, W. 1960. 'Regenerationsversuche am Gehirn von *Periplaneta americana* unter Berücksichtigung von Verhaltensverändrung und Neurosekretion.' *Z. Morph. Ökol. Tiere*, **48**, 576–649.

DU BOIS, A. M. 1938. 'La détermination de l'ébauche embryonnaire chez *Sialis lutaria* L. (Megaloptera).' *Rev. suisse Zool.*, **45**, 1–92.

DU BOIS, A. M. and GEIGY, R. 1935. 'Beiträge zur ökologie, Fortpflanzungsbiologie und Metamorphose von *Sialis lutaria* L. (Studien am Sempachersee).' *Rev. suisse Zool.*, **42**, 169–248.

DUCLAUT, E. 1869. 'De l'influence de froid d'hiver sur le développement de l'embryon du ver á soie et sur l'éclosion de la graine.' *C. R. Acad. Sci.*, *Paris*, **69**, 1021–2.

DUPONT-RAABE, M. 1949a. 'Les chromatophores de la larve du Coréthre.' *Arch. Zool. exp. gén.*, **86**, 32–9.

DUPONT-RAABE, M. 1949b. 'Réactions humorales des chromatophores de la larve du Coréthre.' *C. R. Acad. Sci.*, *Paris*, **228**, 130–2.

DUPONT-RAABE, M. 1951a. 'Étude experimentale de l'adaptation chromatique chez le phasme *Carausius morosus* Bt.' *C. R. Acad. Sci.*, *Paris*, **232**, 886–8.

DUPONT-RAABE, M. 1951b. 'Étude morphologique et cytologique du cerveau de quelques Phasmides.' *Bull. Soc. zool. Fr.*, **76**, 386–97.

DUPONT-RAABE, M. 1952. 'Contribution à l'étude du role endocrine du cerveau et notamment de la pars intercerebralis chez les Phasmides.' *Arch. Zool. exp. gén.*, **89**, 128–38.

DUPONT-RAABE, M. 1954a. 'La rôle endocrine du cerveau dans la régulation des phénomènes d'adaptation chromatique et de la ponte chez les phasmides.' *Pubbl. Zool. Staz. Napoli*, **24**, 63–7.

DUPONT-RAABE, M. 1954b. 'Répartition des activités chromatiques dans le ganglion sus-oesophagien dans la partie deuto- et tritocérébrale.' *C. R. Acad. Sci.*, *Paris*, **238**, 950–1.

DUPONT-RAABE, M. 1956a. 'Quelques données relatives aux phénomènes de neurosécrétion chez les Phasmides.' *Ann. Sci. nat. Zool.*, (11) **18**, 293–303.

DUPONT-RAABE, M. 1956b. 'Rôle des différentes éléments du système nerveux central dans la variation chromatique des Phasmides.' *C. R. Acad. Sci.*, *Paris*, **243**, 1358–60.

DUPONT-RAABE, M. 1956c. 'Mise en évidence, chez les Phasmides, d'une troisième paire de nervi corporis cardiaci, voie possible de cheminement de la substance chromactive tritocérébrale vers les corpora cardiaca.' *C. R. Acad. Sci.*, *Paris*, **243**, 1240–3.

DUPONT-RAABE, M. 1957. 'Les mécanismes de l'adaptation chromatique chez les insectes.' *Arch. Zool. exp. gén.*, **94**, 61–293.

DU PORTE, E. M. 1958. 'The origin and evolution of pupa.' *Canad. Ent.*, **90**, 436–9.

DURCHON, M. 1956. 'Rôle du cerveau dans la maturation génitale et le déclenchement de l'épitoquie chez les Néréidiens.' *Ann. Sci. nat. Zool.*, (11), **18**, 268–73.

DÜRKEN, B. 1907. 'Die Tracheenkiemenmuskulatur der Ephemeriden unter Berücksichtigung der Morphologie des Insektenflügels.' *Z. wiss. Zool.*, **87**, 435–550.

DÜRKEN, B. 1923. 'Ueber die Wirkung farbiges Lichtes auf die Puppen des Kohlweisslings (*Pieris brassicae*) und das Verhalten des Nachkommens.' *Arch. mikr. Anat.*, **99**, 222–389.

DYAR, H. G. 1890. 'The number of molts in Lepidopterous larvae.' *Psyche*, **5**, 420–2.

ÉCHALIER, G. 1955. 'Rôle de l'organe Y dans le déterminisme de la mue de *Carcinides moenas* L.; Expériences d'implantation.' *C. R. Acad. Sci.*, *Paris*, **240**, 1581–3.

ÉCHALIER, G. 1956. 'Effects de l'ablation et de la greffe de l'organe Y sur la mue de *Carcinus moenas* L.' *Ann. Sci. nat. Zool.* (11), **18**, 153–4.

EDE, B. A. 1957. 'The effect of cold shock on developing *Drosophila* embryos.' *Proc. roy. phys. Soc. Edinb.*, **25**, 63–6.

EDELBACHER, S. 1946. 'Das Ganzheitproblem in der Biochemie.' *Experientia*, **42**, 7–18.

EIDMANN, H. 1924a. 'Untersuchungen über Wachstum und Häutung der Insekten.' *Z. Morph. Ökol. Tiere*, **2**, 567–610.

EIDMANN, H. 1924b. 'Untersuchungen über Wachstum und Häutung der Insekten.' *Verh. dtsch. zool. Ges.*, **29**, 124–9.

ELLIS, P. E. and CARLISLE, D. B. 1961. 'The prothoracic gland and colour change in locusts.' *Nature, Lond.*, **190**, 368–9.

EMME, A. M. 1944a. 'Diapause in insects' (in Russian). *Adv. mod. Biol.*, *Moscow*, **18**, 56–71.

EMME, A. M. 1944b. 'On the conformities between the freshly formed eggcell and the diapausing egg' (in Russian). *Adv. mod. Biol.*, *Moscow*, **18**, 397–9.

EMME, A. M. 1947a. 'The breaking of the embryonic diapause in *Bombyx mori* by means of sublethal temperature doses. I. The developmental variability in thermoreactivity' (in Russian). *C. R. Acad. Sci. U.R.S.S.*, **6**, 769–76.

EMME, A. M. 1947b. 'New information on the diapause of insects' (in Russian). *Adv. mod. Biol.*, *Moscow*, **24**, 154–7.

EMME, A. M. 1949a. 'The role of temperature on the exhaustion of the embryonic diapause by the mulberry silkworm' (in Russian). *C. R. Acad. Sci. U.R.S.S.*, **67**, 589–92.

EMME, A. M. 1949b. 'Combined action with high and low temperature on the eggs of the mulberry silkworm' (in Russian). *C. R. Acad. Sci. U.S.S.R.*, **67**, 747–50.

EMME, A. M. 1950. 'Variation and inheritance of susceptibility to cold of diapause eggs of the mulberry silkworm' (in Russian). *C. R. Acad. Sci. U.R.S.S.*, **75**, 119–22.

EMME, A. M. 1951. 'The stimulating effect of oxygen on the eggs of the mulberry silkworm' (in Russian). *C. R. Acad. Sci. U.R.S.S.*, **81**, 141–4.

EMME, A. M. 1952. 'Detailed study of the developmental variability of thermoreactivity in prediapause silkworm eggs' (in Russian). *C. R. Acad. Sci. U.R.S.S.*, **82**, 825–8.

EMME, A. M. 1953a. 'Activation of the diapausing silkworm eggs by hydrochloric acid' (in Russian). *C. R. Acad. Sci. U.R.S.S.*, **88**, 381–4.

EMME, A. M. 1953b. 'Some questions regarding the theory of insect diapause' (in Russian). *Adv. mod. Biol. Moscow*, **35**, 395–424.

ENAMI, M. 1951. 'Mechanism of control of the chromatophore responses in teleosts and crustaceans.' *J. exp. Morph.*, **7**, 1–22.

ENDERS (SCHIKORA), E. 1956. 'Die hormonale Steuerung rhythmischer Bewegungen von Insekten-Ovidukten.' *Verh. dtsch. zool. Ges.*, **19**, 113–16.

ENGELGARD, V. A. 1945. 'Phosphoric acid and the functions of the cell' (in Russian). *C. R. Acad. Sci. U.R.S.S.*, **2**, 182–96.

ENGELMANN, F. 1957a. 'Bau und Funktion des weiblichen Geschlechtsapparates bei der ovoviviparen Schabe *Leucophaea maderae* (Fabr.) und einige Beobachtungen über die Entwicklung.' *Biol. Zbl.*, **76**, 722–40.

ENGELMANN, F. 1957b. 'Die Steuerung der Ovarfunction bei der ovoviviparen Schabe *Leucophaea maderae* Fabr.' *J. Ins. Physiol.*, **1**, 257–78.

ENGELMANN, F. 1958. 'The stimulation of the corpora allata in *Diploptera punctata* (Blattaria).' *Anat. Rec.*, **132**, **3**, 432–3.

ENGELMANN, F. 1959a. 'Ueber die Wirkung implantierter Prothoraxdrüsen in adulten Weibchen von *Leucophaea maderae*.' *Z. vergl. Physiol.*, **41**, 456–70.

ENGELMANN, F. 1959b. 'The control of reproduction in *Diploptera punctata* (Blattaria).' *Biol. Bull.*, *Wood's Hole*, **117**, 406–19.

ENGELMANN, F. 1960a. 'Mechanisms controlling reproduction in two viviparous cockroaches.' *Ann. N.Y. Acad. Sci.*, **89**, 516–36.

ENGELMANN, F. 1960b. 'Hormonal control of mating behavior in an insect.' *Experientia*, **16**, 69–70.

ENGELMANN, F. and LÜSCHER, M. 1956a. 'Zur Frage der Auslösung der Metamorphose bei Insekten.' *Naturwissenschaften*, **43**, 43–4.

ENGELMANN, F. and LÜSCHER, M. 1956b. 'Die hemmende Wirkung des Gehirns auf die corpora allata bei *Leucophaea maderae* (Orthoptera).' *Verh. dtsch. zool. Ges.*, **19**, 215–220.

ENGELMANN, F. and LÜSCHER, M. 1957. 'Hemmung der Eirefung durch Prothoraxdrüsen bei *Leucophaea maderae* (Orthoptera).' *Naturwissenschaften*, **16**, 455.

ENZMANN, E. V. and HASKINS, C. P. 1938a. 'Morphogenesis studies by means of X-rays. II. Note on an inherited cuticular tumor in *Drosophila*.' *Arch. EntwMech. Org.*, **138**, 159–60.

ENZMANN, E. V. and HASKINS, C. P. 1938b. 'The development of the imaginal eye in the larva of *Drosophila melanogaster*.' *J. Morph.*, **63**, 63–72.

M

EPHRUSSI, B. 1937. 'Revue des expériences de transplantation.' *Bull. Biol.*, **71**, 1–16.

EPHRUSSI, B. 1938. 'Aspects of the physiology of gene action.' *Amer. Nat.*, **72**, 5–23.

EPHRUSSI, B. 1942a. 'Chemistry of "eye color hormones" of *Drosophila*.' *Quart. Rev. Biol.*, **17**, 327–38.

EPHRUSSI, B. 1942b. 'Analysis of eye colour hormones of *Drosophila*.' *Cold Sp. Harb. Symp. quant. Biol.*, **10**, 40–8.

EPHRUSSI, B. 1953. *Nucleo-cytoplasmic relations in micro-organisms; their bearing on cell heredity and differentiation*, Oxford, Univ. Press.

EPHRUSSI, B. and BEADLE, G. W. 1937a. 'Development of eye colours in *Drosophila*. Transplantation experiments on the interaction of vermilion and other eye colours.' *Genetics*, **22**, 65–75.

EPHRUSSI, B. and BEADLE, G. W. 1937b. 'Development of eye colours in *Drosophila*. Production and release of cn + substance by the eyes of different eye colour mutants.' *Genetics*, **22**, 479–83.

EPHRUSSI, B. and CHEVAIS, S. 1937. 'Development of eye colours in *Drosophila*. Relation between pigmentation and release of the diffusible substances.' *Proc. nat. Acad. Sci. U.S.A.* **23**, 428.

EPHRUSSI, B. and HARNBY, M. H. 1936. 'Sur la présence, chez différent insects, des substances intervenant dans la pigmentation des yeux de *Drosophila melanogaster*.' *C. R. Acad. Sci.*, *Paris*, **203**, 1028–30.

EPHRUSSI, B., KHOUVINE, Y., and CHEVAIS, S. 1938. 'Genetic control of morphogenetic substance in *Drosophila*.' *Nature, Lond.*, **141**, 204–5.

EPSTEINS, F. F. 1937. 'Zur Physiologie der Metamorphosis bei *Drosophila melanogaster*. I. Verpuppung.' *Biol. Jaarb.*, **4**, 362–377.

ERGENE, S. 1952. 'Farbanpassung entsprechend der jeweiligen Substratfärbung bei *Acrida turrita*.' *Z. vergl. Physiol.*, **34**, 69–74.

EVANS, A. C. 1936. 'Histolysis of muscle in the pupa of the blow-fly *Lucilia sericata* Meig.' *Proc. roy. ent. Soc. Lond.* (A), **11**, 52–4.

EVANS, J. J. T. 1962. 'Insect neurosecretory material separated by differential centrifugation.' *Science*, **136**, 314–15.

EWEST, A. 1937. 'Struktur und erste Differenzierung im Ei des Mehlkäfers *Tenebrio molitor*.' *Arch. EntwMech. Org.*, **135**, 689–752.

FÁBIÁN, G. 1948. 'Phänogenetische Untersuchungen an einer Sterilitätsmutante ("bordo-steril") von *Drosophila melanogaster*.' *Arch. Klaus-Stift. VererbForsch.*, **23**, 512–17.

FAHLENDER, K. 1940. 'Die Segmentalorgane der Diplopoda, Symphyla und Insecta Apterygota.' *Zool. Bidr. Uppsala*, **18**, 243–51.

FARKAS, G. and TANG, H. 1926. 'Die Wirkung von Adrenalin und Cholin auf die Entwicklungszeit der Seidenraupen.' *Biochem. Z.*, **172**, 350–4.

FAULHABER, I. 1959. 'Biochemische Untersuchungen zum Eiweissstoffwechsel der Letalmutante lethal giant larvae (lgl) von *Drosophila melanogaster*.' *Z. VererbLehre*, **90**, 299–334.

FAVRELLE, M. 1943. 'Effect de l'ablation des corpora allata chez *Bacillus rossii.*' *C. R. Acad. Sci.*, *Paris*, **216**, 215–16.

FEDERLEY, H. 1936. 'Sex-limited hereditary cancer in Lepidopterous larvae.' *Hereditas*, *Lund*, **22**, 193–216.

FEDOTOV, D. M. 1936. 'Ueber die späte postembryonale Entwicklung des Frostspanners (*Operophtera brumata* L.)' (in Russian). *C. R. Acad. Sci. U.R.S.S.*, **4**, 237–40.

FEDOTOV, D. M. 1939. 'On the phenomenon of regressive changes in some bag-worm moths (Psychidae).' *C. R. Acad. Sci. U.R.S.S.*, **24**, 616–619.

FEDOTOV, D. M. 1940. 'The contemporary state of the problems of organ reduction and research carried out by the Institute of evolutionary morphology of the Academy of Sciences of the U.R.S.S.' (in Russian). *Adv. mod. Biol.*, *Moscow*, **13**, 354–70.

FEDOTOV, D. M. 1944a. 'Two types of organ regression in the ontogeny of insects' (in Russian). *C. R. Acad. Sci. U.R.S.S.*, **44**, 133–6.

FEDOTOV, D. M. 1944b 'Some observations in the internal state of the imago of *Eurygaster integriceps*' (in Russian). *C. R. Acad. Sci. U.R.S.S.*, **42**, 408–11.

FEDOTOV, D. M. 1945a. 'Evolutionary significance of regressive changes in ontogenesis' (in Russian). *Bull. Soc. nat. Moscow* (NS), **50**, 18–30.

FEDOTOV, D. M. 1945b. 'Postembryonic development and regression in *Pachytelia unicolor* Hufn. (Lepidoptera, Psychidae)' (in Russian). *Bull. Acad. Sci. U.R.S.S.*, *Sér. Biol.*, 623–53.

FEDOTOV, D. M. 1947. 'Changes in the internal state of *Eurygaster integriceps* imagoes during the year' (in Russian). *Vriednaia tcherepachka (Eurygaster integriceps)*, *Moscow*, **1**, 35–80.

FEDOTOV, D. M. 1956. 'Les phénomènes de regression dans la développe-ment de certain insectes supérieurs.' *Proc. XIVth int. Congr. Zool.*, 1953, 493–4.

FINKELSTEIN, A. 1944. 'Tumour growth in invertebrates' (in Russian). *Adv. mod. Biol. Moscow*, **17**, 320–48.

FINLAYSON, L. H. 1956. 'Normal and induced degeneration of abdominal muscles during metamorphosis in the Lepidoptera.' *Quart. J. micr. Sci.*, **97**, 215–33.

FINLAYSON, L. H. 1957. 'Abnormal metamorphosis in Saturniid moths infected by a microsporidian.' *Nature*, *Lond.*, **180**, 713–14.

FISCHER, F. *et al.* 1962. 'Sind die Neurohormone der Arthropoden identisch, mit fluoreszierenden Substanzen aus dem Nervensystem.' *Z. Naturf.*, **17b**, 833–6.

FISCHER, F. *et al.* 1931. 'Interactions between a sporozoan and its insect hosts.' Purdue Univ., Ph.D. Thesis, Zoology.

FISCHER, J. 1942. *Grundriss der Gewebezüchtung*, G. Fischer, Jena.

FLEISCHMANN, W. 1929. 'Zur Frage der Beeinflussung wirbelloser durch Wirbeltierinkrete.' *Pflüg. Arch. ges. Physiol.*, **221**, 591–3.

FLEISCHMANN, W. 1937. *Vergleichende Physiologie der inneren Sekretion,* Wien u. Leipzig, Perles.

FLOREY, E. 1952a. In Pflugfelder, *Entwicklungsphysiologie der Insekten,* Leipzig, Akad. Verlag, p. 182.

FLOREY, E. 1952b. 'Untersuchungen über die Natur der Farbwechselhormone der Crustaceen.' *Biol. Zbl.,* **71,** 499–611.

FOA, A. 1927. 'Osservazione ed esperienze sul bivoltinismo del baco da ceta.' *Ann. R. Inst. Agr. Portica,* **3,** 2.

FORMIGONI, A. 1956. 'Neurosécrétion et organes endocrinnes chez *Apis mellifica* L.' *Ann. Sci. nat. Zool.,* **11,** 282–91.

FRAENKEL, G. 1934. 'Pupation of flies initiated by a hormone.' *Nature, Lond.,* **133,** 834.

FRAENKEL, G. 1935a. 'A hormone causing pupation in the blow-fly *Calliphora erythrocephala.*' *Proc. roy. Soc.* (B), **118,** 1–12.

FRAENKEL, G. 1935b. 'Observations and experiments on the blow-fly *Calliphora erythrocephala* during the first day after emergence.' *Proc. zool. Soc. Lond.,* **118,** 893–904.

FRAENKEL, G. 1951. 'Effect and distribution of vitamin Bp.' *Arch. Biochem. Biophys.,* **34,** 457–77.

FRAENKEL, G. and BLEWETT, M. 1942. 'Biotin as a possible growth factor for insects.' *Nature, Lond.,* **149,** 301.

FRAENKEL, G. and HSIAO, C. 1962. 'Hormonal and nervous control of tanning in the fly.' *Science,* **138,** 27–9.

FRAENKEL, G. and RUDALL, M. 1940. 'A study of the physical and chemical properties of the insect cuticle.' *Proc. roy. Soc.* (B), **129,** 1–35.

FRAENKEL, G. and RUDALL, M. 1947. 'The structure of insect cuticle.' *Proc. roy. Soc.* (B), **134,** 111–43.

FRAENKEL, G. and SCHNEIDERMAN, H. A. 1958. 'The effect of nitrogen, argon, and sulphur hexafluoride on the development of insects.' *J. Cell. comp. Physiol.,* **52,** 431–52.

FRANKENBERGER, Z. 1944. 'On the problem of the morphological origin of insect wings' (in Czech). *Sbor. ent. odd. nár. Mus. Praha,* **2122,** 408–19.

FRASER, A. 1957. 'Neurosecretory cells in the brain of the larva of *Lucilia caesar* L.' *Nature, Lond.,* **179,** 257–8.

FRASER, A. 1958. 'Humoral control of metamorphosis and diapause in the larvae of certain Calliphoridae.' *Proc. roy. Soc. Edinb.* (B), **67,** 127–40.

FRASER, A. 1959a. 'Observations on the endocrine control of development of the larvae of certain Calliphoridae.' *Ent. mon. Mag.,* **95,** 159–66.

FRASER, A. 1959b. 'The anatomy of the central nervous system and retrocerebral endocrine organs of the larvae of *Lucilia caesar* and certain other Diptera Cyclorrapha.' *Proc. roy. ent. Soc. Lond.* (A), **34,** 186–92.

FREE, J. B. 1955. 'Queen production in colonies of bumble bees.' *Proc. roy. ent. Soc. Lond.* (A), **30,** 19–25.

FRIEDRICH, H. 1930. 'Zur Kenntnis der Regeneration der Extremitäten bei *Carausius morosus.*' *Z. wiss. Zool.,* **137,** 578–605.

FRÖBRICH, G. 1953. 'Der Tribolium-Imago-Faktor (TIF) durch Carnitin ersetzbar.' *Naturwissenschaften*, **40**, 556.

FRÖBRICH, G. 1954. 'Darstellung von Konzentraten des "Tribolium-Imago-Factors" und seine vermutliche chemische Natur.' *Naturwissenschaften*, **40**, 344–54.

FRUTON, J. S. 1955. *Aspects of synthesis and order in growth*, Princeton Univ. Press, pp. 15–42.

FUKAYA, M. 1955. 'The role of the brain in the metamorphosis of the rice stem borer, *Chilo suppressalis*' (in Japanese). *Jap. J. appl. Zool.*, **2**, 179–83.

FUKAYA, M. and MITSUHASHI, J. 1958. 'The hormonal control of larval diapause in the rice stem borer, *Chilo suppressalis*. II. The activity of the corpora allata during the diapause.' *Jap. J. appl. Zool.*, **2**, 223–6.

FUKUDA, S. 1937. 'Note préliminaire sur la transformation de la peau larvaire en puparium chez les larves de *Sturmia sericariae*.' *Proc. imp. Acad. Japan*, **13**, 114–16.

FUKUDA, S. 1939. 'Acceleration of development of silkworm ovary by transplantation into young pupa.' *Proc. imp. Acad. Japan*, **15**, 19–21.

FUKUDA, S. 1940a. 'Determination of voltinism in the silkworm with special reference to the pigment formation in the serosa of the egg.' *Zool. Mag.*, *Tokyo*, **52**, 415–29.

FUKUDA, S. 1940b. 'Induction of pupation in silkworm by transplanting the prothoracic gland.' *Proc. imp. Acad. Japan*, **16**, 417–20.

FUKUDA, S. 1941a. 'Induction of metamorphosis in the silkworm by transplanting pupal prothoracic gland.' *Zool. Mag.*, *Tokyo*, **53**, 12.

FUKUDA, S. 1941b. 'Role of the prothoracic gland in differentiation of the imaginal character in the silkworm pupa.' *Annot. zool. jap.*, **20**, 9–13.

FUKUDA, S. 1942–3. 'Precocious development of the silk gland following ablation of the corpora allata in the silkworm' (in Japanese). *Zool. Mag.*, *Tokyo*, **54**, 11–13 (abstract in *Jap. J. Zool.*, **10**, 18).

FUKUDA, S. 1944. 'The hormonal mechanism of larval molting and metamorphosis in the silkworm.' *J. Fac. Sci. Tokyo Univ.*, **6** (4), 477–537.

FUKUDA, S. 1951a. 'Factors determining the production of the diapause eggs in the silkworm.' *Proc. Japan. Acad.*, **27**, 582–6.

FUKUDA, S. 1951b. 'The production of the diapause eggs by transplanting the suboesophageal ganglion in the silkworm.' *Proc. Japan. Acad.*, **27**, 672–7.

FUKUDA, S. 1951c. 'Alteration of voltinism in the silkworm by decapitating the pupa.' *Zool. Mag.*, *Tokyo*, **60**, 119–21.

FUKUDA, S. 1952. 'Function on the pupal brain and suboesophageal ganglion in the production of non-diapause and diapause eggs in the silkworm.' *Annot. zool. Jap.*, **25**, 1–2, 149–55.

FUKUDA, S. 1953a. 'Determination of voltinism in the univoltine silkworm.' *Proc. Japan. Acad.*, **29**, 381–4.

FUKUDA, S. 1953b. 'Determination of voltinism in the multi-voltine silkworm.' *Proc. Japan. Acad.*, **29**, 385–8.

FUKUDA, S. 1953c. 'Alteration of voltinism in the silkworm following transection of pupal oesophageal connectives.' *Proc. Japan. Acad.*, **29**, 389–91.

FUKUDA, S. 1955. 'Endocrinological studies on the metamorphosis and voltinism of the silkworm *Bombyx mori*.' *Acta Int. Seric. Techn. Conf. Ales*, **7**, 11–12.

FÜLLER, H. B. 1960. 'Morphologische und experimentelle Untersuchungen über die neurosekretorischen Verhältnisse im Zentral-nervensystem von Blattiden und Culiciden.' *Zool. Jb.*, Abt. 3, **69**, 223–50.

FURAKAWA, H. 1930. 'Can the skin of the imago be made to moult?' *Proc. imp. Acad. Japan*, **11**, 158–60.

FURZEAU-BRAESCH, S. 1961. 'Les déterminismes de la diapause chez les insectes.' *Année biol.*, **37**, 43–69.

GABE, M. 1951. 'Données histologiques sur la néurosecretion chez les Pterotracheidae.' *Rev. canad. Biol.*, **10**, 391–410.

GABE, M. 1953a. 'Sur l'existence chez quelques Crustacés malacostracés d'un organe comparable à la glande de la mue des insectes.' *C. R. Acad. Sci.*, *Paris*, **237**, 1111–13.

GABE, M. 1953b. 'Quelques acquisitions récentes sur les glandes endocrines des Arthropodes.' *Experientia*, **9**, 352–6.

GABE, M. 1953c. 'Données histologiques sur les glandes céphaliques de quelques Thysanoures.' *Bull. Soc. zool. Fr.*, **78**, 177.

GABE, M. 1955. 'Particularités histologiques des cellules neurosecretrices chez quelques lamellibranches.' *C. R. Acad. Sci.*, *Paris*, **240**, 1810–1912.

GABE, M. 1956. 'Histologie comparée de la glande de mue (organne Y) des Crustacés malacostracés.' *Ann. Sci. nat. Zool.*, **18**, 145–52.

GAINES, J. C. and CAMPBELL, F. L. 1935. 'Dyar's rule as related to the number of instars of the corn ear worm *Heliothis obsoleta* (Fab.) collected in the field.' *Ann. ent. Soc. Amer.*, **28**, 445–61.

GALE, E. F. 1956. *Enzymes: units of biological structure and function.* Acad. Press Inc., New York, p. 49.

GALTON, A. W. 1952. 'Hormones in plants and invertebrates, by K. V. Thiman.' *Nature, Lond.*, **170**, 724–5, 4331.

GANGULY, D. N. and BANERJEE, M. 1961. 'Morphological study of the neurosecretory system of the plant bug *Macrocerœa grandis*.' *Proc. zool. Soc. Lond.*, **13**, 71–90.

GANGULY, D. N. and BASU, B. D. 1962. 'Studies on some chemical contents of the neurosecretory cells of adult silk worm *Bombyx mori*.' *Acta histochem.* **13**, 31–46.

GANGULY, D. N. and BASU, B. D. 1962. 'Studies on some cytoplasmic inclusions of the neurosecretory cells of the adult silk worm *Bombyx mori*.' *Anat. Anz.*, **111**, 81–90.

GANGULY, D. N. and DEB, D. C. 1960. 'Studies on the cephalic incretory pathways of *Chrysocoris stolli* Wolff.' *Anat. Anz.*, **109**, 28–35.

GANTES, H. 1949. 'Morphologie externe et croissance de quelques larves de Formicides.' *Bull. Soc. Hist. nat. Afr.*, **40**, 71–97.

GARDNER, E. J. 1948. 'A case of genetically controlled cytoplasmic influence in *Drosophila*.' *Drosophila Inform. Serv.*, **22**, 70; cf. *Rec. Gen. Soc. Amer.*, **18**, 87–8.

GAULDEN, M. E. and CARLSON, I. G. 1951. 'Differentiation of histoblasts in tissue cultures of grasshoppers.' *Exp. Cell Res.*, **2**, 416–33.

GAY, H. 1960. 'Nuclear control of the cell.' *Sci. Amer.*, **202**, 126–36.

GAW, Z. Y., LIU, N. T. and ZIA, T. U. 1958. 'Tissue culture methods for cultivation of virus grasserie.' *Acta vir.* (Engl. ed.), **3**, suppl., 55.

GEIGY, R. 1931a. 'Erzeugung rein imaginaler Defekte durch ultraviolette Eibestrahlung bei *Drosophila melanogaster*.' *Arch. EntwMech. Org.*, **125**, 406–47.

GEIGY, R. 1931b. 'Action de l'ultra-violet sur le pole germinal dans l'œuf de *Drosophila melanogaster* (castration et mutabilé).' *Rev. suisse Zool.*, **38**, 187–288.

GEIGY, R. 1937. 'Beobachtungen über die Metamorphose von *Sialis lutaria* L.' *Mitt. schweiz. ent. Ges.*, **17**, 144–57.

GEIGY, R. 1938. 'Entwicklungsphysiologische Untersuchungen über Anuren und Urodellen Metamorphose. I.' *Verh. schweiz. Naturf. Ges.*, **116**, 160–2.

GEIGY, R. 1941. 'Die Metamorphose als Folge gewebspezifischer Determination.' *Rev. suisse Zool.*, **48**, 483–94.

GEIGY, R. 1948. 'Étude expérimentale de la métamorphose de *Sialis lutaria* L.' *Bull. Biol.*, **33**, suppl., 62–7.

GEIGY, R. and ABOIM, A. N. 1944. 'Gonadenentwicklung bei *Drosophila* nach frühembryonaler Ausschaltung der Geschlechtszellen.' *Rev. suisse Zool.*, **51**, 410–17.

GEIGY, R. and LÜSCHER, M. 1942. 'Imaginale Bein-Doppelbildungen nach Ultraviolett-Bestrahlung von Schmetterlingseiern (*Tineola bisselliella* Hum.).' *Rev. suisse Zool.*, **49**, 206–10.

GEIGY, R. and OCHSÉ, W. 1940a. 'Versuche über die inneren Faktoren der Verpuppung bei *Sialis lutaria*, L.' *Rev. suisse Zool.*, **47**, 225–41.

GEIGY, R. and OCHSÉ, W. 1940b. 'Schnürungsversuche an Larven von *Sialis lutaria* L.' *Rev. suisse Zool.*, **47**, 193–4.

GEIGY, R. and PORTMANN A. 1941. 'Versuch einer morphologischen Ordnung der tierischen Entwicklungsvorgänge.' *Naturwissenschaften*, **29**, 734–43.

GEIGY, R. and RAHM, U. 1951. 'Beiträge zur experimentellen Analyse der Metamorphose von *Sialis lutaria* L.' *Rev. suisse Zool.*, **58**, 408–13.

GEISPITZ, K. F. 1949. 'The light as a factor regulating the developmental cycle in *Dendrolimus pini* L.' (in Russian). *C. R. Acad. Sci. U.R.S.S.*, **68**, 781–4.

GEISPITZ, K. F. 1958. 'The adaptive character in the resection and its role in the ecology of *Dendrolimus pini* L.' (in Russian). *Ann. Leningr. Univ.*, **240**, 21–33.

GELDIAY, S. 1959. 'Neurosecretory cells in ganglia of the roach, *Blaberus craniifer.*' *Biol. Bull., Wood's Hole,* 117, 267.

GELELOVICH, S. 1950. 'Une nouvelle tumeur héréditaire chez la *Drosophila.*' *C. R. Acad. Sci. U.R.S.S.,* 230, 1002–4.

GERSCH, M. 1952. 'Experimentelle Untersuchungen über den Verdauungstractus der Larve von *Chaoborus.*' *Z. vergl. Physiol.,* 34, 346–369.

GERSCH, M. 1955a. 'Untersuchungen über Auslösung und Steuerung der Darmbewegungen bei der Larve von *Chaoborus* (Corethra).' *Biol. Zbl.,* 74, 603–28.

GERSCH, M. 1955b. 'Ergebnisse und Probleme der Verdauungsphysiologie der wirbellosen Tiere.' *Experientia,* 11, 413–16.

GERSCH, M. 1956a. 'Das Hormonsystem der Insekten auf Grund neuer Forschungsergebnisse.' *Ber. Hundertj. dtsch. ent. Ges. Berlin,* 146–67.

GERSCH, M. 1956b. 'Untersuchungen zur Frage der hormonalen Beeinflussung der Melanophoren bei der *Corethra*-Larve.' *Z. vergl. Physiol.,* 39, 190–208.

GERSCH, M. 1957a. 'Das Hormonsystem der Insekten'. *Forsch. Fortschr. dtsch. Wiss.,* 31, 9–15.

GERSCH, M. 1957b. 'Wesen und Wirkungsweise von Neurohormonen im Tierreich.' *Naturwissenschaften,* 20, 525–32.

GERSCH, M. 1958a. 'Neurohormonale Beeinflussung der Herztätigkeit bei der Larve von *Corethra.*' *J. Ins. Physiol.,* 2, 281–97.

GERSCH, M. 1958b. 'Neurohormone bei wirbellosen Tieren.' *Verh. dtsch. zool. Ges.,* pp. 40–76.

GERSCH, M. 1959a. 'Weitere Untersuchungen über neurohormonale Beziehungen bei Insekten.' *Acta Symp. Ontog. Insects, Praha,* pp. 127–132.

GERSCH, M. 1959b. 'Untersuchungen über Neurohormone bei Insekten.' *Proc. XVth int. Congr. Zool., London,* 493–6.

GERSCH, M. 1960a. 'Neurosekretion und Neurohormone bei wirbellosen Tieren.' *Symp. Biol. Hung.,* 1, 153–80.

GERSCH, M. 1960b. 'New findings on neurosecretion and on the effects of the neurohormones in insects.' *J. gen. Biol., Moscow,* 21, 245–60.

GERSCH, M. 1961. 'Insect metamorphosis and the activation hormone.' *Amer. Zoologist,* 1, 53–7.

GERSCH, M. 1962a. 'The activation hormone of the metamorphosis of insects.' *Gen. comp. Endocrinol.,* suppl., 1, 322–9.

GERSCH, M. 1962b. 'Hormone und Hormonforschung bei niederen Tieren.' *Mat. med. Nordmark,* pp. 1–31.

GERSCH, M. and ALTHAUS, B. 1959. 'Ueber herzanregende Faktoren aus dem Nervensystem von Spinnen.' *Mber. dtsch. Acad. Wiss.,* 1, 376–9.

GERSCH, M. and BERGER, H. 1962. 'Die Wirkung isolierter Neurohormone aus *Periplaneta americana* auf die Pupariumbildung der Schmeissfliege *Calliphora erythrocephala.*' *Naturwissenschaften,* 11, 262.

GERSCH, M. and DEUSE, M. 1957. 'Die Wirkung von Neurohormonen aus Insekten auf das Froschherz.' *Biol. Zbl.*, **76**, 436–42.

GERSCH, M. and DEUSE, M. 'Ueber herzaktive Faktoren aus dem Nervensystem von *Aplysia*.' *Zool. Jb. (Phys.)*, **68**, 519–34.

GERSCH, M., FISCHER, M., UNGER, H. and KOCH, H. 1960. 'Die Isolierung neurohormonaler Faktoren aus dem Nervensystem der Küchenschabe *Periplaneta americana*.' *Z. Naturf.*, **15b**, 319–22.

GERSCH, M. and MOTHES, G. 1956. 'Neurohormonaler Wirkungsantagonismus beim Farbwechsel von *Dixippus morosus*.' *Naturwissenschaften*, **43**, 542.

GERSCH, M. and UNGER, H. 1957. 'Nachweis von Neurohormonen aus dem Nervensystem von *Dixippus morosus* mit Hilfe papierchromatographischer Trennung.' *Naturwissenschaften*, **44**, 117.

GERSCH, M., UNGER, H. and FISCHER, F. 1957. 'Die Isolierung eines Neurohormons aus dem Nervensystem von *Periplaneta americana* und einige biologische Testverfahren.' *Wiss. Z. Univ. Jena, math-nat. Reihe*, **6**, 125–9.

GHILYAROV, M. S. 1949. 'The characteristics of soil as a living medium and its importance in the evolution of insects' (in Russian). *C. R. Acad. Sci. U.R.S.S.*, **67**, 280.

GHILYAROV, M. S. 1957. 'Evolution of the postembryonic development and the types of insect larvae' (in Russian). *Zool. Zh.*, **36**, 1683–97.

GHILYAROV, M. S. 1958. 'Biologically active substances produced by insects' (in Russian). *Adv. mod. Biol., Moscow*, **46**, 208–16.

GHILYAROV, M. S. 1959. 'The laws of morphological and physiological changes in arthropods during their transition to life on dry land' (in Russian). *Trudy Inst. Morf. Zhiv. (Acad. Sci. U.R.S.S.)*, **27**, 118–33.

GIARD, A. 1889. 'Sur la castration parasitaire des *Typhlocyba* par une larve d'Hymenoptère (*Aphelopus melalucus* Dalm.) et par une larve de Diptère (*Atelenerva spuria* Meig.).' *C. R. Acad. Sci., Paris*, **109**, 708.

GIERSBERG, H. 1928. 'Ueber den morphologischen und physiologischen Farbwechsel der Stabheuschrecke *Dixippus morosus*.' *Z. vergl. Physiol.*, **7**, 657–95.

GIERSBERG, H. 1929. 'Die Färbung der Schmetterlingen, I.' *Z. vergl. Physiol.*, **9**, 523–40.

GIERSBERG, H. 1931. 'Ueber den Zusammenhang von morphologischen und physiologischen Farbwechsel. Nach Untersuchungen an Insekten und Fischen.' *Arch. zool. ital.*, **16**, 363–70.

GIERSBERG, H. 1933. 'Neuere Untersuchungen zur Physiologie des Farbwechsels.' *Iber. schles. Ges. vaterl. Cult.*, **106**, 110–14.

GIERYNG, R. 1959. 'The central nervous system of *Leptinotarsa decemlineata* with special consideration of the brain.' *Ann. Univ. M. Curie-Sklodowska*, **14**, 141–59.

GIERYNG, R. 1960. 'Histological structure of the brain of *Cicadetta adusta*.' *Ann. Univ. M. Curie-Sklodowska*, **15**, 205–12.

GIERYNG, R. 1961. 'Studies on the ontogenetic development of the central nervous system of *Leptinotarsa decemlineata*.' *Zool. Listy*, 10, 117–18.

GILBERT, L. I. 1962. 'Maintenance of the prothoracic gland by the juvenile hormone in insects.' *Nature, Lond.*, 193, 1205–7.

GILBERT, L. I. and SCHNEIDERMAN, H. A. 1957. 'The quantitative assay of the juvenile hormone of insects.' *Anat. Rec.*, 128, 55.

GILBERT, L. I. and SCHNEIDERMAN, H. A. 1958. 'Occurrence of substances with juvenile hormone activity in adrenal cortex of Vertebrates.' *Science*, 128, 844.

GILBERT, L. I. and SCHNEIDERMAN, H. A. 1959a. 'Prothoracic gland stimulation by juvenile hormone extracts of insects.' *Nature, Lond.*, 184, 171–3.

GILBERT, L. I. and SCHNEIDERMAN, H. A. 1959b. 'Sexual dimorphism in lipid content, juvenile hormone content and size of corpora allata in Lepidoptera.' *Anat. Rec.*, 134, 569.

GILBERT, L. I. and SCHNEIDERMAN, H. A. 1960a. 'The development of a bioassay for the juvenile hormone of insects.' *Trans. amer. micr. Soc.*, 79, 38–67.

GILBERT, L. I. and SCHNEIDERMAN, H. A. 1961a. 'The content of juvenile hormone and lipid in Lepidoptera: sexual differences and developmental changes.' *Gen. comp. Endocrin.*, 1, 453–72.

GILBERT, L. I. and SCHNEIDERMAN, H. A. 1961b. 'Some biochemical aspects of insect metamorphosis.' *Amer. Zool.*, 1, 11–51.

GILLET, J. D. 1957. 'Variation in time of release of the ovarian development hormone in *Aedes aegypti*.' *Nature, Lond.*, 180, 656.

GILLET, J. D. 1958. 'Induced ovarian development in decapitated mosquitoes by transfusion of haemolymph.' *J. exp. Biol.*, 35, 685–93.

GILMOUR, D. 1961. *Biochemistry of Insects*, New York and London, Acad. Press Inc.

GIRARDIE, A. 1962. 'Étude biométrique de la croissance ovarienne après ablation et implantation de corpora allata chez *Periplaneta americana*.' *J. Ins. Physiol.*, 8, 199–204.

GLASS, B. 1958. *A summary of the McCollum-Pratt Symposium on the chemical basis of development*, Baltimore, Johns Hopkins Press, pp. 855–922.

GLAUERT, A. M. and GLAUERT, R. H. 1959. 'Einleitung in Araldit-Harzstoffe für Elektronmikroskopie.' *J. biophys. biochem. Cytol.*, 4, 191.

GLOOR, H. 1947. 'Phänokopie-Versuche mit Aether an *Drosophila*.' *Rev. suisse Zool.*, 54, 637–712.

GOBEIL, A. R. 1941. 'La diapause chez les Tenthredes, I, II.' *Canad. J. Res.*, 19, 363–416.

GOETSCH, W. 1937. 'Die Entstehung der "Soldaten" im Ameisenstaat.' *Naturwissenschaften*, 25, 803–8.

GOETSCH, W. 1948. 'Vitamin T.' *Oest. zool. Z.*, 2, 533–626.

GOLDSCHMIDT, R. 1919. 'Intersexualität und Geschlechtsbestimmung.' *Biol. Zbl.*, 39, 498–512.

GOLDSCHMIDT, R. 1920a. *Mechanismus und Physiologie der Geschlechts-bestimmung*, Berlin, Borntraeger, 251 pp.

GOLDSCHMIDT, R. 1920b. 'Untersuchungen zur Entwicklungsphysiologie des Flügelmusters der Schmetterlinge.' *Arch. EntwMech. Org.*, **47**, 654–667.

GOLDSCHMIDT, R. 1920c. 'Untersuchung über Intersexualität.' *Z. indukt. Abstamm- u. VererbLehre*, **23**, 1–199.

GOLDSCHMIDT, R. 1923. 'Einige Materialien zur Theorie der abgestimmten Reaktionsgeschwindigkeiten.' *Arch. mikr. Anat.*, **98**, 292–313.

GOLDSCHMIDT, R. 1927. *Physiologische Theorie der Vererbung*, Berlin, Springer.

GOLDSCHMIDT, R. 1931a. *Die sexuellen Zwischenstüfen*, Berlin.

GOLDSCHMIDT, R. 1931b. 'Neue Untersuchungen über die Umwandlung der Gonaden bei intersexuellen *Lymantria dispar*.' *Arch. EntwMech. Org.*, **124**, 618–53.

GOLDSCHMIDT, R. 1931c. 'Analysis of intersexuality in the gipsy moth.' *Quart. Rev. Biol.*, **6**, 125–42.

GOLDSCHMIDT, R. 1934. 'Lymantria.' *Bibliogr. genet.*, **11**, 1–186.

GOLDSCHMIDT, R. 1935. 'Gen und Aussencharakter III.' *Biol. Zbl.*, **55**, 535–54.

GOLDSCHMIDT, R. 1938. *Physiological genetics*, New York, McGraw-Hill.

GOLDSCHMIDT, R. 1940. *The material basis of evolution*, Boston, Yale Univ. Press.

GOLDSCHMIDT, R. 1945. 'Addition data on phenocopies and genetic action.' *J. exp. Zool.*, **100**, 193–201.

GOLYSCHEV, N. 1928. 'Gasaustausch bei *Bombyx mori* in allen Stadien der Metamorphose.' *Arch. Zentr. Forsch. Stat. Seide u. Seidenraupenzucht*, *U.R.S.S.*, **3**, 129–60.

GOMORI, G. 1941. 'Observations with differential stains in human islets of Langerhans.' *Amer. J. Path.*, **17**, 395–406.

GOOD, P. N. 1949. 'Paper chromatography of pterins.' *Nature, Lond.*, **163**, 31.

GOODCHILD, A. J. P. 1954. 'Culture of insect tissues.' *Nature, Lond.*, **173**, 504–5.

GORBMAN, A. and HOWARD, A. 1962. *A textbook of comparative endocrinology*, New York, J. Wiley & Sons, p. 16.

GORDON, C. and SANG, J. H. 1941. 'The relation between nutrition and exhibition of the gene Antennales.' *Proc. roy. Soc.* (B), **130**, 151–84.

GORYSHIN, N. I. 1959. 'Influence of photoperiodism on the development of diapause in *Leptinotarsa decemlineata*.' *Mezhd. Metod. Kom. Kolorad. Zhuk.*, *Akad. Nauk S.S.S.R.*, p. 278.

GÖSSWALD, K. and BIER, H. 1953. 'Untersuchungen zur Kastendetermination in der Gattung *Formica*.' *Naturwissenschaften*, **40**, 38–9.

GÖSSWALD, K. and BIER, H. 1954. 'Untersuchungen zur Kastendetermination in der Gattung *Formica*.' *Insectes sociaux*, **3**, 229–46.

GOTTSCHEWSKI, G. H. M. 1958. 'Ueber das Wachstum von *Drosophila* Augenimaginalscheiben in vitro.' *Naturwissenschaften*, **45,** 400.

GRACE, T. D. C. 1954. 'Culture of insect tissues.' *Nature, Lond.*, **174,** 187–8.

GRACE, T. D. C. 1958a. 'Effects of various substances on growth of silkworm tisses in vitro.' *Aust. J. biol. Sci.*, **11,** 407–11.

GRACE, T. D. C. 1958b. 'The prolonged growth and survival of ovarian tissue of the promethea moth (*Callosamia promethea*) in vitro.' *J. gen. Physiol.*, **41,** 1027–34.

GRANDORI, L. and CARÉ, E. 1954. 'Studie anatomo-istologico sui sistema neurosecretore in *Musca domestica* e *Calliphora erythrocephala.*' *Pubbl. Staz. zool. Napoli*, **24,** suppl., 50–1.

GRASSÉ, P. P. 1946. 'La structure des sociétés d'Invertébrés.' *Rev. suisse Zool.*, **53,** 432–1.

GRASSÉ, P. P. 1949. 'Isoptères.' In *Traité de Zoologie*, **9,** 408–544, Paris, Masson.

GRASSÉ, P. P. 1952. 'Le polymorphisme des termites et la détermination des castes.' *Trans. IXth int. Congr. Ent.*, 1951, 51–62.

GRASSÉ, P. P. and LESPERON, L. 1936. 'Mue et excrétion chez le ver a soie.' *C. R. Soc. Biol.*, **122,** 1013.

GRASSÉ, P. P. and NOIROT, C. 1946a. 'La production du sexes néoténiques chez le termite à con jaune (*Calotermes ruficollis* F.): inhibition germinalle et inhibition somatique.' *C. R. Acad. Sci.*, *Paris*, **223,** 569–71.

GRASSÉ, P. P. and NOIROT, C. 1946b. 'Le polymorphisme sociale du termite à cou jaune (*Calotermes flavicollis* F.). La production des soldats.' *C. R. Acad. Sci.*, *Paris*, **223,** 929–31.

GRASSÉ, P. P. and NOIROT, C. 1947. 'Le polymorphisme social du termite à cou jaune (*Calotermes flavicollis* F.). Les faux ouvrières ou pseudoergates et les mues régressives.' *C. R. Acad. Sci.*, *Paris*, **224,** 219–21.

GRASSÉ, P. P., NOIROT, C., CLÉMENT, G., and BUCHLI, H. 1950. 'Sur la significance de la caste des ouvriers chez les termites.' *C. R. Acad. Sci.*, *Paris*, **230,** 892–5.

GREEN, D. F. 1956. *Enzymes: Units of biological structure and function*, New York, Acad. Press Inc., p. 465.

GRISON, P. 1947. 'Développement sans diapause des chenilles des *Euproctis phaeorrhaea* (Lep. Liparides).' *C. R. Acad. Sci.*, *Paris*, **225,** 1089–90.

GRISON, P. 1949. 'Effects d'implantation de cerveaux chez le doriphore (*Leptinotarsa decemlineata* Say) en diapause.' *C. R. Acad. Sci.*, *Paris*, **228,** 428–30.

GRISON, P. and ROEHRICH, R. 1944. 'Comparison du développement (des chenilles d'*Operophtera brumata* L. and *Euproctis*) à different températures constantes.' *Bull. Soc. ent. Fr.*, **54,** 12–16.

GROB, H. 1952. 'Entwicklungsphysiologische Untersuchungen an den Speicheldrüsen, dem Darmtractus und den Imaginalscheiben einer Letalrasse (lgl) von *Drosophila melanogaster.*' *Z. indukt. Abstamm- u. VererbLehre*, **84,** 320–60.

GROOT, A. P. DE and VOOGD, S. 1954. 'On the ovary development in queenless worker bees (*Apis mellifera* L.)' *Experientia,* 10, 384–5.

GRÜNFELD, E. K. 1948. 'The role of the brain in the metamorphosis of the larvae of *Aporia crataegi.*' *C. R. Acad. Sci. U.R.S.S.,* 60, 1085–7.

HACHLOW, W. 1931. 'Zur Entwicklungsmechanik der Schmetterlinge.' *Arch. EntwMech. Org.,* 125, 26–49.

HACKMANN, R. H. 1953. 'Chemistry and insect cuticle. 3. Hardening and darkening of the cuticle.' *Biochem. J.,* 54, 371–7.

HACKMANN, R. H., PRYOR, M. G. M. and TODD, A. R. 1948. 'The occurrence of phenolic substances in Arthropoda.' *Biochem. J.,* 43, 474–7.

HADORN, E. 1937a. 'Hormonale Kontrolle der Pupariumbildung bei Fliegen.' *Naturwissenschaften,* 25, 681–2.

HADORN, E. 1937b. 'An accelerating effect of normal "ring glands" on puparium formation in lethal larvae of *Drosophila.*' *Proc. nat. Acad. Sci. Wash.,* 23, 478–84.

HADORN, E. 1938. 'Die Degeneration der Imaginalscheiben bei letalen *Drosophila*-Larven der Mutation "lethal-giant".' *Rev. suisse Zool.,* 45, 425–9.

HADORN, E. 1939. 'Die Verpuppung der Fliegen als Beispiel eines hormonal bedingten Prozesses bei wirbellosen.' *Mitt. naturw. Ges. Thun,* 4, 99–113.

HADORN, E. 1942. 'Hormonale und genetische Voraussetzungen der Metamorphose.' *Rev. suisse Zool.,* 48, 495–509.

HADORN, E. 1948a. 'Genetische und entwicklungsphysiologische Probleme der Insektenontogenese.' *Folia biotheor., Leiden* (B), 3, 109–26.

HADORN, E. 1953. 'Regulation and differentiation within field-districts in imaginal discs of *Drosophila.*' *J. Embr. exp. Morph.,* 1, 213–16.

HADORN, E. 1954. 'Approaches to the study of biochemical and developmental effects of mutations.' (*Proc. 9th int. Congr. genet. 1953*) *Caryologia,* suppl. 6, 326–337.

HADORN, E. 1956. 'Erbkonstitution und Merkmalsbildung.' *Verh. schweiz. naturf. Ges.,* 136, 52–66.

HADORN, E. 1957. 'Ueber die Bildung der roten Augenpigmente von *Drosophila* in Transplantaten.' *Rev. suisse Zool.,* 64, 317–25.

HADORN, E. 1958. 'Role of genes in developmental processes.' *Symp. Chem. Basis Develop.,* Johns Hopkins Press. pp. 779–92.

HADORN, E., ANDERS, G. and URSPRUNG, H. 1959. 'Kombinate aus teilweise dissoziierten Imaginalscheiben verschiedener Mutanten und Arten von *Drosophila.*' *J. exp. Zool.,* 142, 159–75.

HADORN, E, and BERTANI, G. 1948. 'Induktion männlicher Pigmentierung in somatischen Zellen von *Drosophila*-Ovarien.' *Rev. suisse Zool.,* 55, 232–44.

HADORN, E., BERTANI, G. and GALLERA, J. 1949. 'Regulationsfähigkeit und Feldorganisation der männlichen Genital-Imaginalscheiben von *Drosophila melanogaster.*' *Arch. EntwMech. Org.,* 144, 31–70.

HADORN, E. and FRIZZI, W. 1949. 'Experimentelle Untersuchungen zur Melanophoren-Reaktion von *Corethra*.' *Rev. suisse Zool.*, **56**, 306–16.

HADORN, E. and FRIZZI, W. 1950. 'Veränderungen am transplantierten weiblichen Geschlechtsapparat von *Drosophila melanogaster* nach Behandlung der Imaginalscheibe in Salzlösungen.' *Rev. suisse Zool.*, **57**, 477–88.

HADORN, E. and GLOOR, H. 1946. 'Transplantationen zur Bestimmungen des Anlagemusters in der weiblichen Genital-Imaginalscheibe von *Drosophila melanogaster*.' *Rev. suisse Zool.*, **53**, 495–501.

HADORN, E. and NEEL, J. 1938a. 'The accelerating effect of ring gland injection upon puparium formation in normal and hybrid *Drosophila melanogaster* larvae.' *Genetics*, **23**, 151.

HADORN, E. and NEEL, J. 1938b. 'Der hormonale Einfluss der Ringdrüse (corpus allatum) auf die Pupariumbildung bei Fliegen.' *Arch. EntwMech. Org.*, **138**, 281–304.

HADORN, E. and NIGGLI, H. 1946. 'Mutations in *Drosophila* after chemical treatment of gonads in vitro.' *Nature, Lond.*, **157**, 162–3.

HADORN, E. and SCHARRER, B. 1938. 'The structure of the ring gland in normal and lethal larvae of *Drosophila melanogaster*.' *Proc. Nat. Acad. Sci. Wash.*, **24**, 236–42.

HADORN, E. and STUMM-ZOLLINGER, E. 1953. 'Untersuchungen zur biochemischen Auswirkung der Mutation "lethal-translucida" von *Drosophila melanogaster*.' *Rev. suisse Zool.*, **60**, 506–16.

HAECKEL, F. 1906. *Prinzipien der generellen Morphologie der Organismen*, Berlin.

HAHN, J. 1928. 'Sur l'influence de la glande thyroide sur les invertébrés' (in Polish with French summary). *Mem. Soc. Sci. Bohème*, **4**, 1–31.

HAHN, J. 1929. 'Ueber den Einfluss von Schilddrüsenfütterung auf die Metamorphose der *Vanessa io* und *Tenebrio molitor*.' *Arch. EntwMech. Org.*, **115**, 336–59.

HALBWACHS, M. C., JOLY, L. and JOLY, P. 1957. 'Resultats d'implantations de "glandes ventrales" à *Locusta migratoria* L.' *J. Ins. Physiol.*, **1**, 143–9.

HALLER, P. H. 1948. 'Morphologische, biologische und histologische Beiträge zur Kenntnis der Metamorphose der Trichopteren.' *Mitt. Schw. ent. Ges.*, 21, **3**, 301–60.

HAMASAKI, S. 1932. 'On the effect of castration in the silkworm *Bombyx mori*.' *Proc. imp. Acad. Tokyo.*, **8**, 267–70.

HANČ, O. 1959. *Hormone (Einführung in ihre Chemie und Biologie)*, Jena, G. Fischer, pp. 1–633.

HANDLIRSCH, A. 1927. 'Die postembryonale Entwicklung.' In Schröder, *Handbuch der Entomologie*, **1**, 1117–85.

HANSER, G. 1957. 'Wirkung eines Metamorphose-Hormons bei *Ephestia kühniella*.' *Zool. Anz.*, **20**, 209–15.

HANSTRÖM, B. 1926. 'Untersuchungen über die relative Grösse der

Gehirnzentren verschiedener Arthropoden unter Berücksichtigung der Lebensweise.' *Z. mikr.-anat. Forsch.*, **7**, 135–90.

HANSTRÖM, B. 1936a. 'Ein eigenartiges Rhynchotengehirn.' *Opusc. ent.*, **1**, 20–6.

HANSTRÖM, B. 1936b. 'Inkretorische Organe und Hormonfunktionen bei den Wirbellosen.' *Ergebn. Biol.*, **14**, 143–224.

HANSTRÖM, B. 1936c. 'Ueber eine Substanz im Insektenkopf, die zusammenfallend auf das Pigment der Garneelenchromatophoren wirkt.' *K. fysiogr. Sälsk. Lund Förh.*, **6**, 1–5.

HANSTRÖM, B. 1937. 'Vermischte Beobachtungen über die chromatophoraktivierenden Substanzen der Augenstiele der Crustaceen und des Kopfes der Insekten.' *Acta Univ. Lund* (N.S.), **32**, 1–11.

HANSTRÖM, B. 1938. 'Zwei Probleme betreffs des hormonalen Lokalisation im Insektenkopf.' *K. fysiogr. Sällsk. Lund Handl.*, **49**, 1–17.

HANSTROM, B. 1939. *Hormones in invertebrates*, Oxford, Clarendon Press.

HANSTRÖM, B. 1940a. 'Die chromatophoraktivierende Substanz des Insektenkopfes.' *Acta Univ. Lund* (N.S.), **36**, 1–20.

HANSTRÖM, B. 1940b. 'Inkretorische Organe, Sinnesorgane und Nervensystem des Kopfes einiger niederer Insektenordnungen.' *K. svenska VetenskAkad. Handl.*, **18**, 1–265.

HANSTRÖM, B. 1941. 'Einige Paralellen im Bau und in der Herkunft der inkretorischen Organe der Arthropoden und Vertebraten.' *Acta Univ. Lund* (N.S.), **37**, 1–19.

HANSTRÖM, B. 1942. 'Die Corpora cardiaca und allata der Insekten.' *Biol. gen.*, **15**, 485–531.

HANSTRÖM, B. 1943a. 'Der Lobus dorsomedialis von *Lygaeus equestris*.' *Acta Univ. Lund* (N.S.), **38**, 1–12.

HANSTRÖM, B. 1943b. 'Ergänzende Beobachtungen über das Corpus cardiacum und das Stirnauge der Machiliden und das Gehirn der Campodeiden.' *K. fysiogr. Sällsk. Lund Förh.*, **13**, 215–19.

HANSTRÖM, B. 1949. 'Three principal incretory organs in the animal kingdom.' *Bull. Biol.*, **33**, suppl., 182–209.

HANSTRÖM, B. 1953. 'Neurosecretory pathways in the head of crustaceans, insects and vertebrates.' *Nature, Lond.*, **171**, 72–3.

HANSTRÖM, B. 1956. 'The comparative aspect of neurosecretion with special reference to the hypothalamo-hypophysis system.' *Proc. VIIIth Symp. Colston Res. Soc.*, pp. 23–7.

HANSTRÖM, B. 1957. 'Reflections on the secretory role of the brain.' *Nova Acta R. Soc. Sci. upsal.*, **17**, 3–12.

HARKER, J. E. 1958. 'Experimental production of midgut tumours in *Periplaneta americana*.' *J. exp. Biol.*, **35**, 251–9.

HARKER, J. E. 1960a. 'The effect of perturbations in the environmental cycle of the diurnal rhythm of activity of *Periplaneta americana*.' *J. exp. Biol.*, **37**, 154–63.

HARKER, J. E. 1960b. 'Endocrine and nervous factors in insect circadian rhythms.' *Cold Sp. Harb. Symp. quant. Biol.*, **25**, 279–87.

HARKER, J. E. 1961. 'Internal factors controlling the suboesophageal ganglion neurosecretory cycle in *Periplaneta americana*.' *J. exp. Biol.*, **37**, 164–70.

HARNACK, M. 1958a. 'Histophysiological studies on the corpora allata of *Leucophaea maderae*. II. The effect of starvation.' *Biol. Bull.*, **115**, 521–529.

HARNACK, M. 1958b. 'The effect of starvation on the endocrine control of the ovary by the corpus allatum in the insect *Leucophaea maderae*.' *Anat. Rec.*, **130**, 446.

HARNACK, M. and SCHARRER, B. 1956. 'A study of the corpora allata of gonadectomized *Leucophaea maderae*.' *Anat. Rec.*, **125**, 558.

HARRIS, R. S. and MARRIAN, G. F. 1959. *Vitamins and Hormones, Advances in Research and Application*, London, Acad. Press Inc., 359 pp.

HARTUNG, E. W. 1942. 'The effect of roentgen radiation on tumour incidence in *Drosophila*.' *Cancer Res.*, **2**, 837–40.

HARTUNG, E. W. 1949. 'Roentgen radiation of tumors in *Drosophila melanogaster*.' *Science*, **109**, 565–6.

HARTZELL, A. 1958. 'Insect tissue culture: a review.' *Proc. Xth int. Congr. Ent.*, **2**, 319–25.

HARVEY, W. 1951. *Generationes animalium, ex. 45 a 50*, Amsterdam.

HARVEY, W. R. 1962. 'Metabolic aspects of insect diapause.' *Ann. Rev. Ent.*, **7**, 57–80.

HARVEY, W. R. and WILLIAMS, C. M. 1953. 'Changes in the cyanide sensitivity of the heart-beat of the *Cecropia* silkworm during the course of metamorphosis.' *Anat. Rec.*, **117**, 544.

HARVEY, W. R. and WILLIAMS, C. M. 1958a. 'Physiology of insect diapause. XI. Cyanide sensitivity of the heart-beat of the *Cecropia* silkworm with special reference to the anaerobic capacity of the heart.' *Biol. Bull.*, *Wood's Hole*, **114**, 23–35.

HARVEY, W. R. and WILLIAMS, C. M. 1958b. 'Physiology of insect diapause: XII. The mechanism of carbon-monoxide-sensitivity and insensitivity during the pupal diapause of the cecropia silkworm.' *Biol. Bull.*, *Wood's Hole*, **114**, 36–53.

HARVEY, W. R. and WILLIAMS, C. M. 1961. 'The injury metabolism of the *Cecropia* silkworm. I. Biological amplification of the effects of localized injury.' *J. Ins. Physiol.*, **7**, 81–99.

HASE, A. 1936. 'Ueber Hormone bei Insekten und über ihre Bedeutung für die Metamorphose und Eiproduktion.' *Naturwissenschaften*, **34**, 271–2.

HASEGAWA, K. 1951. 'Studies on the voltinism in the silkworm *Bombyx mrio* L. with special reference to the organs concerning determination of voltinism (a preliminary note).' *Proc. Japan. Acad.*, **27**, 557–671.

HASEGAWA, K. 1957. 'The diapause hormone of the silkworm, *Bombyx mori*.' *Nature, Lond.*, **179**, 1300–1.

HASSAN, A. I. 1939. 'The biology of some British Delphacidae and their parasites with special reference to the Strepsiptera.' *Trans. roy. ent. Soc. Lond.*, **89**, 345–84.

HAVELKA, J, and WINKLER, J. 1953. 'Hysterotely in *Graphoderes bilineatus* Degeer.' *Acta Soc. ent. Čsl.*, **47**, 159–162.

HAYDAK, M. H. 1943. 'Larval food and development of castes in the honey bee.' *J. econ. Ent.*, **36**, 778–92.

HEIMS, A. 1956. 'Ueber die Kutikulamuster der Wachsmotte *Galleria mellonella.*' *Arch. EntwMech. Org.*, **148**, 538–68.

HELLER, J. 1947. 'Recherches sur la métamorphose des insectes. XIV. Le mécanisme de régulation du métabolisme pendant le stade nymphal. Le rôle de la tyrosinase.' *Acta Biol. exp. Vars.*, **14**, 229–37.

HELLER, J. and SWIECHOWSKA, W. 1948. 'Investigations on insect metamorphosis.' *Zool. Polon.*, **4**, 73–82.

HENKE, K. 1924. 'Die Färbung und Zeichnung der Feuerwanze (*Pyrrhocoris apterus*) und ihre experimentelle Beeinflussbarkeit.' *Z. vergl. Physiol.*, **1**, 297–439.

HENKE, K. 1933. 'Zur Morphologie und Entwicklungsphysiologie der Tierzeichnungen.' *Naturwissenschaften*, **21**, 633–9, 654–9. 665–73, 683–690.

HENKE, K. 1947. 'Einfache Grundvorgänge in der tierischen Entwicklung. I. Ueber Zellteilung, Wachstum und Formbildung in der Organenentwicklung der Insekten.' *Naturwissenschaften*, **34**, 149–57, 180–6.

HENKE, K. 1948. 'Ueber Ordnungsvorgänge in der Spätentwicklung der Insekten.' *Rev. suisse Zool.*, **55**, 319–37.

HENNEGUY, L. F. 1904. *Les Insectes*, Paris.

HENSON, H. 1946. 'The theoretical aspect of insect metamorphosis.' *Biol. Rev.*, **21**, 1–14.

HERLANT-MEEWIS, H. 1956. 'Croissance et néurosecretion chez *Eisenia foetida.*' *Ann. Sci. nat., Zool.*, (11), **18**, 184–98.

HERLANT-MEEWIS, H. and PAQUET, L. 1956. 'Neurosécrétion et mue chez *Carausius morosus.*' *Ann. Sci. nat., Zool.*, (11), **18**, 163–9.

HERTZ, M., and IMMS, A. D. 1937. 'On the responses of the African migratory locust to different types of background.' *Proc. roy. Soc.* (B), **22**, 281–97.

HESLOP-HARRISON, G. 1958. 'On the origin and function of the pupal stadia in holometabolous insects.' *Proc. Univ. Durham phil. Soc.*, **13**, 59–79.

HESS, A. 1958. 'The fine structure of nerve cells and fibers, neuroglia and sheaths of the ganglion chain in the cockroach *Periplaneta americana.*' *J. biophys. biochem. Cytol.*, **4**, 731–7.

HESS, G. 1942. 'Ueber den Einfluss der Weisellosigkeit und des Fruchtsbarkeitsvitamins E auf die Ovarien der Bienenarbeiterin.' *Schweiz. Bienenztg*, **2**, 33–110.

HEYMONS, R. 1899. 'Über bläschenförmige Organe bei den Gespensterheuschrecken.' *S. B. preuss. Akad. Wiss. Berlin, phys. mat. Kl.*, pp. 563–75.

HIDAKA, I. 1956. 'Recherches sur le déterminisme hormonal de la coloration pupale chez Lépidoptères. I. Les effets de la ligature, de l'ablation des ganglions, de l'incision des nerfs chez prepupes et larves de quelque Papilionides.' *Annot. zool. jap.*, **29**, 69–74.

HIDAKA, I. 1957. 'Recherches sur le cas de deux nymphalides.' *Annot. zool. jap.*, **30**, 83–5.

HIDAKA, I. and YONEKAWA, M. 1959. 'The distension of the body in the full grown caterpillars as a result of extirpation of the prothoracic ganglion.' *Zool. Mag.*, **1**, 27–31.

HIGHNAM, K. C. 1958a. 'Activity of the brain (corpora cardiaca system) during pupal diapause "break" in *Mimas tiliae* (Lep.).' *Quart. J. micr. Sci.*, **99**, 73–88.

HIGHNAM, K. C. 1958b. 'Activity of the corpora allata during pupal diapause in *Mimas tiliae* (Lep.).' *Quart. J. micr. Sci.*, **99**, 171–80.

HIGHNAM, K. C. 1960. 'The histology of the neurosecretory system of the adult female Desert-Locust, *Schistocerca gregaria*.' *Quart. J. micr. Sci.*, **102**, 27–38.

HIGHNAM, K. C. 1961. 'Induced changes in the amounts of material in the neurosecretory system of the Desert Locust.' *Nature, Lond.*, **191**, 199–200.

HIGHNAM, K. C. 1962. 'Neurosecretory control of ovarian development in *Schistocerca gregaria*.' *Quart. J. micr. Sci.*, **103**, 57–72.

HIGHNAM, K. C. and LUSIS, O. 1962. 'The influence of mature males on the neurosecretory control of ovarian development in the desert locust.' *Quart. J. micr. Sci.*, **103**, 73–83.

HILL, L. 1962. 'Neurosecretory control of haemolymph protein concentration during ovarian development in the desert locust.' *J. Ins. Physiol.*, **8**, 609–19.

HINTON, H. E. 1946. 'Concealed phases in the metamorphosis of insects.' *Nature, Lond.*, **157**, 552–3.

HINTON, H. E. 1948. 'On the origin and function of the pupal stage.' *Trans. roy. ent. Soc. Lond.*, **99**, 395–409.

HINTON, H. E. 1949. 'On the function, origin and classification of pupae.' *Proc. S. Lond. ent. nat. Hist. Soc.*, 1947–8, 111–54.

HINTON, H. E. 1951. 'The structure and function of the endocrine glands of the Lepidoptera.' *Proc. S. Lond. ent. nat. Hist. Soc.*, 1950–1, 124–60.

HINTON, H. E. 1953. 'The initiation, maintenance and rupture of diapause—a new theory.' *Entomologist*, **86**, 279–91.

HINTON, H. E. 1955a. 'On the structure, function and distribution of the prolegs of the Panorpoidea with a criticism of the Berlese-Imms theory.' *Trans. roy. ent. Soc. Lond.*, **106**, 455–556.

HINTON, H. E. 1955b. 'Caste determination in bees and termites.' *Sci. Progr., London*, **43**, 316–26.

HINTON, H. E. 1957. 'Some aspects of diapause.' *Sci. Progr., London*, **45**, 307–20.

HINTON, H. E. 1958a. 'The phylogeny of the panorpoid orders.' *Ann. Rev. Ent.*, **3**, 181–206.

HINTON, H. E. 1958b. 'Concealed phases in the metamorphosis of insects.' *Sci. Progr., London.*, **46**, 260–75.

HINTON, H. E. 1958c. 'On the nature and metamorphosis of the colour pattern of *Thaumalea* (Dipt.)'. *J. Ins. Physiol.*, **2**, 249–60.

HINTON, H. E. 1959a. 'How the indirect flight muscles of insects grow.' *Sci. Progr., London*, **47**, 321–33.

HINTON, H. E. 1960. 'The ways in which insects change colour.' *Sci. Progr., London*, **48**, 341–50.

HISAW, F. L. 1959. 'Endocrine adaptation of the mammalian oestrous cycle and gestation.' In *A textbook of comparative endocrinology*, New York, J. Wiley & Sons, pp. 533–67.

HOARDT, K. 1943. 'Ueber die Ausprägungsweise und Ausprägungsbedingungen der Mutation kurzflügelig bei *Ephestia kühniella*.' *Biol. Zbl.*, **63**, 478–87.

HODEK, I. and ČERKASOV, I. 1958. 'Imaginal wintering of *Semiadalia undecimnotata* Schneid. in the open' (in Czech). *Mém. Soc. zool. tchécosl.*, **22**, 180–92.

HODEK, I. and ČERKASOV, I. 1959. 'Experimental influencing of the imaginal diapause of *Coccinella septempunctata*.' *Acta Soc. zool. Čsl.*, **25**, 70–90.

HODGSON, E. S. and GELDIAY, S. 1959. 'Experimentally induced release of neurosecretory materials from roach corpora cardiaca.' *Biol. Bull., Wood's Hole*, **117**, 275–83.

HOGAN, T. W. 1960. 'The onset and duration of diapause in eggs of *Acheta commodus*.' *Austr. J. biol. Sci.*, **13**, 14–29.

HOGBEN, L. T. and HOBSON, D. D. 1924. 'Studies of internal secretion. III. The action of pituitary extract and adrenaline on contractile tissues of certain invertebrata.' *Brit. J. exp. Biol.*, **1**, 487–500.

HOLDSWORTH, R. P., jr. 1945. 'Development of insect wings.' *Summ. Theses Harvard Univ.*, Cambridge, Mass., pp. 50–2.

HÖLLDOBLER, K. 1959. 'Über die Ameise als Einzelwesen und über die Bedeutung dieser Individualität für den Ameisenstaat als Individuum höherer Ordnung.' *Mitt. schweiz. ent. Ges.*, **32**, 357–73.

HOLMGREN, N. 1909. 'Termitenstudien, I.' *K. svenska VetensAkad. Handl.*, **44**, 1–215.

HOLTFRETER, J. 1948. 'Concepts on the mechanism of embryonic indication and its relation to parthenogenesis and malignancy.' *Symp. Soc. exp. Biol.*, **2**, 17–49.

HOOP, M. 1933. 'Häutungshistologie einiger Insekten.' *Zool. Jb.*, Abt. 2, **57**, 433–64.

HOOPINGARNER, R. and BECK, S. 1960. 'Manometric calibration for insect respiration.' *Ann. ent. Soc. Amer.*, **53**, 697–8.

HORIKAWA, M. and SUGAHARA, T. 1960. 'Studies on the effects of radiation on living cells in tissue culture. II. Radiosensitivity of cells isolated from various imaginal discs and organs of larvae of *Drosophila melanogaster.*' *Radiation Res.*, **13**, 6.

HOSSELET, C. 1925. 'Les Oenocytes des *Culex annulatus* et l'étude de leur chondrionne au cours de leur sécrétion.' *C. R. Acad. Sci.*, *Paris*, **180**, 399–401.

HOUSE, H. L. and BARLOW, J. S. 1960. 'Effects of oleic and other fatty acids on the growth rate of *Agria affinis.*' *J. Nutr.*, **72**, 409–14.

HOVANITZ, W. 1947. 'Occurrence of parallel series of associated physiological and morphological characters in diverse groups of mosquitoes and other insects.' *Contr. Lab. Vertebr. Biol. Univ. Mich.*, no. **32**, 24 pp.

HRDÝ, I. 1952. 'The postembryonic development of the cricket (*Gryllus domesticus*).' Thesis of the Biological Faculty, Charles University, Prague.

HRDÝ, I., NOVÁK, V. J. A. and ŠKROBAL, D. 1959. 'The influence of the queen inhibitory substance of the honey bee on the development of supplementary sexuals in *Kalotermes flavicollis.*' *Acta Symp. Evol. Ins.*, *Prague*, pp. 172–4.

HRDÝ, I., and NOVÁK, V. J. A. 1960. 'A contribution to the question of non-specificity of the exohormones.' *Proc. XIth. int. Congr. Ent.*, *Wien*, **3**, 222–5.

HUECK, H. J. 1951. 'Influence of light upon the hatching of winter eggs of the fruit tree red-spider.' *Nature, Lond.*, **167**, 993–4.

HULTIN, I. 1947. 'The corpora allata in various castes of ants.' *K. fysiogr. Sällsk. Lund Förh.*, **17**, 107–13.

HUOT, L., LECLERQ, J. and FLORKIN, M. 1959. 'Croissance disharmonique du phosphore total chez les larves, les prénymphes et les nymphes de deux races de *Tenebrio molitor* L.' *Arch. int. Physiol.*, **67**, 461–7.

HUXLEY, J. S. 1932. *Problems of relative growth*, London, Methuen.

HUXLEY, J. S. 1950. 'Relative growth and form transformation.' *Proc. roy. Soc.* (B), **137**, 465–9.

HYKEŠ, O. V. 1926. 'L'influence de quelques substances endocrines sur l'activité du cœur chez les invertébrés.' *C. R. Soc. Biol.*, *Paris*, **95**, 203–6.

HYKEŠ, O. V. 1932. 'Adrenalinwirkung am Herzen der Avertebraten.' *Čas. lék. čes.*, pp. 129–133.

HYKEŠ, O. V. and HYKEŠOVÁ. 1932. 'Influence de l'extrait du cœur d'Escargot sur le cœur de la larve du moucheron.' *C. R. Soc. Biol.*, *Paris*, 130.

ICHIKAWA, M. and NISHIITSUTSUJI, J. 1951. 'Studies on the insect metamorphosis. I. Role of brain in the imaginal differentiation of Lepidoptera.' *Annot. zool. jap.*, **24**, 205–11.

ICHIKAWA, M. and NISHIITSUTSUJI, J. 1952. 'Studies on the insect metamorphosis. II. Determination of the critical period of pupation in the Eri-silkworm, *Philosamia cynthia.*' *Annot. zool. jap.*, **25**, 143–8.

ICHIKAWA, M. and NISHIITSUTSUJI, J. 1957. 'Effect of the Papilio-brain on the imaginal differentiation of *Leuhdorfia* pupa.' *J. Fac. Sci.*, *Hokkaido Univ.*, (6), **13**, 390–3.

ICHIKAWA, M. and NISHIITSUTSUJI, J. 1959. 'Studies on the role of the corpus allatum in the Eri-silkworm, *Philosamia cynthia ricini.*' *Biol. Bull., Wood's Hole,* **116,** 88–94.

ICHIKAWA, M., NISHIITSUTSUJI, J. and YASHIKA, K. 1953. 'Studies on the insect metamorphosis. III. Activity of the brain in the postembryonic development of Lepidopterans.' *Mém. Coll. Sci. Univ. Kyoto* (B), **20,** 145–50.

ICHIKAWA, M., NISHIITSUTSUJI, J. and YASHIKA, K. 1955a. 'Studies on the insect metamorphosis. IV. Prothoracic glands of *Ephestia cautella.*' *Mém. Coll. Sci. Univ. Kyoto* (B), **22,** 1–9.

ICHIKAWA, M., NISHIITSUTSUJI, J. and YASHIKA, K. 1955b. 'Studies on the insect metamorphosis. V. Implantations of larval brains into the pupae of *Leuhdorfia japonica.*' *Mém. Coll. Sci. Univ. Kyoto* (B), **22,** 11–15.

IMMS, A. D. 1937. *Recent advances in entomology,* London, Methuen.

IMMS, A. D. 1946. *Textbook of entomology,* London, Methuen.

ITO, H. 1918. 'Glandular nature of the corpora allata of the Lepidoptera.' *Bull. Imp. Tokyo Seric. Coll.,* **I,** 64–103.

ITO, T. 1951. 'Integument in silkworm.' *Bull. Seric. Exp. Stat. Japan,* **13,** 585–611.

ITO, T. 1960. 'Karnitin as a growth stimulator in insects.' *Protein nucleic Acid Enzyme,* **5,** 26–30.

ITO, T. 1961. 'Sterol requirements of the silkworm *Bombyx mori.*' *Nature, Lond.,* **191,** 882–3.

IVANOV, S. P. 1932. '*Loxostege sticticalis* L. in the chief areas of turnip cultivation in 1930' (in Russian). *Izd. U.N.I.S.A., Kiev,* pp. 5–20.

IVANOV, P. P. and MESCHERSKAYA, K. A. 1935. 'Die physiologischen Besonderheiten der geschlechtlich unreifen Insektenovarien und die zyklischen Veränderungen ihrer Eigenschaften.' *Zool. Jb.,* Abt. 3, **55,** 281–348.

IVANOVA, M. S. 1947. 'The development of the base of the wing in *Calliptamus italicus* L.' (in Russian). *C. R. Acad. Sci. U.R.S.S.,* **56,** 885–7.

IVANOVA-KAZAS, O. 1959. 'Yolk system of insects and its evolution in Hymenoptera' (in Russian). *Vestn. Leningr. Univ.,* no. **21,** 78–91.

IWASAKI, J. 1927. 'Sur quelques phénomènes provoqués chez les chenilles de papillons par introduction de corps étrangers.' *Arch. mikr. Anat.,* **23,** 319–340.

JANDA, V. 1930. 'Ueber den Einfluss der Schilddrüsenfütterung auf das Wachstum, Metamorphose und Artscharaktere von *Anthrenus museorum* und *Dixippus morosus.*' *Acta Soc. ent. Čsl.,* **27,** 36–45.

JANDA, V. 1933a. 'On the influence of radium irradiation on the colouring, development and the oxygen-consumption in *Tenebrio molitor.*' *Mém. Soc. sci. Bohème,* pp. 1–26.

JANDA, V. 1933b. 'On the development and oxygen-consumption of the isolated parts of the pupal body in *Tenebrio molitor.*' *Acta Soc. ent. Čsl.,* **30,** 1–14.

JANDA, V. 1934. 'Contribution to the knowledge of the periodical colour change in *Dixippus morosus.' Mém. Soc. sci. Bohème*, pp. 1–30.

JANDA, V. 1935. 'On the present stage of investigation of hormonal processes in invertebrates.' *Příroda*, **28**, 33–39.

JANDA, V. 1936a. 'On the colour change in the transplanted skin and artificially joined fragment of the body in *Dixippus morosus.' Rozpr. české Akad.*, **46**, 1–10.

JANDA, V. 1936b. 'Ueber den Farbwechsel transplantierter Hautstücke und küntslich verbundener Körperfragmente bei *Dixippus morosus.' Zool. Anz.*, **115**, 177–85.

JANDA, V. 1937. 'Contribution to the knowledge of the colour change process in *Chrysopa vulgaris* Sch.' *Mém. Soc. sci. Bohème*, pp. 1–11.

JANDA, V. 1939. 'A few experiments for determination of the quick colour change in Orthoptera.' *Sbor. přír. Klubu, Třebíč*, **3**, 66–72.

JANDA, V. and KOCIÁN, V. 1933. 'Ueber den Sauerstoffverbrauch der Puppen von *Tenebrio molitor* L. während der Metamorphose.' *Zool. Jb.*, **52**, 561–708.

JANDA, V., jr. 1952. 'The total metabolism in insects. II. The influence of temperature on oxygen consumption of different instars in *Dixippus morosus.' Mém. Soc. zool. tchécosl.*, **16**, 3–4, 237–8.

JANET, CH. 1899. 'Sur les nerfs céphaliques, les corpora allata et le tentorium de la fourmi *Myrmica rubra.' Mém. Soc. zool. Fr.*, **12**, 295–335.

JÁNSKÝ, L. 1955. 'Der Gesamtstoffwechsel der Insekten. IV. Anderungen in den Fetten während der Entwicklung der Puppe von *Musca domestica* L.' *Mém. Soc. zool. tchécosl.*, **19**, 249–58.

JÁNSKY, L. 1956. 'Der Einfluss der Kulturtemperatur auf die Aenderungen in den Eigenschaften der Fette und im Fettgehalt in den Puppen von *Musca domestica.' Mém. Soc. zool. tchécosl.*, **20**, 1–15.

JEANNEL, R. 1949. 'Évolution et géonémie des insectes.' In P. P. Grassé, *Traité de Zoologie*, **9**, 86–110.

JENIAUX, C. 1961. 'Activité chitinolytique de l'hémolymphe de *Bombyx mori* au cours des métamorphoses.' *Arch. int. Physiol. Biochim.*, **69** (5), 750–1.

JENSEN, P. B. 1948. 'A determination theory.' *Physiol. Plant.*, **1**, 156–169.

JERMY, T. and SÁRINGER, G. 1955. 'Die Role der Photoperiode in der Auslösung der Diapause des Kartoffelkäfers (*Leptinotarsa decemlineata* Say) und des amerikanischen weissen Bärenspinners (*Hyphantria cunea* Drury).' *Acta agron. hung.*, **5**, 3–4, 419–40.

JESCHIKOV, J. J. 1929. 'Zur Frage über die Entstehung der vollkommenen Verwandlung.' *Zool. Jb.*, Abt. 2, **50**, 601–50.

JESCHIKOV, J. J. 1936. 'Metamorphose, Cryptometabolie und direkte Entwicklung.' *Zool. Anz.*, **114**, 141–52.

JESCHIKOV, J. J. 1940. 'Ueber frühe Embryonalstadien und ihren Zusammenhang mit den Typen der postembryonalen Entwicklung bei den Insekten' (in Russian). *C. R. Acad. Sci. U.R.S.S.* (N.S.), **28**, 574–6.

JESCHIKOV, J. J. 1941. 'Die Dottermenge im Ei und die Typen der post-embryonalen Entwicklung bei den Insekten.' *Zool. Anz.*, **134**, 71–87.

JOHANSSON, A. S. 1953. 'Diapause and pupal morphology and colour in *Pieris brassicae* L.' *Norsk. ent. Tidsskr.*, **9**, 79–86.

JOHANSSON, A. S. 1955. 'The relationship between corpora allata and reproductive organs in starved *Leucophaea maderae*.' *Biol. Bull.*, *Wood's Hole*, **108**, 40–4.

JOHANSSON, A. S. 1957a. 'The nervous system of the milkweed bug *Oncopeltus fasciatus*.' *Trans. Amer. ent. Soc.*, **83**, 119–83.

JOHANSSON, A. S. 1957b. 'Neurosecretion and metamorphosis in the milk-weed bug *Oncopeltus fasciatus*.' *Experientia*, **13**, 1–3.

JOHANSSON, A. S. 1957c. 'Neurosecretion in the milkweed bug *Oncopeltus fasciatus*. II.' *Int. Symp. Neurosecret. Lund*, pp. 98–101.

JOHANSSON, A. S. 1958a. 'Relation of nutrition to endocrine-reproductive functions in the milkweed bug *Oncopeltus fasciatus*.' *Nytt. Mag. Zool.*, **7**, 1–132.

JOHANSSON, A. S. 1958b. 'Hormonal regulation of reproduction in the milkweed bug, *Oncopeltus fasciatus*.' *Nature, Lond.*, **181**, 198–9.

JOHANSSON, A. S. 1959. 'Nutritional endocrine regulation of insect reproduction.' *Acta Symp. Evol. Insect.*, *Prague*, pp. 133–6.

JOHNSON, B. 1959a. 'Effect of parasitization by *Aphidius platensis* Bréthes on the developmental physiology of its host, *Aphis craccivora* Koch.' *Ent. exp. appl.*, **2**, 82–99.

JOHNSON, B. 1959b. 'Studies on the degeneration of the flight muscles of alata aphids. II. Histology and control of muscle breakdown.' *J. Ins. Physiol.*, **3**, 367–7.

JOHNSON, B. and BIRKS, P. R. 1960. 'Studies on wing polymorphism in aphids. I. The developmental process involved in the production of the different forms.' *Ent. exp. appl.*, **3**, 327–39.

JOLY, L. 1954. 'Résultats d'implantation systématique de corpora allata à des jeunes larves de *Locusta migratoria*.' *C. R. Soc. Biol.*, *Paris*, **148**, 479–583.

JOLY, L. 1955. 'Analyse du fonctionnement des corpora allata chez la larve de *Locusta migratoria*.' *C. R. Soc. Biol.*, *Paris*, **149**, 584–7.

JOLY, L. 1958. 'Comparison des divers types d'adultoides chez *Locusta migratoria*.' *Insectes sociaux*, **5**, 373–8.

JOLY, L. 1960. 'Functions des corpora allata chez *Locusta migratoria* L.' Thèse, Strasbourg, pp. 1–93.

JOLY, P. 1940. 'Recherche, par voie chimique, des principles vitamines et hormones cétoniques dans le sang de la reine de *Bellicositermes natalensis* (Hav.).' *C. R. Soc. Biol.*, *Paris*, **134**, 408–10.

JOLY, P. 1942a. 'Sur l'insensibilité des insectes aux hormones génitales des vértebrés.' *C. R. Acad. Sci.*, *Paris*, **214**, 133–5.

JOLY, P. 1942b. 'Sur le rôle des corpora allata dans la ponte des Dytiscides.' *C. R. Acad. Sci.*, *Paris*, **214**, 807–9.

JOLY, P. 1945a. 'La fonction ovarienne et son control humoral chez les Dytiscides.' *Arch. Zool. exp. gén.*, **84**, 49–164.

JOLY, P. 1945b. 'Les corrélations humorales chez les insectes.' *Année biol.*, **21**, 1–34.

JOLY, P. 1948. 'Les hormones sexuelles des insectes.' *Bull. biol. Suppl.*, **33**, 81–6.

JOLY, P. 1949a. 'Complexe endocrine rétro-cérébral de la larve de Dytisque (*Macrodytes marginalis*).' *Bull. Soc. zool. Fr.*, **73**, 196–200.

JOLY, P. 1949b. 'Le système endocrine-rétro-cérébral et son fonctionnement chez les Acridiens migrateurs.' *Ann. Sci. nat., Zool.*, (11), **11**, 255–262.

JOLY, P. 1950. 'Functionnement ovarien des carabes.' *C. R. Soc. Biol., Paris*, **144**, 1217–1220.

JOLY, P. 1951. 'Déterminisme endocrine de la pigmentation chez *Locusta migratoria*.' *C. R. Soc. Biol., Paris*, **145**, 1362–6.

JOLY, P. 1952. 'Déterminisme de la pigmentation chez *Acrida turrita*.' *C. R. Acad. Sci., Paris*, **235**, 1054–6.

JOLY, P. 1954. 'Étude de la croissance alaire chez *Locusta migratoria* L.' *C. R. Soc. Biol., Paris*, **148**, 2082–7.

JOLY, P. 1955. 'Chronology of mitosis in *Locusta migratoria*.' *Arch. Anat., Strasbourg*, **37**, 88–96.

JOLY, P. 1956. 'Croissance et indice de grégarisation chez *Locusta migratoria*.' *Insectes sociaux*, **3**, 17–24.

JOLY, P. 1957. 'Remarques sur la métamorphose chez les Acridiens.' *Acta Soc. Linn. Bordeaux*, **97**, 1–5.

JOLY, P. 1958. 'Les corrélations humorales chez les Acridiens.' *Année biol.*, **34**, 97–118.

JOLY, P. 1959. 'Un cas de gynandromorphisme chez *Locusta migratoria*.' *Bull. Soc. zool. Fr.*, **84**, 407–10.

JOLY, P. 1961. 'Régulation endocrine des phases chez les orthoptères grégarisables.' *Symp. gen. Biol. ital.*, **10**, 203–18.

JOLY, P. 1962. 'Rôle joué par les corpora allata dans la réalisation du polymorphisme de phase chez *Locusta migratoria*.' *Colloques int. Centr. natn. Rech. scient.*, **114**, 77–88.

JOLY, P. and JOLY, L. 1953. 'Résultats de greffes de corpora allata chez *Locusta migratoria*.' *Ann. Sci. nat., Zool.*, (11), **15**, 331–45.

JOLY, P. and BILL, M. 1955. 'Croissance et métamorphose alaire chez les Acridiens.' *Acta 74. Congr. Caen, Ass. Fr. Avanç. Sci.*, pp. 1–5.

JOLY, P., BILL, M. and HALBWACHS, M. 1956. 'Contrôle humoral du développement chez *Locusta migratoria*.' *Ann. Sci. nat., Zool.*, (11), **18**, 256–61.

JONES, B. M. 1953. 'Activity of the incretory centres of *Locustana pardalina* during embryogenesis. Function of the prothoracic glands.' *Nature, Lond.*, **172**, 551.

JONES, B. M. 1956a. 'Endocrine activity during insect embryogenesis.

Function of the ventral head gland in locust embryos (*Locustana pardalina* and *Locusta migratoria*).' *J. exp. Biol.*, **33**, 174–85.

JONES, B. M. 1956b. 'Endocrine activity during insect embryogenesis. Control of events in development following the embryonic moult (*Locusta migratoria* and *Locustana pardalina*).' *J. exp. Biol.*, **33**, 685–96.

JONES, B. M. 1958. 'Enzymatic oxidation of protein as a rate-determining step in the formation of highly stable surface membranes.' *Proc. roy. Soc.* (B), **148**, 263–77.

JONES, B. M. and CUNNINGHAM, J. 1960. 'Growth by cell division in insect tissue culture.' *Nature, Lond.*, **187**, 1072–4.

JONES, B. M. and SINCLAIR, W. 1958. 'Induction of melanin patterns as separate process in the cuticle of Albino locust with internally absorbed phenol substrates.' *Nature, Lond.*, **181**, 926–7.

JONES, B. M. and WILSON, R. S. 1959. 'Studies on the action of phenylthiourea on the respiratory metabolism and spinning behavior of the *Cynthia* silkworm.' *Biol. Bull.*, *Wood's Hole*, **117**, 482–91.

JONES, D. F. 1936. 'Tumors in *Drosophila melanogaster* resulting from somatic segregation.' *Science*, **84**, 135.

JÖRSCHKE, H. 1914. 'Die Fazettenaugen der Orthoptera und Termiten.' *Z. wiss. Zool.*, **III**, 153–280.

JUCCI, C. 1956. 'Richerche sulle ghiandolle endocrine nelle termiti.' *Insectes sociaux*, **3**, 283–4.

JUNQUA, C. 1956. 'Étude morphologique et histophysiologique des organes endocrines de l'*Hydrocyrius columbiae* Spin.' *Bull. Biol.*, *Wood's Hole*, **90**, 154–62.

KAHN, R. H. 1921. 'Ueber Schilddrüsenfütterung an Wirbellosen.' *Pflüg. Arch. ges. Physiol.*, **192**, 81–92.

KAISER, P. 1949. 'Histologische Untersuchungen über die Corpora allata und Prothoraxdrüsen der Lepidopteren im bezug auf ihre Funktion.' *Arch. EntwMech. Org.*, **144**, 99–131.

KAISER, P. 1955. 'Die Inkretorgane der Termiten im Kastendifferenzierungsgeschehen.' *Naturwissenschaften*, **42**, 303–4.

KALMUS, H. 1938. 'Tagesperiodisch verlaufende Vorgänge an der Stabheuschrecke (*Dixippus morosus*) und ihre experimentelle Beeinflussung.' *Z. vergl. Physiol.*, **25**, 494–508.

KAMENSKI, S. and PAIKIN, D. 1939. 'The causes of several years dormancy in *Bothynoderes punctiventris* beetles' (in Russian). *Věst. Zashch. rast.*, **I**, 49–54.

KANN, F. 1933. 'Temperatureinflüsse auf die Wachstumsstadien von *Dixippus morosus* (*Carausius*) Br. et Redt.' *Anz. Akad. Wiss. Wien*, **10**, 4–5.

KARAWAIEV, V. N. 1898. 'Die nachembryonale Entwicklung von *Lasius flavus*.' *Z. wiss. Zool.*, **64**, 385–478.

KARLSON, P. 1954. 'Biometrische Probleme der Insektenmetamorphose.' *Verh. dtsch. zool. Ges.*, pp. 68–85.

KARLSON, P. 1955. 'Die Prothorakaldrüsenhormone der Insekten: chemische Eigenschaften und physiologische Bedeutung.' *Proc. III. int. Congr. Biochem., Bronx.*

KARLSON, P. 1956a. 'Chemische Untersuchungen über die Metamorphose-hormone der Insekten.' *Ann. Sci. nat., Zool.*, (11), **18**, 125–37.

KARLSON, P. 1956b. 'Biochemical studies on insect hormones.' *Vitam. Horm.*, **14**, 227–66.

KARLSON, P. 1957. 'Ueber die Häutungshormone der Arthropoden.' *Zool. Anz.*, Suppl., **20**, 203–8.

KARLSON, P. 1959. 'Zur Chemie und Wirkungsweise der Insektenhormone.' *Proc. IVth Int. Congr. Biochem.*, **12**, 37–47.

KARLSON, P. 1962a. 'Zur vergleichenden Biochemie der Vitamine und Hormone.' *Münch. med. Wschr.*, **104**, 1697–1703.

KARLSON, P. 1962b. 'Morphogenese und Metamorphose der Insekten.' *Colloquium Ges. physiol. Chem.*, pp. 101–18.

KARLSON, P. 1962c. 'New concepts on the mode of action of hormones.' (*Proc. Soc. Endocrinol.* 85); *J. Endocrinol.*, **24**, 4–12.

KARLSON, P. 1962d. 'Insektenhormone und ihre Wirkungsweise.' *Proc. VIIIth Symp. dtsch. Ges. Endocrinol. München*, pp. 90–8.

KARLSON, P. and BÜCKMANN, D. 1956. 'Experimentelle Auslösung der Umfärbung bei *Cerura*-Raupen durch Prothorakaldrüsenhormon.' *Naturwissenschaften*, **43**, 44–5.

KARLSON, P. and BUTENANDT, A. 1959. 'Pheromones (Ectohormones) in Insects.' *Ann. Rev. Ent.*, **4**, 39–58.

KARLSON, P. and HANSER, G. 1952. 'Ueber die Wirkung des Puparisie-rungshormon bei der Wildform der Mutante lgl von *Drosophila melanogaster*.' *Z. Naturf.*, **7b**, 80–3.

KARLSON, P. and HANSER, G. 1953. 'Bildungsort und Erfolgsorgan des Puparisierungshormons der Fliegen.' *Z. Naturf.*, **8b**, 91–6.

KARLSON, P. and HOFFMEISTER, H. 1961. 'Insektenhormone.' *Scientia, Bologna*, **16**, 1–6.

KARLSON, P. and LÖFFLER, U. 1962. 'Isolierung von Speicheldrüsen-Chromosomen durch differentielle Zentrifugation.' *Hoppe-Seyl. Z.*, **32**, 286–8.

KARLSON, P. and LÜSCHER, M. 1959a. 'Pheromone (Ein Nomenklaturvorschlag für eine Wirksstoffklasse).' *Naturwissenschaften*, **2**, 63–4.

KARLSON, P. and LÜSCHER, M. 1959b. ' "Pheromones": a new term for a class of biologically active substances.' *Nature, Lond.*, **183**, 55.

KARLSON, P. and SCHLOSSBERGER-RAUKE, I. 1962. 'Zum Tyrosinstoff-wechsel der Insekten. VIII. Die Sklerotizierung der Cuticula bei der Wild-form und Albinomutante von *Schistocerca gregaria*.' *J. Ins. Physiol.*, **8**, 441–52.

KARLSON, P. and SCHMIALEK, P. 1959. 'Nachweis der Exkretion von Juvenilhormon.' *Z. Naturf.*, **14b**, 821.

KARLSON, P. and SCHMIED, H. 1955. 'Ueber die Tyrosinase der *Calliphora*-Larven.' *Hoppe-Seyl. Z.*, **300**, 35–41.

KARLSON, P. and SEKERIS, C. 1962a. 'N-Acetyl-dopamine as sclerotizing agent of the insect cuticle.' *Nature, Lond.*, **195**, 183–4.

KARLSON, P. and SEKERIS, C. 1962b. 'Zum Tyrosinstoffwechsel der Insekten. IX. Kontrolle des Tyrosinstoffwechsels durch Ecdyson.' *Biochim. biophys. Acta*, **63**, 489–95.

KARLSON, P. and STAMM-MENÉNDEZ, M. D. 1956. 'Notiz über den Nachweis von Metamorphose-Hormon in den Imagines von Bombyx mori.' *Hoppe-Seyl. Z.*, **306**, 109–11.

KARLSON, P. and WECKER, E. 1955. 'Die Tyrosinaseaktivität während der Pupariumbildung von Calliphora erythrocephala.' *J. physiol. Chem.*, **300**, 42–8.

KAWETSKI, P. E. 1946–7. 'Experimental cancer research in U.R.S.S.' (in Russian). *Ann. Rev. Sov. Med.*, **4**, 322–7.

KE, O. 1930. 'Morphological variation of the prothoracic gland in the domestic and the wild silkworm.' *Bull. Sci. fac. Terkult, Kjusu Imp. Univ.*, **4**, 12–21.

KELLOG, V. L. 1904. 'Influence of the primary reproduction organs on the secondary sexual characters.' *J. exp. Zool.*, **1**, 601–5.

KEMPER, H. 1931. 'Beiträge zur Biologie der Bettwanze (Cimex lectularius). II. Ueber die Häutung.' *Z. Morph. Oekol. Tiere*, **22**, 53–109.

KERR, W. E. 1950. 'Evolution of caste determination in the genus Melipona.' *Evolution*, **4**, 7–13.

KETCHEL, M. and WILLIAMS, C. M. 1952. 'Relationship between the hemaglutination factor and the growth and differentiation hormone in the cecropia silkworm.' *Anat. Rec.*, **113**, 83.

KETCHEL, M. and WILLIAMS, C. M. 1953. 'The prothoracic gland hormone as a sustained stimulus for the growth and differentiation of insect tissues.' *Anat. Rec.* **117**, 542.

KEVAN, D. K. 1944. 'The bionomics of the neotropical cornstalk borer, Diatraea lineolata, in Trinidad.' *Bull. ent. Res.*, **35**, 23–30.

KEY, K. H. L. 1936. 'Observations on rate of growth, coloration and the abnormal six-instar life cycle in Locusta migratoria migratorioides R. and F.' *Bull. ent. Res.*, **27**, 77–85.

KEY, K. H. L. 1957. 'Centromorphic phases in three species of Phasmidea.' *Austr. J. Zool.*, **3**, 247–84

KEY, K. H. L. and DAY, M. F. 1954a. 'A temperature-controlled physiological colour response in the grasshopper Kosciuscola tristis.' *Austr. J. Zool.*, **2**, 309–39.

KEY, K. H. L. and DAY, M. F. 1954b. 'The physiological mechanism of colour change in the grasshopper Kosciuskola tristis.' *Austr. J. Zool.*, **2**, 340–63.

KEY, K. H. L. and EDNEY, E. B. 1936. 'Precocious adults resulting from the omission of the fifth instar in Locusta migratoria migratorioides.' *Proc. roy. ent. Soc. Lond.* (A), **11**, 55–8.

KHOUVINE, Y., EPHRUSSI, B. and CHEVAIS, S. 1938. 'Development of eye colours in Drosophila: nature of the diffusible substances; effects of yeast, peptones and starvation on their production.' *Biol. Bull.*, *Wood's Hole*, **75**, 425–46.

KHOUVINE, Y., EPHRUSSI, B. and HARNBY, M. 1936. 'Extraction et solubilité des substances intervenant dans la pigmentation des yeux de *Drosophila melanogaster*.' *C. R. Acad. Sci.*, *Paris*, **203**, 1542–4.

KIKKAWA, H. 1941. 'Mechanism of pigment formation in *Bombyx mori* and *Drosophila melanogaster*.' *Genetics*, **26**, 587–607.

KIM, CH. 1959. 'The differentiation centre inducing the development from larval to adult leg in *Pieris brassicae*.' *J. Embryol. exp. Morph.*, **7**, 572–82.

KIN, J. 1939. 'On the corpus allatum hormone in *Bombyx mori*.' *J. Seric. Sci. Japan*, **10**, 86–97.

KIRCHNER, E. 1960. 'Untersuchungen über neurohormonale Faktoren bei *Melolontha vulgaris*.' *Zool. Jb.*, **69**, 43–62.

KLATT, B. 1919. 'Keimdrüsentransplantation beim Schwammspinner.' *Z. indukt. Abstamm- u. VererbLehre*, **22**, 1–50.

KLATT, B. 1920. 'Beiträge zur Sexualphysiologie des Schwammspinners.' *Biol. Zbl.*, **40**, 539–58.

KLOOT, W. G. VAN DER. 1960. 'Neurosecretion in insects.' *Ann. Rev. Ent.*, **5**, 35–52.

KLOOT, W. G. VAN DER. 1961. 'Inhibition in the neuro-endocrine systems in invertebrates.' Reprint from '*Nervous Inhibition*', *Proc. Int. Symp.*, Oxford, London, New York, Paris, pp. 447–58.

KLOOT, W. G. VAN DER and WILLIAMS, C. M. 1954. 'Cocoon construction by the *Cecropia* silkworm. III. The alteration of spinning behavior by chemical and surgical techniques.' *Behaviour*, **6**, 233–55.

KLOOT, W. G. VAN DER and WILLIAMS, C. M. 1955. 'The control of neurosecretion and diapause by physiological changes in the brain of the *Cecropia* silkworm.' *Biol. Bull.*, *Wood's Hole*, **109**, 276–94.

KLUG, H. 1958. 'Neurosecretion and Aktivitätsperiode bei Carabiden.' *Naturwissenschaften*, **45**, 141–2.

KNIGHT, H. H. 1922. 'Studies on the life history and biology of *Perillus bioculatus* Fabr. including observations on the nature of the color patterns.' *Rep. Minn. Ent.*, **19**, 50–96.

KNOWLES, F. G. H. 1956. 'Some problems in the study of colour changes in Crustaceans.' *Ann. Sci. nat.*, *Zool.*, (11), **18**, 315–23.

KNOWLES, F. G. H. 1959. 'Hormones in insects and crustaceans.' *Biology*, **24**, 23–8.

KNOWLES, F. G. H., CARLISLE, D. B. and DUPONT-RAABE, M. 1955. 'Studies on pigment activating substances in animals. I. The separation by paper electrophoresis of chromactivating substances in arthropods.' *J. Mar. Biol. Ass. U.K.*, **34**, 611–35.

KOBAYASHI, K. 1956. 'On the neurosecretory cells of the suboesophageal ganglion of the fifth instar larvae in *Bombyx mori*.' *Sanshi-Kaiho*, **25**, 3.

KOBAYASHI, K. 1958. 'Effect of larval brain on the imaginal differentiation in the silkworm.' *Nature*, *Lond.*, **182**, 110–11.

KOBAYASHI, K. 1960a. 'Endocrinology in the silkworm.' *Proc. XIth Conf. Techn. seric. Inst. Murcie*, pp. 279–82.

KOBAYASHI, K. 1960b. 'Function of the corpus allatum in "Dauer-pupa" of the silkworm *Bombyx mori*.' *Nature, Lond.*, **187**, 346–7.

KOBAYASHI, K. and BURDETTE, W. 1961. 'Effect of brain hormone from *Bombyx* on metamorphosis of *Calliphora erythrocephala*.' *Proc. Soc. exp. Biol. N.Y.*, **107**, 240–2.

KOBAYASHI, K., FUKAYA, M. and MITSUHASHI, J. 1960. 'Imaginal differentiation of "Dauer pupae" in the silkworm.' *J. seric. Sci. Tokyo*, **29**, 337–40.

KOBAYASHI, K. and KIRIMURA, J. 1958. 'The "brain" hormone in the silkworm, *Bombyx mori*.' *Nature, Lond.*, **181**, 1217.

KOBAYASHI, K. and NAKASONE, S. 1960a. 'Imaginal differentiation in artificially induced diapausing brainless pupae of the silkworm by treatment with carbon monoxide or oxygen.' *Bull. seric. Exp. Sta. Japan*, **16**, 100–12.

KOBAYASHI, K. and NAKASONE, S. 1960b. 'Inhibitory effect of low temperature on the secretion of the brain hormone in silkworm pupae.' *J. seric. Sci. Tokyo*, **29**, 203–5.

KOBAYASHI, K. and YAMASHITA, Y. 1959. 'A function of corpus allatum in neurosecretory system in the silkworm.' *J. seric. Sci. Tokyo*, **28**, 336–9.

KOCIAN, V. 1931. 'Thyroxin und Atmung.' *Zool. Jb.*, Abt. 3, **50**, 47–60.

KOGURE, M. 1933. 'The influence of light and temperature on certain characters of the silkworm *Bombyx mori*.' *J. Dep. Agr. Kyushu Univ.*, **4**, 1–93.

KÖHLER, W. 1933. 'Die Entwicklung der Flügel bei der Mehlmotte *Ephestia kühniella* mit besonderer Berücksichtigung des Zeichnungsmusters.' *Z. Morph. Oekol. Tiere*, **24**, 582–681.

KÖHLER, W. 1941. 'Experimentelle Untersuchungen über die Determination des Zeichnungsmusters bei der Mehlmotte *Ephestia kühniella*. II. Veränderungen des Musters nach partieller ultravioletter Bestrahlung und örtlicher Hitzebehandlung des jungen Puppenflügels.' *Vjschr. naturf. Ges. Zürich*, **86**, 77–151.

KÖHLER, W. and FELDOTTO, W. 1937. 'Morphologische und experimentelle Untersuchungen über Farbe, Form und Struktur der Schuppen von *Vanessa urticae* und ihre gegenseitigen Beziehungen.' *Arch. EntwMech. Org.*, **136**, 313–99.

KOLLER, G. 1929. 'Die innere Sekretion bei wirbellosen Tieren.' *Biol. Rev.*, **4**, 269–306.

KOLLER, G. 1938. 'Hormone bei wirbellosen Tieren.' *Probl. Biol.*, **1**, Leipzig, Verlagsges.

KOLLER, G. 1948. 'Rhythmische Bewegungen und hormonale Steuerung bei den Malpighischen Gefässen der Insekten.' *Biol. Zbl.*, **67**, 201–11.

KOLLER, G. 1954a. 'Neurosekretorische Steuerung der Darmbewegungen von Insekten.' *Pubbl. Staz. zool. Napoli*, **24**, 67.

KOLLER, G. 1954b. 'Zur Frage der hormonalen Steuerung bei rhythmischen Eingeweidebewegung von Insekten.' *Verh. dtsch. zool. Ges.*, pp. 417–422.

KOLLER, G. 1955. 'Zur Frage der hormonalen Steuerung bei rhythmischen Eingeweidebewegungen von Insekten.' *Zool. Anz.*, suppl., **18**, 417–22.

KOLLER, P. CH. 1932. 'Der Einfluss chemisch reines Thyroxins auf die Entwicklung von Drosophila melanogaster.' *Arch. EntwMech. Org.*, **125**, 663–72.

KOMAROWA, O. S. 1949. 'The factors inducing diapause in *Polychrosis botrana*' (in Russian). *C. R. Acad. Sci. U.R.S.S.*, **68**, 789–92.

KONOK, I. 1955. 'Investigations into the physiology of moulting. I. Influence of external factors on the moulting and pupation of the larvae of *Tenebrio molitor* L.' (in Hungarian). *Ann. Inst. Biol. Tihany*, **23**, 37–52.

KONOK, I. 1958. 'Untersuchungen der neurosekretorischen Aktivität während der Häutung und Metamorphosis der Raupe *Deilephila euphorbiae*.' *Ann. Inst. Biol. Tihany*, **25**, 37–45.

KONOK, I. 1960. 'Die Neurosekretion und ihre Rolle bei den Insekten.' *Symp. Biol. Hung.*, **1**, 181–9.

KONSTANTINOV, A. S. and LUZINA, A. V. 1961. 'On the cytological principles of growth in chironomid larvae *Tendipes*' (in Russian). *Citologija*, **3**, 341–4.

KOPEĆ, S. 1908. 'Experimentaluntersuchungen über die Entwicklung der Geschlechtscharaktere bei Schmetterlingen.' *Bull. int. Acad. Sci. Cracovie*, pp. 893–918.

KOPEĆ, S. 1910. 'Ueber morphologische und histologische Folgen der Kastration und Transplantation bei Schmetterlingen.' *Bull. Acad. Sci. Cracovie, ser. B.*, 186–198.

KOPEĆ, S. 1912a. 'Untersuchungen über die Kastration und Transplantation bei Schmetterlingen.' *Arch. EntwMech. Org.*, **33**, 1–116.

KOPEĆ, S. 1912b. 'Ueber die Funktionen des Nervensystems der Schmetterlinge während der successiven Stadien der Metamorphose.' *Zool. Anz.*, **40**, 353–60.

KOPEĆ, S. 1912c. 'Regeneration of appendages in Lepidoptera.' *Chin. Sci. mat.-nat. B*, 1096–1102; 47–481.

KOPEĆ, C. 1913. 'Untersuchungen über die Regeneration von Larvalorganen und Imaginalscheiben.' *Arch. EntwMech. Org.*, **37**, 440–72.

KOPEĆ, S. 1915. 'Nochmals über die Unabhängigkeit der Ausbildung sekundärer Geschlechtscharaktere von den Gonaden bei Schmetterlingen.' *Zool. Anz.*, **43**, 65–74.

KOPEĆ, S. 1917. 'Experiments on metamorphosis of insects.' *Bull. int. Acad. Sci. Cracovie (B)*, pp. 57–60.

KOPEĆ, S. 1922a. 'Studies on the necessity of the brain for the inception of insect metamorphosis.' *Biol. Bull., Wood's Hole*, **42**, 323–42.

KOPEĆ, S. 1922b. 'Physiological self-differentiation of the wing-germs grafted on caterpillars of the opposite sex.' *J. exp. Zool.*, **36**, 469–75.

KOPEĆ, S. 1922c. 'Mutual relationship in the development of the brain and eyes of Lepidoptera.' *J. exp. Zool.*, **36**, 459–66.

KOPEĆ, S. 1923. 'The influence of the nervous system on the development and regeneration of muscles and integument in insects.' *J. exp. Zool.*, **37**, 15–25.

KOPEĆ, S. 1924a. 'Studies on the influence of inanition on the development and duration of life in insects.' *Biol. Bull.*, *Wood's Hole*, **46**, 1–21.

KOPEĆ, S. 1926. 'Is the insect metamorphosis influenced by thyroid feeding?' *Biol. Bull.*, *Wood's Hole*, **50**, 339–54.

KOPEĆ, S. 1927. 'Über die Entwicklung der Insekten unter dem Einfluss der Vitaminzugabe.' *Biol. gen.*, **3**, 375–84.

KOPENETZ, A. 1949. 'Farbwechsel der Larve von *Corethra plumicornis*.' *Z. vergl. Physiol.*, **31**, 490–505.

KÖPF, H. 1957a. 'Über Neurosekretion bei *Drosophila*, I.' *Biol. Zbl.*, **76**, 28–42.

KÖPF, H. 1957b. 'Zur Topographie und Morphologie neurosekretorischer Zentren bei *Drosophila*.' *Naturwissenschaften*, **44**, 121–2.

KÖPF, H. 1958. 'Beitrag zur Topographie und Histologie neurosekretorischer Zentren bei *Drosophila*.' *Verh. dtsch. zool. Ges.*, pp. 439–43.

KORNHAUSER, S. I. 1919. 'The sexual characteristics of the membracid *Thelia bimaculata*. I. External changes induced by *Aphelopus theliae*.' *J. Morph.*, **32**, 531–636.

KOSHANCHIKOV, I. V. 1938. 'The geographic distribution and physiological characteristics of *Pyrausta nubilalis*' (in Russian). *Zool. Zh.*, **17**, 246–59.

KOSHANCHIKOV, I. V. 1946a. 'The features of respiratory adaptation to the environmental conditions in insects' (in Russian). *J. gen. Biol.*, *Moscow*, **7**, 49–64.

KOSHANCHIKOV, I. V. 1946b. 'On the physiology and biological significance of the pupal stage in the development cycle of metamorphosing insects (Holometabola)' (in Russian). *Bull. Acad. Sci. U.R.S.S.*, *Biol.*, pp. 171–82.

KOSHANCHIKOV, I. V. 1948a. 'Hibernation and diapause in Lepidoptera' (in Russian). *Bull. Acad. Sci. U.R.S.S.*, *Biol.*, pp. 653–73.

KOSHANCHIKOV, I. V. 1948b. 'On the possibility of hibernation in the oak-silkworm eggs (*Antherea pernyi*)' (in Russian). *Proc. Lenin Acad. agric. Sci.*, **13**, 25–31.

KOSHANCHIKOV, I. V. 1949a. 'The day and night range of temperature as a factor in the development of the larvae of *Antherea pernyi*' (in Russian). *C. R. Acad. Sci. U.R.S.S.*, **67**, 381–4.

KOSHANCHIKOV, I. V. 1949b. 'The importance of seasonal changes in the leaves of the host plants in the development of *Ocneria dispar*' (in Russian). *C. R. Acad. Sci. U.R.S.S.*, **66**, 1203–6.

KOSHANCHIKOV, I. V. 1949c. 'The features of influence of negative temperatures on the embryonal development in insects' (in Russian). *J. gen. Biol. Moscow*, **10**, 50–67.

KOSHANCHIKOV, I. V. 1950. 'The characteristics of hibernation and diapause in *Lymantria dispar*' (in Russian). *C. R. Acad. Sci. U.R.S.S.*, **73**, 605–7.

KOSHANCHIKOV, I. V. 1952. 'On the question of the temperature optimum. IX. The temperature amplitude as a factor in the development of *Lymantria dispar* and *Antherea pernyi*' (in Russian). *Rev. ent. U.R.S.S.*, **32**, 27–42.

KOWALEWSKY, A. 1887. 'Beiträge zur Kenntnis der nachembryonalen Entwicklung der Musciden.' *Z. wiss. Zool.*, **45**, 542–94.

KOWALSKI, J. 1919/20. 'Cinése atypique dans les cellules adipeuses de larves de *Pyrrhocoris apterus* avec quelques remarques sur le centrosome.' *Cellule*, **30**, 81–118.

KRAMER, S. and WIGGLESWORTH, V. B. 1950. 'The outer layers of the cuticule in the cockroach *Periplaneta americana* and the function of the oenocytes.' *Quart. J. micr. Sci.*, **91**, 63–72.

KRAUSE, G. 1934. 'Analyse erster Differenzierungsprozesse im Keim der Gewächshausheuschrecke durch künstlich erzeugte Zwillings-Doppel- und Mehrfachbildungen.' *Arch. EntwMech. Org.*, **132**, 115–205.

KRAUSE, G. 1953. 'Die Aktionsfolge zur Gestaltung des Keimstreifs von *Tachycines*, insbesondere das morphogenetische Konstruktionsbild bei *Duplicitas parallela*.' *Arch. EntwMech. Org.*, **146**, 275–370.

KREUSCHER, A. 1922. 'Der Fettkörper und die Oenozyten von *Dytiscus marginalis*.' *Z. Zool.*, **119**, 247–87.

KREYENBERG, J. 1929. 'Experimentell-biologische Untersuchungen über *Dermestes lardarius* L. und *D. vulpinus* F. Ein Beitrag zur Frage nach der Inconstanz der Häutungszahlen bei Coleopteren.' *Z. angew. Ent.*, **14**, 140–188.

KRISHNAKUMARÁN, A. 1961. 'Ribonucleic acids in the moult cycle of an insect.' *Nature, Lond.*, **189**, 243–45.

KRISHNAKUMARÁN, A. 1962a. 'Endocrine control of metabolism in Arthropods.' *Ergeb. Biol.*, **25**, 79–92.

KRISHNAKUMARÁN, A. 1962b. 'On some biochemical aspects of the moult cycle in *Gryllus*.' *Biol. Zbl.*, **81**, 529–38.

KRIVOSHEYNA, N. P. 1959. 'On the morphological changes in ontogenetical development of several dipterous larvae' (in Russian). *IV. Symp. Vsesoyuz. ent. obshch.*, **1**, 71–3.

KŘÍZENECKÝ, J. 1914. 'Ueber die Beschleunigung der Einwirkung des Hungerns auf die Metamorphose.' *Biol. Zbl.*, **34**, 46–59.

KROEGER, P. 1960. 'The induction of new puffing patterns by transplantation of salivary gland nuclei into egg cytoplasm of *Drosophila*.' *Chromosoma*, **11**, 129–45.

KRUMINSCH, R. 1952. 'Die Borstenentwicklung bei der Wachsmotte *Galleria mellonella* L.' *Biol. Zbl.*, **71**, 183–210.

KÜHN, A. 1936. 'Weitere Untersuchungen über den Gen-A-Wirkstoff bei der Mehlmotte *Ephestia kühniella*.' *Nachr. Ges. Wiss. Göttingen*, **2**, 239–249.

KÜHN, A. 1937. 'Hormonale Wirkungen in der Insektenentwicklung.' *Forsch. Fortschr.*, **13**, 49–50.

KÜHN, A. 1938. 'Zur Entwicklungsphysiologie der Schmetterlingsmetamorphose.' *Proc. VIIth Int. Congr. Ent. Berlin*, pp. 780–96.

KÜHN, A. 1960. 'Über den Ausfärbungsverläuf der Imaginalanlagen von *Ephestia*-Genotypen in der Puppe.' *Biol. Zbl.*, **79**, 385–92.

KÜHN, A., CASPARI, E. and PLAGGE, E. 1935. 'Über hormonale Genwirkung bei *Ephestia kühniella*.' *Nachr. Ges. Wiss. Göttingen*, **2**, 1–30.

KÜHN, A. and HENKE, K. 1929. 'Genetische und entwicklungsphysiologische Untersuchungen an der Mehlmotte *Ephestia kühniella*. VIII–XII.' *Abh. Ges. Wiss. Göttingen*, **15**, 1–121.

KÜHN, A. and PIEPHO, H. 1936. 'Über hormonale Wirkungen bei der Verpuppung der Schmetterlinge.' *Nachr. Ges. Wiss. Göttingen*, **2**, 141–154.

KÜHN, A. and PIEPHO, H. 1938. 'Die Reaktionen der Hypodermis und Versonschen Drüsen auf das Verpuppungshormon bei *Ephestia kühniella*.' *Biol. Zbl.*, **58**, 12–51.

KÜHN, A. and PIEPHO, H. 1940. 'Über die Ausbildung der Schuppen in Hauttransplantaten von Schmetterlingen.' *Biol. Zbl.*, **60**, 1–22.

KÜHN, A. and PLAGGE, R. 1937. 'Prädetermination der Raupenaugenpigmentierung bei *Ephestia kühniella* Zell. durch den Genotypus der Mutter und durch arteigene und artfremde Implantate.' *Biol. Zbl.*, **57**, 113–26.

KÜHNE, H. 1957. 'Untersuchungen über die Neurosekretion bei Spinnen.' *Naturwissenschaften*, **55**, 431.

KURLAND, G. and SCHNEIDERMAN, H. A. 1959. 'The respiratory enzymes of diapausing silkworm pupae: a new interpretation of carbon monoxide-insensitive respiration.' *Biol. Bull.*, *Wood's Hole*, **116**, 136–61.

KUSKE, G., PENNER, M. and PIEPHO, H. 'Zur Metamorphose des Schmetterlingsbeines.' *Biol. Zbl.*, **80**, 347–51.

KUWABARA, M. 1947. 'Über die Regulation im weisellosen Volke der Honigbiene *Apis mellifica*, besonders die Bestimmung des neuen Weisels.' *J. Fac. Sci. Hokkaido Univ.*, **9**, 359–82.

KUSNYETZOV, N. J. 1953. *The principles of insect physiology* (in Russian), 2 vols., Moscow.

LAHARGUE, J. 1957. 'L'implantation des corps allates imaginaux haterait la chrysalidation chez les vers à soie décapités, alors qu'elle la diffère chez les vers entiers.' *C. R. Acad. Sci.*, *Paris*, **245**, 910–11.

LAHARGUE, J. 1959. 'Action des corps allates imaginaux sur les jeunes vers à soie expérimentalement privés de leurs propres corps allates.' *C. R. Acad. Sci.*, *Paris*, **248**, 3486–7.

LAMBREFF, J. 1944. 'Die Wirkung der Hormone der Wirbellosen auf die Wirbeltiere. I. Hormone der Insekten, die auf die Pigmentzellen der Wirbeltiere wirken' (in Bulgarian with German summary). *Annu. Univ. Sofia* (*phys.-mat.*), **40**, 243–66.

N

LAMPEL, G. 1962. 'Formen und Steuermechanismen des Generationwechsels bei Insekten.' *Zool. Anz.*, **168**, 1–26.

LARSEN, J. R. 1958. 'Hormone-induced ovarian development in mosquitoes.' *Science*, **127**, 587–8.

LARSEN, J. R. and BODENSTEIN, D. 1959. 'The humoral control of egg maturation in the mosquitoes.' *J. exp. Zool.*, **140**, 343–82.

LAUFBERGER, V. 1925. 'The influence of several iodine compounds of the known chemical composition on the metamorphosis in tadpoles' (in Czech). *Lék. sborník*, **26**, 527–36.

LAUFBERGER, V. 1925. 'The biological meaning of the endocrines' (in Czech). *Čas. lék. čes.*, **64**, 806–9.

LAUFBERGER, V. 1946. *Praktická fysiologie* (in Czech), Prague, 161 pp.

LAUFER, H. 1960. 'Blood proteins in insect development.' *Ann. N.Y. Acad. Sci.*, **89**, 490–8.

LAUFER, H. 1961. 'Identification of the volatile factor involved in spermatocyte differentiation in vitro.' *Science*, **133**, 34–6.

LE BERRE, J. R. 1959. 'Caractères biologiques des *Locusta* de la faune de France et étude d'un exemple diapause embryonnaire.' *Ann. Épiphyt.*, **10**, 101–254.

LECOMTE, J. 1952. 'Hétérogénéité dans le comportement agressif des ouvrières d'*Apis mellifica*.' *C. R. Acad. Sci., Paris*, **234**, 890–1.

LEE H. TSUI-JING. 1948. 'A comparative morphological study of the prothoracic glandular bands of some Lepidopterous larvae with special reference to their innervation.' *Ann. ent. Soc. Amer.*, **41**, 200–5.

LEES, A. D. 1941. 'Operations on the pupal wing of *Drosophila melanogaster*.' *J. Genet.*, **42**, 115–42.

LEES, A. D. 1950a. 'Diapause and photoperiodism in the fruit tree spider mite (*Metatetranychus ulmi*).' *Nature, Lond.*, **166**, 874–5.

LEES, A. D. 1950b. 'The physiology of diapause.' *Sci. Progr., London*, **38**, 735–42.

LEES, A. D. 1954. 'Photoperiodism in Arthropods.' *Proc. Int. Protobiol. Congr., Amsterdam*, pp. 36–45.

LEES, A. D. 1955. *The physiology of diapause in Arthropods*, I–II, Cambridge Univ. Press.

LEES, A. D. 1956. 'The physiology and biochemistry of diapause.' *Ann. Rev. Ent.*, **1**, 1–16.

LEES, A. D. 1959. 'The role of photoperiod and temperature in the determination of parthenogenetic and sexual forms in the Aphid *Megoura viciae* Buck. I. The influence of these factors on apterous virginoparae and their progeny.' *J. Ins. Physiol.*, **3**, 92–117.

LEES, A. D. 1960a. 'The role of photoperiod and temperature in the determination of parthenogenetic and sexual forms in the Aphid *Megoura viciae* Buck. II. The operation of the "Interval Timer" in young clones.' *J. Ins. Physiol.*, **4**, 154–75.

LEES, A. D. 1960b. 'Some aspects of animal photoperiodism.' *Cold Sp. Harb. Symp. quant. Biol.*, **25**, 261–8.

LEES, A. D. 1961. 'Clonal polymorphism in aphids.' Repr. from *Insect polymorphism*, ed. by J. S. Kennedy, London, Roy. ent. Soc., pp. 68–79.

LEES, A. D. and PICKEN, L. E. R. 1945. 'Shape in relation to fine structure in the bristles of *Drosophila melanogaster*.' *Proc. roy Soc.* (B), **132**, 396–423.

LEGAY, J. M. 1950. 'Note sur l'évolution des corpora allata au cours de la vie larvaire de *Bombyx mori*.' *C. R. Soc. Biol., Paris*, **144**, 512–13.

LEGAY, J. M. 1960. 'Physiologie du ver à soie.' *Ann. Épiphyt.*, **10**, 501–36; **11**, 81–141.

LEGAY, J. M. 1962. 'Caractère des processus métaboliques au cours de la diapause des insectes.' *Ann. Nutr. Aliment.*, **16**, 65–89.

LEGAY, J. M. and PASCAL, M. 1957. 'Effects d'une castration unilatérale précoce chez le ver à soie sur la ponte de l'adulté.' *C. R. Acad. Sci., Paris*, **244**, 1831–3.

LEMPENNAU, M. 1960. 'Regenerattypen der Flügelimaginalscheiben bei *Antherea pernyi* und anderen Grosschmetterlingen.' *Experientia*, **16**, 539–540.

LENGERKEN, H. 1928. 'Über die Entstehung bilateral-symmetrischer Insektengynander aus verschmolzenen Eiern.' *Biol. Zbl.*, **48**, 26–31.

LENGERKEN, H. 1932. 'Nachhinkende Entwicklung und ihre Folgeerscheinungen beim Mehlkäfer.' *Jena. Z. Naturw.*, **67**, 260–73.

LEVENBOOK, L. 1959. 'Biochemistry of Insects.' *Proc. IVth Int. Congr. Biochem. Vienna*, 1958, **12**, 239–52.

LEVINSON, L. B. and PLATONOVA, G. I. 1948. 'On the relation between basophilous materials and neurosecretion in the nervous cell' (in Russian). *C. R. Acad. Sci. U.R.S.S.*, **58**, 9–12.

LEVY, R. I. and SCHNEIDERMAN, H. A. 1958. 'An experimental solution to the paradox of discontinuous respiration in insects.' *Nature, Lond.*, **182**, 491–3.

L'HÉLIAS, C. 1951. 'Expérience de ligatures chez la larve d'*Apis mellifica*.' *C. R. Soc. Biol., Paris*, **145**, 233–7.

L'HÉLIAS, C. 1952a. 'Étude des glandes endocrines postcérébrales et du cerveau de la larve des *Lophyrus pini* (L.) et *rufus* (André).' *Bull. Soc. zool. Fr.*, **78**, 106–12.

L'HÉLIAS, C. 1952b. 'Étude de la glande prothoracique chez la larve d'*Apis mellifica* (Hyménoptère).' *Bull. Soc. zool. Fr.*, **77**, 191–5.

L'HÉLIAS, C. 1953a. 'L'organe leucopoiétique des Tenthrédes.' *Bull. Soc. zool. Fr.*, **78**, 76–83.

L'HÉLIAS, C. 1953b. 'Role des corpora allata dans le métabolisme des glucides, de l'azote et des lipides chez le phasme *Dixippus morosus*.' *C. R. Acad. Sci., Paris*, **236**, 2164–6.

L'HÉLIAS, C. 1953c. 'Étude comparée de l'azote total et de l'azote non proteinique chez le phasme *Dixippus morosus* aprés ablation des corpora allata.' *C. R. Acad. Sci., Paris*, **236**, 2489–91.

L'HÉLIAS, C. 1954a. 'Étude des phosphatases chez le phasme *Dixippus morosus* aprés ablation des corpora allata.' *C. R. Acad. Sci., Paris*, **238**, 2352–4.

L'HÉLIAS, C. 1954b. 'Étude du métabolisme basal chez le phasme *Dixippus morosus* aprés ablation des corpora allata.' *C. R. Acad. Sci., Paris*, **239**, 778–80.

L'HÉLIAS, C. 1955a. 'Recherches préliminaires sur les hormones du cerveau et du complexe post-cérébral des phasmes *Carausius morosus* et *Cuniculina cuniculina*.' *C. R. Acad. Sci., Paris*, **240**, 1141–3.

L'HÉLIAS, C. 1955b. 'Recherches sur les hormones du complexe post-cérébral chez *Carausius morosus*.' *C. R. Acad. Sci., Paris*, **241**, 770–2.

L'HÉLIAS, C. 1955c. 'Variations des métabolismes glucidiques, acoté et lipidique aprés ablation des corpora allata chez le phasme *Dixippus morosus*.' *Physiol. comp.*, **4**, 74–88.

L'HÉLIAS, C. 1956a. 'Identification de facteurs hormonaux dans le cerveau et le complexe rétrocérébral du phasme *Carausius morosus*.' *Ann. Sci. nat., Zool.* (11), **18**, 274–81.

L'HÉLIAS, C. 1956b. 'Les hormones du complexe rétrocérébral du phasme *Carausius morosus*; action chimique et identification du squelette commun de ces hormones.' *Année biol.*, **32**, 203–19.

L'HÉLIAS, C. 1957a. 'Le rôle des ptérines dans le mécanisme hormonal du complexe rétrocérébral chez les insectes.' *Proc. IInd. int. Symp. Neurosecret., Lund*, pp. 91–5.

L'HÉLIAS, C. 1957b. 'Biochimie de la métamorphose et rôle du complexe rétrocérébral chez les insectes.' *Act. Soc. linn. Bordeaux*, **97**, 1–11.

L'HÉLIAS, C. 1957c. 'Action du complexe rétrocérébral sur la métabolisme chez le phasme *Carausius morosus*.' *Bull. biol.*, **44**, suppl., 1–96.

L'HÉLIAS, C. 1960. 'Tumour induction factor provoked by folic acid in *Pieris brassicae* during the diapause.' *Folia biol., Praha*, **6**, 310–18.

L'HÉLIAS, C. 1962. 'Rétablissement du cycle bisexuell par la bioptérine et l'acide folique chez le Puceron parthenogénétique *Sappaphis plantaginea*.' *C. R. Acad. Sci., Paris*, **255**, 388–90.

LHOSTE, J. 1951. 'Les modifications de structure des glandes ventrales chez *Forficula auricularia* L. au cour du développement.' *Bull. Soc. zool. Fr.*, **75**, 285–92.

LIGHT, S. F. 1942. 'The determination of the castes of social insects.' *Quart. Rev. Biol.*, **17**, 312–26; **18**, 46–63.

LIGHT, S. F. 1944. 'Experimental studies on ectohormonal control of the development of supplementary reproductives in the termite genus *Zootermopsis*.' *Univ. Calif. Publ. Zool.*, **43**, 413–54.

LIGHT, S. F. and WEESNER, F. M. 1951. 'The production of supplementary reproductives in *Zootermopsis* (Isoptera).' *J. exp. Zool.*, **117**, 397–414.

LIGHT, S. F. and WEESNER, F. M. 1955. 'The production and replacement of soldiers in incipient colonies of *Reticulitermes hesperus* Banks.' *Insectes sociaux*, **2**, 347–54.

LINDEMANN, W. 1950. 'Untersuchungen zur postembryonalen Entwicklung schweizerischen Collembolen.' *Rev. suisse Zool.*, **57**, 353–431.

LINZEN, B. and BÜCKMANN, D. 1961. 'Biochemische und histologische Untersuchungen zur Umfärbung der Raupe von *Cerura vinula*.' *Z. Naturf.*, **16b**, 6–17.

LITVINOVA, H. F. 1946. 'Histological changes in the integument of the caterpillars of Chinese oak silkmoth *Antherea pernyi* G.M.' (in Russian). *Bull. Acad. Sci. U.R.S.S.* (*biol.*), pp. 391–402.

LIU, N. I., SHICH, T. E. and GAW, Z. Y. 1958. 'Cultivation of silkworm tissue' (in Chinese). *Sci. Sinica*, **7**, 219.

LÖBBECKE, E. A. 1958. 'Über die Entwicklung der imaginalen Epidermis des Abdomens von *Drosophila*, ihre Segmentierung und die Determination der Tergite.' *Biol. Zbl.*, **77**, 209–37.

LOEWE, S. 1931. 'Hormonale Sexualität bei den Schmetterlingen.' *Naturwissenschaften*, **19**, 775.

LOEWE, S., RANDENBUSCH, W., VOSS, H. E. and HEUERN, J. W. C. VAN. 1922. 'Nachweis der Sexualhormone-Vorkommens bei Schmetterlingen.' *Biochem. Z.*, **244**, 347–56.

LOEWI, O. 1937. *Die chemische Übertragung der Nervenwirkung*, Stockholm.

LOHER, W. 1960. 'The chemical acceleration of the maturation process and its hormonal control in the male of the desert locust.' *Proc. roy. Soc.* (B), **153**, 380–97.

LOHER, W. 1961. 'Die Beschleunigung der Reife durch ein Pheromon des Männchens der Wüstenheuschrecke und die Funktion der Corpora allata.' *Naturwissenschaften*, **21**, 657–61.

LOHER, W. 1962. 'Die Kontrolle des Weibchengesanges von *Gomphocerus rufus* L. durch die Corpora allata.' *Naturwissenschaften*, **17**, 406.

LOOSLI, R. 1958. 'Vergleich von Entwicklungspotenzen in normalen, transplantierten und mutierten Halteren-Imaginalscheiben von *Drosophila melanogaster*.' *Devl. Biol.*, **1**, 24–64.

LORITZ, J. 1957. 'Addenda aux observations du Dr F. Benz et à mes propres recherches, faites sur des chenilles mutilées du *Celerio euphorbiae* L.' *Bull. Soc. Ent. Mülh.*, pp. 13–18.

LOULOUDES, J., SHORTINO, T. J. and BROWN, N. L. 1962. 'Hydroxy-Lecithin emulsions for treating insects.' *J. econ. Ent.*, **55**, 819.

LOZINA-LOZINSKI, L. K. 1935. 'Anabiosis in *Pyrausta nubilalis* caterpillars during freezing.' *C. R. Acad. Sci. U.R.S.S.*, **2**, 328–32.

LOZINA-LOZINSKI, L. K. 1943. 'The fluctuation of the respiratory activity of insects during development.' *Bull. Acad. Sci. U.R.S.S.* (*biol.*), **3**, 125–34.

LUBBOCK, J. 1883. *The origin and metamorphosis of insects*, London, Macmillan.

LUDWIG, D. 1932. 'The effect of temperature on the growth curves of *Popillia japonica*.' *Physiol. Zool.*, **5**, 431–47.

372 *Insect Hormones*

LUDWIG, D. 1953. 'Cytochrome oxidase activity during diapause and metamorphosis of the Japanese beetle.' *J. gen. Physiol.*, **36**, 751–7.

LUDWIG, D. and BARSA, M. C. 1955. 'The activity of succinic dehydrogenase during diapause and metamorphosis of the Japanese beetle *Popillia japonica*.' *J. N.Y. ent. Soc.*, **63**, 161–5.

LUDWIG, D. and BARSA, M. C. 1959. 'Activities of respiratory enzymes during the metamorphosis of the housefly *Musca domestica* L.' *J. N.Y. ent. Soc.*, **67**, 151–6.

LUI-CHUN-SHEN. 1960. 'The hormonal mechanism of voltinism in the mulberry silkworm.' *Autoreferat, Tashkent*.

LUKOSCHUS, F. 1952. 'Über die Prothorakaldrüsen der Honigbiene.' *Naturwissenschaften*, **5**, 116.

LUKOSCHUS, F. 1955a. 'Untersuchungen zur Metamorphose der Honigbiene *Apis mellifica*.' *Insectes sociaux*, **2**, 147–62.

LUKOSCHUS, F. 1955b. 'Die Bedeutung des innersekretorischen Systems für die Ausbildung epidermaler Kastenmerkmale bei der Honigbiene.' *Insectes sociaux*, **2**, 221–36.

LUKOSCHUS, F. 1957. 'Die Kastenentwicklung bei der Honigbiene. Avitaminose oder endocrine Anaplasie?' *Verh. dtsch. zool. Ges.*, pp. 278–283.

LÜSCHER, M. 1944. 'Experimentelle Untersuchungen über die larvale und die imaginale Determination im Ei der Kleidermotte *Tineola biselliella*.' *Rev. suisse Zool.*, **51**, 531–627.

LÜSCHER, M. 1948a. 'The regeneration of legs in *Rhodnius prolixus*.' *J. exp. Biol.*, **25**, 334–43.

LÜSCHER, M. 1948b. 'Gewebekultur "in vivo" bei *Rhodnius prolixus*.' *Rev. suisse Zool.*, **55**, 227–32.

LÜSCHER, M. 1951a. 'Die Production und Elimination von Ersatzgeschlechtstieren bei der Termite *Kalotermes flavicollis* Fabr.' *Z. vergl. Physiol.*, **34**, 123–41.

LÜSCHER, M. 1951b. 'Über die Determination der Ersatzgeschlechtstiere bei der Termite *Kalotermes flavicollis* Fabr. (Vorläufige Mitteilung).' *Rev. suisse Zool.*, **58**, 404–8.

LÜSCHER, M. 1952a. 'Die Ursachen der tierischen Regeneration.' *Experientia*, **8**, 81.

LÜSCHER, M. 1952b. 'Untersuchungen über das individuelle Wachstum bei der Termite *Kalotermes flavicollis* Fabr. (Beitrag zum Kastenbildungsproblem).' *Biol. Zbl.*, **71**, 529–43.

LÜSCHER, M. 1953. 'Kann die Determination durch eine monomolekulare Reaktion ausgelöst werden?' *Rev. suisse Zool.*, **60**, 524–8.

LÜSCHER, M. 1955. 'Zur Frage der Übertragung sozialer Wirkstoffe bei Termiten.' *Naturwissenschaften*, **7**, 186.

LÜSCHER, M. 1956a. 'Hemmende und förndernde Faktoren bei der Entstehung der Ersatzgeschlechtstiere bei der Termite *Kalotermes flavicollis* Fabr.' *Rev. suisse Zool.*, **63**, 261–7.

LÜSCHER, M. 1956b. 'Die Entstehung von Ersatzgeschlechtstieren bei der Termite *Kalotermes flavicollis*.' *Insectes sociaux*, **3**, 119–28.

LÜSCHER, M. 1957a. 'Ersatzgeschlechtstiere bei Termiten und die Beeinflussung ihrer Entstehung durch die Corpora allata.' *Verh. dtsch. Ges. angew, Ent.*, **14**, 144–50.

LÜSCHER, M. 1957b. 'Experimentelle Erzeugung von Soldaten bei der Termite *Kalotermes flavicollis*.' *Naturwissenschaften*, **3**, 69–70.

LÜSCHER, M. 1958. 'Über die Entstehung der Soldaten bei Termiten.' *Rev. suisse Zool.*, **65**, 372–7.

LÜSCHER, M. 1959. 'Die Physiologie der Differenzierung der Kasten bei der Termite *Kalotermes flavicollis*.' *Acta Symp. Evol. Ins.*, *Prague*, pp. 161–6.

LÜSCHER, M. 1960a. 'Hormonal control of caste differentiation in Termites.' *Ann. N.Y. Acad. Sci.*, **89**, 549–63.

LÜSCHER, M. 1960b. 'Sozialwirkstoffe bei Termiten.' *Proc. XIth Int.Congr. Ent.*, **1**, 579–82.

LÜSCHER, M. 1961a. 'Air-conditioned termite nests.' *Sci. Amer.*, **205**, 138–45.

LUSCHER, M. 1961b. 'Demonstration of a trail pheromone in termites.' *Symp. gen. Biol. ital.*, **11**, 189–92.

LÜSCHER, M. 1962. 'Hormonal regulation of development in termites.' *Symp. gen. Biol. ital.*, **10**, 1–111.

LÜSCHER, M. and ENGELMANN, F. 1955. 'Über die Steuerung der Corpora allata-Function bei der Schabe *Leucophaea maderae*.' *Rev. suisse Zool.*, **62**, 649–57.

LÜSCHER, M. and ENGELMANN, F. 1960. 'Histologische und experimentelle Untersuchungen über die Auslösung der Metamorphose bei *Leucophaea maderae*.' *J. Ins. Physiol.*, **5**, 240–58.

LÜSCHER, M. and KARSLON, P. 1958. 'Experimentelle Auslösung von Häutungen bei der Termite *Kalotermes flavicollis*.' *J. Ins. Physiol.*, **1**, 341–5.

LÜSCHER, M. and SPRINGHETTI, 1960. 'Untersuchungen über die Bedeutung der Corpora allata für die Differenzieurung der Kasten bei der Termite *Kalotermes flavicollis*.' *J. Ins. Physiol.*, **5**, 190–212.

LYONETT, P. 1762. *Traité anatomique de la chenille qui ronge la bois du saule*, La Haye.

LYSENKO, T. D. 1936. *The theoretical basis of yarovisation* (in Russian), Moscow, Selchosgis, pp. 5–94.

LYSENKO, T. D. 1949. *Agrobiologia* (in Russian), Moscow, Selchosgis.

MAAS, A. H. 1948. 'Über die Auslösbarkeit von Temperaturmodifikationen während der Embryonalentwicklung von *Drosophila melanogaster*.' *Arch. EntwMech. Org.*, **143**, 515–72.

MCDONALD, S. and BROWN, A. W. A. 1952. 'Cytochrome oxidase and cyanide sensitivity of the larch sawfly during metamorphosis.' *Rep. ent. Soc. Ont.*, **83**, 30–4.

MCLEOD, D. G. R. and BECK, S. D. 1963. 'Photoperiodic termination of diapause in an insect.' *Biol. Bull., Wood's Hole,* **124,** 84–96.

MAGNUSSEN, K. 1933. 'Untersuchungen zur Entwicklungsphysiologie des Schmetterlingsflügels.' *Arch. EntwMech. Org.,* **128,** 447–97.

MAINX, J. 1947. 'Die Schleifenkerne der Dipterenlarven.' *Mikroskopie,* **2,** 314–18.

MALUCELLI, P. 1934. 'Nuove experienze per la schiusura estemporanea dell'uovo di *Bombyx mori.*' *Ann. Staz. bacol. sper. Padova,* **48,** 12–22.

MARCUS, H. 1951. 'Observationes morfologicas en *Dinjapyx marcussi.*' *Folia univ. Cochabamba,* **5,** 83–106.

MARCUS, W. 1962. 'Untersuchungen über die Polarität der Rumpfhaut von Schmetterlingen.' *Arch. EntwMech. Org.,* **154,** 56–102.

MARKOVICH, N. J. 1941. 'New data on the biology of *Anopheles bifurcatus.*' *Med. Parasit.,* **10,** 1–23.

MARTIGNONI, M. E. 1960. 'Problems of insect tissue cultures.' *Experientia,* **15,** 125–8.

MARTIGNONI, M. E., ZITGER, M. E. and WAGNER, R. P. 1958. 'Preparation of cell suspensions from insect cuticle for in vitro cultivations.' *Science,* **128,** 360–1.

MARTINI, E. and AKHUNDOV, I. 1929. 'Versuche über Farbanpassung bei Culiciden.' *Zool. Anz.,* **81,** 25–44.

MARTYNOV, A. V. 1937. 'On the termite wings in connection with the phylogeny of this and relative groups of insects' (in Russian). *Sb. Acad. N. V. Nasonov. Tzd. A.N.S.S.S.R.,* 83–150.

MASATOSHI, KOBAYASHI and KIRIMURA, J. 1958. 'The brain hormone in the silkworm *Bombyx mori* L.' *Nature, Lond.,* **181,** 1217.

MASLENIKOVA, V. A. 1961. 'Influence of the hormones of the host on the diapause in *Pteromalus puparum.*' *C. R. Acad. Sci. U.R.S.S.,* **139,** 249–52.

MATSUDA, R. 1961a. 'Studies of relative growth in Gerridae (1–3).' *Ann. ent. Soc. Amer.,* **54,** 578–98.

MATSUDA, R. 1961b. 'Studies of relative growth in Gerridae (4).' *J. Kansas ent. Soc.,* **34,** 5–17.

MATSUDA, R. 1962a. 'Studies of relative growth in Gerridae. VI. Comparison of two species of *Trepobates.*' *Univ. Kansas Sci. Bull.,* **47,** 113–29.

MATSUDA, R. 1962b. 'A study of relative growth in two strains of *Pycnoscelus surinamensis* Linn.' *Growth,* **26,** 129–35.

MATSUDA, R. 1962c. 'A study of relative growth of leg and antennal segments in some species of Heteroptera.' *Contr. Dept. Ent. Kansas Univ.,* **30,** 152–9.

MATSUDA, R. and ROHLF, F. J. 1961. 'Studies of relative growth in Gerridae (5). Comparison of two populations.' *Growth,* **25,** 211–17.

MATTHÉE, I. I. 1945. 'Biochemical differences between the solitary and gregarious phases of locusts and noctuids.' *Bull. ent. Res.,* **36,** 343–71.

MATTHÉE, I. I. 1951. 'The structure and physiology of the egg of *Locustana pardalina* Walk.' *Bull. Dept. Agric. S. Afr.,* **316,** 1–83.

MATZ, G. 1961. 'Étude histologique des tumeurs expérimentales chez *Leucophaea maderae* Fabr. et *Locusta migratoria* L.' *Bull. Soc. Zool. Fr.*, 86, 148–56.

MAUSER, E. 1938. 'Synchrone Metamorphose deplatierter Vorderbeine mit dem Wirtstiere *Dixippus morosus*.' *Biol. gen.*, 14, 179–211.

MAZIA, D. 1956. *Enzymes: units of biological structure and function.* New York, Acad. Press Inc., p. 261.

MEANS, O. W. 1942. 'Cholinesterase activity of tissues of adult *Melanoplus differentialis*.' *J. Cell. comp. Phys.*, 20, 319–24.

MEDNIKOVA, M. B. 1952. 'The endocrine glands, corpora allata and corpora cardiaca of mosquitoes' (in Russian). *Zool. Zh.*, 31, 676–85.

MEDVEDEVA, N. 1935. 'The problem of the specific reaction of invertebrates to the vertebrate hormones' (in Russian, with German summary). *Med. Z. vseukrain. Acad. Nauk*, 4, 667–75.

MEDVEDEVA, N. 1939. 'The evolution of the humoral regulation of the life processes' (in Russian, with English summary). *Adv. mod. Biol.*, *Moscow*, 10, 222–48.

MEGUSHAR, F. 1907. 'Die Regeneration der Coleopteren.' *Arch. EntwMech. Org.*, 25, 148–234.

MEHROTRA, K. N. 1960. 'Development of the cholinergic system in insects eggs.' *J. Ins. Physiol.*, 5, 129–42.

MEISENHEIMER, J. 1908a. 'Ergebnisse einiger Versuchsreihen über Extirpation und Transplantation der Geschlechtsdrüsen bei Schmetterlingen.' *Zool. Anz.*, 32, 393–400.

MEISENHEIMER, J. 1908b. 'Über den Zusammenhang von Geschlechtsdrüsen und sekundären Geschlechtsmerkmalen bei den Arthropoden.' *Verh. dtsch. Ges. zool.*, 84–95.

MEISENHEIMER, J. 1909a. *Experimentelle Studien zur Soma und Geschlechtsdifferenzierung. I. Über den Zusammenhang primärer und sekundärer Geschlechtsmerkmale bei den Schmetterlingen*, Jena, Fischer, 186 pp.

MEISENHEIMER, J. 1909b. 'Über die Beziehungen zwischen orimärer und sekundärer Geschlechtsmerkmalen bei den Schmetterlingen.' *Naturwissenschaft. Wochenschr.*, 8, 545–53.

MEISENHEIMER, J. 1910. 'Zur Ovarialtransplantationen bei Schmetterlingen.' *Zool. Anz.*, 35, 446–50.

MEISENHEIMER, J. 1930. *Geschlecht und Geschlechter im Tierreiche. II. Die allgemeinen Probleme.* Jena, Fischer.

MELLANBY, K. 1936. 'The later embryology of *Rhodnius prolixus*.' *Quart. J. micr. Sci.*, 79, 1–42.

MELLANBY, K. 1938/39. 'Diapause und Metamorphosis of the blowfly *Lucilia sericata*.' *Parasitology*, 30, 392–402.

MENDES, M. V. 1947. 'Glandulas endocrinas e hormonias nos insectos.' *Ann. Acad. bras. Sci.*, 19, 259–75.

MENDES, M. 1948. 'Histology of the corpora allata of *Melanoplus differentialis*.' *Biol. Bull.*, *Wood's Hole*, 94, 194–207.

MENG, K. 1958. '5-Hydroxytriptamin und Acetylcholin als Wirkungsantagonisten beim *Helix*-Herzen.' *Naturwissenschaften*, **19**, 470.

MERCER, E. H. and BRUNET, P. C. J. 1959. 'The electron microscopy of the left colleterial gland of the cockroach.' *J. biophys. biochem. Cytol.*, **5**, 257–62.

MERCIER, L. 1920. 'Les glandes salivaires des Panorpes sont-elles sous la dépendance des glandes génitales ?' *C. R. Soc. Biol.*, *Paris*, **83**, 470–1.

METALNIKOV, S. 1907. 'Zur Verwandlung der Insekten.' *Biol. Zbl.*, **27**, 396–405.

MEYER, G. F. and PFLUGFELDER, O. 1958. 'Elektronenmikroskopische Untersuchungen an den Corpora cardiaca von *Carausius morosus*.' *Z. Zellforsch.*, **48**, 556–64.

MEYER, J. H. 1953. 'Die Bluttransfusion als Mittel zur Überwindung letaler Keimkombination bei Lepidopteren-Bastarden.' *Z. wien. ent. Ges.*, **38**, 41–80.

MEYER, K. E. and BÜCKMANN, D. 1962. 'Die Häutungen des Pantopoden *Pycnogonum litorale*.' *Verh. dtsch. zool. Ges.*, **53**, 604–9.

MEYER, R. K. and ME SHAN, W. H. 1950. 'Hormone-enzyme relationship.' *Rec. Progr. Hormone Res.*, **5**, 465–516.

MIKHAILOV, E. N. 1936. 'The technique of the spring preservation of the silkworm eggs in refrigerators' (in Russian). *Trans. Centralasiat. Seric. Inst. Tashkent*, **4**, 1–52.

MIKHAILOV, E. N. 1950. *Manual of silkworm culture* (in Russian). Selchosgis, Moscow. 496 pp.

MIKHIN, B. N. and ZOLOTAREV, E. CH. 1938. 'The influence of temperature during the spring incubation of the oak-silkworm (*Antherea pernyi*) eggs and pupae on the changes in its voltinism' (in Russian). *Sehlkovodstvo (Sericulture)*, **5**, 54–9.

MILBURN, N., WEIANT, E. A. and ROEDER, K. D. 1960. 'The release of efferent nerve activity in the roach, *Periplaneta americana*, by extracts of the corpus cardiacum.' *Biol. Bull.*, *Wood's Hole*, **118**, 111–19.

MIKALONIS, S. J. and BROWN, R. H. 1941. 'Acetylcholine and cholinesterase in the insect central nervous system.' *J. Cell. comp. Physiol.*, **18**, 401–3.

MILLER, E. M. 1942. 'The problem of castes and caste differentiation in *Prorhinotermes simplex* Hagen.' *Bull. Univ. Miami*, **15**, 1–27.

MILLER, L. W. 1950. 'Factors influencing diapause in the European red mite.' *Nature, Lond.*, **166**, 875.

MISSONIER, J. 1960. 'Action du facteur temperature sur le développement nymphal de *Chortophila brassicae* Bouché (Dipt., Muscidae).' *C. R. Acad. Sci. Paris*, **251**, 1424–6.

MIURA, E. and TORII, E. 1944. 'Physiological studies on the cause of molting and metamorphosis in the silkworm *Bombyx mori*.' *Sci. Rep. Kyoto Seric. Coll.*, **2**, 251–312.

MOCHIDO, O. and YOSHIMEKI 1962. 'Relations with development of the gonads, dimensional changes of the corpora allata and duration of post-diapause period in hibernating larvae of the rice stem borer.' *Jap. J. appl. Ent. Zool.*, **6**, 114–23.

MOKIA, G. G. 1941. 'Contribution to the study of hormones in insects' (in Russian). *C. R. Acad. Sci. U.R.S.S.*, (N.S.) **30**, 371–3.

MOLL, M. H. 1949. 'Estudio bibliografico sobre el corpus allatum an los insettos.' *Rev. Acad. Cienc. Zaragoza* (2), **4**, 87–94.

MONCHADSKII, A. S. 1935. 'On the role of contact moisture in *Pyrausta nubilalis* larvae after the winter diapause' (in Russian). *Plant Prot.*, Leningrad, fasc. **3**, 39–50.

MONCHADSKII, A. S. 1949. 'On the types of the reaction of insects to the environmental temperature changes' (in Russian). *Bull. Acad. Sci. U.R.S.S. (biol.)*, **2**, 171–200.

MONOD, J. and POULSON, D. 1937. 'Specific reactions of the ovary to inter-specific transplantations among members of the melanogaster group of *Drosophila*.' *Genetics*, **22**, 257–63.

MONRO, J. 1958. 'Cholinesterase and the secretion of the brain hormone in insects.' *Austr. J. biol. Sci.* **11**, 399–406.

MORAN, M. R. 1959a. 'Changes in the fat content during metamorphosis of the mealworm, *Tenebrio molitor* L.' *J. N.Y. ent. Soc.*, **67**, 213–16.

MORAN, M. R. 1959b. 'Changes in the distribution of nitrogen during meta-morphosis of the mealworm *Tenebrio molitor* L'. *J. N.Y. ent. Soc.*, **67**, 217–22.

MOROHOSHI, S. 1939a. 'Studies on the molting character in the silkworm *Bombyx mori*. I. Endocrine influencing the molt and metamorphosis of insects and a discussion on the number of molts.' *Bull. sci. Fak. Agr. Kjusu Univ.*, **8**, 232–41.

MOROHOSHI, S. 1939b. 'idem'. 'II. Genetical studies on the molting charac-ter.' *Bull. sci. Fak. terk. Kjusu Univ.*, **8**, 242–63.

MOROHOSHI, S. 1939c. 'idem'. 'III. Variation of the molting character by temperature and moisture shocks.' *Bull. sci. Fak. Agr. Kjusu Univ.*, **8**, 264–81.

MOROHOSHI, S. 1939d. 'idem'. 'IV. Variation of the molting character by blood transfusion.' *Bull. sci. Fak. Agr. Kjusu Univ.*, **8**, 282–5.

MOROHOSHI, S. 1943a. 'idem'. 'VI. On the process of the variation of the molting character,' *Jap. J. Genet.*, **20**, 75–8.

MOROHOSHI, S. 1943b. 'idem'. 'VII. On the prothetely found in natura and a self-regulating mechanism of the silkworm.' *Jap. J. Genet.*, **20**, 79–87.

MOROHOSHI, S. 1947a. 'Mutual relation of the developmental process in the silkworm.' *Jap. J. Genet.*, **22**, 20–1.

MOROHOSHI, S. 1951a. 'Genetical studies between the molting character and the voltine of the silkworm *Bombyx mori*. I. Correlation between the molting character and the superfluous abdominal legs.' *Papers Coord. Comm. Res. Genet.*, **2**, 179–81.

MOROHOSHI, S. 1951b. 'idem'. 'II. The interaction among the molting, the voltine and the superfluous abdominal legs.' *Papers Coord. Comm. Res. Genet.*, **2**, 181–4.

MOROHOSHI, S. 1957. *Physiogenetical studies on moltinism and voltinism in* Bombyx mori: *a new hormonal antagonistic balance theory on the growth.* Jap. Soc. Prom. Sci., Tokyo. 202 pp.

MOROHOSHI, S. 1959. 'Hormonal studies on the diapause and non-diapause eggs of the silkworm *Bombyx mori* L.' *J. Ins. Physiol.*, **3**, 28–40.

MOROHOSHI, S., MIYAZAWA, H. and KIKUKHI, R. 1956. 'Production of the non-diapause eggs by transplanting the corpora allata and brain-corpora allata complex in the silkworm.' *Jap. J. Genet.*, **31**, 305–8.

MOROHOSHI, S., MIYAZAWA, H. and KIKUKHI, R. 1957. 'Studies on the voltinism in the silkworm. VII. Functions on the corpora allata and sub-oesophageal ganglion.' *J. seric. Sci. Tokyo*, **26**, 232–3.

MOTHES, G. 1960. 'Weitere Untersuchungen über den physiologischen Farbwechsel von *Carausius morosus*.' *Zool. Jb.*, Abt. 3, **69**, 133–62.

MRÁZEK, A. 1906. 'Brachyptere Mermithogynen bei den Ameisen.' *Z. wiss. Insektenbiol.*, **2**, 109–11.

MRÁZEK, A. 1908. 'Brachyptere Mermithogynen bei *Lasius alienus*.' *Čas. čs. spol. ent.*, **5**, 139–46.

MÜLLER, J. 1928. 'Über ein eigentümliches, dem Nervus sympathicus analoges Nervensystem der Eingeweide bei den Insekten.' *Nova Acta Acad. Caesar. Leop. Carol.*, **14**, 71–108.

MÜLLER, J. 1957. 'Über die Diapause von *Stenocranus minutus* Fabr.' *Beitr. Ent.*, **7**, 203–25.

MUNEZ, J. A. 1954. 'Über das Vorkommen von Prothoraxdrüsen bei *Anisotarsus cupripennis*.' *Biol. Zbl.*, **73**, 602–10.

MUROGA, H. 1940. 'Development of the prothoracic glands of the silkworm and the effect of its transplantation and pupation.' *J. seric. Sci. Tokyo*, **11**, 231–40.

MURRAY, F. V. and TIEGS, O. W. 1935. 'The metamorphosis of *Calandra oryzae*.' *Quart. J. micr. Sci.*, **77**, 405–95.

MÜSSBICHLER, A. 1952. 'Die Bedeutung äusserer Einflüsse und der Corpora allata bei der Afterweiselentstehung von *Apis mellifica*.' *Z. vergl. Physiol.*, **34**, 207–21.

NABERT, A. 1913. 'Die Corpora allata der Insekten.' *Z. wiss. Zool.*, **104**, 181–358.

NAGATOMO, T. 1956. 'Function of the brain-suboesophageal ganglion complex in the silkworm *Bombyx mori*.' *Proc. Japan Acad.*, **32**, 500–3.

NAGEL, R. H. 1934. 'Metathetely in larvae of the confused flour beetle (*Tribolium confusum* Duval).' *Ann. ent. Soc. Amer.*, **27**, 425–8.

NAISSE, J. 1958. 'Phénomènes neurosécrétoires chez les opilions.' *Proc. XVth Int. Congr. Zool.*, **6**, 1003–4.

NATON, E. 1960a. 'Ueber die Entwicklung des schwarzbraunen Mehlkäfers *Tribolium destructor*.' Teil I. *Z. angew. Ent.*, **46**, 233–44.

NATON, E. 1960b. ibid. Teil II. *Z. angew. Ent.*, **47**, 256–74.

NATON, E. 1961. ibid. Teil III. *Z. angew. Ent.*, **48**, 58–74.

NATON, E. 1962. ibid. Teil. IV. *Zool. Beitr.*, **8**, 95–123.

NAYAR, K. K. 1935a. 'Corpus allatum in *Iphita limbata* Stål.' *Curr. Sci.*, **22**, 241–2.

NAYAR, K. K. 1953b. 'Thoracic glands of *Iphita limbata* Stål.' *Nature, Lond.*, **172**, 768.

NAYAR, K. K. 1953c. 'Neurosecretion in *Iphita limbata* Stål.' *Curr. Sci.*, **22**, 149.

NAYAR, K. K. 1954a. 'Metamorphosis in the integument of caterpillars with omission of the pupal stage.' *Proc. roy. ent. Soc. Lond.* (A), **29**, 129–34.

NAYAR, K. K. 1954b. 'The structure of the corpus cardiacum of *Locusta migratoria*.' *Quart. J. micr. Sci.*, **95**, 245–50.

NAYAR, K. K. 1955a. 'Studies on the neurosecretory system of *Iphita limbata* Stål. I. Distribution and structure of the neurosecretory cells of the nerve ring.' *Biol. Bull., Wood's Hole*, **108**, 296–307.

NAYAR, K. K. 1955b. 'idem'. 'II. Acid phosphatase and cholinesterase in the neurosecretory cells.' *Proc. Indian. Acad. Sci.*, **42**, 27–30.

NAYAR, K. K. 1955c. 'Neurosecretory cells in the larvae of gall midges.' *Curr. Sci.*, **24**, 90–1.

NAYAR, K. K. 1955d. 'Enzyme complex of the corpus allatum of the female *Iphita limbata* Stål.' *Curr. Sci.*, **24**, 306–7.

NAYAR, K. K. 1956a. 'Studies on the neurosecretory system of *Iphita limbata* Stål. III. The endocrine glands and the neurosecretory pathways in the adult.' *Z. Zellforsch.*, **44**, 697–705.

NAYAR, K. K. 1956b. 'The structure of the corpus allatum of *Iphita limbata*.' *J. micr. Sci.*, **97**, 83–8.

NAYAR, K. K. 1956c. 'Effect of extirpation of neurosecretory cells on the metamorphosis of *Iphita limbata*.' *Curr. Sci.*, **25**, 192–3.

NAYAR, K. K. 1956d. 'Competence of the integument to undergo metamorphosis in *Iphita limbata*.' *J. zool. Soc. India*, **8**, 139–48.

NAYAR, K. K. 1957a. 'Water content and release of neurosecretory products in *Iphita limbata*.' *Curr. Sci.*, **26**, 25.

NAYAR, K. K. 1957b. 'Studies on the neurosecretory system of *Iphita limbata* Stål. IV. Observations on the structure and functions of the corpora cardiaca of the adult insect.' *Proc. Nat. Inst. Sci. India* (B), **22**, 171–84.

NAYAR, K. K. 1958. 'idem'. 'V. Probable endocrine basis of oviposition in the female insect.' *Proc. Indian Acad. Sci.* (B), **47**, 233–51.

NAYAR, K. K. 1961. 'Studies on the juvenile hormone extracts of the butterfly *Terias hecabe* Linn.' *Beitr. Ent.*, **11**, 914–22.

NEEDHAM, J. 1942. *Biochemistry and morphogenesis*, Cambridge, Univ. Press; New York, Macmillan, 935 pp. (cf. pp. 28–34).

NEEDHAM, J. 1952. *Regeneration and wound healing*, London, Methuen; New York, J. Wiley & Son, 152 pp.

NEEDHAM, J. 1957. 'The quadratic relation in differential growth.' *Nature, Lond.*, **180**, 1293.

NEISWANDER, C. R. 1947. 'Variations in the seasonal history of the european cornborer in Ohio.' *J. econ. Ent.*, **40**, 707–12.

NEWBY, W. W. 1949. 'Abnormal growth on the head of *Drosophila melanogaster*.' *J. Morph.*, **85**, 177–96.

NIEMIERKO, W. 1947a. 'Contribution to the biochemistry of silkworm metamorphosis.' *Acta Biol. exp.*, **14**, 151–5.

NIEMIERKO, W. 1947b. 'The fatty acids metabolism in the silkworm caterpillars.' *Acta Biol. exp.*, **14**, 138–50.

NIEMIERKO, W. 1962. 'Pyro and polyphosphates in insects.' *Colloques int. Centre natn. Rech. scient.*, no. **106**, 615–23.

NISHIITSUTSUJI-ÜWO, J. 1960. 'Fine structure of the neurosecretory system in Lepidoptera.' *Nature, Lond.*, **188**, 953.

NOIROT, C. 1952. 'Le polymorphisme social chez les termites et son déterminisme.' *Colloques int. Centre natn. Rech. scient.*, **34**, 103–16.

NOIROT, C. 1953. 'Les soins et l'alimentation des jeunes chez les termites.' *Ann. Sci. nat., Paris, Zool.*, **14**, 405–14.

NOIROT, C. 1954. 'Le polymorphisme des termites supérieurs.' *Année biol.*, **30**, 461–74.

NOIROT, C. 1955. 'Recherches sur le polymorphisme des termites supérieurs.' *Ann. Sci. nat., Paris, Zool.*, **17**, 399–595.

NOIROT, C. 1957. 'Neurosécrétion et sexualité chez la Termite á cou jaune (*Kalotermes flavicollis*).' *C. R. Acad. Sci., Paris.* **245**, 743–5.

NOLAND, J. L. and BAUMANN, C. A. 1949. 'Effects of certain azo-dyes upon the cockroach *Blatella germanica*.' *Proc. Soc. exp. Biol. N.Y.*, **71**, 365–8.

NOVÁK, V. J. A. 1948. 'On the question of the origin of pathological creatures (pseudogynes) in ants of the genus *Formica*.' *Acta Soc. zool. Čsl.*, **12**, 97–131.

NOVÁK, V. J. A. 1951a. 'New aspects of the metamorphosis in insects.' *Nature, Lond.*, **167**, 132.

NOVÁK, V. J. A. 1951b. 'The metamorphosis hormones and morphogenesis in *Oncopeltus fasciatus* Dal.' *Acta Soc. zool. Čsl.*, **15**, 1–48.

NOVÁK, V. J. A. 1954. 'The growth of the corpora allata during the postembryonal development in insects.' *Acta Soc. zool. Čsl.*, **18**, 98–133.

NOVÁK, V. J. A. 1955a. 'The question of the origin and evolution of the metamorphosis in insects from the point of view of the findings on the metamorphosis hormones.' *Acta Soc. ent. Čsl.*, **52**, 31–43.

NOVÁK. V. J. A. 1955b. 'To the knowledge of the mechanism conditioning the development of the ventral black pattern in the abdomen of the bug *Oncopeltus fasciatus* Dal.' *Acta Soc. zool. Čsl.*, **19**, 233–46.

NOVÁK, V. J. A. 1955c. 'Die Frage der Formentwicklung aus dem Standpunkt der Erkenntnisse über die Metamorphose der Insekten (GF-Theorie der Morphogenese).' *Čslká Biol.*, **4**, 566–74.

NOVÁK, V. J. A. 1955d. 'The question of the gradient factor and its function in insect metamorphosis. Observations to H. E. Hinton paper: the initiation, maintenance and rupture of diapause: a new theory.' *Beitr. Ent.*, **5**, 457–61.

NOVÁK, V. J. A. 1956a. Review: V. B. Wigglesworth, 1954. 'The physiology of insect metamorphosis' (in Russian). *Rev. Ent. U.R.S.S.*, 35, 962–4.

NOVÁK, V. J. A. 1956b. 'The gradient-factor theory, a general conception of the metamorphosis in insects.' *Ann. Soc. zool. Fr.*, 11, 335–7.

NOVÁK, V. J. A. 1956c. Review: A. D. Lees, 'The physiology of diapause in Arthropods.' *Z. angew. Ent.*, 39, 127.

NOVÁK, V. J. A. 1956d. 'Versuch einer zusammenfassenden Darstellung der postembryonalen Entwicklung der Insekten.' *Beitr. Ent.*, 6, 205–493.

NOVÁK, V. J. A. 1957. 'Diapause stages in *Cephaleia abietis*.' *Acta Soc. ent. Čsl.*, 54, 269–76.

NOVÁK, V. J. A. 1958a. 'Der gegenwärtige Stand der Ansichten über das Wesen der Insektenmetamorphose' (in Hungarian). *Biol. Közl. MAV*, 6, 13–22.

NOVÁK, V. J. A. 1959. 'The characters of an artificially produced diapause in silkworm *Bombyx mori*.' *Acta Symp. Evol. Ins.*, Prague, p. 237.

NOVÁK, V. J. A. 1961a. 'Problems of phylogenesis in the holometabolic insects from the point of view of data on the hormones of metamorphosis' (in Russian). *Rev. Ent. U.R.S.S.*, 15, 5–18.

NOVÁK, V. J. A. 1961b. 'Juvenile hormone and morphogenesis.' *Proc. XIth Int. Congr. Ent.*, Vienna, 1, 371–7.

NOVÁK, V. J. A. and ČERVENKOVÁ, E. 1959. 'The function of corpus allatum in the last larval instar of metabolic insects.' *Acta Symp. Evol. Ins.*, Prague, pp. 152–6.

NOVÁK, V. J. A. and GUTMANN, E. 1962. 'On the question of gliosecretion (gliosomata) and other Gomori-positive structures on the central nervous system of the cockroach *Periplaneta americana*.' *Acta Soc. ent. Čsl.*, 59, 314–22.

NOVÁK, V. J. A., PROCHÁZKA, J. and ČERVENKOVÁ, E. 1961. 'The effect of the thymus extractions according to Williams and Schneiderman in *Pyrrhocoris apterus*' (unpublished).

NOVÁK, V. J. A. and ROHDENDORFOVÁ, E. 1959. 'The influence of the implanted corpus allatum on the corpus allatum of the host.' *Acta Symp. Evol. Ins.*, Prague, pp. 157–60.

NOVÁK, V. J. A. and SLÁMA, K. 1959. 'On the question of origin of the pupal instar in insects.' *Acta Symp. Evol. Ins.*, Prague, pp. 65–9.

NOVÁK, V. J. A. and SLÁMA, K. 1962. 'The influence of the juvenile hormone on the oxygen consumption in *Pyrrhocoris apterus*.' *J. Ins. Physiol.*, 8, 145–53.

NOVÁK, V. J. A., SLÁMA, K. and WENIG, K. 1959. 'Effect of implantation of corpus allatum on the oxygen consumption in *Pyrrhocoris apterus*.' *Acta Symp. Evol. Ins.*, Prague, pp. 147–51.

NOVÁK, K. 1960. 'Entwicklung und Diapause der Köcher-fliegenlarven *Anabolia furcata* Br.' *Acta Soc. ent. Čsl.*, 3, 207–72.

NOVOTNÝ, I. 1955. 'The aerobic metabolism of the pupae of *Musca domestica*.' *Acta Soc. zool. Čsl.*, 19, 259–64.

NOVOTNÝ, I. 1962. 'Potassium and caffeine induced increase of oxygen consumption in muscle and its inhibition by drugs.' *XXIInd Int. Congr. Physiol. Sci. Leiden. Excerpta Med.*, Ser. no. 48.

NUNEZ, J. A. 1956. 'Wasserhaushalt und Neurosecretion in dem Käfer *Anisotarsus cupripennis.*' *Z. vergl. Physiol.*, **36,** 341–55.

NUSSBAUM, J. 1889. 'Zur Frage der Segmentierung des Keimstreifs und der Bauchanhänge der Insektenembryonen.' *Biol. Zbl.*, **9,** 516–22.

NUTTING, W. L. 1955. 'Extirpation of roach prothoracic glands. *Scientia,* **122,** 30–1.

NYST, R. H. 1941. 'Contribution à l'étude de l'hormone nymphogène.' *Ann. Soc. zool. Belg.*, **72,** 74–104.

NYST, R. H. 1942. 'Structure et rapports du système nerveux, du vaisseau dorsal et des annexes cardiaques chez *Dixippus morosus.*' *Ann. Soc. zool. Belg.*, **73,** 150–64.

OBENBERGER, J. 1952. '*Entomologie* I.' Přír. naklad., Praha, 872.

OBUCHOWICZ, L. 1962a. 'Respiratory enzymes in the crayfish *Astacus leptodactylus.* I.' *Bull. Soc. Amis Sci. Poznań* (D), **3,** 1–22.

OBUCHOWICZ, L. 1962b. 'Respiratory enzymes in the crayfish *Astacus leptodactylus.* II.' *Bull. Soc. Amis Sci. Poznań* (D), **3,** 23–37.

OCHSÉ, W. 1944. 'Experimentelle und histologische Beiträge zur inneren Metamorphose von *Sialis lutaria* L.' *Rev. suisse Zool.*, **51,** 1–82.

ODA, J. 1959, 'Studies on the proteins of insect haemolymph. Part IX. Chromatography on calcium phosphate columns.' *Bull. agr. chem. Soc. Japan,* **23,** 81–8.

OEDEMANS, J. TH. 1889. 'Falter aus kastrierter Raupen, wie sie aussehen und wie sie sich benehmen.' *Zool. Jb.*, Abt. I, **12,** 71–88.

OERTEL, F. 1930. 'Metamorphosis in the honeybee.' *J. Morph.*, **50,** 295–340.

OEZBAS, S. 1957a. 'Morphological and histological studies on the corpora allata and cardiaca in Orthoptera.' *Commun. Fac. Sci. Ankara* (C), **8,** 19–44.

OEZBAS, S. 1957b. 'Two kinds of secretions in corpora cardiaca of *Locusta migratoria.*' *Commun. Fac. Sci. Ankara* (C), **8,** 45–57.

OEZBAS, S. and HODGSON, E. S. 1958. 'Action of insect neurosecretion upon central nervous system in vitro and upon behavior.' *Proc. nat. Acad. Sci. Wash.*, **44,** 825–30.

O'FARRELL, A. F. 1959. 'Regeneration and development in the cockroach *Blatella germanica.*' *Acta Symp. Evol. Ins., Prague,* p. 140.

O'FARRELL, A. F. 1960a. 'The clock in the cockroach.' Inaugural public lecture, Armidale, N.S.W., Australia, pp. 1–19.

O'FARRELL, A. F. 1962. 'Influence of illumination on moulting and regeneration in the cockroach *Blatella germanica* L.' *Nature, Lond.*, **195,** 1122–3.

O'FARRELL, A. F. and STOCK, A. 1953. 'Regeneration and the moulting cycle in *Blatella germanica* L. I. Single regeneration initiated during the first instar.' *Austr. J. biol. Sci.*, **6,** 485–500.

O'FARRELL, A. F. and STOCK, A. 1954. 'idem'. 'III. Successive regeneration of both metathoracic legs.' *Austr. J. biol. Sci.*, **7**, 525–36.

O'FARRELL, A. F. and STOCK, A. 1958. 'Some aspects of regeneration in cockroaches.' *Proc. XIth Int. Congr. Ent.*, **2**, 253–9.

O'FARRELL, A. F. and STOCK, A. 1962. 'Influence of illumination on moulting and regeneration in the cockroach *Blatella germanica*.' *Nature, Lond.*, **195**, 1122–3.

O'FARRELL, A. F. and MORGAN, J. 1956. 'Regeneration and the moulting cycle in *Blatella germanica* L. IV. Single and repeated regeneration and metamorphosis.' *Austr. J. biol. Sci.*, **9**, 406–22.

OGURA, S. 1933. 'Erblichkeitsstudien am Seidenspinner *Bombyx mori* L. III. Genetische Untersuchung der Häutung.' *Z. indukt. Abstamm- u. Vererb-Lehre*, **64**, 205–68.

OHNISHI, E. and HIDAKA, T. 1955. Effect of environmental factors on the determination of pupal types in some swallowtails, *Papilio xanthus* L. and *P. protenor demetrius* Cr.' *Zool. Mag. Tokyo*, **65**, 185–7.

OHNISHI, E. and HIDAKA, T. 1957. 'Effet des facteurs du milieu ambiant sur la détermination des types de chrysalides de certains papillons diurnes nommés "queue d'hirondelle".' *Bull. Soc. Hist. nat. Toulouse*, **92**, 177–180.

OHTAKI, T. 1960. 'Humoral control of pupal coloration in the cabbage white butterfly, *Pieris rapae crucivora*.' *Annot. zool. jap.*, **33**, 97–103.

ÖRÖSI-PÁL, Z. 1937. 'Pathologische Veränderungen (Geschwülste) im Dünndarm der Honigbiene.' *Zbl. Bakt. II*, **96**, 338–40.

OZAKI, K. 1958a. 'Neurosecretion of earwig *Anisolabis maritima*.' *Sci. Pap. Coll. gen. Educ. Tokyo*, **8**, 85–92.

OZAKI, K. 1958. 'Effects of corpus allatum hormone on development of male genital organs of the earwig *Anisolabis maritima*.' *Sci. Pap. Coll. gen. Educ. Tokyo*, **8**, 69–75.

OZAKI, K. 1958c. 'Effects of the corpus allatum hormone on postembryonic development of the female of the earwig *Anisolabis maritima*.' *Sci. Pap. Coll. gen. Educ. Tokyo*, **8**, 187–200.

OZAKI, K. 1959a. 'Further studies on the effects of the corpus allatum hormone on the development of the genital organs in males of the earwig *Anisolabis maritima*.' *Sci. Pap. Coll. gen. Educ. Tokyo*, **9**, 127–34.

OZAKI, K. 1959b. 'Secretion of moulting hormone from the ventral glands of the earwig *Anisolabis maritima*.' *Sci. Pap. Coll. gen. Educ. Tokyo*, **9**, 255–62.

OZAKI, K. 1960. 'Hormonal control of molting in the earwig *Anisolabis maritima*.' *Sci. Pap. Coll. gen. Educ. Tokyo*, **10**, 87–97.

OZAKI, K. 1961. 'Secretion of the juvenile hormone in the imago of the earwig *Anisolabis maritima*.' *Sci. Pap. Coll. gen. Educ. Tokyo*, **11**, 101–7.

PACLT, J. 1956. *Biologie der primär flügellosen Insekten*, Jena, G. Fischer, pp. 1–258.

PAIN, J. 1954a. 'La "substance de fécondité" dans le developpement des ovaires des ouvrières des abeilles (*Apis mellifica*).' *Insectes sociaux*, **1**, 59–70.

PAIN, J. 1954b. 'Sur l'ectohormone des reines d'abeilles.' *C. R. Acad. Sci. Paris*, **239**, 1869–70.

PAIN, J. 1955. 'Influence des reines mortes sur le développement ovarien de jeunes ouvrières d'abeilles (*Apis mellifica*).' *Insectes sociaux*, **2**, 34–43.

PAIN, J. 1956. 'La développement des ovaires des ouvrières des abeilles et l'ectohormone des reines.' *Experientia*, **12**, 354–7.

PAIN, J. 1959. 'Étude de l'apparition de l'attractivité chez les reines d'abeilles.' *C. R. Acad. Sci., Paris*, **248**, 3211–12.

PAIN, J. 1960. 'De l'influence du nombre des abeilles encagées sur la formation des œufs dans le ovaires de l'ouvrière.' *C. R. Acad. Sci., Paris*, **250**, 2629–31.

PAIN, J. and BARBIER, M. 1960. 'Mise en évidence d'une substance attractive extraite du corps des ouvrières d'abeilles par chromatographie en phase gazeuze.' *C. R. Acad. Sci., Paris*, **250**, 1126–7.

PAIN, J., HÜGEL, M. and BARBIER, M. 1960. 'Sur les constituants du mélange attractif des glandes mandibulaires des reines d'abeilles à différentes stades de leur vie.' *C. R. Acad. Sci., Paris*, **251**, 1046–8.

PALADE, G. E. 1956. *Enzymes: Units of biological structure and function*, New York, Acad. Press Inc., 185 pp.

PALM, N. B. 1947. 'Notes on the structure of the corpus allatum in *Gryllotalpa*.' *Forh. K. fisiogr. Sällsk. Lund*, **17**, 130–40.

PALM, N. B. 1949. 'Sexual differences in size and structure of the corpora allata in some insects.' *K. svensk. Vetensk. Akad. Handl.*, **6**, 1–24.

PANOV, A. A. 1957b. 'The structure of the insect brain in the subsequent stages of postembryonic development' (in Russian). *Rev. Ent. U.R.S.S.*, **36**, 269–84.

PANOV, A. A. 1959a. 'The morphogenesis of the glomerous structure of neuropyle of the olfactory lobe in insects' (in Russian). *Zool. Zh.*, **38**, 775–7.

PANOV, A. A. 1959b. 'The structure of the cerebral ganglion in insects in the subsequent stages of the postembryonic development. II. Central body' (in Russian). *Rev. Ent. U.R.S.S.*, **38**, 301–11.

PANOV, A. A. 1962a. 'The distribution of the neurosecretory cells in the ventral nerve cord of Orthoptera.' *C. R. Acad. Sci. U.R.S.S.*, **145**, 1409–12.

PANOV, A. A. 1962b. 'The character of cell reproduction in the central nervous system of the nymph of *Gryllus domesticus*' (in Russian). *C. R. Acad. Sci. U.R.S.S.*, **143**, 471–4.

PAPENHEIMER, A. M. and WILLIAMS, C. M. 1952. 'The effects of diphteria toxin on the cecropia silkworm.' *J. gen. Physiol.*, **35**, 727–40.

PARDI, L. 1946. 'Ricerche sui Polistini, 7. La "dominazione" e il ciclo ovarico annuale in *Polistes gallicus*.' *Boll. Ist. Ent. Univ. Bologna*, **15**, 24–84.

PARHON, C. I. and DEREVIZI, H. 1932. 'L'hormone parathyroidienne agit-elle chez les invertébrés ?' *C. R. Soc. Biol., Paris*, **110**, 643–4.

PARKER, G. H. 1948. *Animal colour changes and their neurohumours,* Cambridge, Univ. Press.

PASSONEAU, J. V. and WILLIAMS, C. M. 1953. 'The moulting fluid of the cecropia silkworm.' *J. exp. Biol.,* **30,** 545–60.

PATAY, R. 1946. 'Apropos de l'évolution nymphale de l'intestin moyen des Coléoptères.' *Bull. Soc. ent. Fr.,* **41,** 22–3.

PATAY, R. 1949. 'Apropos de l'évolution nymphale de l'intestine moyen de *Macrodytes marginalis* L.' *Bull. Soc. Sci. Bretagne,* **23,** 35–44.

PATTERSON, T. L. 1928. 'Growth and development of flesh flies as influenced by the feeding of hypophysis.' *Arch. EntwMech. Org.,* **113,** 267–86.

PAUL, H. 1937. 'Transplantation und Regeneration der Flügel zur Untersuchung ihrer Formbildung bei einem Schmetterling mit Geschlechtsdimorphismus *Orgyia antiqua.*' *Arch. EntwMech. Org.,* **136,** 64–111.

PAUTSCH, F. 1950. 'The effect of monochromatic light on the melanin formation in the *Dixippus morosus.*' *Bull. Acad. Pol. Sci.,* pp. 277–87.

PAUTSCH, F. 1952a. 'Chromatographic principles of the walking stick *Dixippus morosus* as colour change activators in some amphibians and marine crustaceans.' *Bull. Acad. Pol. Sci.,* pp. 1–32.

PAUTSCH, F. 1952b. 'Some analogies in the endocrine systems of vertebrates and invertebrates.' *Endokrin. Polska III,* pp. 73–84.

PEACOCK, A. D. and BAXTER, A. T. 1950. 'Studies in Pharaoh's ant, *Monomorium pharaonis* (L) 3. Life History.' *Ent. mon. Mag.,* **86,** 171–8.

PEACOCK, A. D., SMITH, I. C., HALL, D. W. and BAXTER, A. T. 1954. 'idem'. '8. Male production by parthenogenesis.' *Ent. mon. Mag.,* **90,** 154–8.

PEPPER, J. H. 1937. 'Breaking the dormancy in the sugar beet web-worm, *L. sticticalis* L. by means of chemicals.' *J. econ. Ent.* **30,** 380.

PEREDELSKI, A. 1930. 'On the question of the role of nervous system in the metamorphosis of Lepidoptera' (in Russian). *Arb. zentr. ForschSta. Seide, Moskau,* **4,** 41–62.

PEREDELSKI, A. 1939a. 'Endocrinology of invertebrates' (in Russian). *Adv. mod. Biol., Moscow,* **10,** 51–95.

PEREDELSKI, A. 1939b. 'The influence of vertebrate hormones upon the invertebrates' (in Russian). *Adv. mod. Biol., Moscow,* **8,** 441–66.

PEREDELSKI, A. 1940. 'Specific effects of the metamorphosis hormones of invertebrates on the metamorphosis of vertebrates' (in Russian). *C. R. Acad. Sci. U.R.S.S.,* **27,** 635–7.

PÉREZ, C. 1902. 'Contribution à l'étude des métamorphoses.' *Bull. sci. Fr. Belg.,* **37,** 195–427.

PÉREZ, C. 1910a. 'Signification phylétique de la nymphe chez les insectes métaboles.' *Bull. sci. Fr. Belg.,* **44,** 221–33.

PÉREZ, C. 1910b. 'Recherches histologiques sur la métamorphose des Muscides (*Calliphora*).' *Arch. Zool. exp. gén.,* **4,** 1–274.

PÉREZ, J. 1886. 'Des effects du parasitisme des *Stylops* sur les apiaires du genre *Andrena.*' *Act. Soc. Linn. Bordeaux,* **40,** 21–60.

PÉREZ, Z. 1940. 'Les cellules sécrétrices du cerveau du quelques Lépidoptères.' *Ann. Fac. Sci. Porto*, **25**, 92–4.

PERKINS, R. C. L. 1918. 'Stylopized bees.' *Ent. mon. Mag.*, **54**, 115–28.

PETIT, C. 1959. 'De la nature des stimulations responsables de la sélection sexuelle chez *Drosophila melanogaster*.' *C. R. Acad. Sci.*, *Paris*, **248**, 3484–5.

PFEIFFER-WEED, I. 1936a. 'Effect of removal of the corpora allata on egg production in the grasshopper *Melanoplus differentialis*.' *Proc. Soc. exp. Biol. N.Y.*, **34**, 883–5.

PFEIFFER-WEED, I. 1936b. 'Experimental study of moulting in the grasshopper *Melanoplus differentialis*.' *Proc. Soc. exp. Biol. N.Y.*, **34**, 885–886.

PFEIFFER-WEED, I. 1939. 'Experimental study of the function of the corpora allata in the grasshopper *Melanoplus differentialis*.' *J. exp. Biol.*, **82**, 439–61.

PFEIFFER-WEED, I. 1941a. 'Further studies on the function of the corpora allata in relation to the ovaries and oviducts of *Melanoplus differentialis*.' *Anat. Rec.*, **78**, 39–40.

PFEIFFER-WEED, I. 1941b. 'Effects of removal of the corpora allata on the fat metabolismus and water content of the grasshopper.' *Anat. Rec.*, **81**, suppl. 57.

PFEIFFER-WEED, I. 1942. 'Suppression of the metamorphosis in the grasshopper *Melanoplus differentialis*.' *Anat. Rec.*, **84**, 486.

PFEIFFER-WEED, I. 1945a. 'Effects of the corpora allata on the metabolism of adult female grasshoppers.' *J. exp. Zool.*, **99**, 183–233.

PFEIFFER-WEED, I. 1945b. 'The influence of the corpora allata over the development of nymphal characters in *Melanoplus differentialis*.' *Trans. Conn. Acad. Arts. Sci.*, **36**, 489–515.

PFLUGFELDER, O, 1937a. 'Vergleichend anatomische, experimentelle und embryologische Untersuchungen über das Nervensystem und die Sinnesorgane der Rhynchota.' *Zoologica, Stuttgart*, **34**, Heft 93, 102 pp.

PFLUGFELDER, O. 1937b. 'Bau, Entwicklung und Funktion der Corpora allata und cardiaca von *Dixippus morosus*.' *Z. wiss. Zool.*, **149**, 477–512.

PFLUGFELDER, O. 1937c. 'Untersuchungen über die Funktion der Corpora allata der Insekten.' *Verh. dtsch. zool. Ges.*, **39**, 121–9.

PFLUGFELDER, O. 1938a. 'Untersuchungen über die histologischen Veränderungen und das Kornwachstum der Corpora allata von Termiten.' *Z. wiss. Zool.*, **150**, 451–67.

PFLUGFELDER, O. 1938b. 'Weitere experimentelle Untersuchungen über die Funktion der Corpora allata von *Dixippus morosus*.' *Z. wiss. Zool.*, **151**, 149–91.

PFLUGFELDER, O. 1938c. 'Farbveränderungen und Gewebsentartungen nach Nervendurchschneidung und Extirpation der Corpora allata von *Dixippus morosus*.' *Verh. dtsch. zool. Ges.*, **40**, 127–37.

PFLUGFELDER, O. 1939a. 'Wechselwirkung von Drüsen innerer Sekretion bei *Dixippus morosus*.' *Z. wiss. Zool.*, **152**, 384–408.

PFLUGFELDER, O. 1939b. 'Hormonale Wirkungen im Lebenslauf der Stabheuschrecken.' *Forsch. Fortschr.*, **15**, 162–3.

PFLUGFELDER, O. 1939c. 'Weitere experimentelle Untersuchungen über die Funktion der Corpora allata von *Dixippus morosus.*' *Z. wiss. Zool.*, **152**, 384–408.

PFLUGFELDER, O. 1939d. 'Beeinflussung von Regenerationsvorgängen bei *Dixippus morosus* durch Extirpation und Transplantation der Corpora allata.' *Z. wiss. Zool.*, **152**, 159–84.

PFLUGFELDER, O. 1940. 'Austausch verschiedenalter Corpora allata bei *Dixippus morosus.*' *Z. wiss. Zool.*, **153**, 384–408.

PFLUGFELDER, O. 1941. 'Tatsachen und Probleme der Hormonforschung bei Insekten.' *Biol. gen.*, **15**, 197–235.

PFLUGFELDER, O. 1947a. 'Die Entwicklung embryonaler Teile von *Dixippus morosus* in der Kopfkapsel von Larven und Imagines.' *Biol. Zbl.*, **66**, 372–87.

PFLUGFELDER, O. 1947b. 'Geschwulstartige Wucherungen durch Implantation von Embryonen in Larven und Imagines von *Dixippus morosus*, nach Störung des Hormonhaushaltes.' *Biol. Zbl.*, **66**, 170.

PFLUGFELDER, O. 1947c. 'Über die Ventraldrüsen und einige andere inkretorische Organe des Insektenkopfes.' *Biol. Zbl.*, **66**, 211–35.

PFLUGFELDER, O. 1948a. 'Volumetrische Untersuchungen an den Corpora allata der Honigbiene *Apis mellifica.*' *Biol. Zbl.*, **67**, 223–41.

PFLUGFELDER, O. 1948b. 'Atypische Gewebsdifferenzierungen bei Stabheuschrecken nach experimenteller Störung der inneren Sekretion.' *Z. Krebsforsch.*, **56**, 107–20.

PFLUGFELDER, O. 1948c. 'Mechanismus der Amitose und Pseudoamitose bei experimentellen Geschwulstbildungen und nach Giftwirkung.' *Verh. dtsch. Zool. Kiel*, 49–58.

PFLUGFELDER, O. 1949. 'Die Funktion der Pericardialdrüsen der Insekten.' *Zool. Anz.*, **14**, suppl., 169–73.

PFLUGFELDER, O. 1952. *Entwicklungsphysiologie der Insekten*, Leipzig, Akad. Verlagsges. 284 pp.

PFLUGFELDER, O. 1958. *Entwicklungsphysiologie der Insekten*, Leipzig, 2nd ed. 435 pp.

PHIPPS, J. 1949. 'The structure and maturation of the ovaries in British Acrididae.' *Trans. roy. ent. Soc. Lond.*, **100**, 233–47.

PHIPPS, J. 1950. 'The maturation of the ovaries and the relation between weight and maturity in *Locusta migratoria migratorioides.*' *Bull. ent. Res.*, **40**, 539–57.

PIEPHO, H. 1938a. 'Wachstum und totale Metamorphose an Hautimplantaten bei der Wachsmotte *Galleria mellonella.*' *Biol. Zbl.*, **58**, 356–366.

PIEPHO, H. 1938b. 'Ueber die Auslösung der Raupenhätung, Verpuppung und Imaginalentwicklung an Hautimplantaten von Schmetterlingen.' *Biol. Zbl.*, **58**, 481–95.

PIEPHO, H. 1938c. 'Nicht-artspezifische Metamorphosehormone bei Schmetterlingen.' *Naturwissenschaften*, **26**, 383.

PIEPHO, H. 1938d. 'Ueber die experimentelle Auslösbarkeit überzähligen Häutungen und vorzeitiger Verpuppung am Hautstücken bei Kleinschmetterlingen.' *Naturwissenschaften*, **26**, 841–2.

PIEPHO, H. 1939a. 'Hemmung der Verpuppung durch Corpora allata von Jungraupen bei der Wachsmotte *Galleria mellonella*.' *Naturwissenschaften*, **27**, 675–6.

PIEPHO, H. 1939b. 'Raupenhäutungen bereits verpuppter Hautstücke bei der Wachsmotte *Galleria mellonella* L.' *Naturwissenschaften*, **27**, 301–2.

PIEPHO, H. 1939c. 'Über den Determinationszustand der Vorpuppenhypodermis bei der Wachsmotte *Galleria mellonella* L.' *Biol. Zbl.*, **59**, 314–26.

PIEPHO, H. 1940. 'Über die Hemmung der Verpuppung durch Corpora allata.' *Biol. Zbl.*, **60**, 367–93.

PIEPHO, H. 1942. 'Untersuchungen zur Entwicklungsphysiologie der Insektenmetamorphose. Über die Puppenhäutung der Wachsmotte *Galleria mellonella*.' *Arch. EntwMech. Org.*, **141**, 500–83.

PIEPHO, H. 1943. 'Wirkstoffe in der Metamorphose von Schmetterlingen und anderen Insekten.' *Naturwissenschaften*, **31**, 329–35.

PIEPHO, H. 1946. 'Versuche über die Rolle von Wirkstoffen in der Metamorphose der Schmetterlingen.' *Biol. Zbl.*, **65**, 141–8.

PIEPHO, H. 1947. 'Determinationsvorgänge in der Entwicklung der Schmetterlingshaut.' *Nachr. Akad. Wiss. Göttingen*, pp. 27–9.

PIEPHO, H. 1948. 'Zur Frage der Bildungsorgane des Häutungswirkstoffs bei Schmetterlingen.' *Naturwissenschaften*, **35**, 94–5.

PIEPHO, H. 1950a. 'Hormonale Grundlage der Spinntätigkeit bei Schmetterlingsraupen.' *Z. Tierpsychol.*, **7**, 424–34.

PIEPHO, H. 1950b. 'Über die Hemmung der Falterhäutung durch Corpora allata.' *Biol. Zbl.*, **69**, 261–71.

PIEPHO, H. 1950c. 'Über das Ausmass der Artunspezifität von Metamorphosehormone bei Insekten.' *Biol. Zbl.*, **69**, 1–10.

PIEPHO, H. 1951. 'Über die Lenkung der Insektenmetamorphose durch Hormone.' *Verh. dtsch. zool. Ges.*, pp. 62–76.

PIEPHO, H. 1952. 'Die Metamorphose der Lepidopteren in ihrer Anhängigkeit von Hormonen.' *Z. Lepid.*, **2**, 105–19.

PIEPHO, H. 1955a. 'Über die polare Orientieurung der Bälge und Schuppen auf dem Schmetterlingsrumpf.' *Biol. Zbl.*, **74**, 467–74.

PIEPHO, H. 1955b. 'Über die Ausrichtung der Schuppenbälge und Schuppen am Schmetterlingsrumpf.' *Naturwissenschaften*, **42**, 1–3.

PIEPHO, H. 1960. 'Hormonal control of molting behavior and scale development in insects.' *Ann. N.Y. Acad. Sci.*, **89**, 564–71.

PIEPHO, H., BÖDEN, E. and HOLZ, I. 1960. 'Über die Hormonabhängigkeit des Verhaltens von Schwärmerraupen von den Häutungen.' *Z. Tierpsychol.*, **17**, 261–9.

PIEPHO, H. and HEIMS, A. 1952. 'Das Kutikulamuster der Schmetterlings-larve und die hormonale Grundlage seiner Entstehung. Untersuchungen an der Wachsmotte *Galleria mellonella*.' *Z. Naturf.*, **7b**, 231–7.

PIEPHO, H. and HOLZ, I. 1959. 'Verjüngung des Mitteldarms von Schmet-terlingen.' *Biol. Zbl.*, **78**, 417–24.

PIEPHO, H. and MARCUS, W. 1957. 'Wirkungen richtender Faktoren beider Bildung der Schuppen und Bälge des Schmetterlingsrumpfes.' *Biol. Zbl.*, **76**, 23–7.

PIEPHO, H. and MEYER, H. 1961. 'Reaktionen der Schmetterlingshaut auf Häutungshormone.' *Biol. Zbl.*, **70**, 252–60.

PIEPHO, H. and RICHTER, A. 1959. 'Zur Entwicklungsphysiologie des Schuppenkleides bei Ur-Insekten. Untersuchungen an Silberfischen *Lepisma saccharina* L.' *Biol. Zbl.*, **78**, 857–61.

PIERCE, A. 1909. 'A monographic revision of the twisted winged insects comprising the order Strepsiptera Kirby.' *Bull. U.S. nat. Mus.*, **66**, XII + 232 pp.

PIGORINI, L. 1931. 'Contributo alla fisiologia dell'uovo negli insetti.' *Annu. Staz. bacol. sper. Padova*, **46**, 76–263.

PIPA, R. L. 1961. 'Studies on the Hexapod nervous system. IV. A cyto-logical and cytochemical study of neurons and their inclusions in the brain of *Periplaneta americana*.' *Biol. Bull., Wood's Hole*, **121**, 151–534.

PIPA, R. L. 1962. 'A cytochemical study of neurosecretory and other neuroplasmic inclusions in *Periplaneta americana*.' *Gen. comp. Endocrinol.*, **2**, 44–52.

PIPA, R. L., NISHIOKA, R. S. and BERN, H. A. 1962. 'Studies on the Hexapod nervous system. V. The ultrastructure of cockroach gliosomes.' *J. Ultrastruct. Res.*, **6**, 164–70.

PLAGGE, E. 1935. 'Die Pigmentierung der Imaginal- und Raupenaugen der Mehlmotte *Ephestia kühniella* bei verschiedenen Rassen, Transplan-tatträgern und Rassenkreuzungen.' *Arch. EntwMech. Org.*, **132**, 648–670.

PLAGGE, E. 1936a. 'Bewirkung der Augenausfärbung der rotäugigen Rasse von *Ephestia kühniella* durch Implantation artfremder Hoden.' *Nachr. Ges. Wiss. Göttingen (Biol.)*, **2**, 251–6.

PLAGGE, E. 1936b. 'Transplantationen von Augen-Imaginalscheiben zwischen der schwarz- und der rotäugigen Rasse von *Ephestia kühniella*.' *Biol. Zbl.*, **56**, 406–9.

PLAGGE, E. 1936c. 'Der zeitliche Verlauf der Auslösbarkeit von Hoden und Imaginalaugenfärbung durch den A-Wirkstoff bei *Ephestia kühniella* und die zur Ausscheidung einer wirksamen Menge nötige Zeitdauer.' *Z. indukt. Abstamm- u. VererbLehre*, **72**, 127–37.

PLAGGE, E. 1938. 'Weitere Untersuchungen über das Verpuppungshormon bei Schmetterlingen.' *Biol. Zbl.*, **58**, 1–12.

PLAGGE, E. 1939a. 'Genabhängige Wirkstoffe bei Tieren.' *Ergebn. Biol.*, **17**, 105–50.

PLAGGE, E. 1939b. 'Das Verpuppungshormon der Schmetterlinge.' *Forsch. Fortschr. dtsch. Wiss.*, **15**, 175–7.

PLAGGE, E. and BECKER, E. 1938. 'Wirkung arteigener und artfremder Verpuppungshormone in Extrakten.' *Naturwissenschaften*, **26**, 430–1.

PLOTNIKOV, W. 1904. 'Über die Häutung und über einige Elemente der Haut bei den Insekten.' *Z. wiss. Zool.*, **76**, 333–66.

POGOSSIANTZ, H. E. 1946. 'On the problem of the so called tumours in *Drosophila*' (in Russian). *C. R. Acad. Sci. U.R.S.S.*, **52**, 255–8.

POHLEY, H. J. 1959a. 'Über das Wachstum des Mehlmottenflügels unter normalen und experimentellen Bedingungen.' *Biol. Zbl.*, **78**, 232–50.

POHLEY, H. J. 1959b. 'Experimentelle Beiträge zur Lenkung der Organe-entwicklung, des Häutungsrhythmus und der Metamorphose bei der Schabe *Periplaneta americana*.' *Arch. EntwMech. Org.*, **151**, 323–80.

POISSON, R. and SELLIER, R. 1947. 'Brachyptérisme et actions endocrinnes chez *Gryllus campestris*.' *C. R. Acad. Sci., Paris*, **224**, 1074–5.

POLICE, G. 1910. 'Sulla discussa natura di alcune parti del sistema nervoso viscerale degli insetti.' *Arch. zool. ital.*, **4**, 287–314.

POLLISTER, A. W. 1954. *Dynamics of growth processes*, Princeton Univ. Press, p. 33.

POSSOMPÉS, B. 1946. 'Les glandes endocrines post-cérébrales des Diptères. I. Étude chez la larve du *Chironomus plumosus*.' *Bull. Soc. zool. Fr.*, **71**, 99–109.

POSSOMPÉS, B. 1947. 'idem'. 'II. Étude sommaire des corpora allata et des corpora cardiaca chez la larve de *Tipula* sp.' *Bull. Soc. zool. Fr.*, **72**, 57–62.

POSSOMPÉS, B. 1948. 'Technique d'ablation du système nerveux chez la larve de *Calliphora*.' *Bull. Soc. zool. Fr.*, **73**, 100–2.

POSSOMPÉS, B. 1949a. 'Les corpora cardiaca de la larve de *Chironomus plumosus* L.' *Bull. Soc. zool. Fr.*, **73**, 202–6.

POSSOMPÉS, B. 1949b. 'Les glandes endocrines post-cérébrales des Diptères. III. Étude chez la larve de *Tabanus* sp.' *Bull. Soc. zool. Fr.*, **73**, 228–235.

POSSOMPÉS, B. 1949c. 'Ablation fractionnée de l'anneau de Weismann chez la larve de *Calliphora erythrocephala* Meig.' *C. R. Soc. Biol., Paris*, **228**, 1527–9.

POSSOMPÉS, B. 1949d. 'Expériences d'ablation et d'implantation du système nerveux et de l'anneau de Weismann chez la larve de *Calliphora erythrocephala* Meig.' *C. R. XIIIe Conf. int. Zool.*, pp. 474–5.

POSSOMPÉS, B. 1950a. 'Implantation fractionnée de l'anneau de Weismann chez les larves permanentes de *Calliphora erythrocephala* Meig.' *C. R. Soc. Biol., Paris*, **230**, 409–11.

POSSOMPÉS, B. 1950b. 'Rôle du cerveau au cours de la métamorphose de *Calliphora erythrocephala* Meig.' *C. R. Soc. Biol., Paris*, **231**, 594–6.

POSSOMPÉS, B. 1953a. 'Recherches expérimentales sur le déterminisme de la métamorphose de *Calliphora erythrocephala* Meig.' *Arch. Zool. exp. gén.*, **89**, 204–304.

POSSOMPÉS, B. 1953b. 'Les données expérimentales sur la déterminisme endocrine de la croissance des insectes.' *Bull. Soc. zool. Fr.*, **78**, (4), 240–5.

POSSOMPÉS, B. 1954. 'Données expérimentales sur l'activation de l'anneau de Weismann par la cerveau chez *Calliphora erythrocephala* Meig.' *Pubbl. Staz. zool. Napoli*, **24**, 59–63.

POSSOMPÉS, B. 1955. 'Corpus allatum et développement ovarien chez *Calliphora erythrocephala* Meig.' *C. R. Acad. Sci., Paris*, **241**, 2001–3.

POSSOMPÉS, B. 1956. 'Développement ovarien aprés ablation du corpus allatum juvénile chez *Calliphora erythrocephala* Meig. et chez *Sipyloidea sipylus* (Phasmoptère).' *Ann. Sci. nat., zool.*, (11), **18**, 313–14.

POSSOMPÉS, B. 1957. 'Capacité d'accession á l'état imaginal des formes juvéniles du Phasme *Sipyloidea sipylus* W. aprés ablation des corpora allata.' *C. R. Acad. Sci., Paris*, **245**, 2404–6.

POSSOMPÉS, B. 1958. 'Effects de la section des connexions nerveuses entre le cerveau et l'anneau de Weismann sur les cellules neurosécrétrices protocérébrales et sur la glande péritrachéenne de *Calliphora erythrocephala* Meig.' *C. R. Acad. Sci., Paris*, **246**, 322–4.

POSPELOV, V. 1934. 'Imaginal diapause and sterility of butterflies' (in Russian). *C. R. Acad. Sci. U.R.S.S.*, **1**, 347–50.

POULSON, D. F. 1937. 'The embryonic development in *Drosophila*.' *Actual. Scient. ind.*, no. 498.

POULSON, D. F. 1945a. 'Chromosomal control of embryogenesis in *Drosophila*.' *Amer. Nat.*, **79**, 340–63.

POULSON, D. F. 1945b. 'Somatic mosaics and the differentiation of imaginal discs in *Drosophila*.' *Genetics*, **30**, 17.

POULSON, D. F. 1945c. 'On the origin and nature of the ring gland (Weismann's ring) of the higher Diptera.' *Trans. Conn. Acad. Arts. Sci.*, **36**, 449–69.

POULSON, D. F. and WATERHOUSE, D. F. 1958. 'Pole cells and midgut differentiation in Diptera.' *Proc. XVth int. Congr. Zool.*, pp. 606–8.

POYARKOFF, E. 1910. 'Recherches histologiques sur la métamorphose d'un Coléoptère (La Galeruque de l'Orme).' *Thèse Paris Arch. Anat. Micr.*, **62**, 333–48.

POYARKOFF, E. 1914. 'Essai d'une théorie de la nymphe des insectes holométaboles.' *Arch. Zool. exp. gén.*, **54**, 221–65.

POYARKOFF, E. F. 1936. 'The regulation of the number of generations in silkworm' (in Russian). *Priroda*, **5**, 83–93.

POWER, M. E. 1952. 'A quantitative study of the growth of the central nervous system of a holometabolous insect, *Drosophila melanogaster*.' *J. Morph.*, **91**, 389–411.

PREBBLE, M. L. 1941. 'The diapause and related phenomena in *Gilpinia polytoma* (Hartig). I, II.' *Canad. J. Res.*, **19**, 295–322, 323–46.

PRECHT, H. 1953. 'Über Ruhestadium erwachsener Insekten. I. Versuche an Kartoffelkäfern (*Leptinotarsa decemlineata*).' *Z. vergl. Physiol.*, **35**, 326–43.

PREER, J. R. and TELFER, W. H. 1957. 'Some effects of nonreacting substances in the quantitative application of gel diffusion techniques.' *J. Immun.* (4), **79**, 288–93.

PRELL, H. 1914. 'Über den Einfluss der Kastration auf den Antennenbau des Eichenspinners.' *Zool. Anz.*, **44**, 170–4.

PRELL, H. 1915. 'Über die Beziehungen zwischen den primären und sekundären Sexualcharaktern bei Schmetterlingen.' *Zool. Jb.*, Abt. 3, **35**, 183–224, 593–602.

PRIEBATSCH, I. 1933. 'Der Einfluss des Lichtes auf den Farbwechsel und Phototaxis von *Dixippus morosus*.' *Z. vergl. Physiol.*, **19**, 453–88.

PRINGLE, J. W. S. and HUGHES, G. N. 1948. 'Transmission of effects from the endings of nerve fibres.' *Nature, Lond.*, **162**, 558–60.

PRUTHI, H. S. 1924. 'Studies in insect metamorphosis. I. Prothetely in mealworms, *Tenebrio molitor* and other insects.' *Biol. Rev.*, **1**, 139–47.

PRYOR, M. G. M. 1940. 'On the hardening of the cuticle of insects.' *Proc. roy. Soc.* (B.), **128**, 393–407.

PRZIBRAM, H. 1919. 'Tierische Regeneration als Wachstumsbeschleunigung.' *Arch. EntwMech. Org.*, **45**, 1–38.

PRZIBRAM, H. 1935. 'Wachstum von Anhängen an verwandelten Fangheuschrecken (*Mantis, Sphodromantis*). Zugleich: Aufzucht der Gottesanbeterinnen XI und Homoeosis bei Arthropoden IX.' *Biol. gen.*, **11**, 189–202.

PRZIBRAM, H. and MEGUSHAR, F. 1912. 'Wachstumsmessungen an *Sphodromantis bioculata* Burm. I. Länge und Masse.' *Arch. EntwMech. Org.*, **34**, 680–741.

PRZIBRAM, H. and WEBER, E. F. 1907. 'Aufzucht, Farbwechsel und Regeneration unserer europäischen Gottesanbeterin (*Mantis religiosa*).' *Arch. EntwMech. Org.*, **23**, 615–31.

PUNT, A. 1950. 'The respiration in insects.' *Physiol. comp.*, **2**, 59–74.

PUNT, A. 1956a. 'Further investigation on the respiration in the insects.' *Physiol. comp.*, **4**, 121–9.

PUNT, A. 1956b. 'The influence of carbon dioxide on the respiration of *Carabus nemoralis* Müll.' *Physiol. comp.*, **4**, 132–41.

PUNT, A., PARSER, W. J. and KUKHKIN, J. 1957. 'Oxygen uptake in insects with cyclic CO_2 release.' *Biol. Bull., Wood's Hole*, **112**, 108–19.

PYLE, R. W. 1945. 'Changes in the nervous system of Lepidoptera during metamorphosis.' *Sum. Theses Ph.D. Harv.*, pp. 55–7.

QUO-FU. 1958. 'The comparative study of the corpora allata in normal and castrated specimens of grasshoppers.' *Acta ent. sinica*, **8**, 355–60.

QUO-FU. 1959a. 'The research of reproduction in East-migratory locust. Physiological effect of castration and mating.' *Acta ent. sinica*, **9**, 464–476.

QUO-FU. 1959b. 'Reciprocal transplantation of gonads of the adult oriental migratory locust in the *Locusta migratoria manilensis* M.' *Sci. Rec. Chunking*, **11**, 567–72.

RAABE, M. 1959a. 'Einfluss der Extirpation von Gehirn und Corpora cardiaca auf den Wasserhaushalt in *Carausius morosus.' C. R. Acad. Sci., Paris*, **252**, 2310–12.

RAABE, M. 1959b. 'Neurohormones chez les insectes.' *Bull. Soc. zool. Fr.*, **84**, 272–316.

RABAUD, E. 1929. 'Étude sur *Polistes gallicus* infesté par *Xenos vesparum.' Arch. micr. Anat.*, **25**, 280–93.

RABAUD, E. and MILLOT, J. 1927. 'Sur les Guêpes (*Polistes gallicus*) infestées par les Stylops.' *C. R. Soc. Biol., Paris*, **96**, 944–6.

RADTKE, A. 1942. 'Hemmung der Verpuppung bei Mehlkäfer *Tenebrio molitor.' Naturwissenschaften*, **30**, 451–2.

RAE, C. A. 1955. 'Possible new elements in the endocrine complex of cockroaches.' *Austr. J. Sci.*, **18**, 33–4.

RAE, C. A. 1957. 'Prothoracic glands in a mantid (*Orthodera ministralis* Fabr.).' *Austr. J. Sci.*, **19**, 229.

RAE, C. A. and O'FARRELL, A. F. 1959. 'The retrocerebral and ventral glands of the primitive Orthopteroid *Grylloblatta campodeiformis* Walk, with a note on the homology of the muscle cord of the "prothoracic gland" in Dictyoptera.' *Proc. roy. ent. Soc. Lond.* (A), **34**, 76–83.

RAHMS, U. H. 1952. 'Die innersekretorische Steuerung der postembryonalen Entwicklung von *Sialis lutaria* L.' *Rev. suisse Zool.*, **59**, 173–237.

RAPOPORT, J. A. 1939. 'Specific morphoses in *Drosophila* induced by chemical compounds.' *Bull. Biol. Méd. exp. U.R.S.S.*, **7**, 415–17.

RAVOUX, P. H. 1947. 'Observations sur l'anamorphose de *Scutigerella immaculata.' Arch. Zool. exp. gén.*, **85**, 189–98.

READIO, P. A. 1931. 'Dormancy in *Reduvius personatus.' Ann. ent. Soc. Amer.*, **24**, 19–39.

REES, J. 1888. 'Beiträge zur Kenntnis der inneren Metamorphose von *Musca vomitoria.' Zool. Jb.*, Abt. 2, **3**, 1–34.

REGEN, J. 1909. 'Kastration und Folgerscheinung bei *Gryllus campestris* Männchen.' *Zool. Anz.*, **34**, 477–8.

REGEN, J. 1910. 'Kastration und Folgerscheinung bei *Gryllus campestris* Männchen.' *Zool. Anz.*, **35**, 427–32

REHM, M. 1950. 'Sekretionsperioden neurosekretorischer Zellen im Gehirn von *Ephestia kühniella.' Z. Naturf.*, **56**, 167–9.

REHM, M. 1951. 'Die zeitliche Folge der Tätigkeitsrhythmen inkretorischer Organe von *Ephestia kühniella* während der Metamorphose und des Imaginallebens.' *Arch. EntwMech. Org.*, **145**, 205–8.

REMPEL, J. G. 1940. 'Intersexuality in Chironomidae induced by Nematode parasitism.' *J. exp. Zool.*, **84**, 261–89.

REMY, P. 1923. 'L'iode et le développement des insectes.' *Bull. Soc. Sci. Nancy* (4), **2**, 45–52.

REMY, P. 1924. 'Les sécrétions internes et les metamorphoses.' *Ann. Sci. nat., Paris*, **7**, 41–82.

RESNICHENKO, M. S. 1927. 'Zur Frage über die spezifische Wirkung der Schilddrüse und Ca- und K-jonen auf die Entwicklung von *Drosophila melanogaster.*' *Trans. Lab. exper. Biol. Zoopark, Moscow,* **3,** 27–35.

RHEIN, W. 1933. 'Über die Entstehung des weiblichen Dimorphismus.' *Arch. EntwMech. Org.,* **129,** 601–65.

RHEIN, W. 1951. 'Über die Entstehung des weiblichen Dimorphismus im Bienenstaate und ihre Beziehung zum Metamorphoseproblem (vorläufige Mitteilung).' *Verh. dtsch. zool. Ges.,* pp. 99–101.

RIBBANDS, C. R. 1953. *The behaviour and social life of honey bees,* London.

RICHARD, G. 1952. 'L'innervation sensorielle pendant les mues chez les insectes.' *Bull. Soc. zool. Fr.,* **77,** 99–106.

RICHARD, G. 1954. 'Organogenèse des nerfs et des trachées alaires du termite *Kalotermes flavicollis* Fabr.' *Insectes sociaux,* **1,** 177–88.

RICHARDS, O. W. 1953. *The social insects,* London, MacDonald.

RINTERKNECHT, E. 1961. 'Étude de la cicatrisation chez *Locusta migratoria* L.' *Bull. Soc. zool. Fr.,* **86,** 87–98.

RISLER, H. 1950. 'Kernvolumenänderung in der Larvenentwicklung von *Ptychopoda seriata* Schrk.' *Biol. Zbl.,* **69,** 11–28.

RIZKI, M. T. M. 1950. 'A method of preparation of *Drosophila* eggs for micromanipulation.' *Drosophila Information Service,* **24,** 98.

RIZKI, M. T. M. 1953. 'A micro-injection assembly for *Drosophila.*' *Drosophila Information Service,* **27,** 121–2.

RIZKI, M. T. M. 1960. 'Melanotic tumor formation in *Drosophila.*' *J. Morph.,* **106,** 147–57.

RIZKI, M. T. M. and RIZKI, M. R. 1962. 'Cytodifferentiation in the Rosy mutant of *Drosophila melanogaster.*' *J. Cell. Biol.,* **12,** 149–58.

ROBBINS, W. E. and SHORTINO, T. J. 1962. 'Effect of cholesterol in the larval diet on ovarian development in the adult house-fly.' *Nature, Lond.,* **194,** 502–3.

ROBERTSON, C. W. 1936. 'The metamorphosis of *Drosophila* including an accurately timed account of the principal morphological changes.' *J. Morph.,* **59,** 351–99.

ROCKSTEIN, M. 1956. 'Metamorphosis, a physiological interpretation.' *Science,* **123,** 534–6.

ROCKSTEIN, M. 1957. 'Some aspects of intermediary metabolism of carbohydrates in insects.' *Ann. Rev. Ent.,* **2,** 19–36.

ROCKSTEIN, M. 1959. 'Metachemogenesis—postemergence biochemical maturation in insects.' In Clarke *et al.,* 'Studies in invertebrate morphology.' *Smithson. misc. Coll.,* **137,** 263–86.

ROHDENDORF, B. B. 1959. 'Die Bewegungsorgane der Zweiflügler-Insekten und ihre Entwicklung. I–III.' *Wiss. Z. Humboldt-Univ. Berl.,* **8,** 73–119, 269–308, 435–54.

ROEDER, K. D. 1953. *Insect Physiology,* New York and London.

RÖLLER, H. 1962. 'Über den Einfluss der Corpora allata auf den Stoffwechsel der Wachsmotte.' *Naturwissenschaften,* **22,** 525.

ROMEIS, B. and WÜST, I. 1929a. 'Die Wirkung von Thyroxin auf den Gasstoffwechsel von Schmetterlingspuppen. Zugleich ein Beitrag zur Frage der Wirkung kleinster Mengen.' *Arch. EntwMech. Org.*, **118**, 534–633.

ROMEIS, B. and WÜST, I. 1929b. 'Über die Wirkung kleinster Thyroxindosen auf den Gasstoffwechsel von Wirbellosen.' *Naturwissenschaften*, **17**, 104–5.

ROMEIS, B. and WÜST, I. 1932. 'Die Wirkung von Thyroxin auf den Gasstoffwechsel von Schmetterlingspuppen. II. Teil.' *Arch. EntwMech. Org.*, **125**, 673–736.

ROMEIS, B. and DOBKIEWICZ, L. 1920. 'Der Einfluss von Schilddrüsenfütterung auf Entwicklung und Wachstum der Schmeissfliege (*Calliphora erythrocephala*).' *Arch. EntwMech. Org.*, **47**, 118–30.

ROMEIS, B. and DOBKIEWICZ, L. 1932. 'Die Wirkung von Thyroxin auf den Gasstoffwechsel von Schmetterlingspuppen. III. Teil-ergänzende mikroskopische Untersuchungen.' *Arch. EntwMech. Org.*, **125**, 737–69.

ROONWAL, M. L. 1937. 'Studies on the embryology of the African migratory locust, *Locusta migratoria migratorioides* Reiche (Orthoptera, Acrididae). II. Organogeny.' *Phil. Trans. R. Soc.* (B), **227**, 175–244.

ROONWAL, M. L. 1947. 'On variations in the number of ovarioles and its probable origin in the desert locust *Schistocerca gregaria*.' *Rec. ind. Mus.*, **44**, 375–80.

ROTH, L. and STAY, B. 1959. 'Control of oöcyte development in cockroaches.' *Science*, **130**, 271–2.

ROTH, L. and STAY, B. 1961. 'Oöcyte development in *Diploptera punctata*.' *J. Ins. Physiol.*, **7**, 186–202.

ROTH, L. and STAY, B. 1962. 'A comparative study of Oöcyte development in false ovoviviparous cockroaches.' *Psyche*, **69**, 165–208.

RÖTTGEN, H. 1960. 'Untersuchungen zur Entwicklungsgeschichte des Randfransenmusters der Mehlmotte *Ephestia kühniella*.' *Biol. Zbl.*, **79**, 641–55.

ROUBAUD, E. 1922. 'Étude sur le sommeil d'hiver préimaginal des Muscides.' *Bull. biol.*, **56**, 455–544.

ROUBAUD, E. 1927a. 'L'anhydrobiose reactivante dans le cycle évolutif de la Pyrale du Maïs.' *C. R. Acad. Sci., Paris*, **186**, 792–3.

ROUBAUD, E. 1927b. 'L'heterodynamie et la rôle de l'athermobiose dans le cycle évolutif de *Phlebotomus pappatasii*.' *Bull. Soc. path. exot.*, **20**, 613–19.

ROZEBOOM, L. E. 1961. 'The effect of the gonadotropic hormone cycle of the adult mosquito on development of the malaria parasite'. *J. Parasit.*, **47**, 597–99.

RUSSELL, E. S. 1940. 'A comparison of "benign" and "malignant" tumors in *Drosophila melanogaster*.' *J. exp. Zool.*, **84**, 363–85.

RUSSELL, E. S. 1942. 'The inheritance of tumors in *Drosophila melanogaster* with especial reference to an isogenic strain of st sr tumor 36a.' *Genetics*, **27**, 612–18.

RUSSO-CAIA, S. 1960a. 'Aspetti biochimici della metamorphosi degli insetti. L'acido derossi ribonucleico durante lo sviluppo larvale e la metamorfosi di *Musca domestica* L' *R. C. Accad. Lincei*, **29**, 215–20, 630–33.

RUSSO-CAIA, S. 1960b. 'Aspetti biochimici della metamorphosi degli insetti. Il metabolismo delle sostanze azotate durante lo sviluppo larvale e la metamorfozi di *Musca domestica*.' *Riv. Biol.*, **53**, 409–30.

RUSSO-CAIA, S. 1960c. 'Cucidi e lipidi nella metamorfosi di *Musca domestica*.' *Ric. sci.*, **30**, 1577–83.

RUSSO-CAIA, S. 1960c. 'Aspetti biochimici della metamorfosi degli insetti. Osservazioni su alcuni prodotti terminali del metabolismo azotato nello sviluppo larvale e nella metamorfosi di "*Musca domestica* L.".' *Rend. Ist. Sci. Camerino*, **1**, 67–81.

RUSSO-CAIA, S. 1960d. 'Aspetti biochimici della metamorfosi degli insetti. Idrolisi enzymatica dell'atp durante lo sviluppo larvale e la metamorfozi di *Musca domestica*.' *Acta Embryol. Morphol. exp.*, **3**, 286–95.

SABROSKY, C., LARSON, J. and NABOURS, R. 1933. 'Experiments with light upon reproduction growth and diapause in Grouse locusts (Acrididae, Tetriginae).' *Trans. Kans. Acad. Sci.*, **36**, 298–300.

SACKTOR, B. 1951. 'Some aspects of respiratory metabolism during metamorphosis of normal and DDT-resistant house-flies, *Musca domestica*.' *Biol. Bull., Wood's Hole*, **100**, 229–43.

SACKTOR, B. 1952. 'The cytochrome c oxidase and the house-fly *Musca domestica*'. *J. gen. Physiol.*, **35**, 397–407.

SÄGESSER, H. 1960. 'Über die Wirkung der Corpora allata auf den Sauerstoffverbrauch bei der Schabe *Leucophaea maderae*.' *J. Ins. Physiol.*, **5**, 264–85.

SAKAGAMI, S. F. 1954. 'Occurrence of an aggressive behavior in queenless hives with consideration on the social organisation of honey bee.' *Insectes sociaux*, **1**, 331–43.

SALHAROV, N. L. 1930. 'Studies in cold resistance of insects.' *Ecology*, **11**, 505–17.

SALT, G. 1927. 'The effects of stylopization on aculeate Hymenoptera.' *J. exp. Zool.*, **48**, 223–319.

SALT, G. 1931. 'A further study of the effects of stylopization on wasps.' *J. exp. Zool.*, **59**, 133–63.

SALT, G. 1937. 'The egg-parasite of *Sialis lutaria*: a study of the influence of the host upon a dimorphic parasite.' *Parasitology*, **29**, 539–53.

SALT, G. 1941. 'The effects of hosts upon their insect parasites.' *Biol. Rev.*, **16**, 239–64.

SALT, G. 1952. 'Trimorphism in the ichneumonid parasite *Gelis corruptor*.' *Quart. J. micr. Sci.*, **93**, 453–74.

SALT, R. W. 1947. 'Some effects of temperature on the production and elimination of diapause in the wheat stem sawfly, *Cephus cinctus*.' *Canad. J. Res.*, **25**, 66–86.

SAMOKHVALOVA, G. V. 1951. 'The origin of hereditary changes in aphids in connection with the change of the host plant' (in Russian). *J. gen. Biol.*, *Moscow*, **3**, 176–91.

SAMUELS, A. 1956. 'The effects of sex and allatectomy on the oxygen consumption of the thoracic musculature of the insect *Leucophaea maderae*.' *Biol. Bull.*, *Wood's Hole*, **110**, 179–83.

SANBORN, R. C. and WILLIAMS, C. M. 1950. 'The cytochrome system in the Cecropia silkworm with special reference to the properties of a new component.' *J. gen. Physiol.*, **33**, 579–88.

SANDERSON, A. R. and HALL, D. W. 1948. 'The cytology of the honey bee *Apis mellifica*.' *Nature*, *Lond.*, **62**, 34–5.

SATO, H. and JINO, CH. 1935. 'Studies on the voltinism of the silkworm. Activity of the lipase in relation to the voltinism.' *Bull. Ser. Silk. Ind.*, *Uyeda*, **13**, 1–2.

SCHADER, L. 1941. 'The effect of vitamin B_1 (thiamin) on the body length and duration of larval period in *Drosophila melanogaster*.' *Growth*, **5**, 19–26.

SCHALLER, F. 1951. 'Réalisation des charactères de caste au cours de développement perturbées chez l'abeille.' *C. R. Soc. Biol.*, *Paris*, **145**, 1351–4.

SCHALLER, F. 1952. 'Effets d'une ligature postcéphalique sur le développement de larves agées d'*Apis mellifica*.' *Bull. Soc. zool. Fr.*, **77**, 195–204.

SCHALLER, F. 1959b. 'Controle humoral du développement postembryonaire d'*Aeschna cyanea*.' *C. R. Acad. Sci.*, *Paris*, **248**, 2525–7.

SCHARRER, B. 1939. 'Über sekretorisch tätige Nervenzellen bei wirbellosen Tieren.' *Naturwissenschaften*, **75**, 131–8.

SCHARRER, B. 1939. 'The differentiation between neuroglia and connective tissue sheath in the cockroach *Periplaneta americana*.' *J. comp. Neur.*, **70**, 77–88.

SCHARRER, B. 1941a. 'Neurosecretion. II. Neurosecretory cells in the central nervous system of cockroaches.' *J. comp. Neur.*, **74**, 93–108.

SCHARRER, B. 1941b. 'Endocrines in Invertebrates.' *Physiol. Rev.*, **21**, 383.

SCHARRER, B. 1943. 'The influence of the corpora allata on egg development of *Leucophaea maderae*.' *Anat. Rec.*, **87**, 471.

SCHARRER, B. 1945. 'Experimental tumors in insects.' *Proc. Soc. exp. Biol.*, *N.Y.*, **60**, 184–9.

SCHARRER, B. 1946a. 'The role of the corpora allata in the development of *Leucophaea maderae*.' *Endocrinology*, **38**, 35–45.

SCHARRER, B. 1946b. 'The relationship between corpora allata and reproductive organs in adult *Leucophaea maderae*.' *Endocrinology*, **38**, 46–55.

SCHARRER, B. 1946c. 'Section of the nervi corporis cardiaci in *Leucophaea maderae*.' *Anat. Rec.*, **96**, 577.

SCHARRER, B. 1948a. 'Hormones in insects.' In Pincus and Thimann, *Hormones, chemistry and chemical applications*, New York.

SCHARRER, B. 1948b. 'The prothoracic glands of *Leucophaea maderae*.' *Biol. Bull.*, *Wood's Hole*, **95**, 186–98.

SCHARRER, B. 1948c. 'Malignant characteristic of experimentally induced tumors in the insect *Leucophaea maderae.*' *Anat. Rec.,* 100, 774–5.

SCHARRER, B. 1949. 'Gastric cancer experimentally induced in insects by nerve severance.' *J. nat. Cancer Inst.,* 10, 375–6.

SCHARRER, B. 1951. 'The storage of neurosecretory material in the corpus cardiacum.' *Anat. Rec.,* 111, 554–5.

SCHARRER, B. 1952a. 'Hormones in insects.' In K. V. Thimann, *The action of hormones in plants and invertebrates,* New York, Acad. Press. Inc.

SCHARRER, B. 1952b. 'Neurosecretion. XI. The effects of nerve section on the intercerebralis-cardiacum-allatum-system of the insect *Leucophaea maderae.*' *Biol. Bull., Wood's Hole,* 102, 261–72.

SCHARRER, B. 1952c. 'Über endocrine Vorgänge bei Insekten.' *Pflug. Arch. ges. Physiol.,* 255, 154–63.

SCHARRER, B. 1952d. 'The effect of the interruption of the neurosecretory pathway in the *Leucophaea maderae.*' *Anat. Rec.,* 112, 386–7.

SCHARRER, B. 1953. 'Comparative physiology of invertebrate endocrines.' *Ann. Rev. Physiol.,* 15, 457–72.

SCHARRER, B. 1954. 'Neurosecretion in the invertebrates: a survey.' *Pubbl. Staz. zool. Napoli,* 24, 38–41.

SCHARRER, B. 1955a. ' "Castration cells" in the central nervous system of an insect *Leucophaea maderae.*' *Trans. N.Y. Acad. Sci.,* 17, 520–5.

SCHARRER, B. 1955b. 'Aberrations in the distribution of neurosecretory cells in the suboesophageal ganglion of *Leucophaea maderae.*' *Anat. Rec.,* 122, 489–90.

SCHARRER, B. 1955c. In Pincus and Thimann, *The Hormones,* New York, Acad Press Inc., 2nd ed., pp. 121–58.

SCHARRER, B. 1956a. 'Corrélations endocrines dans la reproduction des insectes.' *Ann. Sci. nat., Zool.,* (11), 18, 231–4.

SCHARRER, B. 1956b. 'A study of the corpora allata of gonadectomized *Leucophaea maderae.*' *Anat. Rec.,* 125, 558.

SCHARRER, B. 1958a. 'The corpus allatum of *Leucophaea maderae.*' *Proc. Xth int. Congr. Ent.,* 2, 57.

SCHARRER, B. 1958a. 'Neuro-endocrine mechanism in insects.' *Proc. IInd int. Symp. Neurosecret.,* 79–84.

SCHARRER, B. 1959. 'The role of neurosecretion in neuroendocrine integration.' *Symp. comp. Endocrin.,* pp. 134–148.

SCHARRER, B. 1961. 'Functional analysis of the corpus allatum of *Leucophaea maderae* with the electron microscope.' *Biol. Bull., Wood's Hole,* 121, 370.

SCHARRER, B. 1962a. 'Ultrastructure and function in the corpus allatum of an insect *Leucophaea maderae.*' *Anat. Rec.,* 142, 275.

SCHARRER, B. 1962b. 'The neurosecretory system of *Leucophaea maderae* and its role in neuroendocrine integration.' *Gen. comp. Endocrinol.,* 2, 30.

SCHARRER, B. and HADORN, E. 1938. 'The structure of the ring gland (corpus allatum) in normal and lethal larvae of *Drosophila.*' *Proc. nat. Acad. Sci., Wash.*, 24, 236–47.

SCHARRER, B. and HADORN, E. 1961. 'Histophysiological studies on the corpus allatum of *Leucophaea maderae*. III. Effect of castration.' *Biol. Bull., Wood's Hole*, 121, 193–208.

SCHARRER, B. and SZABÓ-LOCKHEAD, M. 1950. 'Tumors in the invertebrates' (a review). *Cancer Res.*, 10, 403–19.

SCHARRER, B. and SCHARRER, E. 1937. 'Über Drüsennervenzellen und neurosekretorische Organe bei Wirbellosen und Wirbeltieren'. *Biol. Rev.*, 12, 185–216.

SCHARRER, B. and SCHARRER, E. 1944. 'Neurosecretion. VI. A comparison between the intercerebralis-cardiacum-allatum system of insects and the hypothalamo-hypophysial system of Vertebrates.' *Biol. Bull., Wood's Hole*, 87, 242–51.

SCHARRER, E. 1952. 'The general significance of the neurosecretory cell.' *Scientia*, 4, 177–83.

SCHARRER, E. 1958. 'Molting cycles in the toad *Bufo marinus*.' *Anat. Rec.*, 130, 369.

SCHARRER, E. 1959. 'Neuroendocrine relations. General and phylogenetic interpretations of neuroendocrine interrelations.' In *A textbook of comparative endocrinology*, New York, J. Wiley & Sons, pp. 233–249.

SCHARRER, E. and SCHARRER, B. 1945. 'Neurosecretion.' *Physiol. Rev.*, 25, 171–81.

SCHARRER, E. and SCHARRER, B. 1954a. 'Neurosecretion.' In Möllendorf, *Handbuch der mikroskopischen Anatomie der Menschen*, Berlin, Springer, 4, 953–1066.

SCHARRER, E. and SCHARRER, B. 1954b. 'Hormones produced by neurosecretory cells.' *Recent Progr. Hormone Res.*, 10, 183–240.

SCHARRER, E. and SCHARRER, B. 1958. 'Neurosecretion.' *Science*, 127, 1396–8.

SCHEER, B. T. 1957. 'The hormonal control of metabolism in Decapod Crustaceans.' In B. T. Scheer (Ed.). *Recent advances in invertebrate physiology*. Eugene, Oregon, Univ. Oregon Publ., pp. 213–27.

SCHEER, B. T. 1960. 'The neuroendocrine system of arthropods.' *Vitam. Horm.*, 18, 141–204.

SCHICK, V. 1953. 'Ueber die Wirkung von Giftstoffen auf die Tänze der Bienen.' *Z. vergl. Physiol.*, 35, 105–28.

SCHIEBLER, T. H. 1951. 'Zur Histochemie der neurosekretorischen hypothalamisch-neurohypophysären Systems.' *Acta anat.*, 13, 233–55.

SCHIEBLER, T. H. 1952. 'Cytochemische und elektronenmikroskopische Untersuchungen an granulösen Fraktionen der Menschenhypophyse des Rindes.' *Z. Zellforsch.*, 36, 563–76.

SCHINDLER, A. K. 1902. 'Die Metamorphose der Insekten.' *Z. Naturw.*, 75, 349–56.

o

SCHLEIP, W. 1911. 'Der Farbwechsel von *Dixippus morosus*.' *Zool. Jb.*, Abt. 3, **30**, 45–132.

SCHLEIP, W. 1915. 'Über die Frage nach der Beteiligung des Nervensystems beim Farbwechsel von *Dixippus morosus*.' *Zool. Jb.*, Abt. 3, **35**, 225–32.

SCHLEIP, W. 1921. 'Über den Einfluss des Lichtes auf die Färbung von *Dixippus morosus* und Frage der Erblichkeit des erworbenen Farbkleides.' *Zool. Anz.*, **52**, 151–60.

SCHMIEDER, R. G. 1933. 'The polymorphic forms of *Mellitobia chalybii* and the determining factors involved in their production.' *Biol. Bull.*, *Wood's Hole*, **65**, 338–54.

SCHMIEDER, R. G. 1942. 'The control of metamorphosis in Hymenoptera.' *Anat. Rec.*, **84**, 514.

SCHMIDT, E. L. and WILLIAMS, C. M. 1951. 'An analysis of metamorphosis hormones of Lepidoptera by the method of tissue culture.' *Anat. Rec.*, **111**, 162.

SCHMIDT, E. L. and WILLIAMS, C. M. 1953. 'Physiology of insect diapause. V. Assay of the growth and differentiation hormone of Lepidoptera by the method of tissue culture.' *Biol. Bull.*, *Wood's Hole*, **105**, 174–87.

SCHMIDT, G. H. 1961a. 'Sekretionsphasen und cytologische Beobachtungen zur Funktion der Oenocyten während der Puppenphase verschiedener Kasten und Geschlechter von *Formica polyctena*.' *Z. Zellforsch.*, **55**, 707–23.

SCHMIDT, G. H. 1961b. 'Histophysiologische Untersuchungen zur Bedeutung der Oenozyten während der Metamorphose der roten Waldameise *Formica polyctena*.' *Verh. dtsch. zool. Ges. Saarbrücken, Zool. Anz.*, **25**, Suppl.' pp. 329–37.

SCHMIDT, G. H. 1961c. 'Histologische Untersuchungen zur Funktion der Corpora allata während der Metamorphose von *Formica polyctena*.' *Symp. gen. Biol. ital.*, *Pavia*, **10**, 43–72.

SCHNEIDER, F. 1951. 'Einige physiologische Beziehungen zwischen Syrphidenlarven und ihren Parasiten.' *Z. angew. Ent.*, **33**, 150–62.

SCHNEIDERMAN, H. A. 1953. 'The discontinuous release of carbon dioxide by diapausing pupal insects.' *Anat. Rec.*, **117**, 540.

SCHNEIDERMAN, H. A. 1959. 'The chemistry and physiology of insect growth hormones.' *Cell, Organism and Milieu*, Ronald Press Comp., pp. 157–87.

SCHNEIDERMAN, H. A., FEDER, N. and KETCHEL, M. 1951. 'The cytochrome system in relation to in vitro spermatogenesis in the cecropia silkworm.' *Anat. Rec.*, **111**, 164.

SCHNEIDER, H. A. and GILBERT, L. I. 1957. 'The distribution and chemical properties of the juvenile hormone of insects.' *Anat. Rec.*, **128**, 618.

SCHNEIDERMAN, H. A. and GILBERT, L. I. 1958a. 'The inactivation of juvenile hormone extracts by pupal silkworms.' *Anat. Rec.*, **131**, 557–8.

SCHNEIDERMAN, H. A. and GILBERT, L. I. 1958b. 'Substances with juvenile hormone activity in crustacea and other invertebrates.' *Biol. Bull.*, *Wood's Hole*, **115**, 530–5.

SCHNEIDERMAN, H. A. and WEINSTEIN, J. M. 1960. 'Juvenile hormone activity in microorganisms and plants.' *Nature, Lond.*, **188**, 1041.

SCHNEIDERMAN, H. A., KETCHEL, M. and WILLIAMS, C. M. 1953. 'The physiology of insect diapause. VI. Effects of temperature, oxygen tension and metabolic inhibitors on in vitro spermatogenesis in the cecropia silkworm.' *Biol. Bull., Wood's Hole*, **105**, 188–99.

SCHNEIDERMAN, H. A. and WILLIAMS, C. M. 1952. 'The terminal oxidases in diapausing and non-diapausing insects.' *Anat. Rec.*, **113**, 4.

SCHNEIDERMAN, H. A. and WILLIAMS, C. M. 1953a. 'Metabolic effects of localized injury to the integument of the cecropia silkworm.' *Anat. Rec.*, **117**, 640–1.

SCHNEIDERMAN, H. A. and WILLIAMS, C. M. 1953b. 'Discontinuous carbon dioxide output by diapausing pupae of the giant silkworm *Platysamia cecropia*.' *Biol. Bull., Wood's Hole*, **105**, 382.

SCHNEIDERMAN, H. A. and WILLIAMS, C. M. 1953c. 'The physiology of insect diapause. VII. The respiratory metabolism of the Cecropia silkworm during diapause and development.' *Biol. Bull., Wood's Hole*, **105**, 320–34.

SCHNEIDERMAN, H. A. and WILLIAMS, C. M. 1954a. 'idem'. 'VIII. Qualitative changes in the metabolism of the Cecropia silkworm during diapause and development.' *Biol. Bull., Wood's Hole*, **106**, 210–29.

SCHNEIDERMAN, H. A. and WILLIAMS, C. M. 1954b. 'idem'. 'IX. The cytochrome oxidase system in relation to the diapause and development of the Cecropia silkworm.' *Biol. Bull., Wood's Hole*, **106**, 238–52.

SCHNEIDERMAN, H. A. and WILLIAMS, C. M. 1955. 'An experimental analysis of the discontinuous respiration of the Cecropia silkworm.' *Biol. Bull., Wood's Hole*, **109**, 123–43.

SCHNEIRLA, T. C. and BROWN, R. Z. 1952. 'Sexual broods and the production of young queens in two species of terrestrial army ants.' *Zoologica*, **37**, 5–37.

SCHOONHOVEN, L. M. 1959. 'The break of diapause in *Bupalus piniarius* L.' *Acta Physiol. Pharmacol. Néerland*, **8**, 578.

SCHOONHOVEN, L. M. 1962. 'Diapause and the physiology of host-parasite synchronization in *Bupalus piniarius* L. and *Eucarcelia rutilla*.' *Arch. Néerland. Zool.*, **15**, 111–74.

SCHRADER, K. 1938. 'Untersuchungen über die Normalentwicklung des Gehirns und Gehirntransplantationen bei der *Ephestia kühniella* nebst einigen Bemerkungen über Corpus allatum.' *Biol. Zbl.*, **58**, 52–90.

SCHRÖDER, D. 1957. 'Über die Gewebsatmung des Kartoffelkäfers *Leptinotarsa decemlineata* in der Winterruhe und in Wachzustand.' *J. Ins. Physiol.*, **1**, 131–42.

SCHULTZ, R. L. 1960. 'Electron microscopic observations of the corpora allata and associated nerves in the moth *Celerio lineata*.' *J. Ultrastruct. Res.*, **3**, 320–7.

SCHÜRFELD, W. 1935. 'Die physiologische Bedeutung der Versondrüse, untersucht im Zusammenhang mit ihrem feineren Bau.' *Arch. EntwMech. Org.*, **133**, 728–59.

SCHWAN, H. 1940. 'Beitrag zur Kenntnis der Atmung holometaboler Insekten während der Metamorphose.' *Ark. Zool.*, **32**, 1–15.

SCHWEIGER, A. and KARLSON, P. 1962a. 'Zur Wirkungsweise des Prothorakaldrüsenhormons Ecdyson.' *Symp. gen. Biol. ital.*, **10**, 12–21.

SCHWEIGER, A. and KARLSON, P. 1962b. 'Zum Thyrosinstoffwechsel der Insekten. X. Die Aktivierung der Präphenoloxydase und das Aktivatorenzym.' *Hoppe-Seyl. Z.*, **329**, 210–21.

SCHWERDTFEGER, H. 1931. 'Beiträge zum Vorkommen und zur Wirkung der weiblichen Sexualhormone.' *Arch. exp. Path. Pharmak.*, **163**, 487–492.

SCHWINCK, J. 1951. 'Veränderung der Epidermis, der Perikardialzellen und der Corpora allata in der Larvenentwicklung von *Panorpa communis* unter normalen und experimentellen Bedingungen.' *Arch. EntwMech. Org.*, **145**, 62–108.

SCUDAMORE, H. H. 1942. Thesis, Northwestern University; in part in *Anat. Rec.*, **84**, suppl., 514–16.

SEAMANS, L. and WOODRUFF, L. C. 1939. 'Some factors influencing the number of moults of the german roach.' *J.Kans. ent. Soc.*, **12**, 73–6.

SEDEE, J. W. 'Qualitative vitamin requirements for growth of larvae of *Calliphora*.' *Experientia*, **9**, 142–3.

SEIDEL, F. 1924. 'Die Geschlechtsorgane in der embryonalen Entwicklung von *Pyrrhocoris apterus* L.' *Z. Morph. Oekol. Tiere*, **1**, 429–506.

SEIDEL, F. 1931. 'Das Differenzierungssystem in Libellenkeim; die dynamischen Voraussetzungen der Determination und Regulation.' *Arch. EntwMech. Org.*, **131**, 135–87.

SEIDEL, F. 1936. 'Entwicklungsphysiologie des Insektenkeims.' *Verh. dtsch. zool. ges.*, **38**, 291–336.

SEKERIS, C. and KARLSON, P. 1962. 'Zum Tyrosinstoffwechsel der Insekten. VII.' *Biochim. biophys. Acta*, **62**, 103–13.

SEILER, J. 1937. 'Ergebnise aus der Kreuzung parthenogenetischer und zweigeschlechtlicher Schmetterlinge. 5. Die *Solenobia*-Intersexe und die Deutungen des Phänomens der Intersexualität.' *Rev. suisse Zool.*, **44**, 283–307.

SEILER, J. 1951. 'Analyse des intersexen Fühlers von *Solenobia triquetrella*.' *Rev. suisse Zool.*, **58**, 489–95.

SELLIER, R. 1946. 'Transplantation et mue induite d'appendices d'adultes chez *Acheta campestris*.' *C. R. Soc. Biol., Paris*, **140**, 965–6.

SELLIER, R. 1949. 'Diapause larvaire et macroptérisme chez *Gryllus campestris*.' *C. R. Soc. Biol., Paris*, **228**, 2055–6.

SELLIER, R. 1950. 'La différenciation sexuelle des élytres chez les Orthoptères gryllidés.' *C. R. Soc. Biol., Paris*, **231**, 180–2.

SELLIER, R. 1951. 'La glande prothoracique des Gryllides.' *Arch. Zool. exp. gén.*, **88**, 61–72.

SELLIER, R. 1956. 'Gonades, cerveau et morphogenèse alaire chez les Grillons.' *Ann. Sci. nat., Zool.*, (II), **18**, 251–5.

SEMBRAT, K. 1958. 'Hormones and evolution.' *Proc. XVth int. Congr. Zool.*, London, **6**, 529–31.

SEN GUPTA, K. 1961. 'Studies on insect tissue culture. I. Culture of tissues from the wax moth *Galleria mellonella* L. in vitro.' *Folia Biol.*, **7**, 400–8.

SERDIUKOVA, G. V. 1951. 'The hibernation of *Ixodes ricinus* eggs in the conditions of the Karelian neck' (in Russian). *C. R. Acad. Sci. U.R.S.S.*, **81**, 1171–3.

SERDIUKOVA, G. V. 1952. 'New data on the development of the *Ixodes ricinus* larvae and nymphs in natural conditions.' *C. R. Acad. Sci. U.R.S.S.*, **83**, 769–73.

SHAKHBAZOV, V. G. 1961. 'The reaction to the length of daylight and the light receptor of the pupa of the Chinese oak silkworm *Antherea pernyi* G.' *C. R. Acad. Sci. U.R.S.S.*, **140**, pp. 944–6.

SHAPPIRIO, D. G. 1960. 'Oxidative enzymes and the injury metabolism of diapausing *Cecropia silkworms*.' *Ann. N.Y. Acad. Sci.*, **89**, 537–48.

SHAPPIRIO, D. G. and WILLIAMS, C. M. 1952. 'Spectroscopic studies of the cytochrome system of the Cecropia silkworm at the temperature of liquid nitrogen.' *Anat. Rec.*, **113**, 78.

SHAPPIRIO, D. G. and WILLIAMS, C. M. 1953. 'Cytochrome E in individual tissues of the Cecropia silkworm.' *Anat. Rec.*, **117**, 542–3.

SHAPPIRIO, D. G. and WILLIAMS, C. M. 1957a. 'Spectrophotometric studies of oxidative enzyme systems in the wing epithelium.' *Proc. roy. Soc.* (B), **147**, 233–46.

SHAPPIRIO, D. G. and WILLIAMS, C. M. 1957b. 'Spectroscopic studies of individual tissues.' *Proc. roy. Soc.* (B), **147**, 218–32.

SHAROV, A. G. 1953. 'The development of Thysanura in connection with the problem of morphology of Insects' (in Russian). *C. R. Acad. Sci. U.R.S.S.*, **8**, 83–150.

SHAROV, A. G. 1957a. 'Comparative onthogenetical method and its importance in phylogenetical research in insects.' *Zool. Zh.*, **36**, 64–84.

SHAROV, A. G. 1957b. 'The types of metamorphosis in insects and their interelations on basis of comparative-onthogenetical and paleontological data' (in Russian). *Rev. Ent. U.R.S.S.*, **36**, 569–76.

SHAROV, A. G. 1958. 'Evolution as the process of ontogeny alteration.' *Pro. XVth int. Congr. Zool.*, London, **1**, 1–4.

SHATOURY, H. H. EL. 1955a. 'A genetically controlled malignant tumour in *Drosophila*.' *Arch. EntwMech. Org.*, **147**, 496–522.

SHATOURY, H. H. EL. 1955b. 'The structures of the lymph glands in *Drosophila* larvae.' *Arch. EntwMech. Org.*, **147**, 489–95.

SHATOURY, H. H. EL. 1955c. 'Lethal no-differentiation and the development of the imaginal discs during the larval stage in *Drosophila*.' *Arch. EntwMech. Org.*, **147**, 523–38.

SHATOURY, H. H. EL. 1956a. 'An immunological hypothesis of tumour development in *Drosphila*.' *Arch. EntwMech. Org.*, **148**, 391–401.

SHATOURY, H. H. EL. 1956b. 'Developmental interactions in the development of the imaginal muscles of *Drosophila*.' *J. Embryol. exp. Morph.*, **4**, 228–39.

SHATOURY, H. H. EL. 1956c. 'Differentiation and metamorphosis of the imaginal optic glomeruli in *Drosophila*.' *J. Embryol. exp. Morph.*, **4**, 228–39.

SHATOURY, H. H. EL. 1957. 'Behavior of lethal-no-imaginal bud larvae towards imaginal bud and lymph gland transplants.' *Arch. EntwMech. Org.*, **150**, 61–4.

SHAVER, J. R. 1953. 'Stages in the introduction of cleavage in the frog egg.' *J. exp. Zool.*, **122**, 169–192.

SHELFORD, V. E. 1927. 'An experimental investigation of the relations of the codling moth to weather and climate.' *Bull. Ill. nat. Hist. Surv.*, **16**, 311–440.

SHELTON, E. and SCHNEIDER, W. C. 1952. 'On the usefulness of tetranolium salts as histochemical indicators of dehydrogenase activity.' *Anat. Rec.*, pp. 112–61.

SHULOV, A. H. and PENER, M. P. 1961. 'Environmental factors in interruption of development of Acrididae eggs.' Reprinted from *Cryptobiotic stages in biological systems*, Amsterdam.

SHUMAKOV, E. M., EDELMAN, N. M. and BORISOVA, A. E. 1959. 'Experiments on raising phytophagous insects upon artificial media.' *C. R. Acad. Sci., U.R.S.S.*, **130**, 237–41.

SHU-YI WANG and DIXON, S. E. 1960. 'Studies on the transaminase activity of muscle tissue from allatectomized roaches *Periplaneta americana*.' *Canad. J. Zool.*, **38**, 275–83.

SHVANVICH, B. N. 1949. *Text-book of general entomology* (in Russian), Sov. nauka, 900 pp.

SIANG-HSU. 1948. 'The Golgi material and mitochondria in the salivary glands of the larva of *Drosophila*.' *Quart. J. micr. Sci.*, **89**, 401–14.

SIMMONDS, F. J. 1944. 'Observations on the parasites of the *Cydia pomonella* in Southern France.' *Sci. Agr.*, **25**, 1–30.

SIMMONDS, F. J. 1948. 'The influence of maternal physiology on the incidence of diapause.' *Phil. Trans.*, **233**, B, 385–414.

SINGH, T. 1958. 'Ovulation and corpus luteum formation in *Locusta migratoria migratorioides* Reich and Fairmaire and *Schistocerca gregaria* Fors.' *Trans. roy. ent. Soc. Lond.*, **110**, 1–20.

SISAKYAN, J. M. 1951. 'Fermentative activity of protoplasmic structures' (in Russian). *Bakh. Chten.*, 5.

SISAKYAN, J. M. and WEYNOVA. M. K. 1955. 'The character of proteins of the pupal body fluid in *Bombyx mori*' (in Russian). *C. R. Acad. Sci. U.R.S.S.*, **101**, 531–4.

SKELLAM, J. G., BRIAN, M. V. and PROCTOR, J. R. 1959. 'The simultaneous growth of interacting systems.' *Acta biotheor. Leiden*, **13**, 131–44.

SLÁMA, K. 1957. 'Wachstum und Sauerstoffverbrauch während der Post-embryonalentwicklung bei der Blattwespe *Athalia colibri*.' *Mém. Soc. zool. Čsl.*, **21**, 289–99.

SLÁMA, K. 1959a. 'The total metabolism during the larval development in several sawfly species.' *Acta soc. ent. Čsl.*, **56**, 113–25.

SLÁMA, K. 1959b. 'Metabolism during diapause and development in sawfly metamorphosis.' *Acta Symp. Evol. Ins.*, *Prague*, pp. 195–201.

SLÁMA, K. 1959c. 'The succinic dehydrogenase activity in different organs of the sawfly *Cephaleia abietis* L. during diapause and development.' *Acta Symp. Evol. Ins.*, *Prague*, pp. 222–5.

SLÁMA, K. 1959d. 'The question of the U-shaped curves of oxygen consumption in the intermoulting periods of holometabolous and hetero-metabolous insect larvae.' *Acta Symp. Evol. Ins.*, *Prague*, 189.

SLÁMA, K. 1960a. 'Oxygen consumption during the postembryonic development of *Pyrrhocoris apterus* and its comparison with that of Holometabola.' *Ann. ent. Soc. Amer.*, **53**, 606–10.

SLÁMA, K. 1960b. 'Continuous respiration in diapausing prepupae and pupae in certain sawflies.' *J. Ins. Physiol.*, **5**, 341–8.

SLÁMA, K. 1961. 'The pseudojuvenilizing effects in insects.' *Acta Soc. ent. Čsl.*, **58**, 117–20.

SLEPECKY, R. A. and GILBERT, L. I. 1961. 'The antimicrobial activity of some insect extracts possessing juvenile hormone activity.' *Experientia*, **17**, 1–5.

SLIFER, E. H. 1932. 'Insect development. V. Qualitative studies on the fatty acids from grasshopper eggs.' *Physiol. Zool.*, **5**, 448–57.

SLIFER, E. H. 1946. 'The effect of xylol and other solvents in diapause in the grasshopper eggs together with a possible explanation for the action of these agents.' *J. exp. Zool.*, **102**, 333–56.

SLOPER, J. C. 1957. 'Presence of a substance rich in protein-bound cystine or cysteine in the neurosecretory system of an insect.' *Nature, Lond.*, **179**, 148.

SLOPER, J. C. 1958. 'The application of newer histochemical and isotope technique for the localization of protein-bound cystine or cysteine to the study of hypothalamic neurosecretion in normal and pathological conditions.' *Proc. IInd Int. Symp. Neurosekr. Lund*, 18–20.

SMITH, C. W. and COLE, M. 1941. 'Effect of length of day on the activity and hibernation of the american dog tick *Dermacentor variabilis*.' *Ann. ent. Soc. Amer.*, **34**, 426–31.

SMITH, G. 1909. 'On the correlation between primary and secondary sexual characters.' *Quart. J. micr. Sci.*, **54**, 577–604.

SMITH, G. and HAMM, A. H. 1914. 'Studies in the experimental analysis of sex. II. *Stylops* and stylopization.' *Quart. J. micr. Sci.*, **60**, 435–461.

SMOLKA, H. 1958. 'Untersuchungen an Kleinorganen im Integument der Mehlmotte.' *Biol. Zbl.*, **77**, 437–78.

SNODGRASS, R. F. 1953. 'The metamorphosis of a fly's head.' *Smithson Misc. Coll.*, **122**, 1–25.

SNODGRASS, R. F. 1954. 'Insect metamorphosis.' *Smithson Misc. Coll.*, **122**, 1–124.

SOLODOVNIKOVA, O. P. 1950. 'The developmental cycle of the fat body and its connection with the fecundity in mosquitoes.' (in Russian). *Zool. Zh.*, **29**, 545–55.

SOUTHWOOD, T. R. E. 1961. 'A hormonal theory of the mechanism of wing polymorphism in Heteroptera.' *Proc. roy. ent. Soc. Lond.* (A), **36**, 4–6.

SPEMANN, H. 1942. 'Über das Verhalten embryonalen Gewebes im erwachsenen Organismus.' *Arch. EntwMech. Org.*, **141**, 693–769.

SPIELMANN, A. 1957. 'The inheritance of ontogeny in the *Culex pipiens* complex of mosquitoes.' *Ann. J. Biol.*, **65**, 404–25.

SQUIRE, F. A. 1940. 'On the nature and origin of the diapause in *Platyedra gossypiella*.' *Bull. ent. Res.*, **31**, 1–6.

SRIVASTAVA, U. S. 1959. 'The prothoracic glands of some coleopteran larvae.' *Quart. J. micr. Sci.*, **100**, 51–64.

SRIVASTAVA, U. S. 1960. 'Secretory cycle and disappearance of prothoracic glands in *Tenebrio molitor* L.' *Experientia*, **16**, 445–6.

SRIVASTAVA, U. S. and PRASAD, O. 1960. 'A comparative study of the neurosecretory cells in certain insects.' *Proc. nat. Acad. Sci., India* (B), 25.

SRIVASTAVA, U. S. and PRASAD, O. 1961. 'Studies on the structure and function of neurosecretory cells in insects' (in Hindi). *Res. J. Hindi Sci. Acad.*, **4**, 129–30.

STAAL, IR. G. B. 1959. 'Endocrine effects in phase development in *Locusta*.' *Acta Symp. Evol. Ins.*, *Prague*, pp. 142–6.

STAAL, IR. G. B. 1961. 'Studies on the physiology of phase induction, in *Locusta migratoria migratorioides*.' *Publ. Fonds. Landb. Export Bur.*, no. 40, *Meded. Lab. Ent. Wageningen*, no. 72, 1–125.

STAAL, IR. G. B. and DE WILDE, J. 1962. 'Endocrine influences on the development of phase characters in *Locusta*.' *Colloques int. Centre natn. Rech. scient.*, **114**, 89–105.

STAMM, M. D. 1958. 'Isolement d'hormones de métamorphose dans l'orthoptère *Dociostaurus maroccanus*.' *Rev. exp. Physiol.*, **14**, 263–8.

STAMM, M. D. 1959. 'Estudios sobre hormones de invertebrados. II. Aistamiendo de hormonas de la metamorfosis en el Ortóptero *Dociostaurus maroccanus*.' *An. Fis. Quim.* (B), **55**, 171–8.

STARK, M. B. 1918. 'A hereditary tumor in *Drosophila*.' *J. Cancer Res.*, **3**, 279–301.

STAUDINGER, F. 1930. 'Heteromorphose an Stigmen und anderen Gebilden bei *Carausius* (*Dixippus*) *morosus*.' *Arch. EntwMech. Org.*, **122**, 316–78.

STAY, B. 1959a. 'Distribution of glycogen and lipoid during the larval and pupal stages.' *J. Morph.*, **105**, 427–56.

STAY, B. 1959b. 'Distribution of phosphatases, dehydrogenases and cytochrome oxidase during larval and pupal stages.' *J. Morph.*, **105**, 457–494.

STEEN, S. B. 1961. 'The effect of juvenile hormone on the respiratory

metabolism of silkworm pupae, as recorded with a new semimicro device.'
Acta Physiol. Scand., **51**, 275–82.

STEFANI, ST. 1931. 'Equivalenza e specifita degli ormoni morfogenetici'.
Riz. spec. policlin.' *Sec. med.*, **38**, 99–104.

STEGWEE, D. 1960. 'The role of esterase inhibition in tetraethyl – pyrophosphate poisoning in the housefly *Musca domestica*.' *Canad. J. Biochem.
Physiol.*, **38**, 1417–30.

STEGWEE, D. and KAMMEN-WERTHEIM, A. R. 1962. 'Respiratory chain
metabolism in the Colorado potato beetle. I.' *J. Ins. Physiol.*, **8**, 117–26.

STEIDLE, H. 1930. 'Über die Verbreitung des weiblichen Sexualhormons.'
Arch. exp. Path. Pharmak., **157**, 89–90.

STEINACH, E., DOHRN, M., SCHOELLER, W., HOHLWEG, A. and FAURE,
W. 1928. 'Über die biologischen Wirkungen des weiblichen Sexualhormons.' *Pflug. Arch. ges. Physiol.*, **219**, 306–24.

STEINBERG, D. M. 1938a. 'Regulatory processes in insect metamorphosis.
I. Experimental studies on the regeneration of wings in some Lepidoptera'
(in Russian). *Biol. Zh.*, **7**, 295–310.

STEINBERG, D. M. 1938b. 'idem'. 'II. The embryonic territories of wing and
leg in the hypodermis of the caterpillars of *Galleria mellonella*' (in Russian).
Biol. Zh., **7**, 993–1012.

STEINBERG, D. M. 1938c. 'Growth and differentiation of the female sexual
gland in Lepidoptera' (in Russian). *Arch. anat. hist. embryol.*, **8**, 178–99.

STEINBERG, D. M. 1939. 'Regulatory processes in insect metamorphosis.
III. The effect of the regeneration process on the pupation of caterpillars'
(in Russian). *Bull. Acad. Sci. U.R.S.S. (biol.)*, pp. 502–9.

STEINBERG, D. M. 1945. 'idem'. 'IV. Autoregulation of the wing in Lepidoptera' (in Russian). *C. R. Acad. Sci. U.R.S.S.*, **48**, 71–2.

STEINBERG, D. M. 1947. 'Experimentally produced chimeras in the wing
of Lepidoptera' (in Russian). *C. R. Acad. Sci. U.R.S.S.*, **58**, 945–6.

STEINBERG, D. M. 1948. 'Hormones in insects' (in Russian). *Adv. mod.
Biol.*, **25**, 401–18.

STEINBERG, D. M. 1949a. 'Morphogenetical potencies of hypodermis during
the development of wing in *Galleria mellonella*' (in Russian). *Bull. Acad.
Sci. U.R.S.S. (biol.)*, pp. 340–74.

STEINBERG, D. M. 1949b. 'Regulation processes during the metamorphosis
in beetles' (in Russian). *Ann. Leningr. Univ. (biol.)*, **20**, 207–28.

STEINBERG, D. M. 1950a. 'Comparative evaluation of the regeneration
abilities in insects' (in Russian). *Zool. Zh.*, **29**, 267–76.

STEINBERG, D. M. 1950b. 'The possibility of the development of wings
in Lepidoptera following the transplantation of their imaginal discs into
the body cavity' (in Russian). *C. R. Acad. Sci. U.R.S.S.*, **71**, 1159–62.

STEINBERG, D. M. 1951. 'Morphogenetical basis of the segmentation of
appendages in insects' (in Russian). *Rev. Ent. U.R.S.S.*, **31**, 450–62.

STEINBERG, D. M. 1956a. 'Interrelations of tissues in grafts and transplantations in plants and animals' (in Russian). *Zool. Zh.*, **35**, 793–803.

STEINBERG, D. M. 1956b. 'Morphogenetical analysis of the development of imaginal discs in Insecta-Holometabola' (in Russian). *Rev. Ent. U.R.S.S.*, **35**, 503–9.

STEINBERG, D. M. 1956c. 'The ways of evolution of metamorphosis in arthropods' (in Russian). *Probl. mod. biol.*, **4**, 172–84.

STEINBERG, D. M. 1956d. 'Analyse morphogénétique du Développement des Organes imaginaux chez les Insectes holométaboles.' *Proc. Xth int. Congr. Ent.*, **2**, 261–6.

STEINBERG, D. M. 1957. 'The survey of the chief investigations in the insect morphology during the 40 years of Soviet government' (in Russian). *Rev. Ent. U.R.S.S.*, **36**, 4.

STEINBERG, D. M. 1959a. 'The importance of the methods of experimental morphology for the study of insect evolution' (in Russian). *IV. Syezd vsoyuz. ent. obschch.*, **1**, 196–7.

STEINBERG, D. M. 1959b. Review of the 1st edition of the book 'Insektenhormone' by J. V. A. Novák (in Russian). *Rev. Ent. U.R.S.S.*, **38**, 941–3.

STELWAAG-KITTLER, F. 1954. 'Zur Physiologie der Käferhäutung. Untersuchungen am Mehlkäfer *Tenebrio molitor*.' *Biol. Zbl.*, **73**, 12–49.

STENDEL, W. 1911. 'Über Drüsenzellen bei Lepidopteren.' *Zool. Anz.*, **38**, 582–5.

STENDEL, W. 1912. 'Beiträge zur Kenntnis der Oenozyten von *Ephestia kühniella*.' *Z. wiss. Zool.*, **102**, 136–68.

STERN, C. 1941a. 'The growth of testes in *Drosophila*. II. The nature of interspecific differences.' *J. exp. Zool.*, **87**, 113–58.

STERN, C. 1941b. 'The growth of testes in *Drosophila*. II. The nature of interspecific differences.' *J. exp. Zool.*, **87**, 159–80.

STERN, C. and HADORN, E. 1939. 'The relation between the colour of testes and vasa efferentia in *Drosophila*.' *Genetics*, **24**, 162–79.

STIENNON, J. A. and DROCHMANS, P. 1961. 'Electron microscope study of neurosecretory cells in Phasmidae.' *Gen. comp. Endocrinol.*, **1**, 287–94.

STOCK, A. and O'FARRELL, A. F. 1954. 'Regeneration and the moulting cycle in *Blatella germanica*. II. Simultaneous regeneration of both metathoracic legs.' *Austr. J. biol. Sci.*, **7**, 302–7.

STOSSBERG, M. 1938. 'Die Zellvorgänge bei der Entwicklung der Flügelschuppen von *Ephestia kühniella*.' *Z. Morph. Oekol. Tiere*, **34**, 173–206.

STRANGWAYS-DIXON, J. 1959. 'Hormones, selective feeding and reproduction in *Calliphora erythrocephala*.' *Acta Symp. Evol. Ins. Prague*, pp. 137–9.

STRANGWAYS-DIXON, J. 1961a. 'The relationship between nutrition hormones and reproduction in the blowfly *Calliphora erythrocephala*.' *J. exp. Biol.*, **38**, 225–35.

STRANGWAYS-DIXON, J. 1961b. 'idem'. 'II. The effect of removing the ovaries, the corpus allatum and the median neurosecretory cells upon selective feeding and the demonstration of the corpus allatum cycle.' *J. exp. Biol.*, **38**, 637–46.

STRELNIKOV, J. D. 1936. 'Water exchange and diapause in *Antherea pernyi*' (in Russian). *C. R. Acad. Sci. U.R.S.S.*, **6**, 257–60.

STRELNIKOV, J. D. 1959. 'The meaning of the body size in insects on their structure, physiology and interrelations with the environment.' *Proc. IVth Conf. U.R.S.S. ent. Soc.*, **1**, 169–70.

STRICH, M. C. 1953. 'Étude de la glande ventrale chez *Locusta migratoria migratorioides.*' *Ann. Sci. nat. Zool.*, **16**, 399–410.

STRICH-HALBWACHS, M. 1954a. 'Rôle de la glande ventrale chez *Locusta migratoria.*' *C. R. Soc. Biol., Paris*, **148**, 2087–90.

STRICH-HALBWACHS, M. 1954b. 'Action de la glande ventrale pour le développement ovarian de la *Locusta migratoria.*' *J. Ins. Physiol.*, **1**, 346–351.

STRICH-HALBWACHS, M. 1959. 'Contrôle de la mue chez *Locusta migratoria.*' *Ann. Sci. nat., Zool.*, **12**, 483–570.

STRICH-HALBWACHS, M., JOLY, L. and JOLY, P. 1957. 'Résultats d'implantations des glandes ventrales à *Locusta migratoria.*' *J. Ins. Physiol.*, **1**, 143–9.

STRICKLAND, E. H. 1911. 'Some parasites of *Simulium* larvae and their effects in the development of the host.' *Biol. Bull., Wood's Hole*, **21**, 302–38.

STRICKLAND, E. H. 1913. 'Parasites of *Simulium* larvae.' *J. Morph.*, **24**, 43–105.

STERNSEE-ZOLLINGER, E. 1957. 'Histological study of regeneration processes after transection of the nervi corporis cardiaci in transplanted brains of the cecropia silkworm.' *J. exp. Zool.*, **134**, 315–26.

STRONG, L. 1962. 'A simple apparatus for use in removing corpora allata from locusts.' *Bull. ent. Res.*, **54**, 19–21.

STUMPF, H. 1959. 'Die Wirkung von Hitzreizen auf die Entwicklungsvorgänge in Puppenflügel von *Drosophila.*' *Biol. Zbl.*, **78**, 116–42.

STUTINSKI, F. 1952a. 'Étude du complexe rétrocérébral du quelques insectes avec l'hématoxiline chromique.' *Bull. Soc. zool. Fr.*, **77**, 61–7.

STUTINSKI, F. 1952b. 'Einfluss der Extrakte von Corpora cardiaca and neurosekretorischen Gehirnzellen und die Exkretion des Wassers in der Ratte.' *Bull. Soc. zool. Fr.*, **78**, 202–4.

STUTINSKY, F. 1953. 'Mise on evidence d'une substance antidiuretique dans le cerveau et le complex retrocérébral d'une Blatte (*Blabera fusca* Brunn.).' *Bull. Soc. zool. Fr.*, **78**, 202–4.

SÜFFERT, F. 1924. 'Bestimmungsfaktoren des Zeichnungsmusters beim Saisondimorphismus von *Araschnia levana.*' *Biol. Zbl.*, **44**, 173–88.

ŠULC, K. 1927. 'Das Tracheensystem von *Lepisma* und Phylogenie der Pterygogenea.' *Acta Soc. Sci. nat. Morav.*, **4**, 1–43.

SUSSMANN, A. 1952. 'Tyrosinase and the respiration of pupae of *Platysamia cecropia.*' *Biol. Bull., Wood's Hole*, **102**, 39–47.

SUSSMANN, A. 1960. *Animal growth and development.* Found. Modern. Biol. ser., Englewood Cliffs, New Jersey, pp. 1–114.

SUSTER, P. 1933a. 'Beinregeneration nach Ganglienextirpation bei *Sphodromantis bioculata.*' *Zool. Jb.*, Abt. 3, **53**, 41–8.

SUSTER, P. 1933b. 'Beinregeneration nach Ganglienextirpation bei *Sphodromantis bioculata.*' *Zool. Jb.*, Abt. 3, **53**, 49–66.

SWAMMERDAM, J. 1957. *The book of nature or the history of insects*, London.

SZTERN, H. 1914. 'Wachstumsmessungen an *Sphodromantis bioculata*. II. Länge, Breite und Höhe.' *Arch. EntwMech. Org.*, **40**, 429–95.

TAGAWA, K., *et al.* 1957. 'Crystalline cytochrome c – crystallization of cytochrome c from fish.' *Nature, Lond.*, **179**, 249.

TAKAKOA, M. 1959. 'Studies of the metamorphosis in insects. III. Relation between pupation and oxygen tension in *Drosophila*.' *Embryologia*, **4**, 237–46.

TAKAKOA, M. 1960a. 'idem'. 'Inhibition of pupation by carbon dioxide in the mature larva of *Drosophila melanogaster*.' *Embryologia*, **5**, 78–84.

TAKAKOA, M. 1960b. 'idem'. 'V. Factors controlling the larval period of the squash-fly, *Zengodacus depressus*.' *Embryologia*, **5**, 259–69.

TAKAMI, T. 1958. 'In vitro culture of embryos in the silkworm *Bombyx mori* L. I. Culture in silkworms egg extract with special reference to some characteristics of the diapause eggs.' *J. exp. Biol.*, **35**, 286–96.

TAMANO, N. 1960. 'Effect of some drugs acting on the central and autonomic nervous system and of some mitotic inhibitors of the growth and metamorphosis of the silkworm and on the properties of its cocoon and thread.' *Folia Pharm. jap.*, **56**, 882–97.

TARAO, WAKAMORI. 1924. 'Preliminary notes on effects of thyroid feeding on the silkworm *Bombyx mori*.' *Jap. Med. World*, **4**, 68–71.

TARAO, WAKAMORI. 1931. 'Influence of the feeding of the thyroid gland and the anterior lobe of hypophysis on the second generation of the silkworm *Bombyx mori*.' *Proc. imp. Acad. Japan*, **7**, 205–7.

TAUBER, J. (TAABOR, H.). 1925. 'Exometamorphose der Schmetterlinge und Einwirkung von Hormonen.' *Biol. Listy*, **10**, 371–87.

TEISSIER, G. 1931. 'Recherches morphologiques et physiologiques sur la croissance des insectes.' *Trav. Sta. biol. Roscoff.*, **9**, 29–238.

TEISSIER, G. 1936. 'La loi de Dyar et la croissance des Arthropods.' *Libre jubil. Bouvier*, pp. 335–42.

TEISSIER, G. 1947. 'Functionnement des chromatophores de la larve de Corèthre.' *C. R. Acad. Sci., Paris*, **225**, 204–5.

TELFER, W. H. 1953. 'Further studies on a sex-limited blood protein of a saturniid silkworm.' *Anat. Rec.*, **117**, 541.

TELFER, W. H. 1954. 'Immunological studies of insect metamorphosis. II. The role of a sex limited blood protein in egg formation by the cecropia silkworm.' *J. gen. Physiol.*, **37**, 539–58.

TELFER, W. H. and WILLIAMS, C. M. 1951. 'An immunological study of the blood proteins during the metamorphosis of the cecropia silkworm.' *Anat. Rec.*, **111**, 3.

TELFER, W. H. and WILLIAMS, C. M. 1952. 'The relation of the blood proteins to egg formation in the cecropia silkworm.' *Anat. Rec.*, **113,** 82.

TELFER, W. H. and WILLIAMS, C. M. 1953. 'Immunological studies of insect metamorphosis. I. Qualitative and quantitative description of the blood antigens of the cecropia silkworm.' *J. gen. Physiol.*, **36,** 389–413.

TEPLYAKOVA, M. 1947. 'Postembryonic development in the internal reproductive organs in the year cycle of *Eurygaster integriceps*' (in Russian). *Izd. Akad. Nauk. Moscow*, **1,** 81–119.

THÉVENARD, P. 1949. 'Note préliminaire concernant l'étude radiographique de la métamorphose de la Mouche et l'application de cette méthode de recherche a la pathologie chez cet insect.' *C. R. Acad. Sci., Paris*, **228,** 863–4.

THOMPSON, J. H. 1929. 'Effects of feeding silkworm on extract of the anterior lobe of the pituitary gland.' *Arch. EntwMech. Org.*, **114,** 578–82.

THOMPSON, W. R. 1923. 'Sur le déterminisme de l'aptérisme chez un Ichneumonide parasite *Pezomachus sericeus* Först.' *Bull. Soc. ent. Fr.*, 40–2.

THOMSEN, E. 1940. 'Relation between corpus allatum and ovaries in adult flies.' *Nature, Lond.*, **145,** 28–9.

THOMSEN, E. 1941. 'Ringdrüse und Corpus allatum bei Musciden.' *Naturwissenschaften*, **29,** 605–6.

THOMSEN, E. 1942. 'An experimental and anatomical study of the corpus allatum in *Calliphora erythrocephala*.' *Vidensk. Medd. dansk. naturh. Foren Kbh.*, **106,** 320–405.

THOMSEN, E. 1947. 'The gonadotropic hormones in the Diptera.' Lecture, Conf. Sci. Intern. Endocrinol., Paris.

THOMSEN, E. 1948a. 'The gonadotropic hormones in the Diptera.' *Bull. biol.*, **33,** 68–80.

THOMSEN, E. 1948b. 'Effect of removal of neurosecretory cells in brain of adult *Calliphora erythrocephala*.' *Nature, Lond.*, **161,** 439–40.

THOMSEN, E. 1949. 'Influence of the corpus allatum on the oxygen consumption of adult *Calliphora erythrocephala*.' *J. exp. Biol.*, **26,** 137–49.

THOMSEN, E. 1952. 'Functional significance of the neurosecretory brain cells and the corpus cardiacum in the female blowfly *Calliphora erythrocephala*.' *J. exp. Biol.*, **29,** 137–72.

THOMSEN, E. 1954a. 'Studies on the transport of neurosecretory materials in *Calliphora erythrocephala* by means of ligaturing experiments.' *J. exp. Biol.*, **31,** 322–30.

THOMSEN, E. 1954b. 'Experimental evidence for the transport of secretory material in the axons of the neurosecretory cells of *Calliphora erythrocephala*.' *Pubbl. Staz. zool. Napoli*, **24,** 48–50.

THOMSEN, E. 1955. 'Oxygen consumption of castrated females of the blowfly *Calliphora erythrocephala*.' *J. exp. Biol.*, **32,** 692–9.

THOMSEN, E. 1956. 'Observations on the oenocytes of the adult *Calliphora erythrocephala*.' In Wingstrand, *Bertil Hanström, Zool. papers in honour of his 65th birthday*, pp. 298–306.

THOMSEN, E. 1959. 'Further studies on the function of the neurosecretory cells of the brain of the adult *Calliphora erythrocephala* female.' *Acta Symp. Evol. Ins., Prague*, pp. 121–5.

THOMSEN, E. and HAMBURGER, K. 1955. 'Oxygen consumption of castrated females of the blowfly *Calliphora erythrocephala*.' *J. exp. Biol.*, **32**, 692–9.

THOMSEN, E. and MÖLLER, I. 1959. 'Neurosecretion and intestinal proteinase activity in an insect, *Calliphora erythrocephala*.' *Nature, Lond.*, **183**, 1401–2.

THOMSEN, E. and THOMSEN, M. 1954. 'Dark field microscopy of living neurosecretory cells.' *Experientia*, **10**, 206–7.

THOMSEN, M. 1943. 'Effect of corpus cardiacum and other insect organs on the colour change of the shrimp *Leander adspersus*.' *Biol. Medd. Kbh.*, **19**, 1–38.

THOMSEN, M. 1948. 'Reactions of crustacea to insect hormones.' *Bull. Biol. Fr. Belg.*, **33**, suppl., 57–61.

THOMSEN, M. 1951. 'Weismann's ring and related organs in larvae of Diptera.' *Biol. Skr.*, **6**, 1–32.

THOMSEN, M. 1954a. 'Neurosecretion in some Hymenoptera.' *Biol. Skr.*, **7**, 1–24.

THOMSEN, M. 1954b. 'Observations on the cytology of neurosecretion in various insects.' *Pubbl. Staz. zool. Napoli*, **24**, 46–8.

THORNTON, D. 1947. 'The effect of 2, 4-Dinitrofenol on the larval growth of *Drosophila*.' *Growth*, **11**, 51–60.

TIEGS, O. W. 1922. 'Researches on the insect metamorphosis.' *Trans. roy. soc. S. Austr.*, **46**, 319–527.

TILMENBAJEV, A. I. 1960. 'The development of the preimaginal phases in the bug *Aelia sibirica* Reut' (in Russian). *Tr. In-ta Zool. Acad. Sci. KazSR*, **11**, 145–56.

TIMON-DAVID, J. 1940. 'Hormones and internal environment.' *Ann. Fac. Sci. Marseilles* (2), **13**, 239–307.

TITSCHAK, E. 1926. 'Growth and moulting in *Tineola*.' *Z. wiss. Zool.*, **128**, 509–69.

TOBIAS, J. M. 1948. 'Potassium, sodium and water interchange irritable tissues and haemolymph of an omnivorous insect, *Periplaneta americana*.' *J. Cell. Comp. Physiol.*, **31**, 125–42.

TONON, A. 1927. 'Variabilita dei caratteri embryologica dell'uovo di fillugello duerante la diapause.' *Annu. Staz. bacol. sper. Padova*, **45**, 47–55.

TOYAMA, K. 1902. 'Contribution to the study of silkworm. I. On the embryology of the silkworm.' *Bull. Coll. Agric. Tokyo*, **5**, 73–118.

TRAGER, W. 1937. 'Cell size in relation to the growth and metamorphosis of the mosquito, *Aedes aegypti*.' *J. exp. Zool.*, **76**, 467–89.

TRAGER, W. 1947. 'Insect nutrition.' *Biol. Rev.*, **22**, 148–77.

TRAGER, W. 1959. 'The tse-tse-fly tissue culture and the development of trypanosomes to the infective stage.' *Ann. trop. Med. Parasit.*, **53**, 473–91.

TULESHKOV, R. 1935. 'Über Ursachen der Überwinterung der *Lymantria dispar* and *L. monacha* und anderer Lymantriiden im Eisstadium.' *Z. angew. Ent.*, **22**, 97–117.

TURNER, R. S. 1949. 'Observations with central nervous system of *Leptinotarsa articola.' J. comp. Neur.*, **85**, 52–65.

TUXEN, L. S. 1949. 'Über den Lebenszyklus und die postembryonale Entwicklung zweier dänischer Proturengattungen.' *Biol. Skr.*, 6, no. 3, 1–49.

TWOHY, D. W. and ROZEBOOM, L. E. 1957. 'A comparison of food reserves in autogeneous and anautogenous *Culex pipiens* populations.' *Ann. J. Hyg.*, **65**, 316–24.

UBISCH, L. V. 1911. 'Über Flügelregeneration beim Schwammspinner *Lymantria dispar.' Arch. EntwMech. Org.*, **31**, 637–53.

UMEYA, Y. 1924. 'On the internal secretion of the silkworm.' *Chosen Hakubugakkai kaiho*, 2.

UMEYA, Y. 1926a. 'Studies on the silkglands of the silkworm (*Bombyx mori*, L.).' *Bull. ser. Exp. Sta. Chosen*, 1, 27–48.

UMEYA, Y. 1926b. 'Experiments on ovarian transplantations and blood transfusion in silkworm with special reference to the alternation of voltinism.' *Bull. ser. Exp. Sta. Chosen*, 1, 1–26.

UNGER, H. 1956. 'Neurohormonale Steuerung der Herztätigkeit bei Insekten.' *Naturwissenschaften*, **43**, 66–7.

UNGER, H. 1957. 'Untersuchungen zur neurohormonalen Steuerung der Hertztätigkeit bei Insekten.' *Biol. Zbl.*, **76**, 204–25.

URSPRUNG, H. 1959. 'Fragmentierungs-und Bestrahlungsversuche zur Bestimmung von Determinationszustand und Anlageplan der Genitalscheiben von *Drosophila melanogaster.' Arch. EntwMech. Org.*, **151**, 504–558.

URVOY, J. 1962. 'Transplantation de patte sur les tergites de la Blatte *Blabera craniifer* Burm.' *Bull. Soc. Sci. Bretagne*, **37**, 113–18.

USHATINSKAYA, R. S. 1949. 'The direction of several processes in insect body at low temperature.' *C. R. Acad. Sci. U.R.S.S.*, **68**, 1101–4.

USHATINSKAYA, R. S. 1950a. 'The general cold resistance of *Calandra granaria* and *Sitophilus oryzae*' (in Russian). *Proc. Acad. Sci. U.R.S.S. (biol.)*, 1, 17–28.

USHATINSKAYA, R. S. 1950b. 'The influence of the environment and food humidity in *Calandra granaria*' (in Russian). *Zool. Zh.*, **29**, 341–9.

USHATINSKAYA, R. S. 1951. 'Physiological and ecological basis of cold resistance in insects' (in Russian). *Zool. Inst. Acad. Sci. U.R.S.S.*, pp. 1–26.

USHATINSKAYA, R. S. 1952. 'The direction of several physiological processes of the insect body in the period preliminary to hibernation' (in Russian). *C. R. Acad. Sci. U.R.S.S. (biol.)*, 1, 101–14.

USHATINSKAYA, R. S. 1955. 'The physiological characteristics of *Eurygaster integriceps* quiescence in the period of quiescence in the mountains and in the plain' (in Russian). *Vred. cherepashka*, 3, 134–70.

USHATINSKAYA, R. S. 1956. 'The physiological research of insect diapause.' *Ber. 100jr. dtsch. ent. Ges.*, Berlin, pp. 250–63.

USHATINSKAYA, R. S. 1957. *The principles of cold resistance in insects* (in Russian), Moscow, Acad. Sci. U.R.S.S., 314 pp.

USHATINSKAYA, R. S. 1958. 'Origin of insect diapause in the zone of temperate climate and its role in the formation of biological cicles.' *Proc. XVth int. Congr. Zool.*, pp. 1051–3.

USHATINSKAYA, R. S. 1959. 'Some of the physiological and biochemical characteristics of the diapause and winter dormancy in *Leptinotarsa decemlineata*' (in Russian). *Int. Symp. Colorado beetle, Acad. Sci. U.R.S.S.*, pp. 57–8.

UTIDA (1959). 'The differences in the respiration intensity between the short-wing and long-wing leafhoppers.' *Jap. J. appl. Ent. Zool.*, **3**, 212–13.

VAGO, C. and CHASTANG, S. 1958. 'Culture in vitro d'un tissue nymphal de lépidoptère.' *Experientia*, **14**, 426.

VANDEL, A. 1930a. 'La production d'intercastes chez la fourmi *Pheidole pallidula*, sous l'action de parasites du genre *Mermis*.' *C. R. Acad. Sci., Paris*, **190**, 770–2.

VANDEL, A. 1930b. 'La production d'intercastes chez la fourmi *Pheidole pallidula* sous l'action de parasites du genre *Mermis*. I. Étude morphologique des individues parasites.' *Bull. biol.*, **64**, 457–94.

VANDEL, A. 1933. 'Un cas d'inversion sexuelle parasitaire produit chez *Odynerus innumerabilis* Sauss. par un Strepsiptère du genre *Pseudoxenos*.' *Bull. biol.*, **67**, 125–34.

VANDEL, A. 1940. 'Le déterminisme de la mue et des métamorphoses chez les insectes.' *Rev. Biol., Paris*, pp. 1–11.

VARLEY, G. C. and BUTLER, C. G. 1933. 'The acceleration of development of insects.' *Parasitology*, **25**, 263–8.

VERSON, E. 1900. 'Beitrag zur Oenozytenliteratur.' *Zool. Anz.*, **23**, 657–61.

VERSON, E. 1911a. 'Zur Kenntnis der Drüsenzellen (sogenannter innerer Sekretion) welche in den Blutlacunen der Insekten vorkommen.' *Zool. Anz.*, **38**, 295–301.

VERSON, E. 1911b. 'Observations on the structure of the exuvial glands and the formation of the exuvial fluid in insects.' *Zool. Anz.*, **38**, 295–301.

VERSON, E. and BISSON, E. 1891. 'Cellule glandulari ipostigmatiche nel *Bombyx mori*.' *Boll. Soc. ent. ital.*, **23**, 3–20.

VIGH, B., *et al.* 1961. 'Gomori-positive secretion in the subcommissural organ of different vertebrates.' *Acta Morphol. Acad. Sci. Hung.*, **10**, 217–35.

VILLEE, C. A. 1942. 'The phenomenon of homeosis.' *Amer. Nat.*, **76**, 494–506.

VILLEE, C. A. 1943. 'Phenogenetic studies of the homeotic mutants of *Drosophila*. 1. The effects of temperature on the expression of aristopedia.' *J. exp. Zool.*, **93**, 75–98.

VILLEE, C. A. 1944. 'idem. 2. The effects of temperature on the expression of proboscipedia.' *J. exp. Zool.*, **96**, 85–102.

VIALANES, H. 1882. 'Recherches sur l'histologie des insectes.' *Ann. Sci. nat.*, *Zool.*, **14**, 1–348.

VLADIMIRSKI, N. T. (1935). 'Wirkt tatsächlich die Farbe des Substrates auf die Puppen durch die Augen der Raupe? Versuche mit der Kohlmotte-*Plutella maculipennis.*' *Trans. Dynam. Develop.*, *Moscow*, **10**, 375–83.

VOGT, M. 1940a. 'Die Förderung der Eireifung innerhalb heteroplasmatisch transplantierter Ovarien von *Drosophila* durch die gleichzeitige Implantation der arteigener Ringdrüsen.' *Biol. Zbl.*, **60**, 479–84.

VOGT, M. 1940b. 'Zur Ursache der unterschiedlichen gonadotropen Wirkung der Ringdrüse von *Drosophila funebris* und *D. melanogaster.*' *Arch. Entw-Mech. Org.*, **140**, 525–46.

VOGT, M. 1941a. 'Weiterer Beitrag zur Ursache der unterschiedlichen gonadotropen Wirkung der Ringdrüse von *Drosophila funebris* und *D. melanogaster.*' *Naturwissenschaften*, **29**, 80–1.

VOGT, M. 1941b. 'Weiteres zur Frage der Artspezifität gonadotroper Hormone (An *Drosophila*-Arten).' *Arch. EntwMech. Org.*, **141**, 424–54.

VOGT, M. 1941c. 'Zur Artspezifität der Ringdrüsenwirkung auf die Dotterbildung und die imaginale Differenzierung bei *Drosophila*-Arten.' *Biol. Zbl.*, **61**, 242–52.

VOGT, M. 1941d. 'Anatomie der pupalen *Drosophila*-Ringdrüse und ihre mutmassliche Bedeutung als imaginales Metamorphosezentrum.' *Biol. Zbl.*, **61**, 148–58.

VOGT, M. 1941e. 'Bemerkungen zum Corpus allatum von *Drosophila.*' *Naturwissenschaften*, **29**, 725.

VOGT, M. 1942a. 'Zur hormonalen Bedeutung des *Drosophila*-Gehirnes und seiner hormonal bedingten imaginalen Entwicklung.' *Naturwissenschaften*, **30**, 740–1.

VOGT, M. 1942c. 'Induktion von Metamorphoseprozessen durch implantierte Ringdrüsen bei *Drosophila.*' *Arch. EntwMech. Org.*, **142**, 129–82.

VOGT, M. 1942d. 'Die Puparisierung als Ringdrüsenwirkung.' *Biol. Zbl.*, **62**, 149–54.

VOGT, M. 1942e. 'Ein drittes Organ in der larvalen Ringdrüse von *Drosophila.*' *Naturwissenschaften*, **30**, 66.

VOGT, M. 1943a. 'Hormonale Auslösung früher Entwicklungsprozesse in den Augenantennenanlagen von *Drosophila.*' *Naturwissenschaften*, **1**, 200–1.

VOGT, M. 1943b. 'Zur Kenntnis des larvalen und pupalen Corpus allatum von *Calliphora.*' *Biol. Zbl.*, **63**, 56–71.

VOGT, M. 1943c. 'Zur Produktion und Bedeutung metamorphoseförfindernden Hormone während der Larvenentwicklung von *Drosophila.*' *Biol. Zbl.*, **63**, 395–446.

VOGT, M. 1943d. 'Zur Produktion gonadotroper Hormone durch Ringdrüsen des ersten Larvenstadiums bei *Drosophila.*' *Biol. Zbl.*, **63**, 467–470.

VOGT, M. 1944a. 'Zur hormonalen Förderung imaginaler Differenzierungsprozesse bei *Drosophila.*' *Naturwissenschaften*, **32**, 37–39.

VOGT, M. 1944b. 'Beitrag zur Determination der Imaginalscheiben bei *Drosophila.*' *Naturwissenschaften,* **32,** 39–40.

VOGT, M. 1946a. 'Inhibitory effects of the corpora cardiaca and corpus allatum in *Drosophila.*' *Nature, Lond.,* **157,** 512.

VOGT, M. 1946b. 'Zur labilen Determination der Imaginalscheiben von *Drosophila.* II. Die Umwandlung präsumptiven Fühlergewebes im Beingewebe.' *Biol. Zbl.,* **65,** 238–54.

VOGT, M. 1946c. 'Neuer Beitrag zur Determination der Imaginalscheibe bei *Drosophila.*' *Naturwissenschaften,* **33.**

VOGT, M. 1947a. 'Beeinflussung der Antennendifferenzierung durch Colchicin bei der *Drosophila* mutante Aristopedia.' *Experientia,* **3,** 156–7.

VOGT, M. 1947b. 'Fördernde Wirkung eines Eierstocks-Hormons auf die Entwicklung larvaler Imaginalscheiben von *Drosophila.*' *Z. Naturf.,* **11b,** 367–99.

VOGT, M. 1947c. 'Zur labilen Determination der Imaginalscheiben von *Drosophila.* III. Analyse der Manifestierungsbedingungen sowie der Wirkungsweise der zur Antennen-und Palpusverdoppellungen führenden Gen-Mutation.' *Biol. Zbl.,* **66,** 81–105.

VOGT, M. 1947d. 'Fettkörper und Oenozyten der *Drosophila* nach Extirpation der adulten Ringdrüse.' *Z. Zellforsch.,* **34,** 160–4.

VOGT, M. 1947e. 'Zur labilen Determination der Imaginalscheiben von *Drosophila.* V. Beitrag zur Manifestierung der Mutante der Antennales.' *Biol. Zbl.,* **66,** 388–95.

VOGT, M. 1947f. 'Verhalten transplantierter Ringdrüsen, "letaler" *Drosophila*-larven.' *Z. Naturf.,* **2b,** 292–4.

VOITKEVICH, A. A. 1962. 'The role of neurosecretion in the regulation of the amphibian metamorphosis.' *J. gen. Biol.,* pp. 23, 45–55.

VOOGD, S. 1955. 'Inhibition of ovary development in worker bees by extraction fluid of the queen.' *Experientia,* **11,** 181–5.

VOWLES, D. M. 1961. 'The physiology of the insect nervous system.' *Int. Rev. Neurobiol.,* **3,** 349–73.

VUILLAUMME, M. 1958. 'La théorie de Buller sur l'ectohormone des Abeilles et ses limites.' *C. R. Acad. Sci., Paris,* **246,** 1927–9.

WADDINGTON, C. H. 1940a. 'Genes as exvocators in development.' *Growth,* suppl., pp. 37–44.

WADDINGTON, C. H. 1940b. *Organisers and genes,* Cambridge Univ. Press, 185 pp.

WADDINGTON, C. H. 1942. 'Growth and determination in the development of *Drosophila.*' *Nature, Lond.,* **149,** 264–5.

WAGNER, G. 1951. 'Das Wachstum der Epidermiskerne während der Larvenentwicklung von *Calliphora erythrocephala.*' *Z. Naturf.,* **6b,** 86–90.

WAKU, Y. 1957a. 'Pupal oxygen uptake in the chinese oak-silkworm *Antherea pernyi* Guérin and breaking of its diapause.' *Sci. Rep. Tohoku Univ.,* **23,** 143–55.

WAKU, Y. 1957b. 'Seasonal change of the pupal respiratory metabolism in the chinese oak-silkworm *Antherea pernyi* (Guérin) with special regard to its hibernation and diapause.' *Sci. Rep. Tohoku Univ.* (4) **23**, 101–18.

WAKU, Y. 1959. 'Studies on the hibernation and diapause in insects. III. Further notes on the O_2-uptake change and breaking of pupal diapause in the chinese oak-silkworm.' *Sci. Rep. Tohoku Univ.* (4), **25**, 1–12.

WAKU, Y. 1960. ibid. IV. 'Histological observations of the endocrine organs in the diapause and non-diapause larvae of the indian male-moth *Plodia interpunctella* H.' *Sci. Rep. Tohoku Univ.* (4), **26**, 327–40.

WALL, J. B. and RALPH, C. L. 1962. 'Responses of specific neurosecretory cells of the cockroach *Blaberus giganteus* to dehydration.' *Biol. Bull., Wood's Hole,* **122**, 431–8.

WALOFF, Z. 1949. 'Observations on larvae of *Ephestia elutella* H. during diapause.' *Trans. roy. ent. Soc. Lond.,* **100**, 147–58.

WANG SHU-YI and DIXON, S. Z. 1960. 'Studies on the transaminase activity of muscle tissue from allatectomized roaches, *Periplaneta americana.' Canad. J. Zool.,* **38**, 275–83.

WAY, M. J. 1959. 'The effect of temperature, particularly during diapause, on the development of the egg of *Leptohylemyia coarctata*. F.' *Trans. roy. ent. Soc. Lond.,* **111**, 351–64.

WAY, M. J. and HOPKINS, B. A. 1950. 'The influence of photoperiod and temperature on the induction of diapause in *Diataraxia oleracea* L.' *J. exp. Biol.,* **27**, 365–76.

WAY, M. J. and SMITH, M. P. 1949. 'Photoperiodism and diapause in insects.' *Nature, Lond.,* **164**, 615.

WEBER, H. 1933. *Lehrbuch der Entomologie,* Jena, Fischer, pp. 467.

WEBER, H. 1952. 'Morphologie, Histologie und Entwicklungsgeschichte der Articulaten. Gleichzeitig ein Bericht über Fortschritte in der Methodik der Articulatenmorphologie.' *Fortschr. Zool.* (N.F.), **9**, 18–231.

WEED, I. G. 1936a. 'Experimental study of moulting in the grasshopper *Melanoplus differentialis.' Proc. Soc. exp. Biol. Med.,* **34**, 883–5.

WEED, I. G. 1936b. 'Removal of corpora allata on egg production in the grasshopper *Melanoplus differentialis.' Proc. Soc. exp. Biol. Med.,* **34**, 885–886.

WEESNER, F. M. 'The biology of *Tenuirostritermes tenuirostris* (Desneux) with emphasis on caste development.' *Univ. Calif. Publ. Zool.,* **57**, 251–301.

WEIR, J. S. 1959. 'Changes in the retrocerebral endocrine system of larvae of *Myrmica* and their relation to larval growth and development.' *Insectes sociaux,* **6**, 375–86.

WEISMANN, A. 1864. 'Die nachembryonale Entwicklung der Musciden nach Beobachtungen an *Musca vomitoria* und *Sarcophaga carnaria.' Z. wiss. Zool.,* **14**, 187–336.

WEISS, P. 1939. *Principles of development,* New York, Henry Holt.

WEISS, P. 1940. 'The problem of cell individuality in development.' *Amer. Nat.,* **74**, 34–46.

WEISS, P. 1950. 'Perspectives in the field of morphogenesis.' *Quart. Rev. Biol.*, **25**, 117–98.

WEISS, P. 1953. 'The cellular basis of the differentiation.' *J. Embryol. exp. Morph.*, **1**, 181–212.

WEISS, P. and KOVANAN, J. L. 1957. 'A model of growth and growth control in mathematical terms.' *J. gen. Physiol.*, **41**, 1–47.

WEISSENBERG, R. 1906. 'Über die Oenozyten von *Torymus nigricornis* mit besonderer Berücksichtigung der Metamorphose.' *Zool. Jb.*, Abt. **2**, pp. 231–68.

WELLS, M. J. 1954. 'The thoracic glands of Hemiptera and Heteroptera.' *Quart. J. micr. Sci.*, **95**, 231–44.

WELLS, M. J. and WELLS, J. 1959. 'Hormonal control of sexual maturity in *Octopus.*' *J. exp. Biol.*, **36**, 1–33.

WENIG, K. and KEILOVÁ, H. 1951. *Practical course of animal physiology*, Prague (in Czech). 165 pp.

WENSE, T. 1938. *Wirkungen and Vorkommen von Hormonen bei wirbellosen Tieren*, Leipzig, Barth.

WESTWOOD, J. O. 1861. *On the metamorphosis in insects*, Royal Inst. G.B.

WEYER, F. 1928. 'Untersuchungen über die Keimdrüsen bei Hymenopterenarbeiterinnen.' *Z. wiss. Zool.*, **131**, 345–501.

WEYER, F. 1935. 'Ueber drüsenartige Nervenzellen im Gehirn der Honigbiene *Apis mellifica.*' *Zool. Anz.*, **112**, 137–41.

WEYER, F. 1936. 'Regenerationsvorgänge am Mitteldarm der Insekten.' *Verh. dtsch. zool. Ges.*, pp. 157–63.

WHEELER, W. M. 1893. 'A contribution to insect embryology.' *J. Morph.*, **8**, 1–160.

WHITE, P. B. 1921. 'Note on a case of Fibroma in a honey bee.' *J. Path. Bact.*, **24**, 138–9.

WIEDBRAUCK, H. 1953. 'Wiederholung der Metamorphose von Schmetterlingshaut. Versuche an der Wachsmotte *Galleria mellonella.*' *Biol. Zbl.*, **72**, 530–56A.

WIELOWIEISKI, H. 1886. 'Ueber den Fettkörper von *Corethra plumicornis* und seine Entwicklung.' *Zool. Anz.*, **6**, 318–23.

WIGGLESWORTH, V. B. 1933. 'The physiology of the cuticle and of ecdysis in *Rhodnius prolixus* (Triatomidae, Hemiptera); with special reference to the function of the oenocytes and of the dermal glands.' *Quart. J. micr. Sci.*, **76**, 269–318.

WIGGLESWORTH, V. B. 1934a. 'The physiology of ecdysis in *Rhodnius*. II. Factors controlling moulting and "metamorphosis".' *Quart. J. micr. Sci.*, **77**, 191–222.

WIGGLESWORTH, V. B. 1934b. *Insect Physiology*, London.

WIGGLESWORTH, V. B. 1934c. 'Factors controlling moulting and "metamorphosis" in an insect.' *Nature, Lond.*, **135**, 725–6.

WIGGLESWORTH, V. B. 1935. 'Function of the corpus allatum in insects.' *Nature, Lond.*, **136**, 338.

WIGGLESWORTH, V. B. 1936a. 'The function of the corpus allatum in the growth and reproduction of *Rhodnius prolixus*.' *Quart. J. micr. Sci.*, **79**, 91–119.

WIGGLESWORTH, V. B. 1936b. 'The loss of water during ecdysis in *Rhodnius prolixus*.' *Proc. roy. ent. Soc. Lond.* (A), **11**, 104–7.

WIGGLESWORTH, V. B. 1937. 'Wound healing in an insect, *Rhodnius prolixus*.' *J. exp. Biol.*, **14**, 364–81.

WIGGLESWORTH, V. B. 1938. 'The absorption of fluid from the tracheal system of mosquito larvae at hatching and moulting.' *J. exp. Biol.*, **15**, 248–54.

WIGGLESWORTH, V. B. 1939a. 'Häutung bei Imagines von Wanzen.' *Naturwissenschaften*, **27**, 301.

WIGGLESWORTH, V. B. 1939b. 'Source of the moulting hormone in *Rhodnius*.' *Nature, Lond.*, **144**, 953.

WIGGLESWORTH, V. B. 1939c. *The principles of insect physiology*, 1st ed. London, Methuen.

WIGGLESWORTH, V. B. 1940. 'The determination of characters at metamorphosis in *Rhodnius prolixus*.' *J. exp. Biol.*, **17**, 201–22.

WIGGLESWORTH, V. B. 1940b. 'Local and general factors in the development of "pattern" in *Rhodnius prolixus*.' *J. exp. Biol.*, **17**, 180–200.

WIGGLESWORTH, V. B. 1942. 'The significance of "chromatic droplets" in the growth of insects.' *Quart. J. micr. Sci.*, **83**, 141–52.

WIGGLESWORTH, V. B. 1945. *Growth and form in an insect. Essays on growth and form*, Oxford Univ. Press.

WIGGLESWORTH, V. B. 1947a. 'The corpus allatum and the control of metamorphosis in insects.' *Nature, Lond.*, **159**, 872; **160**, 16.

WIGGLESWORTH, V. B. 1947b. 'Endocrinologie des Arthropodes: Rapport général sur l'endocrinologie des insectes.' *Bull. Biol.*, **33**, 174–6.

WIGGLESWORTH, V. B. 1948a. 'The structure and deposition of the cuticle in the adult mealworm.' *Quart. J. micr. Sci*, **89**, 197–217.

WIGGLESWORTH, V. B. 1948b. 'The function of the corpus allatum in *Rhodnius*.' *J. exp. Biol.*, **25**, 1–14.

WIGGLESWORTH, V. B. 1948c. 'The role of the cell in determination.' Symp. Soc. exp. Biol., *Growth* reprint no. **2**, 16 pp.

WIGGLESWORTH, V. B. 1948d. 'The insect cuticle.' *Biol. Rev.*, **23**, 408–451.

WIGGLESWORTH, V. B. 1949a. 'Insect biochemistry.' *Ann. Rev. Biochem.*, pp. 595–614.

WIGGLESWORTH, V. B. 1949b. 'Diskussionsbemerkung zum Vortrag von J. Timon-David, Chimie des hormones d'insectes.' *Bull. biol.*, suppl., **33**, 97.

WIGGLESWORTH, V. B. 1950. *The principles of insect physiology*, 2nd ed., London and New York, 544 pp.

WIGGLESWORTH, V. B. 1951a. 'Metamorphosis in insects.' *Proc. roy. ent. Soc. Lond.* (C), **15**, 78–82.

WIGGLESWORTH, V. B. 1951b. 'Source of moulting hormone in *Rhodnius*.' *Nature, Lond.*, **168,** 558.

WIGGLESWORTH, V. B. 1952a. 'The thoracic gland in *Rhodnius* and its role in moulting.' *J. exp. Biol.*, **29,** 561–70.

WIGGLESWORTH, V. B. 1952b. 'Hormone balance and the control of metamorphosis in *Rhodnius*.' *J. exp. Biol.*, **29,** 620–31.

WIGGLESWORTH, V. B. 1953a. 'Hormones and the development of hybrid Lepidoptera.' *Ent. Rec.*, **65,** 244–5.

WIGGLESWORTH, V. B. 1953b. *The principles of insect physiology*, 3rd ed., London.

WIGGLESWORTH, V. B. 1953c. 'Hormones and metamorphosis with special reference to hemimetabolic insects.' *Trans. IXth int. Congr. Ent.*, **2,** 51–6.

WIGGLESWORTH, V. B. 1953d. 'Determination of cell function in an insect.' *J. Embryol. exp. Morph.*, **1,** 269–77.

WIGGLESWORTH, V. B. 1953e. 'The origin and sensory neurones in an insect, *Rhodnius*.' *Quart. J. micr. Sci.*, **94,** 93–112.

WIGGLESWORTH, V. B. 1954a. 'Growth and regeneration in the tracheal system of an insect, *Rhodnius prolixus*.' *Quart. J. micr. Sci.*, **95,** 115–37.

WIGGLESWORTH, V. B. 1954b. *The physiology of insect metamorphosis*. Cambr. Monogr. Exp. Biol. 1, Cambridge.

WIGGLESWORTH, V. B. 1954c. 'Secretion of juvenile hormone by the corpus allatum of *Calliphora*.' *Nature, Lond.*, **174,** 556.

WIGGLESWORTH, V. B. 1954d. 'Neurosecretion and the corpus cardiacum of insects.' *Pubbl. Staz. zool. Napoli*, **24,** 41–6.

WIGGLESWORTH, V. B. 1955a. 'The breakdown of the thoracic gland in the adult insect *Rhodnius prolixus*.' *J. exp. Biol.*, **32,** 485–91.

WIGGLESWORTH, V. B. 1955b. 'The role of the haemocytes in the growth and moulting of an insect, *Rhodnius prolixus*.' *J. exp. Biol.*, **32,** 649–63.

WIGGLESWORTH, V. B. 1956a. 'Formation and involution of striated muscle fibres during the growth and moulting cycles of *Rhodnius*.' *Quart. J. micr. Sci.*, **97,** 465–80.

WIGGLESWORTH, V. B. 1956b. 'The haemocytes and connective tissue formation in an insect, *Rhodnius prolixus*.' *Quart. J. micr. Sci.*, **97,** 89–98.

WIGGLESWORTH, V. B. 1956c. 'The functions of the amoebocytes during moulting in *Rhodnius*.' *Ann. Sci. Nat., Zool.*, (11), **18,** 139–44.

WIGGLESWORTH, V. B. 1956d. 'Modo d'azione degli ormoni della crescita in *Rhodnius prolixus*.' *Boll. Zool. agr. Bachic.*, **22,** 3–13.

WIGGLESWORTH, V. B. 1956e. 'Hormones and metamorphosis in insects.' *Scientia, Bologna*, **91,** 179–82.

WIGGLESWORTH, V. B. 1956f. 'The function of the corpus allatum in the growth and reproduction of *Rhodnius prolixus*.' *Quart. J. micr. Sci.*, **79,** 91–121.

WIGGLESWORTH, V. B. 1956g. 'La metamorfosi degli insetti.' *R. C. Acad. Bologna* (II), **3,** 1–7.

WIGGLESWORTH, V. B. 1957a. 'The physiology of insect cuticle.' *Ann. Rev. Ent.*, **2**, 37–54.

WIGGLESWORTH, V. B. 1957b. 'The action of growth hormones in insects.' *Symp. Soc. exp. Biol.*, no. **11**, 204–27.

WIGGLESWORTH, V. B. 1958. 'Some methods for assaying extracts of the juvenile hormone in insects.' *J. Ins. Physiol.*, **2**, 73–84.

WIGGLESWORTH, V. B. 1959a. 'The histology of the nervous system of an insect, *Rhodnius prolixus*. I. The peripheral nervous system.' *Quart. J. micr. Sci.*, **100**, 285–98.

WIGGLESWORTH, V. B. 1959b. 'idem'. 'II. The central ganglia.' *Quart. J. micr. Sci.*, **100**, 299–313.

WIGGLESWORTH, V. B. 1959c. 'Metamorphosis, polymorphism, differentiation.' *Sci. Amer.*, **200**, 100–10.

WIGGLESWORTH, V. B. 1959d. 'A simple method for cutting sections in the 0.5 to 1μ range and for sections of chitin.' *Quart. J. micr. Sci.*, **100**, 315–20.

WIGGLESWORTH, V. B. 1959f. *The control of growth and form*, Cornell Univ. Press, p. 140.

WIGGLESWORTH, V. B. 1959g. 'Insect blood cells.' *Ann. Rev. Ent.*, **4**, 1–16.

WIGGLESWORTH, V. B. 1960a. 'Nutrition of the central nervous system of the cockroach *Periplaneta americana*.' *Proc. IXth int. Congr. Ent.*, **1**, 630–1.

WIGGLESWORTH, V. B. 1960b. 'The epidermal cells and the metamorphosis of insects.' *Nature, Lond.*, **188**, 358–9.

WIGGLESWORTH, V. B. 1961. 'Insect polymorphism, a tentative synthesis.' *Symp. roy. ent. Soc. Lond.*, no. **1**, 103–13.

WIGGLESWORTH, V. B. 1962. 'Endocrine regulation during development. I. Hormones in relation to metamorphosis.' *Gen. comp. Endocrinol.*, suppl., **1**, 316–21.

WIGGLESWORTH, V. B. and GILLETT, J. D. 1936. 'The loss of water during ecdysis in *Rhodnius prolixus*.' *Proc. roy. ent. Soc. Lond.* (A), **11**, 104–7.

WILDE, J. DE. 1953. 'Provisional analysis of the imaginal diapause in an insect (*Leptinotarsa decemlineata*).' *Acta physiol. pharm. néerl.*, **3**, 133–8.

WILDE, J. DE. 1958a. 'Perception of the protoperiod by the Colorado beetle.' *Proc. Xth int. Congr. Ent.*, **2**, 213–8.

WILDE, J. DE. 1958b. 'Observations on threshold intensity and sensitivity to different wave length of photoperiodic responses in the Colorado beetle.' *Ent. exp. appl.*, **1**, 301–7.

WILDE, J. DE. 1959a. 'Diapause as a deficiency syndrome of the corpus allatum in the adult Colorado beetle.' *Acta Symp. Evol. Ins. Prague*, pp. 226–30.

WILDE, J. DE. 1959b. 'Fotoperiodiciteit bij insecten.' *Vakb. Biol.*, **39**, 153–162.

WILDE, J. DE. 1961. 'Extrinsic control of endocrine functions in insects.' *Bull. Res. Counc. Israel* (B), **10**, 36–52.

WILDE, J. DE. 1962a. 'Analysis of the diapause syndrome in the Colorado potato beetle; behavior and reproduction.' *Acta physiol. pharm. néerl.*, **11**.

WILDE, J. DE. 1962b. 'Photoperiodism in insects and mites.' *Ann. Rev. Ent.*, **7**, 1–26.

WILDE, J. DE and BOER, J. A. DE. 1961. 'Physiology of diapause in the adult Colorado beetle. II. Diapause as a case of pseudoallatectomy.' *J. Ins. Physiol.*, **6**, 152–61.

WILDE, J. DE and VAN DOESBURG, P. H. 1956. 'Site of hibernation of a Tachinid larva within its host.' *Nature, Lond.*, **177**, 1087.

WILDE, J. DE, DUINTJER, C. S. and MOOK, L. 1959. 'Physiology of diapause in the adult Colorado beetle. I. The photoperiod as a controlling factor.' *J. Ins. Physiol.*, **3**, 75–85.

WILDE, J. DE and STEGWEE, D. 1958. 'Two major effects of the corpus allatum in the adult Colorado beetle (*Leptinotarsa decemlineata*).' *Arch. néerl. Zool.*, **13**, suppl. 1, 277–89.

WILLIAMS, C. M. 1940. 'Production of combinations of pupal and adult characters in individual silkworm pupae by the application of temperature gradients.' *Anat. Rec.*, **78**, suppl., 99.

WILLIAMS, C. M. 1942. 'The effects of temperature gradients on the pupal adult transformation of silkworms.' *Biol. Bull., Wood's Hole*, **82**, 347–55.

WILLIAMS, C. M. 1946a. 'Continuous anaesthesia for insects.' *Science*, **103**, 57.

WILLIAMS, C. M. 1946b. 'Physiology of insect diapause. I. The role of brain in the production and termination of pupal dormancy in giant silkworm *Platysamia cecropia*.' *Biol. Bull., Wood's Hole*, **90**, 234–43.

WILLIAMS, C. M. 1947a. ibid. II. 'Interaction between the pupal brain and prothoracic glands in the metamorphosis in the giant silkworm, *Platysamia cecropia*.' *Biol. Bull., Wood's Hole*, **93**, 89–98.

WILLIAMS, C. M. 1947b. 'The function of the brain in terminating pupal diapause in the giant silkworm *Platysamia cecropia*.' *Anat. Rec.*, **99**, 115.

WILLIAMS, C. M. 1947c. 'The cytochrome system in relation to diapause and development in the cecropia silkworm.' *Anat. Rec.*, **99**, 591.

WILLIAMS, C. M. 1948a. 'Physiology of insect diapause. III. The prothoracic glands in the Cecropia silkworm with special reference to their significance in embryonic and postembryonic development.' *Biol. Bull., Wood's Hole*, **94**, 60–5.

WILLIAMS, C. M. 1948b. 'Extrinsic control of morphogenesis as illustrated in the metamorphosis of insects.' *Growth*, suppl., **12**, 61–76.

WILLIAMS, C. M. 1949a. 'The endocrinology of diapause.' *Bull. biol.*, suppl., **33**, 52–6 (1948).

WILLIAMS, C. M. 1949b. 'The prothoracic glands of insects in retrospect and in prospect.' *Biol. Bull., Wood's Hole*, **97**, 111–14.

WILLIAMS, C. M. 1950. 'A hormonal-enzymatic mechanism for the control of pupal diapause in the cecropia silkworm.' *Abstr. XVIIIth int. Phys. Congr. Copenhagen*, **1**.

WILLIAMS, C. M. 1951a. 'Biochemical mechanics in insect growth and metamorphosis.' *Harvard Univ. Feder. Proc.*, **10**, 546–52.

WILLIAMS, C. M. 1951b. 'Endocrine control of the complete metamorphosis of insects.' *Anat. Rec.*, **111**, 3.

WILLIAMS, C. M. 1952a. 'Physiology of insect diapause. IV. The brain and prothoracic glands as an endocrine system in the cecropia silkworm.' *Biol. Bull., Wood's Hole*, **103**, 120–38.

WILLIAMS, C. M. 1952b. 'Morphogenesis and the metamorphosis in insects.' *The Harvey Lectures*, **47**, 126–55.

WILLIAMS, C. M. 1953. 'Physiology of insect diapause. V. Assay of the growth and differentiation hormone of Lepidoptera by the method of tissue culture.' *Biol. Bull., Wood's Hole*, **105**, 174–87.

WILLIAMS, C. M. 1954. 'Isolation and identification of the prothoracic hormone of insects.' *Anat. Rec.*, **120**, 743.

WILLIAMS, C. M. 1956a. 'The juvenile hormone of insects.' *Nature, Lond.*, **178**, 212.

WILLIAMS, C. M. 1956b. 'Physiology of insect diapause. X. An endocrine mechanism for the influence of temperature on the diapausing pupa of the Cecropia silkworm.' *Biol. Bull., Wood's Hole*, **110**, 201–18.

WILLIAMS, C. M. 1957. 'The juvenile hormone of insects.' *Anat. Rec.*, **128**, 640–1.

WILLIAMS, C. M. 1958a. 'Hormonal regulation of insect metamorphosis.' *Symp. Chem. Basis Develop.*, Johns Hopkins Press, pp. 794–806.

WILLIAMS, C. M. 1958b. 'The juvenile hormone.' *Sci. Amer.*, **198**, 67–74.

WILLIAMS, C. M. 1959. 'The juvenile hormone. I. Endocrine activity of the corpora allata of the adult cecropia silkworm.' *Biol. Bull., Wood's Hole*, **116**, 323–38.

WILLIAMS, C. M. 1960. 'The juvenile hormone.' *Acta endocrin. Copenhagen*, suppl., **50**, 189–91, 397–9.

WILLIAMS, C. M. 1961. 'The juvenile hormone. II. Its role in the endocrine control of molting pupation and adult development in the cecropia silkworm.' *Biol. Bull., Wood's Hole*, **121**, 572–85.

WILLIAMS, C. M., MOORHEAD, L. V. and PULIS, J. F. 1959. 'Juvenile hormone in thymus, human placenta and other mammalian organs.' *Nature, Lond.*, **183**, 405.

WILLIAMS, C. M. and SANBORN, R. C. 1948. 'The cytochrome system in relation to diapause and development in the cecropia silkworm.' *Biol. Bull., Wood's Hole*, **95**, 282–3.

WILSON, E. O. 1953. 'The origin and evolution of polymorphism in ants.' *Quart. Rev. Biol.*, **28**, 136–56.

WILSON, I. T. 1924. 'Two new hereditary tumors in *Drosophila*.' *Genetics*, **9**, 343–62.

WILSON, L. P. 1947. 'Effect of dinitrophenol and excess aminoacids upon melanotic growths in *Drosophila*.' *Anat. Rec.*, **99**, 600.

WILSON, W. T. and SCHARRER, B. 1949. 'Fat metabolism in tumor bearing insects (*Leucophaea maderae*).' *Anat. Rec.*, **105**, 625.

WINKLER, J. 1950. 'Some interesting monstrosities in beetles' (in Czech). *Acta Soc. ent. Čsl.*, **48**, 1–2.

WOJTCZAK, L. and CHMURZYNSKA, W. 1960. 'Inhibition studies on insect polyphenol oxidase.' *Acta biochim. polon.*, **7**, 39–49.

WOLF, B. and WILLIAMS, C. M. 1953. 'Coenzyme A in relation to pupal diapause and adult development in the cecropia silkworm.' *Anat. Rec.*, **117**, 542.

WOLFE, L. S. 1952. 'Investigations on the structure and deposition of the larval, pupal and imaginal cuticles of *Calliphora erythrocephala*.' Thesis, Cambridge Univ.

WOLFE, L. S. 1954. 'The deposition of the third instar larval cuticle of *Calliphora erythrocephala*.' *Quart. J. micr. Sci.*, **95**, 49–66.

WOLSKY, A. 1937. 'Production of local depressions in the development of *Drosophila*.' *Nature, Lond.*, **139**, 1069–70.

WOLSKY, A. 1938. 'The effect of carbon monoxide on the oxygen consumption of *Drosophila* pupae.' *J. exp. Biol.*, **15**, 225–34.

WOLSKY, A. 1941. 'Quantitative changes in the substrate-dehydrogenase system of *Drosophila* pupae during metamorphosis.' *Science*, **94**, 48–49.

WOLSKY, A. and KALICKI, H. G. 1959. 'Oxidative metabolism and puparium formation in the ebony mutant of *Drosophila melanogaster*.' *Nature, Lond.*, **183**, 1129–30.

WOLSKY, A., KALICKI, H. and GRILLO, R. 1961. 'The cyto-physiological basis of hereditary differences in the juvenile hormone activity of *Drosophila melanogaster*.' *Pathol. Biol. Fr.*, pp. 679–82.

WOODRUFF, L. C. 1936. 'Autospasy and regeneration in the roach, *Blatella germanica*.' *J. Kans. ent. Soc.*, **10**, 1–9.

WYATT, S. S. 1956. 'Culture in vitro of tissue from the silkworm, *Bombyx mori* L.' *J. gen. Physiol.*, **39**, 841–52.

YAKHONTOV, V. V. 1945. 'Sur la sécretion interne des insectes.' *C. R. Acad. Sci. U.R.S.S.*, **46**, 127–8.

YAMAMOTO, R. T. and JACOBSON, M. 1962. 'Juvenile hormone activity of isomer of farnesol.' *Nature, Lond.*, **196**, 908–9.

YAMASHITA, Y., TANI, K. and KOBAYASHI, M. 1961. 'The effects of allatectomy on the number of eggs in the silkworm *Bombyx mori*.' *Acta Seric.*, **39**, 12–15.

YASHIKA, K. 1960. 'Studies on the neurosecretory system in Apterygota. I. Histological observation of the corpus allatum and neurosecretory cells in *Ctenolepisma*.' *Mem. Coll. Sci. Univ. Kyoto* (B), **27**, 1–7.

YOKOYAMA, T. 1936. 'Histological observations on a non-moulting strain of silkworm.' *Proc. roy. ent. Soc. Lond.* (A), **11**, 35–44.

YOSSII, R. 1944. 'Über den Determinationszustand der Raupenhaut bei der Mehlmotte *Ephestia kühniella* Zell.' *Biol. Zbl.*, **64**, 305–15.

ZAKHVATKIN, A. A. 1953a. 'Summary of lectures in "Embryology of Arthropods".' In E. S. Smirnov (Ed.), *A. A. Zakhvatkin: Collection of scientific works*, Moscow Univ., pp. 335–78.

ZAKHVATKIN, A. A. 1953b. 'On the question of origin of the larva in holometabola.' In E. S. Smirnov (Ed.), *A. A. Zakhvatkin: Collection of scientific works*, Moscow Univ., pp. 195–204.

ZANDER, E. and BECKER, F. 1925. 'Die Ausbildung des Geschlechtes bei der Honigbiene. II.' *Erlanger Jb. Bienenkunde*, **3**, 161–246.

ZAVŘEL, J. 1926a. 'Metamorphosis in a few new Chironomidae.' *Acta Soc. Sci. nat. Morav.*, **3**, 251–82.

ZAVŘEL, J. 1926b. 'The influence of thyroid on the growth of Chironomidae' (in Czech). *Biol. listy*, **5**, 1–7.

ZAVŘEL, J. 1927. 'Influence de la glande thyroide sur l'acroissement des larves des Chironomides.' *C. R. Soc. Biol., Paris*, **96**, 1087–9.

ZAVŘEL, J. 1930a. 'Untersuchungen über den Einfluss einiger Organenextrakten auf Wachstum und Entwicklung der Chironomiden.' *Arch. EntwMech. Org.*, **121**, 770–99.

ZAVŘEL, J. 1930b. 'Können die Hormone der Wirbeltiere das Wachstum und die Entwicklung der wirbellosen Tiere beeinflussen?' *Publ. Fac. Med. Univ. Masaryk*, **9**, 115–21.

ZAVŘEL, J. 1931. 'Können Wirbeltierhormone das Wachstum und die Entwicklung der Wirbellosen beeinflussen?' *Arch. zool. ital.*, pp. 191–6.

ZAVŘEL, J. 1932. 'Adrenalinwirkung am Herzen der Avertebraten.' *Čas. lék. čes.*, pp. 129–33.

ZAVŘEL, J. 1935a. 'Endokrine Hautdrüsen von *Syndiamesa branicki* Now.' *Publ. Fac. Sci. Univ. Masaryk*, no. 213, 18 pp.

ZAVŘEL, J. 1935b. 'Sur les oenocytes et les glandes de Verson.' *Proc. XIIth int. Congr. Zool.*, 1.

ZAVŘEL, J. 1939. 'The internal secretion in insects' (in Czech). *Výr. zpr. morav. přír. Spol.*, pp. 1–11.

ZEBE, E. 1954. 'Ueber den Stoffwechsel der Lepidopteren.' *Z. vergl. Physiol.*, **36**, 290–317.

ZEE, H. C. and PAI, S. 1944. 'Corpus allatum and corpus cardiacum in *Chironomus* sp.' *Amer. Nat.*, **78**, 472–7.

ZELENÝ, J. 1961. 'Contribution to the knowledge of diapause in insects. 6. Influence of the photoperiod and temperature on the induction of diapause in host and parasite.' *Acta Soc. zool. Čsl.*, **25**, 258–70.

ZIKÁN, J. F. 1944. *Consideracoes sobre a metamorfose dos insetos. Finalidade e importancia fisologica dos filamentos retentivos, embryionários, dos insétos heterometabolicos*, Rio de Janeiro, 51 pp.

ZOLOTAREV, E. CH. 1939. 'The resistance of *Antherea pernyi* eggs in low temperatures and its gas exchange' (in Russian). *Zool. Zh.*, **18**, 387–406.

ZOLOTAREV, E. CH. 1940a. 'Materials on the ecology of voltinism of *Antherea pernyi*' (in Russian). *Zool. Zh.*, **19**, 631–45.

ZOLOTAREV, E. CH. 1940b. *Causes of the origin of pupal diapause in* Antherea pernyi *and the ways of its influencing* (in Russian). Moscow, Selchosgis, pp. 39–62.

ZOLOTAREV, E. CH. 1947. 'Diapause and the development of pupa of the Chinese oak silkworm (*Antherea pernyi*)' (in Russian). *Zool. Zh.*, **26**, 539–544.

ZOLOTAREV, E. CH. 1948. 'Biology of diapause in the *Antherea pernyi* pupae' (in Russian). In *Culture of Chinese Oak silkworm in U.S.S.R.*, Moscow, Selchosgis, pp. 48–63.

ZOLOTAREV, E. CH. 1950. 'On the development of the larvae of *Aporia crategi* during the hibernation period' (in Russian). *Zool. Zh.*, **29**, 152–63.

ZOLOTAREV, E. CH. 1951. 'An example of a successful regulation of the biology of one insect' (in Russian). *Agrobiologia*, **69**, 158–60.

ZWICKI, K. and WIGGLESWORTH, V. B. 1956. 'The course of oxygen consumption during the moulting cycle of *Rhodnius prolixus*.' *Proc. roy. ent. Soc. Lond.* (A), **31**, 153–60.

ZUCKERMANN, S., *et al.* 1950. 'A discussion on the measurement of growth and form.' *Proc. roy. Soc.* (B), **137**, 433–523.

Additional References, 1963–1965

ALLAIS, J. P., BERGERARD, J., ETIENNE, J. and POLONOVSKI, J. 1964. 'Nature et évolution des lipides au cours de l'embryogenèse de *Locusta migratoria migratorioides* L.' *J. Ins. Physiol.*, **5**, 753–72.

ALTMANN, G. 1963. 'Über die Wirkung von gonadotropen Substanzen und Sexualhormonen der Wirbeltiere auf das Ovar der Honigbiene.' *Z. Bienenforsch.*, **5, 6,** 135–6.

ANKERSMIT, G. W. 1964. 'Voltinism and its determination in some beetles of cruciferous crops.' *Meded. Landbouwhogeschool Wageningen*, **64–8,** 1–60.

BARKER, R. J. 1963. 'Inhibition of diapause in *Pieris rapae* L. by brief supplementary photophases.' *Experientia*, **19,** 185.

BARKER, R. J., MAYER, A. and COHEN, CH. F. 1963. 'Photoperiod effects in *Pieris rapae*.' *Ann. ent. Soc. Amer.*, 3, **56,** 292–4.

BEAMENT, J. W. L., TREHERNE, J. E. and WIGGLESWORTH, V. B. 1963. *Advances in insect physiology*. Academic Press, London and New York, vol. I, 512 pp., vol. II, 368 pp., 1965.

BECK, S. D., 1963. 'Physiology and ecology of photoperiodism.' *Bull. ent. Soc. Amer.*, **9,** 1, 8–16.

BECK, S. D. and ALEXANDER, N. 1964a. 'Hormonal activation of the insect brain.' *Science*, **143,** 478–9.

BECK, S. D. and ALEXANDER, N. 1964b. 'Proctodone, an insect developmental hormone.' *Biol. Bull.*, *Wood's Hole*, **126,** 185–98.

BECK, S. D. and ALEXANDER, N. 1964c. 'Chemically and photoperiodically induced diapause development in the European Corn Borer *Ostrinia nubilalis*.' *Biol. Bull.*, *Wood's Hole*, **126,** 175–84.

BEETSMA, J., DE RUITER, L. and DE WILDE, J. 1963. 'Possible influence of neotenine and ecdyson on the signs of phototaxis in the eyed hawk caterpillar (*Smerinthus ocellata* L.).' *J. Ins. Physiol.*, **8,** 251–8.

BELYAEVA, T. G. 1964. 'Secretion of corpora cardiaca and corpora allata and their role in the development of the cricket *Gryllus domesticus* L.' (in Rumanian with English summary). *Zh. obshch. Biol.*, **25,** 443–53.

BERGER, H. 1963. 'Die Wirkung der Neurohormone auf das Metamorphosegeschehen bei *Calliphora erythrocephala* Meig.' *Zool. Publ.*, **70** (2), 245–65.

BERN, A. H. 1963. 'The secretory neuron as a doubly specialized cell.' Reprinted from Mazia, D. and Tyler, A., *General physiology of cell specialization*. McGraw-Hill.

BIELLMAN, G. 1963. 'Effects des rayons X sur des larves de *Locusta migratoria* L.' *Bull. Soc. Zool. Fr.*, **87,** 569–88.

427

BIER, K. 1963. 'Synthese, interzellulärer Transport und Abbau von Ribonukleinsäure im Ovar der Stubenfliege *Musca domestica*.' *J. Cell. Biol.*, **16**, 436–40.

BLAGODATSKAYA, G. I. 1963. 'Developmental changes of neurosecretion in the oak silkworm (*Antherea pernyi*)' (in Russian). *Prace Inst. Zool.*, *Kiev*, 2, **19**, 58–66.

BOCH, R. and SHEARER, D. A. 1963. 'Production of geraniol by honey bees of various ages.' *J. Ins. Physiol.*, **9**, 431–4.

BOER, H. H. 1963. 'A preliminary note on the histochemistry of the neurosecretory material (NSM) of the snail *Lymnaea stagnalis*.' *2nd Confer. Europ. Compar. Endocrinol.*, Abstr. no. 13.

BOWERS, W. S. and THOMPSON, M. J. 1963. 'Juvenile hormone activity: effects of non-isoprenoid and straight-chain alcohols on insects.' *Science*, **142**, 1469.

BOWERS, B. and WILLIAMS, C. M. 1964. 'Physiology of insect diapause. XIII. DNA synthesis during the metamorphosis of the cecropia silkworm.' *Biol. Bull., Wood's Hole*, **126**, 205–19.

BRETTSCHNEIDEROVÁ, Z., and NOVÁK, V. J. A. 1965. 'The effect of juvenile hormone on the protein level in the haemolymph of the bug *Pyrrhocoris apterus* during the metamorphosis.' *Symp. vergl. Endokrin.*, *Jena*, Kurzref., pp. 26–7.

BRIAN, M. V. 1963. 'Studies of caste differentiation in *Myrmica rubra* L. 6. Factors influencing the course of female development in the early third instar.' *Insectes sociaux*, **10**, 91–102.

BRIAN, M. V. and HIBBLE, J. 1963a. 'Larval size and the influence of the queen on growth in *Myrmica*.' *Insectes sociaux*, **10**, 71–82.

BRIAN, M. V. and HIBBLE, J. 1963b. '9-oxodec-trans-2-enoic acid and *Myrmica* queen extracts tested for influence on brood in *Myrmica*.' *J. Ins. Physiol.*, **9**, 25–34.

BÜCKMANN, D. 1963. 'Der Einflus der Temperatur auf das Epidermispigment der Raupen von *Cerura vinula* L.' *Z. naturf.*, **18b**, 255–264.

BURDETTE, W. J. and BULLOCK, M. W. 1963. 'Ecdysone: five biologically active fractions from *Bombyx*.' *Science*, **140**, 1311.

BUTLER, C. G., CALLOW, R. K. and CHAPMAN, J. R. 1964. '9-hydroxy-dec.-trans-2-enoic acid, a pheromone stabilizing honeybee swarms.' *Nature, Lond.*, **201** (4920), p. 733.

CARLISLE, D. B. 1960. 'Softening of chitin for histology'. *Nature, Lond.*, **187**, 1132–3.

CARLISLE, D. B. and ELLIS, P. G. 1963. 'Prothoraco-tropic hormone of Locusts.' *Nature, Lond.*, **200**, 496.

CHINO, H. and GILBERT, L. I. 1964. 'Diglyceride release from insect fat body: a possible means of lipid transport.' *Science*, **143**, 359–61.

CHMURZYŃSKA, W. and WOJTZAK, L. 1963. 'Effect of thiourea on moulting and pupation of the silkworm, *Bombyx mori* L.' *Biol. Bull., Wood's Hole*, **125**, 61–8.

CLARKE, K. U. and LANGLEY, P. A. 1963. 'Effect of the removal of the frontal ganglion on the development of the gonads in *Locusta migratoria*.' *Nature, Lond.*, **198**, 811–12.

CLARKE, K. U., and LANGLEY, P. A. 1964a. 'Studies on the initiation of growth and moulting in *Locusta migratoria migratorioides*. I.' *J. Ins. Physiol.*, **9**, 287–92.

CLARKE, K. U., and LANGLEY, P. A. 1964b. 'Studies on the initiation of growth and moulting in *Locusta migratoria migratorioides*. II.' *J. Ins. Physiol.*, **9**, 363–73.

CLARKE, K. U. and LANGLEY, P. A. 1964c. 'Studies on the initiation of growth and moulting in *Locusta migratoria migratorioides*. III. The role of the frontal ganglion.' *J. Ins. Physiol.*, **9**, 411–21.

CLARKE, K. U. and LANGLEY, P. A. 1964d. 'Studies on the initiation of growth and moulting in *Locusta migratoria migratorioides*. IV. The relationship between the stomatogastric nervous system and neurosecretion.' *J. Ins. Physiol.*, **9**, 423–30.

CLEMENTS, A. N. 1963. *The physiology of mosquitoes*. Pergamon Press, Oxford, London, etc., 394 pp.

CLEVER, U. 1962. 'Genaktivitäten in den Riesenchromatosomen von *Chironomus tentans* und ihre Beziehungen zur Entwicklung. III. Das Aktivitätsmuster in Phasen der Entwicklungsruhe.' *J. Ins. Physiol.*, **8**, 357–76.

CLOUTIER, E. J. and BECK, S. D. 1963. 'Spermatogenesis and diapause in the european corn borer.' *Ann. ent. Soc. Amer.*, **3**, 253–5.

COLHOUN, E. H. 1963. 'The physiological significance of acetylcholine in insects and observations upon other pharmacologically active substances.' *Adv. Ins. Physiol.*, **1**, 1–46.

DAVEY, K. G. 1963a. 'The release by enforced activity of the cardiac accelerator from the corpus cardiacum of *Periplaneta americana*.' *J. Ins. Physiol.*, **9**, 375–381.

DAVIS, N. T. 1964. 'Studies of the reproductive physiology of Cimicidae. I. Fecundation and egg maturation.' *J. Ins. Physiol.*, **6**, 947–63.

DEARDEN, M. 1964. 'Experiments on the effects of farnesol on the development of normal and bar-eyed *Drosophila*.' *J. Ins. Physiol.*, **10**, 195–210.

DELEURANCE, S. and DELEURANCE, E. 1964. 'L'absence de cycle saisonnier de reproduction chez les insectes Coléoptères troglobies (*Bathysciines* et *Trechines*).' *C. R. Acad. Sci., Paris*, **258**, 5995–7.

DELPHIN, F. 1963. 'Histology and possible functions of neurosecretory cells in the ventral ganglia of *Schistocerca gregaria*.' *Nature, Lond.*, **200**, 913–15.

DOANE, W. W. 1963a. 'Carbohydrate metabolism studies in adipose mutants of *Drosophila melanogaster*.' *Proc. XVI Int. Congr. Zool.*, **2**, 202.

DOANE, W. W. 1963b. 'Carbohydrate content of adipose females.' *Dis*, **37**, 73–4.

DUVEAU-HAGÈGE, J. 1963. 'La culture organotypique d'ovaire de *Periplaneta americana.*' *C. R. Acad. Sci.*, **256**, 5429–30.

DUVEAU-HAGÈGE, J. 1964. 'La culture in vitro des gonades de *Galleria mellonella* et *Periplaneta americana.* Development et vitellogenèse.' *Bull. Soc. zool. France*, **89**, 66, 69.

ENGELMANN, F. 1963. 'Die innervation der Genital- und Postgenitalsegmente bei Weibchen der Schabe *Leucophaea maderae.*' *Zool. Jb. Anat.*, **81**, 1–16.

ENGELMANN, F. 1964. 'Inhibition of egg maturation in a pregnant viviparous cockroach.' *Nature, Lond.*, **202**, 724–5.

ENGELMANN, F. 1965. 'Proteinstoffwechsel und Corpus allatum Aktivität bei *Leucophaea maderae.*' *Symp. vergl. Endokrin., Jena*, Kurzref., p. 26.

ENGELMANN, F. and RAU, I. 1965. 'A correlation between feeding and the sexual cycle in *Leucophaea maderae.*' *J. Ins. Physiol.*, **1**, 53–64.

FISHER, F. M. and SANBORN, R. C. 1964. 'Nosema as a source of juvenile hormone in parasitized insects.' *Biol. Bull.*, *Wood's Hole*, **126**, 235–52.

FLOWER, J. W. 1964. 'On the origin of flight in insects.' *J. Ins. Physiol.*, **10**, 1–160.

GABRIEL, C. D. 1965. 'Histologische Veränderungen am neurosekretorischen System, den Pericardialzellen und Oenozyten bei Aphiden während eines Jahreszyklus.' *Symp. vergl. Endokrin., Jena*, Kurzref., p. 12–13.

GEORGE, C. F. 1963. 'Ultrastructure of the retrocerebral complex of the stick insect *Carausius morosus.*' *2nd. Conf. Europ. Compar. Endocrinol.*, Abstr. no. 40.

GERSCH, M. 1963a. 'Weitere Untersuchungen über das neurokrine System der Insekten.' *2nd Conf. Europ. Compar. Endocrinol.*, Abstr. no. 40.

GERSCH, M. 1963b. 'Neurokrinie im Tierreich.' *Forsch. Fortschr. dtsch. Wiss.*, **10**, 289–320.

GERSCH, M. 1963c. 'Hormone als Regulatoren von Lebensvorgängen.' *Ber. sächs. Aka. Wiss., Leipzig/math.-naturwiss.Kl.*, **106**, 1–24.

GERSCH, M. 1964. *Vergleichende Endokrinologie der wirbellosen Tiere.* Akad. Verlagsges., Leipzig, 535 pp.

GERSCH, M. 1965. 'Zur Evolution des Hormonsystems im Tierreich.' *Symp. vergl. Endokrin., Jena.* Kurzref., p. 39.

GERSCH, M. and DRAWERT, J. 1964. 'Zytophotometrische Messungen an neurosekretorischen Zellen.' *Acta histochem.*, **18**, 143–151.

GERSCH, M. and RICHTER, K. 1963. 'Auslösung von Nervenimpulsen durch ein Neurohormon bei *Periplaneta americana.*' *Zool. Jb., Physiol.*, **70**, 301–308.

GERSCH, M., TAPPERT, J., MENSINGER, H. and DRAWERT, J. 1964. 'Über ein einfaches, im Eigenbau konstruirtes Zytophotometer, das den Anforderungen nach hohen Messegenauigkeit entspricht.' *Acta histochem*, **18**, 137–142.

GERSCH, M., UNGER, H., FISCHER, F. and KAPITZA, W. 1964. 'Zur Aufklärung und Kennzeichnung einiger farbwechselaktiver aus dem

Zentralnervensystem von Krebsen und Insekten.' *Zool. Jb., Physiol.*, **70**, 455–488.

GILBERT, L. I. 1963. 'Hormones controlling reproduction and molting in invertebrates.' *Comp. Endocrinol.*, **2**, 1–37.

GILBERT, L. I. 1964. 'Physiology of growth and development. Endocrine aspects.' In Rockstein, M. *Physiology of insects*, Acad. Press, New York, pp. 198–263

GIRARDIE, A. 1962. 'Étude biométrique de la croissance ovarienne après ablation et implantation de corpora allata chez *Periplaneta americana*.' *J. Ins. Physiol.*, **8**, 199–204.

GIRARDIE, A. 1964a. 'Action de la pars intercerebralis sur le développement de *Locusta migratoria* L.' *J. Ins. Physiol.*, **10**, 599–609.

GIRARDIE, A. 1964b. 'Fonction gonadotrope de la pars intercerebralis chez le male de *Locusta migratoria*.' *C. R. Acad. Sci.*, Paris, **258**, 2910–2911.

GOODFELLOW, R. D. and GILBERT, L. I. 1965. 'Endocrinological significance of sterols and isoprenoids in the metamorphosis of the American silkmoth, *Hyalophora cepropia* L.' *Symp. vergl. Endokrin., Jena*, Kurzref., p. 35.

HASEGAWA, K. 1963. 'Studies on the mode of action of the diapause hormone in the silkworm *Bombyx mori*. I. The action of diapause hormone injected into pupae of different ages.' *J. exp. Biol.*, **40**, 517–29.

HASKELL, P. T. and MOORHOUSE, J. E. 1963. 'A blood-borne factor influencing the activity of the central nervous system of the desert locust.' *Nature, Lond.*, **197**, 56–8.

HENTSCHEL, E. 1963. 'Zum neurosekretorischen System der Anostraca, Crustacea.' *Zool. Anz.*, **170**, 187–90.

HERMAN, S. W., GILBERT, I. L. 1965. 'Multiplicity of neuro-secretory cell types and groups in the brain of the saturniid moth *Hyalophora cecropia* (L.).' *Nature, Lond.*, **205**, 926–7.

HIDAKA, T. and AIDA, S. 1963. 'Day length as the main factor of the seasonal form determination in *Polygonia c-aureum*.' *Zool. Mag.*, **72**, 77–83.

HIDAKA, T. and OHTAKI, T. 1963. 'Effet de l'hormone juvénile et du farnesol sur la coloration tégumentaire de la nymphe de *Pieris rapae crucivora* Boids.' *C. R. Soc. Biol.*, Paris, **157**, 928.

HIGHNAM, K. C. 1963. 'Endocrine relationship in insect reproduction.' *R. ent. Soc. Lond., Symp. Insect Reprod.*, **3**, 25–40.

HIGHNAM, K. C. 1965. 'Some aspects of neurosecretion in arthropods.' *Symp. vergl. Endokrin., Jena*, Kurzref., p. 11.

HIGHNAM, K. C. and HASKELL, P. T. 1964. 'The endocrine systems of isolated and crowded *Locusta* and *Schistocerca* in relation to oöcyte growth and the effects of flying upon maturation.' *J. Ins. Physiol.*, **6**, 849–64.

HIGHNAM, K. C., LUSIS, O. and HILL, L. 1963a. 'The role of the corpora

P

allata during oöcyte growth in the desert locust, *Schistocerca gregaria*
Forsk.' *J. Ins. Physiol.*, **9,** 587–96.

HIGHNAM, K. C., LUSIS, O. and HILL, L. 1963b. 'Factors affecting oöcyte
resorption in the desert locust *Schistocerca gregaria.*' *J. Ins. Physiol.*, **9,**
827–37.

HILL, L. 1963. 'Excitation and inhibition of the heart of *Aplysia.*' *Proc.
XVI Int. Congr. Zool.*, **2,** 108.

HINTON, H. E. 1963a. 'Metamorphosis of the epidermis and hormone
mimetic substances.' *Sci. Progr.*, **51,** 306–22.

HINTON, H. E. 1963b. 'The origin and function of the pupal stage.' *Proc.
roy. ent. Soc. Lond.* (A), **38,** 77–85.

HODGSON, E. S. and WRIGHT, A. M. 1963. 'Action of epinephrine and
related components upon the insect nervous system.' *Gen. comp. Endocrin.*, **3,** 519–25.

ICHIKAWA, M. and ISHIZAKI, H. 1963. 'Protein nature of the brain
hormone of insects.' *Nature, Lond.*, **198,** 308–9.

JANDA, V., jr. and SLÁMA, K. 1964. 'Über den Einfluss von Hormonen auf
den Glykogen-, Fett- und Stickstoffmetabolismus bei Adulten *Pyrrhocoris apterus* L.' *Zool. Jb.*, *Physiol.*, **70.**

JOHANSSON, A. S. 1963. 'Feeding and nutrition in reproductive processes
in insects.' *R. ent. Soc., Lond., Symp. Insect Reprod.*, **4,** 41–51.

JOHNSON, B. 1963. 'A histological study of neurosecretion in aphids.'
J. Ins. Physiol., **9,** 727–39.

JOLY, L. 1964, 'Controlle du functionnement ovarien chez *Locusta migratoria* L. I. Effects des castrations totales et de ligatures unilaterales de
l'oviducte.' *J. Ins. Physiol.*, **10,** 437–2.

JOLY, P. 1963. 'Localisation et signification biologique de la substance
provoquant des accidents allergiques chez les personnes exposées à un
contact prolongué avec les grands Acridiens.' *C. R. Soc. Biol., Paris*,
157, 2299.

JOLY, P., JOLY, L. and RIOTTE, C. 1962. 'La métamorphose des organes
du vol chez *Locusta migratoria* L.' *C. R. Socs. sav. Paris & Dép.*, 725–33.

JUBERTHIE-JUPEAU, L. 1963. 'Recherches sur la reproduction et la mue
chez les Symphyles.' *Arch. Zool. exp. gen.*, **102,** 1–172.

JUBERTHIE-JUPEAU, L. 1964a. 'Reproduction et mue chez les Symphyles.'
Ecol. Biol. du sol, **1,** 21–40.

JUBERTHIE-JUPEAU, L. 1964b. 'Destinée du produit de neurosécrétion
de la masse nerveuse sous-oesophagienne et innervation des plaques
paraganglionaires chez un Opilion.' *C. R. Acad. Sci., Paris*, **258,** 2183–
2185.

KARLSON, P. 1963. 'Chemie und Biochemie der Insektenhormone.' *Angew.
Chemie*, **75,** 257–65.

KARLSON, P. 1964. 'Zum Wirkungsmechanismus der Hormone. I. Verteil-
ung von Tritiummarkierten Ecdyson in Larven von *Calliphora erythrocephala.*' *Z. physiol. Chem.*, **336,** 100–6.

KARLSON, P. and AMMON, H. 1964. 'Zum Tyrosinstoffwechsel der Insekten. XI. Biogenese und Schicksal der Azetylgruppe des N-Azetyldopamins.' *Hoppe-Seyl. Z.*

KARLSON, P. and HERRLICH, P. 1965. 'Zum Tyrosinstoffwechsel der Insekten. XVI. Der Tyrosinstoffwechsel der Heuschrecke *Schistocerca gregaria* Forsk.' *J. Ins. Physiol.*, **11**, 79–89.

KARLSON, P. and HOFFMEISTER, H. 1963. 'Zur Biogenese des Ecdysons. I. Umwandlung von Cholesterin in Ecdyson.' *Hoppe-Seyl. Z.*, **331**, 298–300.

KARLSON, P., HOFFMEISTER, H., HOPPE, W. and HUBER, R. 1963. 'Zur Chemie des Ecdysons.' *Liebigs Ann.*, **662**, 1–20.

KARLSON, P. and SCHLOSSBERGER-RAECKE, I. 1962. 'Zum Tyrosinstoffwechsel der Insekten. VIII. Die Sklerotisierung der Cuticula bei der Wildform und der Albinomutante von *Schistocerca gregaria* Forsk.' *J. Ins. Physiol.*, **8**, 441–52.

KARLSON, P. and SCHULZ-ENDERS, A. 1964. 'Über die Wirkung des Thyroxins auf die oxydative Phosphorylierung in Insektenmitochondrien.' *Gen. comp. Endocrin.*

KARLSON, P. and SHAAYA, E. 1964. 'Der Ecdysontiter während der Insektenentwicklung. I. Eine Methode zur Bestimmung des Ecdysongehalts.' *J. Ins. Physiol.*, **10**, 797–804.

KIND, T. V. 1964. 'The neurosecretory system of some Lepidoptera in connection with the diapause and metamorphosis.' *Nauka, Leningrad*, 178–183.

KRISHNAKUMARAN, A., OBERLANDER, H., and SCHNEIDERMAN, H. A. 1965. 'Rates of DNA and RNA synthesis of various tissues during a larval moult cycle of *Samia cynthia ricini* (Lepidoptera).' *Nature, Lond.*, **205**, 1131–3.

KUSKE, G. 1963. 'Untersuchungen zur Metamorphose der Schmetterlingsbiene.' *Roux Arch. EntwMech. Organ.*, **154**, 354–77.

LAUFER, H. 1963a. 'Antigens in insect development.' *Ann. N.Y. Acad. Sci.*, **103**, 1137–54.

LAUFER, H. 1963b. 'Hormones and the development in insects.' *Proc.XVIth Int. Congr. Zool.*, **4**, 215–20.

LAUFER, H. 1964. 'Macromolecular patterns in development and evolution.' From *Taxonomic biochemistry and serology*, Ronald Press, Kansas, pp. 171–89.

LEA, A. O. 1963. 'Some relationship between environment, corpora allata, and egg-maturation in aedine mosquitoes.' *J. Ins. Physiol.*, **9**, 793–809.

LEA, A. O. 1964. 'Studies on the dietary and endocrine regulation of autogenous reproduction in *Aedes taeniorhynchus*.' *J. med. Ent.*, **1**, 40–4.

LEES, A. D. 1963. 'The role of photoperiod and temperature in the determination of parthenogenetic and sexual forms in the aphid *Megoura viciae* Buck. III. Further properties of the maternal switching mechanism in apterous aphids.' *J. Ins. Physiol.*, **2**, 153–64.

L'HÉLIAS, C. 1964. 'Aspects chimiques des mécanismes endocriniens chez les insectes.' *Ann. Biol.*, **3**, 1–26.

LOCKE, M. 1964. 'The structure and formation of the integument in insects.' In Rockstein, M. *The physiology of insects*, pp. 380–466.

LOCKSHIN, R. A. and WILLIAMS, C. M. 1964. 'Programmed cell death. II. Endocrine potentation of the break-down of the intersegmental muscles of silkmoths.' *J. Ins. Physiol.*, **10**, 643–9.

LOCKSHIN, R. A. and WILLIAMS, C. M., 1965. 'Programmed cell death. I. Cytology of degeneration in the intersegmental muscles of the *pernyi* silkmoth.' *J. Ins. Physiol.*, **11**, 123–33.

LOHER, W. 1965. 'Die hormonale Kontrolle der Oocytenentwicklung bei der Heuschrecke *Gomphocerus rufus* L.' *Symp. vergl. Endokrin.*, *Jena*, Kurzref., p. 29.

LOHER, W. and HUBER, F. 1964. 'Experimentelle Untersuchungen am Sexualverhalten des Weibchens der Heuschrecke *Gomphocerus rufus* L.' *J. Ins. Physiol.*, **10**, 13–36.

LÜSCHER, M. 1963. 'Functions of the corpora allata in the development of Termites.' *Proc. 16th int. Congr. Zool.*, **4**, 244–50.

LÜSCHER, M. 1964. 'Die spezifische Wirkung männlicher und weiblicher Ersatzgeschlechtstiere auf die Entstehung von Ersatzgeschlechtstieren bei der Termite *Kalotermes flavicollis* Fabr.' *Insectes sociaux*, **11**, 79–90.

LÜSCHER, M. and WALKER, J. 1963. 'Zur Frage der Wirkungsweise der Königinnenpheromone bei der Honigbiene.' *Rev. suisse Zool.*, **70**, 304–11.

LUSIS, O. 1963. 'The histology and histochemistry of development and resorption in the terminal oocytes of the desert locust *Schistocerca gregaria*.' *Quart. J. micr. Sci.*, **104**, 57–68.

MADDRELL, S. H. P. 1963. 'Excretion of the blood sucking bug, *Rhodnius prolixus* Stål.' *Nature, Lond.*, **194**, 605–6.

MATSUDA, R. 1963a. 'Evolution and relative growth in Arthropods.' *Z. wiss. Zool.*, **169**, 64–81.

MATSUDA, R. 1963b. 'A study of relative growth of leg and antennal segments in two species of *Orthotylus*.' *Proc. R. ent. Soc. Lond.* (A), **38**, 86–9.

MATZ, G. 1963. 'Réactions inflammatoires, cicatrisation et cancérigenèse chez les insectes.' *Bull. Soc. zool. Fr.*, **88**, 650–62.

MATZ, G. 1964. 'Transmission de tumeurs chez les insectes par l'hémolymphe et par filtrats acellulaires du tumeurs broyées.' *J. Ins. Physiol.*, **10**, 141–5.

MATZ, G. *et al.* 1964. 'Transmission du tumeurs chez les insectes par un acide nucleicque extrait des tumeurs.' *C. R. Acad. Sci., Paris*, **258**, 4366–8.

MCLEOD, D. G. R. and BECK, S. D. 1963a. 'The anatomy of the neuroendocrine system of the european corn borer *Ostrinia nubilalis* and its relation to diapause.' *Ann. ent. Soc. Amer.*, **56**, 723–7.

MCLEOD, D. G. R. and BECK, S. D. 1963b. 'Photoperiodic termination of diapause in an insect.' *Biol. Bull., Wood's Hole*, **124**, 84–96.

METCALF, R. L., WINTON, M. Y., and FUKUTO, T. R. 1964. 'The effects of cholinergic substances upon the isolated heart of *Periplaneta americana*.' *J. Ins. Physiol.*, **10**, 353–61.

MIDDLEKANFF, W. W. 1964. 'Effects of photoperiodic upon oögenesis in *Melanoplus devastator* Scudder.' *J. Kans. ent. Soc.*, **37**, 163–8.

MILLES, P. W. 1964. 'Studies on the salivary physiology of plant bugs: oxidase activity in the salivary apparatus and saliva.' *J. Ins. Physiol.*, **10**, 121–9.

MORDUE, W. 1965a. 'Studies on oöcyte production and associated histological changes in the neuro-endocrine system in *Tenebrio molitor* L.' *J. Ins. Physiol.*, **11**, 493–503.

MORDUE, W. 1965b. 'The neuro-endocrine control of oöcyte development in *Tenebrio molitor* L.' *J. Ins. Physiol.*, **11**, 505–11.

MORDUE, W. 1965c. 'Neuro-endocrine factors in the control of oöcyte production in *Tenebrio molitor* L.' *J. Ins. Physiol.*, **11**, 617–25.

MORRISON, P. E. and DAVIES, D. M. 1964. 'Feeding of dry chemically defined diets and egg production in the adult house-fly.' *Nature, Lond.*, **201**, 104–5.

MORSE, R. and GARY, N. E. 1963. 'Further studies on the responses of honey bee colonies (*Apis mellifera*) to queens with extirpated mandibular glands.' *Ann. ent. Soc. Amer.*, **3**, 372–4.

MUTH, W., 1965. 'Effect of 5-florouracil on the development of the scales of *Ephestia*.' *Nature, Lond.*, **205**, 619–20.

NATON, E. 1963a. 'Über die Entwicklung des schwarzbraunen Mehlkäfers *Tribolium destructor*. V. Die Auswirkungen "carnitinfreier" Diäten auf innersekretorische Drüsen und auf die Epidermis.' *Zool. Beitr.*, **8**, 173–86.

NATON, E. 1963b. 'Über die Entwicklung des schwarzbraunen Mehlkäfers *Tribolium destructor*. VI. Beitrag zur Kenntnis der individuellen Empfindlichkeit gegenüber einem Carnitinmangel und abschliessende Diskussion der im Teil IV. und V. beschriebenen Ergebnisse.' *Zool. Beitr.*, **8**, 447–82.

NAYAR, J. K., 1963. 'Effect of synthetic queen substance (9-oxydec-trans-2-enoic acid) on ovary development of the housefly, *Musca domestica* L.' *Nature, Lond.*, **197**, 923–4.

NAYAR, K. K. and ADIYODI, K. G. 1965. 'Effects of administration of Clomiphene on reproduction in female cockroaches.' *Symp. vergl. Endokrin., Jena*, Kurzref., p. 28.

NOVÁK, V. J. A. 1963. 'The endocrine basis of the insect development.' *Proc. 16th int. Congr. Zool.*, **4**, 235–43.

NOVÁK, V. J. A. 1964a. 'The phylogenetic origin of neurosecretion.' *Gen. comp. Endocrinol.*, **4**, 696–703.

NOVÁK, V. J. A. 1964b. 'The juvenile hormone and other morphogenetically active substances in insects.' *Proc. XIIth Int. Congr. Entom.*, 7215.

NOVÁK, V. J. A. 1965a. 'The question of evolution of the juvenile hormone.' *Acta ent. bohemoslov.*, **62**, 165–70.

NOVÁK, V. J. A. 1965b. 'Die Frage des Gradient-Faktors im Lichte der neuesten Erkenntnisse über Metamorphosehormone.' *Symp. vergl. Endokrin.*, *Jena*, Kurzref., p. 24.

NÚNEZ, J. A. 1963. 'Probable mechanismus regulating water economy of *Rhodnius prolixus*.' *Nature, Lond.*, **197**, 312.

O'FARRELL, A. F. 1963. 'Temperature-controlled physiological colour change in some australian damselflies (*Odonata, Zygoptera*).' *Aust. J. Sci.*, **25**, 437–8.

O'FARRELL, A. F. 1964. 'On physiological colour change in some australian *Odonata*.' *J. ent. Soc. Aust.*, **1**, 1–8.

O'FARRELL, A. F. and STOCK, A. 1964. 'Some effects of farnesol methyl ether on regeneration and metamorphosis in the cockroach *Blatella germanica* L.' *Life Sciences*, **3**, 491–7.

ORR, C. W. M. 1964a. 'The influence of nutritional and hormonal factors on the chemistry of the fat body, blood and ovaries of the blowfly *Phormia regina*.' *J. Ins. Physiol.*, **10**, 108–19.

ORR, C. W. M. 1964b. 'The influence of nutritional and hormonal factors on egg development in the blowfly *Phormia regina*.' *J. Ins. Physiol.*, **10**, 53–64.

OZEKI, K. 1965. 'Control on secretion of juvenile hormone in insects.' *Symp. vergl. Endokrin.*, *Jena*, Kurzref., p. 21.

PANITZ, R. 1964. 'Hormonkontrolierte Genaktivitäten in den Riesen-chromosomen von *Acricotopus lucidus*.' *Biol. Zbl.*, **83**, 197–230.

PANOV, A. A. 1963. 'Entstehung und Schicksal der Neuroblasten, Neuronen und Neurogliazellen im Zentralnervensystem von *Antherea pernyi* Guér.' *Rev. Ent. U.R.S.S.*, **42**, 337–50.

PANOV, A. A. and KIND, T. V. 1963. 'The system of neurosecretory cells of the cerebral ganglion in Lepidoptera' (in Russian). *C. R. Acad. Sci. U.R.S.S.*, **153**, 1186–9.

PENER, M. P. 1963. 'Studies on phase differences in the desert locust, *Schistocerca gregaria*, reared under crowded and isolated conditions.' D.S. Thesis, Jerusalem.

PENZLIN, H. 1965. 'Die Bedeutung der Hormone für die Regeneration bei den Insekten.' *Symp. vergl. Endokrin.*, *Jena*, Kurzref., p. 14.

PENZLIN, H. 1964. 'Die Bedeutung des Nervensystems für die Regeneration, bei den Insekten'. *Roux Arch. EntwMech. Organ.*, **155**, 152–61.

PIEPHO, H. 1964. 'Wirkung des Juvenilhormons auf den Mitteldarm der Wachsmotte. I.' *J. Ins. Physiol.*, **9**, 713–19.

RENSING, L. 1965. 'Die Bedeutung der Hormone bei der Steuerung circa-dianer Rhythmen.' *Symp. vergl. Endokrin.*, *Jena*, Kurzref., p. 15.

RIZKI, M. T. M. and RIZKI, M. R. 1963. 'An inducible enzyme system in the larval cells of *Drosophila melanogaster*.' *J. Cell Biol.*, **17**, 87–92.

ROCKSTEIN, M. 1965. *The physiology of insects*. Academic Press, New York and London; vol. II, 905 pp.; vol. III, 692 pp.

ROGOFF, W. M., BELTZ, A. D., JOHNSEN, J. O. and PLAPP, F. W. 1964.

'A sex pheromone in the housefly *Musca domestica*.' *J. Ins. Physiol.*, **10**, 239–46.

ROHDENDORF, E. 1965. 'Effects of allatectomy in adult females of *Thermobia domestica* Packard.' *Symp. vergl. Endokrin., Jena*, Kurzref., p. 30.

RÖLLER, H., PIEPHO, H. and HOLZ, I. 1963. 'Zum Problem der Hormon-abhängigkeit des Paarungverhaltens bei Insekten. Untersuchungen an *Galleria mellonella* L.' *J. Ins. Physiol.*, **2**, 187–94.

ROTH, L. M. 1964. 'Control of reproduction in female cockroaches with special reference to *Nauphoeta cinerea*.—First preoviposition period.' *J. Ins. Physiol.*, **10**, 415–45.

ROTH, L. M. and BARTH, R. H. 1964. 'The control of sexual receptivity in female cockroaches.' *J. Ins. Physiol.*, **10**, 965–75.

ROUSSEL, J. P. 1964a. 'Étude de la consommation d'oxygène chez *Locusta migratoria* L.' *J. Ins. Physiol.*, **9**, 349–61.

ROUSSEL, J. P. 1964b. 'Consommation d'oxygène après ablation des corpora allata chez des femelles adultes de *Locusta migratoria* L.' *J. Ins. Physiol.*, **9**, 721–5.

SCHALLER, F. 1964. 'Croissance occulaire au cours de développements normaux et perturbés de la larve d'*Aeschna cyanea* Mull. (Insecta, Odonata).' *Ann. Endocr., Paris*, **25**, 122–7. (Abstract cf. *Gen. comp. Endocrin.*, **3**, (8), 92.)

SHAPPIRIO, D. G. and HARVEY, W. R. 1965. 'The injury metabolism of the cecropia silkworm. II. Injury-induced alterations in oxidative enzyme systems and respiratory metabolism of the pupal wing epidermis.' *J. Ins. Physiol.*, **11**, 305–27.

SCHARRER, B. 1963. 'Neurosecretion. XIII. The ultrastructure of the corpus cardiacum of the *Leucophae maderae*.' *Z. Zellforsch.*, **60**, 761–96.

SCHARRER, B. 1964. 'Histophysiological studies on the corpus allatum of *Leucophaea maderae*. IV. Ultrastructure during normal activity cycle.' *Z. Zellforsch.*, **62**, 125–48.

SCHEFFEL, H. 1963. 'Zur Häutungsphysiologie der Chilopoden.' *Zool. Jb., Physiol.*, **70**, 284–90.

SCHLOSSBERGER-RAECKE, I. and KARLSON, P. 1964. 'Zum Tyrosin-stoffwechsel der Insekten. XIII. Radioautographische Lokalisation von Tyrosinmetaboliten in der Cuticula von *Schistocerca gregaria* Forsk.' *J. Ins. Physiol.*, **10**, 261–6.

SCHNEIDERMANN, H. A. and GILBERT, L. I. 1964. 'Control of growth and development in insects.' *Science*, **143**, 325–333.

SEHNAL, F. 1965. 'Der Einfluss des Juvenilhormons auf die Metamorphose des Zentralnervensystems der Larven von *Galleria mellonella* L.' *Symp. vergl. Endokrin., Jena*, Kurzref., p. 25.

SEKERIS, C. E. and RAMOS, E. H. 1964. 'On the mechanism of hormone action. II. Ecdysone and protein biosynthesis.' *Arch. Biochem.*, **105**, 483–7.

SHAAYA, E., and KARLSON, P. 1965. 'Der Ecdysontiter während der

Insektenentwicklung. II. Die postembryonale Entwicklung der Schmeiss-fliege *Calliphora erythrocephala* Meig.' *J. Ins. Physiol.*, **11**, 65–68.

SHEARER, D. A., and BOCH, R. 1965. '2-heptanone in the mandibular gland secretion of the honey bee.' *Nature, Lond.*, **206**, 530.

SIEW, Y. C. 1965a. 'The endocrine control of adult reproductive diapause in the chrysomelid beetle, *Galeruca tanaceti* L. I.' *J. Ins. Physiol*, **11**, 1–10.

SIEW, Y. C. 1965b. 'Enfenced occurrence of a meroic type of neurosecretory cell in the chrysomelid beetle, *Galeruca tanaceti* (Linn.).' *Nature, Lond.*, **205**, 523–4.

SLÁMA, K. 1964a. 'Die Einwirkung des Juvenilhormons auf die Epidermis-zellen der Flügelanlagen bei künstlich beschleunigter und verzögerter Metamorphose von *Phyrrhocoris apterus*.' *Zool. Jb., Physiol.*, **70**, 427–54.

SLÁMA, K. 1964b. 'Physiology of sawfly metamorphosis. 2. Hormonal activity during diapause and development.' *Acta Soc. ent. Čsl.*, **61**, 210–19.

SLÁMA, K. 1964c. 'Hormonal control of respiratory metabolism during growth, reproduction and diapause in female adults of *Pyrrhocoris apterus* L.' *J. Ins. Physiol.*, **10**, 283–303.

SLÁMA, K. 1964d. 'Hormonal control of respiratory metabolism during growth, reproduction and diapause in male adults of *Pyrrhocoris apterus* L.' *Biol. Bull., Wood's Hole*, **3**, 499–510.

SLÁMA, K. 1964e. 'Hormonal control of haemolymph protein concentration in the adult of *Pyrrhocoris apterus* L.' *J. Ins. Physiol.*, **10**, 773–82.

SLÁMA, K. 1965a. 'Effect of hormones on growth and respiratory meta-bolism in the larvae of *Pyrrhocoris apterus* L.' *J. Ins. Physiol.*, **11**, 113–22.

SLÁMA, K. 1965b. 'The effect of hormones on the respiration of body fragments in adult *Pyrrhocoris apterus* L.' *Nature, Lond.*

SLÁMA, K. and HRUBEŠOVÁ, H. 1963. 'Übereinstimmung in der Ein-wirkung von larvalen und imaginalen corpora allata auf den Respirations-metabolismus in die Reproduktion bei *Pyrrhocoris apterus* L. Weibchen.' *Zool. Jb., Physiol.*, **70**, 291–300.

STEELE, J. E. 1963. 'The site of action of insect hyperglycemic hormone.' *Gen. comp. Endocrin.*, **3**, 46–52.

STEGWEE, D. 1963–1964. 'Respiratory chain metabolism in the Colorado-potato-beetle. II. Respiration and oxidative phosphorylation in "sarco-somes" from diapausing beetles.' *J. ins. Physiol.*, **10**, 97–102.

STERBA, G. 1963. 'Histochemischer und biochemischer Nachweis der Indentität, zwischen der als Neurosekret nachweisbaren Substanz und dem Trägerprotein der Oxytocin.' *2nd Conf. Europ. Comp. Endocrinol.*, Abstr. no. 97, Gen. comp. Endocrin., 3, 733, Brussels 2.

STERBA, G. 1964. 'Grundlagen des histochemischen und biochemischen Nachweises von Neurosekret (Trägerprotein der Oxytozine) mit Pseudo-isozyanin.' *Acta Histochem.*, **17**, 268–92.

STERBA, G. and WELLNER, K. P. 1963. 'Biochemische Korrelation der Pseudocyanimreaktion zum Nachweis von Neurosekret.' *Naturwissen-schaften*, **8**, 334–5.

STRONG, L. 1963. 'A simple apparatus for use in removing corpora allata from locusts.' *Bull. ent. Res.*, **54,** 19–21.

STRONG, L. 1965a. 'The relationship between the brain, corpora allata and oöcyte growth in the Central American locust, *Schistocerca* sp.—I. The cerebral neurosecretory system, the corpora allata and oöcyte growth.' *J. Ins. Physiol.*, **11,** 135–46.

STRONG, L. 1965b. 'The relationship between the brain, corpora allata, and oöcyte growth in the Central American locust, *Schistocerca* sp.—II. The innervation of the corpora allata, the lateral neurosecretory complex and oöcyte growth.' *J. Ins. Physiol.*, **11,** 271–80.

TOMBES, A. S. 1964. 'Respiratory and compositional study on the aestivating insect, *Hypera postica* (Gyll.) (Curculionidae).' *J. Ins. Physiol.*, **10,** 997–1003.

ULRICH, H. 1963. 'Vergleichend-histologische und zyklische Untersuchungen an den weiblichen Geschlechtsorganen und den innersekretorischen Drüsen adulter Hippobosciden.' *Dtsch ent. Z.*, **10,** 28–71.

UNGER, H. 1965. 'Der Einflus der Neurohormone C und D auf Exkretion und Wasserhaushalt der Stabheuschrecke *Carausius morosus* Br.' *Symp. vergl. Endokrin., Jena*, Kurzref., p. 33.

UNGER, H. 1965b. 'Der Einfluss körpereigner Wirkstoffe auf die Nerventätigkeit von *Periplaneta americana*.' *Symp. vergl. Endokrin., Jena*, Kurzref., p. 38.

URVOY, J. 1963a. 'Étude anatomo-fonctionelle de la patte et de l'antenne de la blatte *Blabera craniifer* Burmeister.' *Théses Fac. Sci. Univ. Renn.*, no. **28,** 1–405.

URVOY, J. 1963b. 'Transplantation de patte prothoracique en place de patte métathoracique chez *Blabera craniifer* Burm.' *Bull. Soc. zool. Fr.*, **88,** 269–73.

VIETINGHOFF, U., PENZLIN, H. and SPANNHOF, L. 1964. 'Kernvolumetrische Untersuchungen an den Pericardialdrüsen regenerierenden Stabheuschrecken *Carausius morosus*.' *Naturwissenschaften*, **15,** 370.

VIGH-TEICHMANN, I. 1963. 'Histochemische Untersuchung der hypothalamischer Ependymsekretion der Ratte.' *2nd Conf. Europ. Comp. Endocrin.*, Abstr. no. 107.

VOJTKEVICH, A. A. 1964. 'Some data on the influence of the hormones of vertebrates on the neurosecretory system of insects' (in Russian). *C. R. Acad. Sci. URSS*, **157,** 236–9.

WALL, B. J. 1965. 'Evidence for regulation of water reabsorption in the rectum of *Periplaneta americana*.' *Symp. vergl. Endokrin., Jena*, Kurzref., p. 32.

WANDERBERG, J. P. 1963. 'The role of the gonadotropic hormone in the synthesis of protein and RNA in *Rhodnius prolixus* (Hemiptera).' *Biol. Bull., Wood's Hole*, **125,** 576–80.

WATSON, J. A. L. 1963. 'The cephalic endocrine system in the Thysanura.' *J. Morph.*, **3,** 359–74.

WATSON, J. A. L. 1964a. 'Moulting and reproduction in the adult firebrat *Thermobia domestica*. I. The moulting cycle and its control.' *J. Ins. Physiol.*, **10**, 305–17.

WATSON, J. A. L. 1964b. 'Moulting and reproduction in the adult of firebrat *Thermobia domestica*. II. The reproductive cycles.' *J. Ins. Physiol.*, **10**, 399–408.

WEISER, J. and SLÁMA, K. 1964. 'Effects of the toxin of *Pyemotes* on the insect prey with special reference to respiration.' *Ann. ent. Soc. Amer.*, **57**, 479–482.

WEIRICH, G. 1963. 'Zur Frage der hormonalen Regulation der Einreihung bei Insekten.' *Inaug. Dissert.*, München, 76 pp.

WHITTEN, J. M. 1964a. 'Haemocytes and the metamorphosis tissues in *Sarcophaga bullata*, *Drosophila melanogaster* and other cyclorraphous Diptera.' *J. ins. Physiol.*, **10**, 447–70.

WHITTEN, J. M. 1964b. 'Connective tissue membranes and their apparent role in transporting neurosecretory and other secretory products in insects.' *Gen. comp. Endocrinol.*, **4**, 176–92.

WIGGLESWORTH, V. B. 1963a. 'The juvenile hormone effect of farnesol and some related compounds: quantitative experiments.' *J. Ins. Physiol.*, **9**, 105–19.

WIGGLESWORTH, V. B. 1963b. 'A further function of the air sacs in some insects.' *Nature, Lond.*, **198**, 106.

WIGGLESWORTH, V. B. 1964. 'The action of moulting hormone and juvenile hormone at the cellular level in *Rhodnius prolixus*.' *J. exp. Biol.*, **40**, 231–45.

WIGGLESWORTH, V. B. 1965a. 'Insect hormones.' *Endeavour*, **24**, 21–6.

WIGGLESWORTH, V. B., 1965b. 'The hormonal regulation of growth and reproduction in insects.' In Beament *et al.*, *Advances in insect physiology*, vol. II, pp. 212–86.

DE WILDE, J. 1964. 'Reproduction-endocrine control.' In Rockstein, M., *The physiology of insects*, vol. I, pp. 69–123.

WILLIAMS, C. M. 1963. 'The juvenile hormone. III. Its accumulation and storage in the abdomens of certain male moths.' *Biol. Bull.*, *Wood's Hole*, **124**, 355–67.

WILLIAMS, C. M. and ADKISSON, P. M. 1964. 'Physiology of insect diapause. XIV. An endocrine mechanism for the photoperiodic control of pupal diapause in the oak silkworm, *Antherea pernyi*.' *Biol. Bull.*, *Wood's Hole*, **127**, 511–25.

YOSHITAKE, N. and TAKAHOSHI, N. 1965. 'Hormone determining the black pupal colour in the silkworm *Bombyx mori* L.' *Nature, Lond.*, **205**, 215.

Index of Topics

441

Index of Zoological Names

Index of Authors

466